CITIES OF THE SOVIET UNION

CITIES OF
THE SOVIET UNION

*Studies in Their Functions, Size,
Density, and Growth*

CHAUNCY D. HARRIS

Samuel N. Harper Professor of Geography

University of Chicago

———

Fifth in the Monograph Series

Published for

Association of American Geographers

by

Rand McNally and Company

Chicago

———

The Monograph Series of the
Association of American Geographers

EDITORS

Derwent Whittlesey 1956

Andrew H. Clark 1957–1961

Thomas R. Smith 1961–1964

Clarence J. Glacken 1964–1966

Marvin W. Mikesell 1966–

EDITOR'S NOTE

CHAUNCY D. HARRIS is one of the relatively small number of American scholars who elected to specialize on the geography of the Soviet Union shortly after the Second World War. In the intervening years he has completed several studies of the economic and urban geography of the USSR, beginning with an article on "The Cities of the Soviet Union" in the 1945 volume of the *Geographical Review*. He has also made a persistent effort to bring the work of Soviet geographers to the attention of his English-speaking colleagues. The latter endeavor has included substantial bibliographic work and editorial supervision of the American editions of Balzak, Vasyutin, and Feigin's *Economic Geography of the USSR* (1949) and *Soviet Geography: Accomplishments and Tasks* (1962). Professor Harris has visited the Soviet Union six times, has participated in meetings of Soviet geographers, and has contributed articles to their journals.

The present work is built on this foundation of prolonged and intimate inquiry. It is a highly original work, for although it contains an elaborate bibliography of the work of Soviet urban geographers, most of the analysis is based upon the use of primary information obtained from census publications and other sources of essentially "raw" data. In offering this study as volume number five of the Monograph Series of the Association of American Geographers, I am confident that it will prove useful to scholars in many countries. The extraordinarily rapid urbanization of the USSR can be regarded as an accelerated counterpart of a process that has also been evident in Europe and the United States. Since pervasive urbanization is a common experience in these realms, there is obviously much to gain from the sharing of information and methods of analysis among urban geographers. It is in this spirit that Professor Harris' study was undertaken, and it is in this spirit that it is offered to the international community of scholars.

MARVIN W. MIKESELL

University of Chicago
Chicago, Illinois

PREFACE

THIS MONOGRAPH IS CONCERNED primarily with 1,247 cities and towns of the Soviet Union of more than 10,000 population for which population data were published in the 1959 census. It treats mainly the economic functions, size relations, distributional patterns, and growth of these Soviet cities.

In Chapter I an attempt is made to give the reader a general areal and historical orientation by depicting urbanization in the Soviet Union in its world-wide space setting and as an historical continuation of a centuries-long process of the old Russian Empire. The rate of urban growth has sharply accelerated, however, during the Soviet period.

Chapter II reviews the contributions made by Soviet geographers to the study of Soviet cities. Since the corpus of relevant literature exceeds a thousand items, only the most salient studies dealing with methodology, theory, or the cities of the country as a whole could be treated. Other articles treating Soviet cities comparatively are listed in the selected bibliography.

Chapter III attempts a functional classification of the 304 Soviet cities of more than 50,000 population in 1959. This classification is based on economic activities as revealed in occupational data from the 1959 census and on size characteristics of the cities.

Chapter IV includes a statistical exploration of thirty characteristics of the 1,247 Soviet cities. The three principal components associated with a large fraction of the variation among these characteristics are then treated in turn: size relationships, areal spacing, and population growth.

Chapter V analyzes the relationship between size, central-place functions, and the administrative hierarchy of the Soviet Union.

Chapter VI is concerned mainly with one characteristic of spacing, density, which is measured by urban population potential and related indicators.

In Chapter VII the long-range trends of growth over the last century and a half are examined.

Chapter VIII is devoted to the growth of cities in the Soviet period with emphasis on the intercensal twenty years, 1939–1959, but with notes both on the earlier intercensal period, 1926–1939, and on the more recent years, 1959–1967.

Finally, Chapter IX contains the summary and conclusions of the study.

It may be well to forewarn the reader of some important and interesting aspects of Soviet cities that are not treated in this monograph, e.g., planning (on which there is a vast literature), internal patterns and land use, points of touristic interest, or history. The work is not directed toward a description of individual cities nor of the urban networks of the various regions of the Soviet Union.

The only data on the 1,247 Soviet cities provided in the published 1959 census concerns their population in 1959 and 1939, and the percentage of increase during this interval. If the Soviet Union is underdeveloped in its recent census publications, it nevertheless provides a wealth of material in earlier censuses and statistical publications, particularly the monumental and detailed censuses of 1897 and 1926. These were useful in studies of the long-term population growth patterns of Soviet cities.

Other types of sources had to be utilized to compensate for the deficiencies of the published census. A whole series of excellent atlases indicate the principal industries of each of the cities of the Soviet Union but they do not, of course, present this information on an exact quantitative basis or in strictly comparable terms. Other map materials, such as the 1:4,000,000 administrative map of the Soviet Union (in four sheets), were generally quite adequate for the purpose of this study in locating and identifying cities of more than 10,000 population by name and symbol for size. The administrative handbooks issued about every two years provided reliable and comparable information. Finally, encyclopedias had to be used for much information. Fortunately these are of a high quality, especially the remarkable *Kratkaia Geograficheskaia Entsiklopediia* (Short Geographic Encyclopedia), which was published in five volumes during the years 1960–1966, and thus provides recent and reliable data.

In this volume two different transliteration schemes are used for rendering Cyrillic letters into the Latin alphabet. For all bibliographical entries the Library of Congress system is adopted, since that is the exact form in which entries will be found in most American libraries which utilize Library of Congress cards or bibliographies. For place names, however, the system of the United States Board on Geographical Names is adopted, since that is the form in which the name is likely to appear in gazetteers and atlases, on maps, or in the geographic literature. The differences are slight, involving principally a "y" in the Board on Geographic Names system in place of an "i" in the Library of Congress system, and an added "y" preceding an initial or post-vowel "e", as for example in the Siberian river, which is spelled "Yenisey" in the Board on Geographic Names system or "Enisei" in the Library of Congress system.

It is my pleasure to record my debt to the American Council of Learned Societies, which made possible under its exchange arrangement with the Academy of Sciences of the USSR three months of research and consultation in the Soviet Union in 1963, during which time this study was launched.

Acknowledgement is made with gratitude for a grant from the National Science Foundation which gave support for the collection of data, its statistical analysis, and its presentation in the forms of maps and tables. The Committee on Slavic Area Studies, the Center for International Studies, and the Library of the University of Chicago have also provided assistance in the work on this monograph.

I am grateful for permission to utilize in Chapter V material from my essay "City and Region in the Soviet Union" in *Urbanization and its Problems: Essays in Honour of E. W. Gilbert*, edited by R. P. Beckinsale and J. M. Houston (Oxford: Basil Blackwell, 1968).

My debt is great to Soviet colleagues who have personally helped with information and material on Soviet work in urban geography, in particular O. A. Konstantinov, V. V. Pokshishevskii, V. G. Davidovich, Iu. G. Saushkin, A. A. Mints, B. S. Khorev, and V. V. Vorob'ëv.

I am profoundly thankful to many individuals who have selflessly helped with the assemblage of original data for this study, Mrs. Chauncy D. Harris, Margaret Harris, William Terechow, Francis M. Leversedge, Dušan Mihelić, and Julie Gordon; with statistical processing through the computer, Robert A. Murdie and Robert J. Tennant; with the drawing of maps, Mrs. Josephine McKenzie, Mrs. Leslie Dienes, and Gerald F. Pyle; and with the typing of the manuscript, Mrs. Dawn H. Townsend. Brian J. L. Berry acted as a consultant on statistical methodology. Arcadius Kahan also made helpful suggestions and Vaclav Laška aided with source materials.

Marvin W. Mikesell, Editor of the Monograph Series of the Association of American Geographers, generously expressed an interest in this study. He has been very helpful in editorial suggestions and in the preparation of the manuscript for publication.

Extensive tables of population data for the 1,247 cities and towns on which this study is based are available separately as "Population of Cities of the Soviet Union, 1897, 1926, 1939, 1959, and 1967: Tables, Maps, and Gazetteer," by Chauncy D. Harris, published as a special issue of *Soviet Geography: Review and Translation,* Volume XI, Number 5 (May, 1970), available from the American Geographical Society of New York.

This study was essentially completed in October, 1968, but later data are included where possible.

CHAUNCY D. HARRIS

University of Chicago
February 1970

TABLE OF CONTENTS

LIST OF FIGURES

LIST OF TABLES

GLOSSARY OF
SOVIET ADMINISTRATIVE-
TERRITORIAL TERMS

Autonomous oblast (AO) — a unit based on a non-Russian ethnic group, lower in status than an autonomous republic (ASSR). There are 8 autonomous oblasts. The 5 in the RSFSR are attached to krays, the 3 in smaller union republics are directly under the republics.

Autonomous republic or, more fully, autonomous soviet socialist republic (ASSR) — a unit based on a non-Russian ethnic group, subordinate to a union republic. Each of the 20 autonomous republics is comparable in area and population to an oblast.

Guberniya — a former administrative division of the Russian Empire and the early days of the Soviet Union, approximately equivalent to a present oblast. The European core of the Russian Empire was divided into 50 guberniyas. Many Russian statistics of the early 19th century are limited to the area covered by these 50 traditional guberniyas.

Industrial management region — a former unit of economic administration for industrial and construction enterprises, formed in 1957 in connection with the so-called geographical or regional principle of administration of industry by regional economic councils (*Sovnarkhozy*). This unit typically encompassed several oblasts but some consisted of a single oblast or a small union republic. These regions were abolished in 1965 after the dismissal of N. S. Khrushchev. See Figure 23 and Table 20.

Kray — a unit in the Russian SFSR, similar to an oblast but being distinguished (with one exception) by including a subordinate autonomous oblast with a non-Russian ethnic group. There were 6 krays in 1967.

Major economic region — one of 18 major regions into which the Soviet Union is divided for statistical or long-range planning purposes but not for administration. Ten of the major economic regions lie within the Russian SFSR and 3 within the Ukrainian SSR. On the other hand the 3 Baltic union republics are grouped into one major economic region, the 3 union republics of the Caucasus into another, and the 4 union republics of Soviet Middle Asia into yet another. Two union republics, the Belorussian SSR and the Kazakh SSR, each form a single major economic region. Thus the major economic regions are much more nearly comparable in area and population than are the union republics, which vary enormously in size and number of inhabitants. The major economic regions are thus particularly useful for statistical and regional comparisons. The Moldavian SSR is not included within any of the 18 major economic regions and thus forms a 19th region. See Figure 22 and Table 6.

National okrug — a minor unit based on a non-Russian ethnic group and subordinate to an oblast or a kray. All 10 national okrugs are located in the RSFSR. They are generally sparsely populated and lie in the northern part of the country, particularly in Siberia.

Oblast — the principal unit into which 6 of the larger union republics are divided. In 1967 there were 105 oblasts: 49 in the Russian Soviet Federated Socialist Republic (RSFSR), 25 in the Ukrainian SSR, 6 in the Belorussian SSR, 9 in the Uzbek SSR, 15 in the Kazakh SSR, and one in the Kirgiz SSR. Nine of the smaller union republics are not subdivided into oblasts.

Rayon — a minor civil division, a small subdivision of an oblast in the larger union republics (or directly of the smaller union republics too small to have oblasts). The number of these units of local government has varied widely over time with administrative reorganizations. On July 1, 1967, there were 2,959 rayons in the Soviet Union, but the number had been as low as 1,833 on April 1, 1963, and as high as 4,368 in 1954.

Russia — the word has two different meanings:

(1) Historically Russia refers to the whole pre-revolutionary Russian Empire, an area similar to but not identical with the present Soviet Union.

(2) Currently the term "Russia" is properly restricted to the Russian Soviet Federated Socialist Republic (RSFSR), only

one of the 15 union republics which constitute the Soviet
Union. This is the area within which the Russian ethnic group
predominates although the RSFSR also includes many smaller
non-Russian groups recognized administratively by the creation
of autonomous republics, autonomous oblasts, and national
okrugs. The RSFSR occupies 76 per cent of the territory of the
Soviet Union and includes 54 per cent of the population.

Soviet socialist republic (SSR) — the designation for each of the
union republics which together compose the Union of Soviet
Socialist Republics (USSR) or the Soviet Union, except that for
the Russian republic the word "federated" is added because
of the many smaller autonomous ethnic units included within
it (thus the Russian Soviet Federated Socialist Republic).

Union republic — one of the 15 major units which together constitute the Soviet Union. Each union republic is based on a different ethnic group, recognized in its name. Besides the Russian SFSR, the union republics are the Ukrainian, Estonian,
Latvian, Lithuanian, Belorussian, Moldavian, Georgian, Armenian, Azerbaydzhan, Kazakh, Kirgiz, Uzbek, Tadzhik, and
Turkmen Soviet Socialist Republics (SSR).

Uyezd — a former minor civil division into which guberniyas were
divided.

I.

Introduction

> The growth of urban population in the
> USSR in volume and rate is without prece-
> dent in the history of mankind.
> — V. G. DAVIDOVICH
> *Voprosy geografii*, sbornik 45,
> 1959, p. 38

> Each city is a link in the chain of the terri-
> torial division of labor.
> — IU. G. SAUSHKIN
> *Vestnik Moskovskogo universiteta*,
> *seriia 5, geografiia*, 1960, no. 1,
> p. 25

THE SOVIET UNION is a land of large cities. Indeed, it vies with the
United States for position of the country with the largest number
of cities of more than 100,000 population in the world (Table 1).
In 1969 the Soviet Union had 209 such cities, compared with 206
for the United States, 135 for Japan, 110 for India, and 103 for the
People's Republic of China. By virtue of smaller total population,
the principal European states, though highly urbanized, had
fewer such cities, e.g., the United Kingdom had 90, the German
Federal Republic, 56, and France, 39.

The number of cities of more than 100,000 in the USSR has
increased rapidly during the Soviet period. The 1926 census recorded only 31 such cities, the 1939 census 82, the 1959 census 146,
and the 1969 estimates, 209. Thus in slightly over 40 years the

TABLE 1

NUMBER OF CITIES OF MORE THAN 100,000 POPULATION IN MAJOR COUNTRIES IN THE MID-1960s

Country	Number of Cities of More Than 100,000 Population	Year
1. Soviet Union	209	1969
2. United States	206*	1965–1966
3. Japan	135	1966
4. India	110	1967
5. People's Republic of China	103	1953–1957
6. United Kingdom	90	1966
7. German Federal Republic	56	1966
8. France	39	1962
9. Italy	36	1965
10. Spain	31	1964–1965
11. Argentina	24	1960
12. Mexico	23	1967
13. Poland	23	1966
14. Nigeria	23	1963
15. Indonesia	22	1961

Sources: Tabulated from United Nations, *Demographic Yearbook 1967* (New York: United Nations, 1968), Table 6, pp. 206–230, and SSSR. Tsentral'noe statisticheskoe upravlenie, *Narodnoe khoziaistvo SSSR v 1968 g. statisticheskii ezhegodnik* (M. Statistika, 1968), pp. 23–32.
* Metropolitan areas. Eighteen other cities of more than 100,000 are included within larger standard metropolitan statistical areas.

number of large cities in the Soviet Union increased more than sixfold.

In terms of total urban population, the Soviet Union occupies second place in the world following the United States (Table 2). In 1959 the Soviet Union had 100.0 million urban dwellers compared with 125.3 million in the United States (1960), 89.2 in the People's Republic of China (1956), and 78.9 million in India (1961). These are also the 4 most populous countries in the world.

When it comes to the percentage which urban population forms of the total population, however, the Soviet Union with 47.9 per cent urban in 1959 occupied an intermediate position between countries with very high levels of urbanization, such as the German Federal Republic, the United Kingdom, the United States, Canada, Japan, and France, all with more than 60 per cent of their populations classified as urban, and countries with low levels of urbanization, such as India, Indonesia, China, and Pakistan, with less than 20 per cent of their population labeled as urban (Table 3). The Soviet Union has about the same level of relative urbanization as Mexico, Poland, Italy, and Brazil (Table 3).

The percentage of the population living in urban settlements has increased sharply in the Soviet Union in recent years, from 18 per cent in the 1926 census to 33 per cent in the 1939 census, 48 per cent in the 1959 census, and 56 per cent in 1969, and is expected to rise to 68 per cent by 1980 and 75 per cent by the year 2000.

The urban population of the Soviet Union increased more than fivefold between 1920 and 1969 from about 24 to 134 million (present boundaries). The highest rate of growth was 1920–1939 and fell into 2 parts: (1) 1920–1926 with recovery from sharp decreases during World War I and the Civil War and (2) 1926–1939 with very rapid urbanization associated with the tempestuous in-

TABLE 2

TOTAL URBAN POPULATION
BY COUNTRY, ABOUT 1960

Country	Total Urban Population (millions)	Year
1. United States	125.3	1960
2. Soviet Union	100.0	1959
(Soviet Union)	(134.2)	(1969)
3. People's Republic of China	89.2	1956 (estimate)
4. India	78.9	1961
5. Japan	66.9	1965
6. United Kingdom	36.8	1961
7. German Federal Republic	33.9	1950
8. Brazil	32.5	1960
9. France	29.3	1962
10. Italy	24.2	1961
11. Mexico	17.7	1960
12. Poland	15.5	1964
13. Indonesia	14.4	1961
14. Canada	12.7	1961
15. Pakistan	12.3	1961
16. Spain	10.3	1950

Sources: United Nations, *Demographic Yearbook 1967*, Table 5, pp. 132–205. Supplementary data from *ibid.*, 1960, Table 9, pp. 373–395; 1962, Table 9, pp. 304–315; 1963, Table 5, pp. 162–230; and 1964, Table 27, pp. 648–664; and SSSR. Tsentral'noe statisticheskoe upravlenie, *Narodnoe knoziaistvo SSSR v 1968 g.*, p. 7.

TABLE 3

PER CENT OF POPULATION URBAN
IN MAJOR COUNTRIES, ABOUT 1960

Country	Per Cent Urban	Year
1. German Federal Republic	78.	1961
2. United Kingdom	76.1	1961
3. United States	69.9	1960
4. Canada	69.7	1961
5. Japan	68.1	1965
6. France	63.0	1962
7. Mexico	50.7	1960
8. Poland	49.4	1964
9. Soviet Union	47.9	1959
(Soviet Union)	(56.2)	(1969)
10. Italy	47.7	1961
11. Brazil	46.3	1960
12. Spain	37.0	1950
13. India	18.0	1961
14. Indonesia	14.8	1961
15. People's Republic of China	14.2	1956 (estimate)
16. Pakistan	13.1	1961

Basic Sources: United Nations, *Demographic Yearbook 1967*, Table 5, pp. 132–205. Supplementary data from *ibid.*, 1960, Table 9, pp. 373–395; 1962, Table 9, pp. 304–315; 1963, Table 5, pp. 162–230; and 1964, Table 27, pp. 648–664, B. S. Khorev, *Gorodskie poseleniia SSSR (problemy rosta i ikh izuchenie); ocherki geografii rasseleniia* (M. Izd. "Mysl'," 1968), p. 12, and SSSR. Tsentral'noe statisticheskoe upravlenie, *Narodnoe khoziaistvo v 1968 g.*, p. 7.

dustrialization of the early Five-Year Plans. Of the 6 major countries, whose urban growth is shown on Figure 1, only Japan had comparably high rates of urban growth during this period before World War II, when its urban population was about half that in the USSR. For the period since World War II the Soviet Union has had a somewhat lower rate of urban growth, while the United States and India have had higher rates than earlier; the rates of growth for the Soviet Union, the United States, and India-Pakistan have been remarkably similar for the period after 1940 (Figure 1). The European countries of earlier urbanization, the United Kingdom, Germany, and France, have had much lower rates. After a heavy loss during World War II, Japan experienced an urban explosion in the decade 1945–1955 that exceeded in rate even the Soviet growth of 1926–1939, which had previously been the world record rate of increase of urban population among countries having at least 20 million urban dwellers.

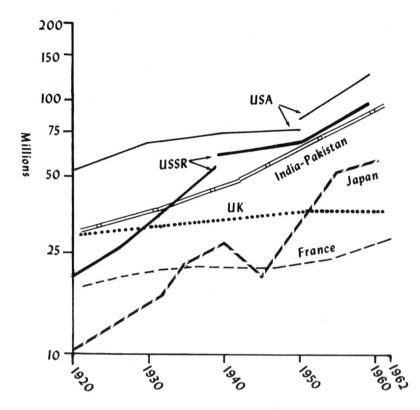

Fig. 1 Growth of urban population ca. 1920–1960 for the United States, USSR, India, Japan, the United Kingdom, and France.

The 1939 double figures for the Soviet Union represent data for old and new boundaries. The 1950 double figure for the United States is for old and new definitions of urban.

Sources: UN, *Demographic Yearbook* 1960, table 9, pp. 373–395, 1962, table 9, pp. 304–315; U. S. Bureau of the Census, *Historical Statistics of the United States,* series A36, p. 9, and official Soviet statistics as given in Table 24 in this monograph.

These international comparisons show that the dramatic upsurge in the urban population of the Soviet Union over the forty-year period 1920–1960 has been at higher rates than in other countries of similarly large urban populations, e.g., the United States and India-Pakistan, especially in the earlier part of the period, and at much higher rates than the European countries of Britain, Germany, and France. On the other hand, the Soviet rate of growth was not unique, since Japan had a slightly higher rate of increase of urban population during this 40-year period.

Looking back over a century and a half of the growth of the urban population of Russia and the Soviet Union, one is struck by the relative regularity of the rate of growth of the units for

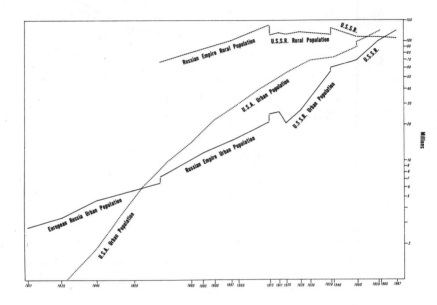

Fig. 2 Growth of urban population in Russia and the Soviet Union, 1811–1967, rural population in the USSR, 1867–1967, and urban population in the United States, 1830–1960.

Double figures for Russia or the Soviet Union for 1867, 1913, and 1939 represent changes in areas covered by the data. Double figures for the United States for 1950 are for old and new definitions of urban.

Sources: Tables 23 and 24 of this monograph and U. S. Bureau of the Census, *Historical Statistics of the United States*, series A36, p. 9.

which comparable data are available at various time periods: of European Russia in the first half of the 19th century, then a slightly higher rate of increase for the Russian Empire (including the Caucasus, Siberia, Middle Asia, and the Far East) in the latter part of the 19th century and early 20th century, and finally within the boundaries of the Soviet Union, a still more rapid rate of increase for the last 50 years (Figure 2). In the Soviet period the highest rates were in the earlier period, especially 1920–1939.

As in the case of the United States, the rural population of the Russian Empire also showed substantial increases during the last half of the 19th century and in the 20th century before World War I, but during the Soviet half century the rural population held relatively constant from 1917 to 1939 and then after World War II began to decline. The rapid growth of urban population has thus been made possible by a massive rural-urban migration.

On the other hand, in the early 19th century the urban population of European Russia was much higher than in the youthful United States. With heavy immigration from Europe, with the expansion of the new country, with the building of railroads, and with the development of industry, the urban population of the United States grew much more rapidly than that of Russia throughout the 19th century. Thus in 1830 the urban population of the United States was less than half that of European Russia, but by 1900 it was about double that of the entire Russian Empire. In 1920 the urban population of the Soviet Union was only two-fifths that of the United States, but since that date the urban population in the USSR has increased more rapidly than in the United States, particularly during the early Five-Year Plans in the Soviet Union and the great depression of the 1930s in the United States. By 1960 the urban population in the USSR was four-fifths that in the United States. The growth curve of urban population in Russia and the Soviet Union is generally concave with increasing rates of growth over the century and a half, while the curve for the United States is generally convex with decreasing rates of growth. These are long-range trends in both countries. As might be expected in recent years as the total urban population of the Soviet Union has become very large and as the proportion of urban population in the total population has risen, the rate of increase of the urban population has begun to taper off.

High rates of growth of the urban population in the Soviet Union depend both on a moderately high natural increase in the population of the country as a whole and on substantial rural-urban migration. A high natural increase provides the human resource for population growth. State economic policy channels this growth into the urban sector and into particular types of cities.

Although the birth rate in the Soviet Union has dropped to only a little over a third the level of 50 years ago, from 45.5 per thousand in 1913 to 17.3 in 1968, the death rate has fallen even more strikingly from 29.1 to 7.7 in the same period (Table 4). The result was the maintenance of a fairly high level of natural increase of the population up to 1960. For example, the 1959 level of rate of natural increase of population of 17.4 per thousand was slightly higher than the level of 1913 (16.4 per thousand). Nevertheless since 1960 the rate of natural increase has dropped dramatically, from 17.8 per thousand in 1960 to 9.6 in 1968, i.e., by almost half. Since 1960 each succeeding year has had a substantially lower rate of natural increase than the previous year.

The very large difference between rural and urban birth rates has been greatly reduced over the past half century. In 1913 the rural birth rate was 48.8 per thousand compared with the urban birth rate of 30.2, a difference of 18.6. In 1968 the difference between the rural and urban birth rates was less than a fourth as much, 4.1 per thousand (19.6 rural and 15.5 urban).

The magnitude of rural-urban migration during the Soviet period is remarkable. For the 32-year period between 1927 and 1959 the net rural-urban migration within the Soviet Union is

TABLE 4

URBAN, RURAL, AND TOTAL BIRTH RATES, DEATH RATES, AND
NATURAL INCREASE IN POPULATION IN THE SOVIET UNION,
1913–1968
(Per Thousand Population)

Year	Birth Rate Urban	Birth Rate Rural	Rural-Urban Difference	Birth Rate Total	Death Rate Total	Natural Increase Total
1913	30.2	48.8	18.6	45.5	29.1	16.4
1926	34.1	46.1	12.0	44.0	20.3	23.7
1940	30.5	31.5	1.0	31.2	18.0	13.2
1959	22.0	27.8	5.8	25.0	7.6	17.4
1968	15.5	19.6	4.1	17.3	7.7	9.6

Source: SSSR. Tsentral'noe statisticheskoe upravlenie, *Narodnoe khoziaistvo SSSR v 1965 g.*, pp. 42–43; *Narodnoe khoziaistvo SSSR v 1968 g.*, pp. 36–37.

estimated at 43 million persons. This flow is of the same magnitude as the total estimated net overseas migration from Europe to the Americas, Africa, and Oceania during the entire 19th century and the 20th century up to World War II.[1]

The number of cities and towns in the USSR has also increased dramatically during the Soviet period. Between 1926 and 1967 their number increased from 1,925 to 5,348.[2] By 1980 they are expected to number 6,900. There are two types of urban settlements officially recognized in the Soviet Union, cities proper (*goroda*) which increased in number in this period from 709 to 1,888 and towns or settlements of urban type (*poselki gorodskogo tipa*), which increased in number from 1,216 to 3,460. The average size of cities and towns obviously increased since the total urban population multiplied 5-fold and the number of urban settlements just under 3-fold. Urban population in the Soviet Union is defined as the population in cities or settlements of urban type. In general cities have more than 10,000 population and settlements of urban type under 10,000, although the criteria for recognition of each depends on function as well as size, varies from republic to republic, and has changed over time.[3] Some small cities are relicts of earlier juridical criteria. But, in any case, about two-thirds of the cities and settlements of urban type have been established as such during the last 40 years. Indeed, settlements of urban type received status as such only during the Soviet period, although many of them were previously urban in function but recognized only as villages.

[1] Frank Lorimer, "Population," *Encyclopedia Britannica*, 1965 ed., vol. 18, p. 234, estimates the total net overseas migration from Europe 1800–1940 at 40–45 million out of a total migration of 60 million during this period.

[2] V. G. Davidovich, "O zakonomernostiakh i tendentsiiakh gorodskogo rasseleniia v SSSR," *Voprosy geografii*, sbornik 66 (M. Izd. "Mysl'," 1965), table 9, p. 21, and *SSSR: Administrativno-territorial'noe delenie soiuznyk respublik na l iiulia 1967 goda* (M. 1967), p. xix.

[3] O. A. Konstantinov, "Sovremennoe sostoianie deleniia naselennykh punktov SSSR na gorodskie i sel'skie," *Izvestiia AN SSSR, seriia geograficheskaia*, 1958, no. 6, pp. 69–78.

V. G. Davidovich, S. A. Kovalev, and V. V. Pokshishevskii, "Ob osnovakh klassifikatsii naselennykh punktov SSSR (v sviazi s zadachami ekonomicheskoi geografii)," *Izvestiia AN SSSR, seriia geograficheskaia*, 1959, no. 4, pp. 106–116.

V. G. Davidovich, "Opredelenie poniatii 'goroda' i 'poselki gorodskogo tipa," in "O razvitii seti gorodov SSSR za 40 let," *Voprosy geografii*, sbornik 45 (M. Geografgiz, 1959), pp. 43–47.

According to the 1959 census about a quarter of the urban dwellers in the Soviet Union live in cities of more than 500,000 population, another quarter in cities 100,000–499,999, another quarter in cities of 20,000–99,999, and about a quarter in cities of less than 20,000 population (Table 5). Of the 4,619 urban units of that date, 1,679 were classed as cities and 2,940 as settlements of urban type. Cities, although fewer in number than settlements of urban type, contained 83 per cent of the urban population.

TABLE 5

NUMBER OF URBAN SETTLEMENTS BY SIZE AND THEIR POPULATION, SOVIET UNION, 1959

Size Category In Population	Number	Total Population
Over 500,000	25	24,162,753
100,000–499,999	123	24,425,829
50,000–99,999	156	10,989,803
20,000–49,999	474	14,828,309
10,000–19,999	798	11,150,064
5,000–9,999	1,296	9,213,576
3,000–4,999	904	3,596,828
Under 3,000	843	1,610,533
Total	4,619	99,977,695
Cities	1,679	82,941,202
Settlement of Urban Type	2,940	17,036,493

Source: SSSR, Tsentral'noe statisticheskoe upravlenie, *Itogi vsesoiuznoi perepisi naseleniia 1959 goda, SSSR (svodnyi tom)* (M. Gosstatizdat, 1962), table 7, p. 35.

Not all parts of the Soviet Union are effectively settled or densely populated. Most of the people live in less than a quarter of the country. This inhabited area may be called the "ecumene." It forms a fertile triangle with a broad base along the western boundary of the Soviet Union and extends eastward as a gradually narrowing wedge halfway across the country to near 90° East Longitude, with a southern extension into the Caucasus region between the Black Sea and the Caspian Sea and another arm sweeping southwestward from the eastern end of the continuous ecumene to include the oases at the bases of the mountains of Soviet Middle Asia. Outliers of the ecumene are stretched like beads along the Trans-Siberian Railroad in the basins at the southern edge of Siberia and the Soviet Far East.

The ecumene is that part of the Soviet Union in which climatic conditions are generally suitable for farming. To the southeast of the ecumene lie the great empty deserts of Soviet Middle Asia. To the north of the ecumene lie the even vaster northern coniferous forests and tundras with very sparse settlement of any kind and only isolated cities. The ecumene on Figure 3 has been

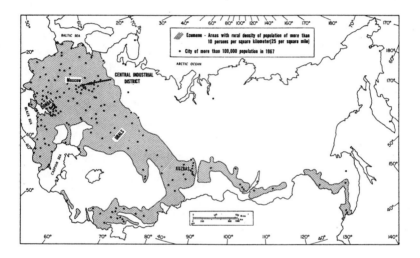

Fig. 3 The distribution of the 201 cities of more than 100,000 population in 1967 in relation to the Soviet Ecumene, the main inhabited portion of the country.

defined as the area with a rural density of population of more than 10 persons per square kilometer (25 per square mile), but most areas outside the ecumene have fewer than one person per square kilometer. The area thus delimited includes about 5 million square kilometers (2 million square miles), or less than a quarter of the total area of the Soviet Union (22.4 million square kilometers or 8.6 square miles). Within it are located 97 per cent of the Soviet cities of more than 100,000 population in 1967 (194 of the 201 such cities). The 6 cities outside the ecumene are mining centers or ports in the vast forests or tundras of the northlands.

The distribution of Soviet cities reveals 2 major types: (1) dispersed central places which are centers of trade, administration, and cultural life and (2) highly localized clusters of cities which have more specialized functions. Central places tend to be evenly spaced throughout the ecumene, each surrounded by its own tributary area and thus distant from a similar city of same rank in the central-place hierarchy. The hierarchy ranges from the capital for the entire country, Moscow, through a group of major regional centers, to centers of oblasts or similar political-administrative units, and then down to centers of rural rayons.

Since the major regional centers and their areas are widely used for orientation purposes, it is well to identify them at this stage (Figure 4 and Table 6). Moscow, the capital of the country, with a 1967 population of 6.5 million stands at the head of the hierarchy of cities. Within the European portion of the Soviet Union the central places for the very largest regions are, in a counterclockwise direction: Leningrad for the Northwest Region, Riga for the Baltic republics, Minsk for Belorussia, Kiev, Odessa,

TABLE 6

Major Regional Centers and Regions
in the Soviet Union

City	Population 1967 Estimated (in thousands)	Region
Moscow	6,507	USSR as a whole
		Central Industrial Region
Leningrad	3,706	Northwest
Riga	780	Baltic
Minsk	680	Belorussia
Kiev	1,413	Southwest in the Ukraine
Odessa	776	South in the Ukraine
Khar'kov	1,125	Donets-Dnepr in the Ukraine
Rostov	757	North Caucasus
Voronezh	611	Central Black Earth
Kuybyshev	992	Volga
Gor'kiy	1,120	Volga-Vyatka
Sverdlovsk	961	Urals
Novosibirsk	1,064	Western Siberia
Irkutsk	420	Eastern Siberia
Khabarovsk	435	Soviet Far East
Tbilisi	842	Caucasus
Alma-Ata	652	Kazakhstan
Tashkent	1,239	Soviet Middle Asia

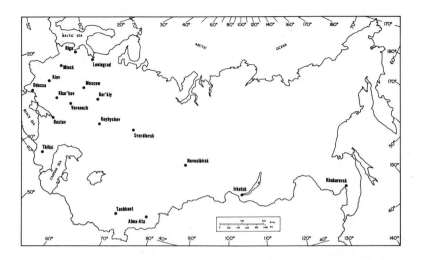

Fig. 4 Major regional centers of the Soviet Union.

and Khar'kov for three portions of the Ukraine, Rostov for the
North Caucasus, Voronezh for the Black-Earth Center, Kuybyshev
for the Volga, and Gor'kiy for the Volga-Vyatka region. Then in
the great sweep eastward from the Urals to the Pacific, Sverdlovsk
is the regional center for the Urals, Novosobirsk for Western Siberia, Irkutsk for Eastern Siberia, and Khabarovsk for the Soviet
Far East. Further to the south Tbilisi serves as a major central
place for the Caucasus, Alma-Ata for Kazakhstan, and Tashkent
for Soviet Middle Asia. Each of these major centers is widely separated from the nearest center of co-ordinate rank and each has a
structured set of subordinate regional centers. The populations
bear some relationship to the size and population of the tributary
region; the only centers with less than half a million population,
Irkutsk and Khabarovsk, lie in the sparsely settled but very large
regions of Eastern Siberia and the Soviet Far East. The vast northern regions with a very small population have no regional center
of comparable rank.

The second type of city is the localized special-function city.
These cities often occur in clusters at or near some resource of
limited distribution, such as a coalfield. The distribution of the
201 cities of more than 100,000 population reveals some of the
more important of these clusters (Figure 3). Just north of the

Black Sea in the southern edge of the European part of the Soviet Union a dozen large cities are bunched together in the rich Donets coal basin (Donbas), which since the late 19th century has been the leading Soviet district for coal mining and related heavy industry, including steel, chemicals, and machinery. None of these cities is an ancient regional center; all are closely tied to highly localized natural resources, to economic utilization of these resources, or to economic activities that have evolved out of the mining and manufacturing in the region. A similar cluster lies at the eastern apex of the continuous ecumene, the Kuznetsk coal basin (Kuzbas) with 7 closely packed large cities, the density of which contrasts sharply with the great open spaces of much of Siberia (Figure 3). The 17 large cities of the Urals are more widely spread among diverse mineral deposits of that great storehouse of metalliferous ores; some are located at iron-ore deposits, others at nonferrous ore deposits, and some at sites of other minerals or at convenient assembly points for processing ores or resulting metals. The Central Industrial District near Moscow is somewhat different. It is the home of the Slavic people and the political center from which the Russian state was formed historically. It has many venerable cities that were centers of small regions. Nevertheless its 23 large cities reveal some clustering qualities based on the early development of manufacturing (similar to New England and Lancashire), at first of textiles but later of a great range of machinery and other products.

TABLE 7

Soviet Cities with More than 100,000 Population 1967
Arranged by Major Economic Region
Republic, and Oblast (or comparable unit).
Population in thousands.

(For location of cities see Figures 5 and 6.)

No.	Name	Oblast	Pop.
		Russia Proper (RSFSR) (R)	
		Northwest (R1)	
2	Leningrad	Leningrad	3706
70	Kaliningrad	Kaliningrad	270
181	Pskov	Pskov	112

TABLE 7 — Continued

SOVIET CITIES WITH MORE THAN 100,000 POPULATION 1967

No.	Name	Oblast	Pop.
188	Novgorod	Novgorod	107
113	Vologda	Vologda	170
119	Cherepovets	Vologda	165
112	Petrozavodsk	Karelian A	171
68	Murmansk	Murmansk	287
61	Arkhangel'sk	Arkhangel'sk	310
164	Severodvinsk	Arkhangel'sk	121
196	Syktyvkar	Komi A	102
		Central (R2)	
1	Moscow	Moscow	6507
121	Podol'sk	Moscow	163
147	Kolomna	Moscow	131
162	Serpukhov	Moscow	121
167	Lyubertsy	Moscow	120
173	Orekhovo-Zuyevo	Moscow	117
174	Elektrostal'	Moscow	117
180	Mytishchi	Moscow	112
194	Noginsk	Moscow	102
33	Yaroslavl'	Yaroslavl'	498
86	Rybinsk	Yaroslavl'	212
92	Kostroma	Kostroma	209
38	Ivanovo	Ivanovo	407
89	Vladimir	Vladimir	211
177	Kovrov	Vladimir	116
60	Ryazan'	Ryazan'	311
45	Tula	Tula	377
153	Novomoskovsk	Tula	126
93	Orël	Orël	209
104	Kaluga	Kaluga	179
67	Bryansk	Bryansk	288
99	Smolensk	Smolensk	196
58	Kalinin	Kalinin	318
		Volga-Vyatka (R3)	
7	Gor'kiy	Gor'kiy	1120
98	Dzerzhinsk	Gor'kiy	201
62	Kirov	Kirov	309
142	Yoshkar-Ola	Mari A	137
107	Cheboksary	Chuvash A	178
129	Saransk	Mordov A	154
		Central Black Earth (R4)	
27	Voronezh	Voronezh	611
151	Belgorod	Belgorod	129
71	Kursk	Kursk	255
72	Lipetsk	Lipetsk	253
88	Tambov	Tambov	211

TABLE 7 — Continued

SOVIET CITIES WITH MORE THAN 100,000 POPULATION 1967

No.	Name	Oblast	Pop.
		Volga (R5)	
9	Kuybyshev	Kuybyshev	992
114	Syzran'	Kuybyshev	169
132	Tol'yatti	Kuybyshev	143
187	Novokuybyshevsk	Kuybyshev	107
65	Ul'yanovsk	Ul'yanovsk	294
14	Kazan'	Tatar A	821
23	Ufa	Bashkir A	704
123	Sterlitamak	Bashkir A	162
53	Penza	Penza	333
22	Saratov	Saratov	720
159	Engel's	Saratov	122
21	Volgograd	Volgograd	743
178	Volzhskiy	Volgograd	114
47	Astrakhan'	Astrakhan'	368
		North Caucasus (R6)	
20	Rostov-na-Donu	Rostov	757
74	Taganrog	Rostov	245
90	Shakhty	Rostov	209
125	Novocherkassk	Rostov	161
186	Novoshakhtinsk	Rostov	107
39	Krasnodar	Krasnodar	407
100	Sochi	Krasnodar	188
138	Armavir	Krasnodar	139
156	Novorossiysk	Krasnodar	123
189	Maykop	Krasnodar (Adygey AO)	106
108	Stavropol'	Stavropol'	177
169	Nal'chik	Kabardino-Balkar A	119
82	Ordzhonikidze	N. Oset A	219
55	Groznyy	Chechen-Ingush A	331
120	Makhachkala	Dagestan A	165
		Urals (R7)	
10	Sverdlovsk	Sverdlovsk	961
44	Nizhniy Tagil	Sverdlovsk	377
124	Kamensk-Ural'skiy	Sverdlovsk	161
183	Pervoural'sk	Sverdlovsk	110
190	Serov	Sverdlovsk	104
13	Chelyabinsk	Chelyabinsk	836
49	Magnitogorsk	Chelyabinsk	357
105	Zlatoust	Chelyabinsk	178
117	Kopeysk	Chelyabinsk	166
160	Miass	Chelyabinsk	122
16	Perm'	Perm'	796
145	Berezniki	Perm'	134

TABLE 7 — Continued

Soviet Cities with More than 100,000 Population 1967

No.	Name	Oblast	Pop.
46	Izhevsk	Udmurt A	376
85	Kurgan	Kurgan	215
56	Orenburg	Orenburg	326
84	Orsk	Orenburg	215

Western Siberia (R8)

8	Novosibirsk	Novosibirsk	1064
34	Novokuznetsk	Kemerovo	493
48	Kemerovo	Kemerovo	364
66	Prokop'yevsk	Kemerovo	290
140	Leninsk-Kuznetskiy	Kemerovo	138
141	Kiselëvsk	Kemerovo	138
175	Anzhero-Sudzhensk	Kemerovo	116
176	Belovo	Kemerovo	116
40	Barnaul	Altay	407
103	Biysk	Altay	181
133	Rubtsovsk	Altay	142
75	Tyumen'	Tyumen'	240
18	Omsk	Omsk	774
57	Tomsk	Tomsk	324

Eastern Siberia (R9)

29	Krasnoyarsk	Krasnoyarsk	576
150	Noril'sk	Krasnoyarsk	129
36	Irkutsk	Irkutsk	420
102	Angarsk	Irkutsk	183
161	Bratsk	Irkutsk	122
185	Cheremkhovo	Irkutsk	109
79	Ulan-Ude	Buryat A	227
96	Chita	Chita	203

Far East (R10)

35	Khabarovsk	Khabarovsk	435
91	Komsomol'sk-na-Amure	Khabarovsk	209
163	Blagoveshchensk	Amur	121
41	Vladivostok	Primorskiy	397
154	Ussuriysk	Primorskiy	124
158	Petropavlovsk-Kamchatskiy	Kamchatka	123

Ukraine (U)
Donets-Dnepr (U1)

6	Khar'kov	Khar'kov	1125
12	Donetsk	Donetsk	840
37	Makeyevka	Donetsk	414
43	Zhdanov	Donetsk	385
51	Gorlovka	Donetsk	343

TABLE 7 — Continued

SOVIET CITIES WITH MORE THAN 100,000 POPULATION 1967

No.	Name	Oblast	Pop.
134	Kramatorsk	Donetsk	141
179	Slavyansk	Donetsk	113
192	Konstantinovka	Donetsk	103
50	Lugansk	Lugansk	352
137	Kadiyevka	Lugansk	139
155	Kommunarsk	Lugansk	124
165	Lisichansk	Lugansk	120
193	Krasnyy Luch	Lugansk	102
15	Dnepropetrovsk	Dnepropetrovsk	816
31	Krivoy Rog	Dnepropetrovsk	510
80	Dneprodzerzhinsk	Dnepropetrovsk	224
184	Nikopol'	Dnepropetrovsk	110
28	Zaporozh'ye	Zaporozh'ye	595
168	Melitopol'	Zaporozh'ye	119
116	Kirovograd	Kirovograd	168
101	Poltava	Poltava	184
143	Kremenchug	Poltava	136
136	Sumy	Sumy	140

Southwest (U2)

3	Kiev	Kiev	1413
139	Chernigov	Chernigov	139
152	Cherkassy	Cherkassy	128
135	Zhitomir	Zhitomir	141
122	Vinnitsa	Vinnitsa	163
200	Rovno	Rovno	100
106	Chernovtsy	Chernovtsy	178
30	L'vov	L'vov	512

South (U3)

17	Odessa	Odessa	776
64	Nikolayev	Nikolayev	300
78	Kherson	Kherson	235
81	Simferopol'	Crimea	223
94	Sevastopol'	Crimea	209
171	Kerch'	Crimea	118

Baltic (Ba)

24	Riga	Latvia (La)	680
52	Tallin	Estonia (E)	340
59	Vil'nyus	Lithuania (Li)	316
69	Kaunas	Lithuania (Li)	284
149	Klaypeda	Lithuania (Li)	131

Belorussia (B)

19	Minsk	Minsk	772
97	Vitebsk	Vitebsk	203
110	Mogilev	Mogilev	176

TABLE 7 — Continued

SOVIET CITIES WITH MORE THAN 100,000 POPULATION 1967

No.	Name	Oblast	Pop.
166	Bobruysk	Mogilev	120
77	Gomel'	Gomel'	237
182	Grodno	Grodno	111
		Moldavia (Mo)	
63	Kishinev		302
		Caucasus (C)	
5	Baku	Azerbaydzhan (Az)	1196
111	Kirovabad	Azerbaydzhan (Az)	174
191	Sumgait	Azerbaydzhan (Az)	104
11	Tbilisi	Georgia (G)	842
126	Kutaisi	Georgia (G)	159
198	Batumi	Georgia (G) (Adzhar A)	100
25	Yerevan	Armenia (A)	665
146	Leninakan	Armenia (A)	133

Kazakhstan (K)
Central and Eastern Kazakhstan (K1)

26	Alma-Ata	Alma-Ata	652
32	Karaganda	Karaganda	498
131	Temirtau	Karaganda	150
95	Semipalatinsk	Semipalatinsk	204
87	Ust'-Kamenogorsk	E. Kazakhstan	212

Tselinnyy Kray (K2) (Virgin Lands)

109	Tselinograd	Tselinograd	176
118	Petropavlovsk	N. Kazakhstan	166
172	Kustanay	Kustanay	118
130	Pavlodar	Pavlodar	154

West Kazakhstan Kray (K3)

144	Aktyubinsk	Aktyubinsk	135
157	Ural'sk	Ural'sk	123
197	Gur'yev	Gur'yev	101

South Kazakhstan Kray (K4)

83	Chimkent	Chimkent	219
128	Dzhambul	Dzhambul	158

Middle Asia (M)
Uzbekistan

4	Tashkent	Tashkent	1239
201	Chirchik	Tashkent	100
195	Bukhara	Bukhara	102
73	Samarkand	Samarkand	248
115	Andizhan	Andizhan	169

TABLE 7 — Continued

Soviet Cities with More than 100,000 Population 1967

No.	Name	Oblast	Pop.
127	Namangan	Andizhan	158
148	Kokand	Fergana	131
		Other republics	
42	Frunze	Kirgizia	396
170	Osh	Kirgizia	119
54	Dushanbe	Tadzhikistan	333
199	Leninabad	Tadzhikistan	100
76	Ashkhabad	Turkmenia	238

Abbreviations:
A Autonomous Soviet Socialist Republic
AO Autonomous Oblast
Boundaries of Major Economic Regions as in *Narodnoe Khoziaistvo SSSR v 1965 g.,* Moskva, 1966, pp. 849-850.
Source: USSR. Prezidium Verkhnogo Soveta. *SSSR. Administrativno-Territorial'noe Delenie Soiuznykh Respublik na l, iiulia 1967 goda.* Moskva, 1967, "Perechen' gorodov s ukazaniem chislennosti naseleniia," pp. 592-604. Estimates for January 1, 1967.

The distribution of the 201 cities of more than 100,000 population in 1967 is shown on Figures 5 and 6. These cities, hereafter called large cities, are listed region by region in Table 7. Within each oblast the cities are arranged in order of size in 1967. The order of listing of regions is that traditionally given in Soviet sources, first the 10 regions of the Russian Soviet Federated Socialist Republic (RSFSR) from west to east, followed by the regions made up of the other republics, beginning with the second most populous republic, the Ukrainian Soviet Socialist Republic (SSR), and followed by the regions of the other republics beginning in the northwest and proceeding first south along the western boundary of the Soviet Union to the Black Sea and then eastward through the Caucasus and Kazakhstan to Soviet Middle Asia.

The Northwest Region of the RSFSR (R1) dominated by Leningrad has 11 large cities which are fairly widely spaced. The Central Region (R2) centered on Moscow has 23 large cities, many of which form clusters, either as suburbs or satellites of Moscow or as industrial cities of the Central Industrial Region north and east of Moscow. The Volga-Vyatka Region (R3) centered on Gor'kiy has 6 large cities including both industrial satellites of Gor'kiy and central-place administrative centers of autonomous republics (ASSR). The Central-Black Earth Region (R4) has only 5 large cities, all of central-place administrative types, the largest of which is Voronezh. The Volga Region (R5) is centered in Kuybyshev and some major regional administrative centers of large size, such as Kazan' (capital of the Tatar ASSR), Ufa (capital of the Bashkir ASSR), and Saratov and Volgograd (both centers of oblasts), each of which has more than 700 thousand population. The North Caucasus Region (R6) has 15 large cities including both central-place and industrial types; Rostov-na-Donu is the regional center. The Urals Region (R7) dominated by mining and industry (with very little agriculture or true rural settlement) has 16 large cities with 3 very large cities, Sverdlovsk, Chelyabinsk, and Perm', each just under a million population. Western Siberia (R8), with its regional center at Novosibirsk, has 14 large cities, 7 of which are clustered together in Kemerovo Oblast; these are the mining and industrial cities of the Kuznetsk Coal Basin (Kuzbas). The vast territory of Eastern Siberia (R9) has 8 large cities, all on the southern fringe; Krasnoyarsk in the west and Irkutsk in the east are the 2 main centers. The last region within the RSFSR, the Soviet Far East (R10), has 6 large cities, with major centers at Khabarovsk and Vladivostok.

The Ukrainian SSR is divided into 3 major regions. The Donets-Dneper Region (U1) with 23 large cities rivals the Central Region in number of cities of more than 100,000 population. The major concentration lies in the cluster of mining and industrial cities of the Donets Coal Basin (Donbas) in Donetsk and Lugansk oblasts (12 cities of more than 100,000 population). This region has 3 very large centers: Khar'kov, one of the largest cities of the country, Donetsk, the center of the Donbas, and Dnepropetrovsk on the Dnepr River, an industrial city between the coalfield and the iron-ore deposits. The Southwest Region (U2) with major centers in Kiev in the east and L'vov in the west has 8 large cities. In contrast to the Donbas cluster of industrial cities, these are all central-place administrative types fairly evenly distributed throughout the region, only one to an oblast and each the administrative center of its oblast. The Southern Region (U3), dominated by Odessa, has 6 large cities.

The other major regions along the western boundary of the Soviet Union include the Baltic Region (Ba) with 5 large cities,

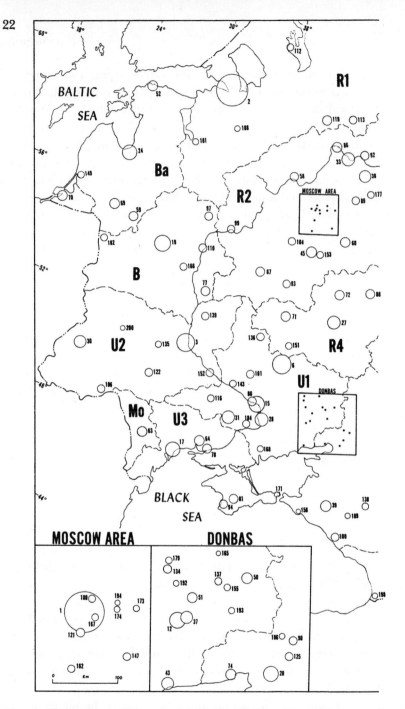

Fig. 5 Cities of more than 100,000 population in 1967: western part of USSR. For identification of regions and cities, see Table 7, or Table 27.

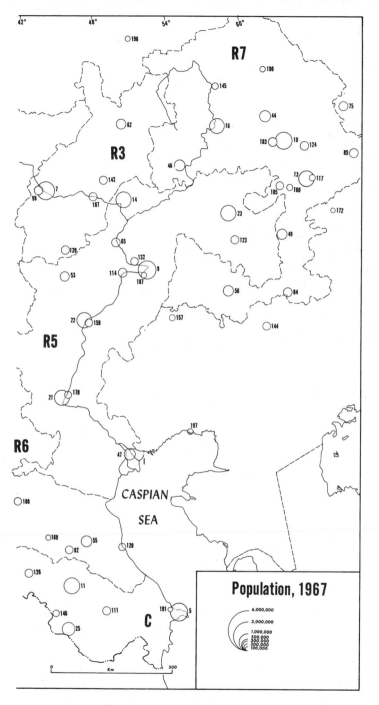

Population, 1967

6,000,000

3,000,000

1,000,000
500,000
300,000
200,000
100,000

0   500
      Km

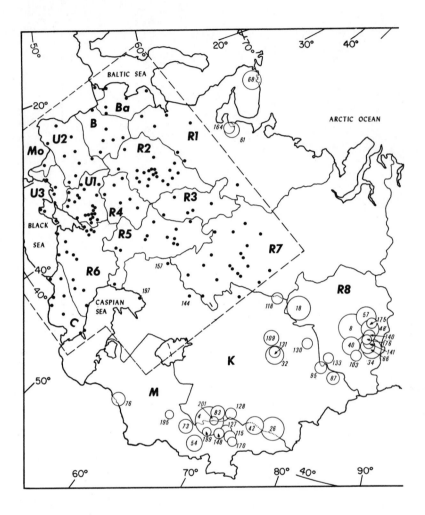

Fig. 6 Cities of more than 100,000 population in 1967: rest of Soviet Union.

among which Riga is the largest, Belorussia (B) with 6 large cities, all of central-place type, centered on Minsk, and the small Moldavian Region (Mo) with only a single large city, Kishinëv.

Along the southern border of the Soviet Union are the regions of the Caucasus, Kazakhstan, and Soviet Middle Asia. The Caucasus Region (C) has 8 large cities with 3 very large cities, each a capital of a union republic: Baku (of the Azerbaydzhan SSR),

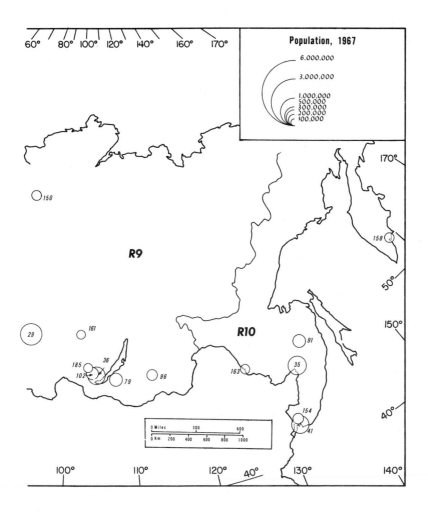

Tbilisi (of the Georgian SSR) and Yerevan (of the Armenian SSR).
Kazakhstan or the Kazakh SSR (K) has 14 large cities. It may be
conveniently but arbitrarily divided into 4 regions for description
here: Central and Eastern Kazakhstan (K1) centered on Alma-Ata,
the capital, and Karaganda, the leading industrial center and mining town; the Virgin Lands Region (Tselinnyy Kray) (K2) centered on Tselinograd in the northern part of the republic; West

Kazakhstan Kray (K3), centered on Aktyubinsk; and South Kazakhstan Kray (K4), centered on Chimkent. The last 3 of these regions formerly existing as krays (an intermediate unit between the Kazakh SSR and the constituent oblasts) lost their official status in the last administrative handbook of the Soviet Union.[4] It might be better to treat the whole of Kazakhstan as a single large region. On the other hand, the 4 union republics of Soviet Middle Asia (M) were earlier grouped into a single large region centered on Tashkent and with 12 large cities; these 4 republics are the Uzbek centered on Tashkent with 7 large cities, the Kirgiz centered on Frunze with 2 large cities, the Tadzhik centered on Dushanbe with 2 large cities, and the Turkmen with only one large city, Ashkhabad, the capital.

The rapid urbanization of the Soviet Union is part of a worldwide process of urbanization, modernization, specialization, interdependence, and economic development, but it has had special features associated with Socialist planning in the Soviet Union. Under a series of Five-Year Plans beginning in 1928, Soviet policy has been directed to the achievement of the most rapid possible industrial development, particularly of heavy industries. Thus in less than 40 years in the period 1928–1967 the production of pig iron rose from 3 to 75 million metric tons, of steel from 4 to 102 million tons, of coal from 36 to 595 million tons, of petroleum from 12 to 288 million tons, of natural gas from 0.3 to 159 billion cubic meters, and of electric power from 5 to 589 billion kilowatt hours, to mention only the most basic indicators of production of metals and energy and fuel.[5]

The high degree of relationship of urbanization and industrialization in the Soviet Union has been measured statistically by Lewis and Rowland.[6] They found a rank correlation among major economic regions of 0.803 between the change in level of urbanization in 1897 and 1961 (as measured by the percentage of the

[4] Based on *SSSR. Administrativno-territorial'noe delenie Soiuznykh Respublik na l iiulia 1967 goda* (Moskva, 1967), pp. 363–395.

[5] SSSR. Tsentral'noe Statisticheskoe Upravlenie, *Strana Sovetov za 50 let: Sbornik Statisticheskikh Materialov.* (Moskva, "Statistika," 1967), p. 53 (for 1928), and *Pravda* and *Izvestiia,* January 25, 1968, pp. 1–2 (for 1967).

[6] Robert A. Lewis and Richard H. Rowland, "Urbanization in Russia and the USSR: 1897–1966," *Annals of the Association of American Geographers,* vol. 59, no. 4 (December, 1969), pp. 776–796. Reference to table 9, p. 791.

population classified as urban in each year) and the change in percentage of the labor force in manufacturing. They also found a rank correlation among major economic regions of 0.828 between level of urbanization in 1959 and percentage of the total labor force in manufacturing in 1961. Industrialization was found to be a modest factor in urbanization in 1897 or in changes in levels of urbanization during the period 1897–1926. However, industrialization has been a major factor in the rapid rises in level of urbanization since 1926.

This tempestuous industrialization, undertaken at a pace unmatched by any other country, at least in the sphere of heavy industry, has been the result of a deliberate governmental policy of industrial and economic development beginning with heavy industry. Since the Soviet government is the owner of all industrial enterprises and of all trade, it has been able to focus a very high fraction of the national income into such development and has thus been able to accelerate its growth at the expense of other segments of the economy, such as agriculture and consumer goods. This industrialization, particularly striking in the early Five-Year Plans, was closely associated with and indeed encouraged the rapid urbanization. Government policy on industrial development will not be explicitly examined in this monograph, though it must always be borne in mind as part of the driving force behind the rapid urbanization and as a factor in the distribution, size characteristics, and economic functions of cities.

II.

Soviet Studies of the Geography
of Cities of the U.S.S.R.

A geography of settlements, and especially of cities, is unknown in Soviet geography.

— Arved Schultz
Geographisches Jahrbuch,
Band 52, 1937, p. 136

Works on the geography of cities of the U.S.S.R. are now numerous.

— O. A. Konstantinov
in *Geografiia naseleniia v SSSR: osnovnye problemy,* 1964, p. 46

THE 1937 ASSERTION OF ARVED SCHULTZ, the German geographer, that Soviet geography did not know any geography of cities was essentially true at that time as there was not then in the Soviet Union a well-recognized separate branch of geography dealing specifically with cities. Today the situation is entirely different. Many Soviet geographers have an interest in cities. A rich literature has developed in Soviet urban geography. My card file of Soviet geographers, who have written papers, chapters, articles, books, or monographs on some phase of Soviet cities includes about four hundred names. My bibliography of works on the geography of Soviet cities runs to more than a thousand items. This impressive corpus of scholarly material is far too extensive to be treated in detail in this monograph. Nevertheless it is ap-

propriate to review very briefly some of the main directions of
this Soviet work in urban geography as a background for the
present study.

The Soviet geographers, O. A. Konstantinov and E. V. Knobel'sdorf, the American geographer, Roland Fuchs, and the German geographer, Dora Fischer, have all reviewed the development of urban geography in the Soviet Union.[1]

In the Soviet Union urban geography is generally considered
a part of population geography, which is recognized as a sub-
field of economic geography.

RISE OF URBAN GEOGRAPHY IN THE SOVIET UNION

The pioneer research monograph on the urban geography of the
present Soviet Union was written by V. P. Semenov-Tian-Shanskii
in 1910.[2] He was impressed that the settlements officially recognized as cities were not identical with the settlements which had
urban functions. On the one hand, many of the official cities were
little more than small villages. On the other hand, many industrial settlements of various types were large in population and
entirely urban in function but were not administratively recognized as cities. Semenov-Tian-Shanskii pioneered in focussing
attention not on juridical status but rather on size and on economic function. He thus anticipated later development of Soviet
urban geography as a branch of economic geography and current bases for the official recognition of cities in which population and industrial employment are given greater weight. Such
large industrial settlements as Donetsk (formerly Yuzovka),

[1] O. A. Konstantinov, "Geograficheskoe izuchenie gorodskikh poselenii v SSSR,"
in *Geografiia naseleniia v SSSR: osnovnye problemy* (M-L: Izd. "Nauka,"
1964), pp. 32–68; O. A. Konstantinov, "Wissenschaftliche Grundprobleme der
sowjetischen Stadtgeographie," *Geographische Berichte*, vol. 10, no. 36 (1965,
no. 3), pp. 202–211; E. V. Knobel'sdorf, "Sovremennye problemy geografii
sovetskikh gorodov," *Voprosy geografii gorodov Pribaltiki*, Publikatsii Estonskogo geograficheskogo obshchestva, 5 (Tallin: Izd. AN Estonskoi SSR, 1962),
pp. 5–25; Dora Fischer, "Siedlungsgeographie in der Sowjetunion," *Erdkunde;
Archiv für wissenschaftliche Geographie*, Band 20, Heft 3 (September, 1966),
pp. 211–227; and Roland J. Fuchs, "Soviet urban geography: an appraisal of
postwar research," *Annals of the Association of American Geographers*, vol. 54,
no. 2 (June, 1964), pp. 276–289.
[2] V. P. Semenov-Tian-Shanskii, "Gorod i derevnia v Evropeiskoi Rossii: ocherk
po ekonomicheskoi geografii," *Zapiski Russkogo geograficheskogo obshchestva
po otdeleniiu statistiki*, tom 10, vypusk 2, S.-Peterburg, 1910, 212 pp.

Nizhniy Tagil, and Izhevsk were given the status of cities only during the Soviet period.

Soviet urban geography had its beginnings in Leningrad in the late 1920s and the 1930s. In an institute devoted to the municipal economy (now an engineering-construction institute), a course in economic geography was developed which devoted special attention to cities.[3] Planning agencies also were concerned with the burgeoning new cities of socialist construction. Early papers of this period especially worthy of mention were written by O. A. Konstantinov and V. V. Pokshishevskii.[4]

The second great impetus to Soviet urban geography came from Moscow. Immediately after World War II, R. M. Kabo helped establish the commission on geography of population and cities in the Moscow branch of the Geographical Society of the USSR (the headquarters of which is in Leningrad) and inaugurated a course on the geography of population at Moscow University (although he was associated mainly with the Moscow Pedagogical Institute named for Lenin). This commission proved to be an important and very productive focus of the interests and activities of many Moscow geographers interested in cities.

N. N. Baranskii of Moscow State University published in 1946 the single most influential paper ever written in Soviet urban geography outlining the field and methods for the economic-geographic study of cities.[5] A high proportion of later work in

---

[3] The early period in Soviet urban geography in Leningrad and the birth of the Moscow group is treated in detail in O. A. Konstantinov, "Istoriia formirovaniia v SSSR geografii gorodov kak osoboi otrasli geograficheskikh znanii (materialy k dokladu Geograficheskoe izuchenie gorodskikh poselenii v SSSR)," in *Materialy po geografii naseleniia*, vypusk 1 (L. Geograficheskoe obshchestvo Soiuza SSR. Otdelenie ekonomicheskoi geografii, 1962), pp. 109–151. Rotaprint.
[4] O. A. Konstantinov, "K voprosu ob ekonomiko-geograficheskom izuchenii gorodov SSSR," *Trudy geografo-ekonomicheskogo nauchno-issledovatel'skogo instituta pri LGU*, vypusk 2, L., 1934, pp. 8–33; O. A. Konstantinov, "Osnovnye problemy ekonomiko-geograficheskogo izucheniia gorodov SSSR," *Trudy pervogo Vsesoiuznogo geograficheskogo s"ezda*, vypusk 4, L. 1934, 67–95; V. V. Pokshishevskii, "O probleme vnutrigorodskoi khoziaistvennoi geografii," *Komunnal'noe delo*, 1929, no. 7; and V. V. Pokshishevskii, "O kraevednoi rabote po kompleksnomu izucheniiu gorodov," *Sovetskoe kraevedenie*, 1931, no. 2; and many others, especially on Leningrad.
[5] N. N. Baranskii, "Ob ekonomiko-geograficheskom izuchenii gorodov," *Voprosy geografii*, sbornik 2 (1946), pp. 19–62; revised in his book *Ekonomicheskaia geografiia; ekonomicheskaia kartografiia* (M. Geografgiz, 1956), pp. 164–214, 2nd ed., 1950, pp. 172–221; and in abbreviated form in his book *Ocherki*

Soviet urban geography has been produced by his students or has been strongly affected by his formulation of the topics to be investigated in this field.

Baranskii addressed himself first to the question of definition of a city and then turned to a typology of cities, citing the work of Harris on a classification of cities of the United States.[6] He then expressed the opinion that in the classification of cities in the Soviet Union 5 aspects should be considered: (1) Time of origin of the city; (2) Economic-geographic location; (3) Functions performed by the city; (4) Size of the city (both in population and area); and (5) Tributary area of the city.

These 5 characteristics have been utilized in various combinations in the later classifications of Soviet cities, especially the time of origin in the so-called genetic classifications, the functions performed in the functional classifications proper, and the population in either simple categorization by size or, more fruitfully, in combination with functions. Economic-geographic location has not lent itself well to quantification or to any sort of universal scheme readily utilizable for all cities. Areas tributary to a city are easily defined for administrative centers but Soviet research on tributary areas of other types of cities is still in an early stage.

Baranskii then proposed that the study of an individual city, the most common form of a Soviet urban study, should include the following topics: introduction, location and natural conditions of the city and its immediate vicinity, historical-geographic sketch, contemporary character of the city as a whole, the microgeography of the city (its internal structure), the immediate vicinity of the city, and in conclusion a look at the future.

A wide range of topics has been studied in the numerous Soviet studies in the urban geography of the Soviet Union, both in specialized papers on specific topics and in general papers devoted to individual regions or cities. Discussion here will be confined, however, to four major topics: (1) classification of Soviet cities,

---

po shkol'noi metodike ekonomicheskoi geografii (M. Uchpedgiz, 1946, 1954, and 1955) and in his *Metodika prepodavaniia ekonomicheskoi geografii* (M. Uchpedgiz, 1960), pp. 250–268.

[6] Chauncy D. Harris, "A functional classification of cities in the United States," *Geographical Review*, vol. 33, no. 1 (January, 1943), pp. 86–99, discussed by Baranskii on pp. 29–30.

(2) size, (3) distribution, or the network of Soviet cities, and (4) growth. These correspond to the subjects treated in chapters III-VIII in this monograph. No attempt will be made to review in the text or to inventory in the selected bibliography the enormous literature on urban planning in the Soviet Union, although major monographs of 2 outstanding planners and geographers deserve special mention, those of V. G. Davidovich of Moscow and the late D. I. Bogorad of Kiev.[7]

CLASSIFICATION OF SOVIET CITIES

O. A. Konstantinov has served as methodologist, reviewer, and bibliographer of Soviet classifications of cities.[8] He first pointed out in 1934 the need for a classification or typology of Soviet cities that would include the economic and social functions performed by a city, differences in growth and development, and regional characteristics.[9] But apparently the first functional classification of cities of the Soviet Union was made by the American geographer, Harris, in 1945.[10] Active work in this field within the Soviet Union dates from since World War II and the publication of the Baranskii paper in 1946.[11] Soviet work on classification of cities has developed rapidly and the literature is now extensive.

[7] V. G. Davidovich, *Planirovka gorodov i rainonov: inzhenerno-ekonomicheskie osnovy* (M. Stroiizdat, 2nd ed., 1964), 325 pp. (1st. ed., Planirovka gorodov, 1947. 316 pp.); V. G. Davidovich, *Rasselenie v promyshlennykh uzlakh (inzhenerno-ekonomicheskie osnovy)* (M. Gosstroiizdat, 1960), 324 pp. D. I. Bogorad, *Raionnaia planirovka; voprosy planirovki promyshlennykh kompleksov* (M. Gosstroiizdat, 1960), 243 pp; and D. I. Bogorad, *Konstruktivnaia geografiia raiona; osnovy raiona; osnovy raionnoi planirovki* (M. Izd. "Mysl'," 1965), 407 p.
[8] O. A. Konstantinov, "Tipologiia i klassifikatsiia gorodskikh poselenii v sovetskoi ekonomiko-geografichskoi nauke," *Materialy po geografii naseleniia,* vypusk 2 (L. Geograficheskoe obshchestvo SSSR, Komissiia geografii naseleniia i gorodov, 1963), pp. 5–53. Bibliography of 93 items. See also his earlier "O klassifikatsii gorodov v ekonomicheskoi geografii," *Voprosy geografii,* sbornik 41 (M. Geografgiz, 1957), pp. 65–92; and "Problema ekonomiko-geograficheskoi klassifikatsii gorodov," *Vtoroi Vsesoiuznyi geograficheskii s"ezd. Tezisy dokladov po sektsii ekonomicheskoi geografii* (M-L. Izd. AN SSSR, 1947).
[9] O. A. Konstantinov, "Osnovnye problemy ekonomiko-geograficheskogo izucheniia gorodov SSSR," *Trudy pervogo Vsesoiuznogo geograficheskogo s"ezda,* vypusk 4. L. 1934, especially pp. 78–82.
[10] Chauncy D. Harris, "The cities of the Soviet Union," *Geographical review,* vol. 35, no. 1 (January, 1945), pp. 107–121, especially pp. 114–120; reviewed by O. A. Konstantinov, "Amerikanskaia klassifikatsiia sovetskikh gorodov," *Izvestiia VGO,* tom 79, vypusk 2 (1947), pp. 218–223.
[11] N. N. Baranskii, "Ob ekonomiko-geograficheskom izuchenii gorodov," *Voprosy geografii,* sbornik 2 (1946), especially pp. 27–32.

Soviet works on classification of cities can be broken down into 2 very general large groups, those that discuss the principles of typology or classification but without examples or at least without any general classification of actual cities, and those that establish a classification of cities for the Soviet Union as a whole, for some region, or for some special type of city, either with or without an explicit discussion of the principles. We are here mainly concerned with the second group.

Utilization of 5 criteria for classification of cities suggested by Baranskii will now be examined in turn: size, economic functions, genesis, tributary area, and economic-geographic location.

Size has been the most widespread and one of the most important criteria for classifying cities. Very little attention has been given, however, to what are the appropriate size categories. Perhaps the most rational classification is that of V. G. Davidovich, who has attempted to study size of city in relation to living conditions, forms of urban transport, municipal services and utilities, forms of construction, and employment structure.[12] Konstantinov has pointed out that classifications by size isolated from other economic-geographic characteristics are of slight value. At the same time he has argued strongly for inclusion of size as one of the elements in a classification, since a small local center and a great metropolitan capital or a tiny industrial settlement with one factory and a diversified center with many large manufacturing establishments are significantly different.

The first Soviet economic-geographic work with a functional classification of cities is reported to be the study of the cities of

---

[12] V. G. Davidovich, "Klassifikatsiia i tipologiia gorodov," in his *Planirovka gorodov i raionov; inzhenerno-ekonomicheskie osnovy* (M. Stroiizdat, 2nd ed., 1964), pp. 18–22, "Kompleksnoe reshenie zadachi razmeshcheniia promyshlennosti v gorode," *ibid.*, pp. 62–70; and "Raschet i razmeshchenie sistemy uchrezhdenii kul'turno-bytovogo obsluzhivaniia," *ibid.*, pp. 212–223; V. G. Davidovich, "Zavisimost' velichiny gorodov ot kharaktera i razmerov ikh narodnokhoziaistvennykh funktsii," in his "O zakonomernostiakh i tendentsiiakh gorodskogo rasseleniia v SSSR," *Voprosy geografii*, sbornik 66 (M. Izd. "Mysl'," 1965), pp. 22–26; V. G. Davidovich, "Klassifikatsiia gorodskikh poselenii po ikh velichine," in his "Velichina gorodskikh poselenii SSSR (po itogam Vsesoiuznoi perepisi naseleniia 1959 g.)," *Voprosy geografii*, sbornik 56 (M. Geografizgiz, 1962), pp. 5–8; and V. G. Davidovich, "Raspredelenie gorodov po gruppam raznoi chislennosti naseleniia," in his "O razvitii seti gorodov SSSR za 40 let," *Voprosy geografii*, sbornik 45 (M. Geografizgiz, 1959), pp. 67–70.

the Kuzbas coal-mining and industrial district of Western Siberia by K. I. Spidchenko in 1947.[13] He classified the 29 urban settlements of this basin into 3 categories: mining, mining and metallurgy, or transport, corresponding to the relatively simple and clearly differentiated structures of that time in this area.

Ten years passed before the second group of classifications of actual cities, but in 1957 three pioneer studies appeared.

E. V. Knobel'sdorf on the basis of the 5 suggested criteria of N. N. Baranskii and his own earlier methodological statement of 1955 proposed a classification for the 19 cities and 26 settlements of urban type of Yaroslavl' and Kostroma oblasts in the Central Industrial Region.[14] He recognized the following categories: (1) large diversified cities having administrative, industrial, and transport functions (populations of more than 100,000); (2) administrative-economic centers with light industry, mainly textiles and food (with populations of 10–50 thousand); (3) cities and workers' settlements, one-industry towns, with large establishments predominantly for textiles or food (small); (4) cities and workers' settlements with wood industries; (5) workers' settlements with peat-mining; (6) small cities with local industry and administrative centers of rayons (the smallest civil division), and (7) workers' settlements with local industry, mainly co-operatives.

V. Sh. Dzhaoshvili classified 65 cities and settlements of urban type in the Georgian SSR in the Caucasus into 7 types: (1) major centers of manufacturing, (2) transport cities, (3) centers of iron and steel, (4) mining towns, (5) producers of building materials, (6) centers of light and food industry, (7) resorts, (8) settlements with mixed or varied industrial or transport functions, and (9) administrative cities and settlements.[15]

[13] K. I. Spidchenko, *Goroda Kuzbassa; ekonomiko-geograficheskii ocherk* (M. Geografgiz, 1947), 148 pp.
[14] E. V. Knobel'sdorf, "K voprosu o tipakh sovetskikh gorodov," *Geograficheskii sbornik*, 11, ekonomicheskaia geografiia (Geograficheskoe obshchestvo SSSR) (M-L. Izd. AN SSSR, 1957), pp. 76–89. See also his "Tipologiia sovetskikh gorodov i zadachi ikh ekonomiko-geograficheskogo izucheniia," *Uchenye zapiski Leningradskogo gosudarstvennogo pedagogicheskogo instituta imeni A. I. Gertsena*, tom 111 (1955), pp. 194–199.
[15] V. Sh. Dzhaoshvili, "K Klassifikatsii gorodov Gruzii," *Soobshcheniia Akademii nauk Gruzinskoi SSR*, tom 19, no. 5 (1957), pp. 563–570.

O. R. Nazarevskii classified the 168 cities and settlements of urban type in Kazakhstan into 9 types: (1) mining towns, (2) factory towns (subdivided into heavy industry and light industry), (3) transport centers, (4) urban settlements growing out of villages, (5) central settlements for state farms, (6) hydroelectric centers, (7) resorts, (8) diversified cities (administrative centers of oblasts), and (9) other.[16]

These 3 classifications appear to be highly diverse but each is based on an analysis of the actual urban settlements in a given region, each recognizes the importance of the economic functions, each includes small as well as large urban settlements, and each distinguishes between the larger diversified administrative centers and the industrial towns, which differ in specialization from region to region.

In the decade following 1957 several score articles have been written on functional classifications of cities based on economic functions.

V. V. Vorob'ëv recognized the following types for Eastern Siberia: (1) large multifunctional centers, (2) mining towns (except coal), (3) coal-mining towns, (4) centers for other types of heavy industry, (5) centers of wood industry, (6) centers of food and light industry, (7) transport centers, (8) other (administrative, agricultural, resort).[17]

Zhuchkevich, Malyshev, and Rogozin classified the cities of Belorussia into 4 types: (1) industrial centers, (2) administrative and cultural centers, (3) railroad junctions, and (4) cities of mixed type.[18]

I. V. Komar in his book on the Urals had a simple classification of cities into: (1) industrial and transport centers, (2) industrial centers, and (3) transport points, but these can be further

[16] O. R. Nazarevskii, "Gorodskoe naselenie i tipy gorodov," in *Kazakhskaia SSR; ekonomiko-geograficheskaia kharakteristika.* Akademiia nauk SSSR, Institut geografii and Akademiia nauk Kazakhskoi SSR, Sektor geografii (M. Geografgiz, 1957), pp. 134–145.
[17] V. V. Vorob'ëv, "Tipy gorodskikh poselenii iuga Vostochnoi Sibiri," *Voprosy geografii,* sbornik 45 (M. Geografgiz, 1959), pp. 99–112.
[18] V. A. Zhuchkevich, A. Ia. Malyshev, and N. E. Rogozin, *Goroda i sela Belorusskoi SSR; istoriko-geograficheskie ocherki* (Minsk: Uchpedgiz BSSR, 1959), 279 pp.

subdivided into subgroups depending on branch of industrial production or type of transportation, whether railroad or river.[19]

M. I. Skliar classified the cities of the Tatar ASSR into: (1) large multifunctional cities, (2) middle-sized complex cities, (3) oil centers, (4) industrial centers, including (a) heavy industry and (b) light and food industry, and (5) transport centers distinguishing (a) railroad junctions, and (b) river towns.[20]

O. R. Nazarevksii classified the new cities of Soviet Middle Asia and Kazakhstan into the following categories: (1) cities of complex development and diverse functions, (2) large cities with several functions (typically industry and transportation), (3) factory towns, (4) mining settlements, (5) transport centers, (6) hydroelectric settlements, (7) centers of trade, distribution, and organization with little industry, (8) resorts, and (9) suburbs.[21]

Knobel'sdorf extended his studies of functional classification to the cities of the Northwest Region of the RSFSR recognizing the following types: (1) cities of a capital type, (2) diversified industrial cities, (3) industrial-port cities, (4) industrial cities with clearly marked specialization, (5) transport cities, (6) residential suburbs, resorts, and palace-museum towns, and (7) local administrative and organizational centers.[22]

The most seminal functional classification was the one by A. A. Mints and B. S. Khorev for the Central Industrial Region.[23] Six types are recognized: (1) capital cities, (2) major diversified economic, administrative-political, and cultural centers, (3) complex industrial cities, (4) specialized industrial cities, (5) nonindus-

[19] I. V. Komar, *Ural; ekonomiko-geograficheskaia kharakteristika* (M. Izd. AN SSSR, 1959), especially pp. 157–179.

[20] M. I. Skliar, "Gorodskie poseleniia Tatarii (osobennosti razvitiia i tipologiia)," *Uchenye zapiski Kazanskogo finansovo-ekonomicheskogo instituta,* vypusk 14 (1960), pp. 205–237.

[21] O. R. Nazarevskii, "Tipologiia i osobennosti formirovaniia novykh poselenii Kazakhstana i sredneaziatskikh respublik," *Voprosy geografii,* sbornik 56 (M. Geografgiz, 1962), pp. 73–94, especially map following p. 84 and table 1 on p. 87.

[22] E. V. Knobel'sdorf, "Funktsional'naia klassifikatsiia gorodov Severo-zapada," in his "Goroda Severo-zapada RSFSR (formirovanie seti gorodov)," Leningradskii gosudarstvennyi pedagogicheskii institut imeni A. I. Gertsena, *Uchenye zapiski,* tom 206 (Leningrad, 1962), pp. 33–34, and map following p. 34.

[23] A. A. Mints and B. S. Khorev, "Opyt ekonomiko-geograficheskoi tipologii sovetskikh gorodov (po materialam Tsentral'no-promyshlennogo raiona)," *Voprosy geografii,* sbornik 45 (M. Geografgiz, 1959), pp. 72–88.

trial cities, and (6) suburbs, mainly industrial. On the basis of the principles proposed in this classification, Mints and Khorev presented in 1961 the first general typology by Soviet geographers for the cities of the entire Soviet Union.[24] Both of these classifications involved a cross-classification of cities not only by function but also by genesis into (1) old cities (a) not developing their pre-revolutionary economic structure or (b) diversifying their economic structure in the Soviet period, or (c) radically altering their economic structure in the Soviet period; or (2) new cities (a) arising on the sites of industrial villages or suburban villages or (b) arising on the site of trade-industrial or handicraft villages, or (c) arising in "empty spaces" or in agricultural settlements.

Knobel'sdorf in 1965 also proposed a general classification of cities of the Soviet Union with a similar combination of functions and history.[25] His classification for the former included (1) diversified cities (centers of union republics, autonomous republics, oblasts, autonomous oblasts, or national okrugs, subdivided by size into 4 categories, with the smallest centers further subdivided by whether they had industry or not, all the larger centers having substantial industrial development), (2) industrial cities (subdivided into those with a diversified structure, either as centers of heavy industry, or light industry, or both, or those with emphasis on a single industry, either heavy or light), and (3) cities with predominant functions other than material production, including local centers (subdivided among those with administrative functions or not and with industrial or transport functions or lacking them), transport centers, suburbs, resorts, scientific centers, and other (naval bases). Each of these functional categories is cross-classified according to the historical development (not mere time of establishment) of the cities involved as follows: (1) arising as a trade, administrative, or fortified center either (a) transformed into an industrial center in the pre-Soviet capitalist period or (b) not transformed in the capitalist period; (2) arising as an indus-

[24] A. A. Mints and B. S. Khorev, "Nekotorye voprosy ekonomiko-geograficheskoi tipologii gorodov," in *Voprosy geografii naseleniia SSSR, sbornik statei k I mezhduvedomstvennomu soveshchaniiu po geografii naseleniia.* (M. Institut geografii AN SSSR, Otdel geografii SSSR, 1961), pp. 44–70.
[25] E. V. Knobel'sdorf, "O sinteticheskoi tipologii sovetskikh gorodov," *Izvestiia VGO*, vol. 97, no. 2 (1965), pp. 119–127.

trial center, either (a) on the site of an industrial village, suburban village, or mining settlement, or (b) on the site of a trade or handicraft village, or (c) on the site of a transport settlement, either a station or a port; and (3) arising with the formation of new socialist establishments, either on an "empty space" or at a settlement of an agricultural character.

The first systematic Soviet functional classification of cities of the Soviet Union including all cities of more than 50,000 population, and not just examples, with related lists and maps was made by B. S. Khorev in 1965.[26] This was a further development of the methods earlier used by Mints and Khorev and Knobel'sdorf. The overly complex earlier schemes involving both economic-functional and genetic categories were simplified by Khorev in his classification to a straightforward economic-functional base but with more explicit recognition of the importance of size. The classification was thus made more comprehensive and consistent, with each category of recognizable significance. His classification was further elaborated and published in his book on the urban settlements of the Soviet Union in 1968.[27] This last classification marks a major advance in that it lists all cities of more than 50,000 population by classification, with percentages occupied in industry, locates them on a map, and discusses in detail the basis of the classification. This study by Khorev has been extensively utilized in the present monograph in the functional classification of Soviet cities in Chapter III.

Iu. G. Saushkin in an entirely different approach to an economic-functional typology proposed a general classification of cities in relation to the territorial division of labor.[28] It is well known that the early stages of processing of raw materials are typically located at or near the natural resources such as lumbering, mining, the processing of perishable foods and so on, that much manufacturing has an intermediate location between raw material

[26] B. S. Khorev, "Issledovanie funktsional'noi struktury gorodskikh poselenii SSSR (v sviazi s zadachami ikh ekonomiko-geograficheskoi tipologii)," *Voprosy geografii*, sbornik 66 (M. Izd. "Mysl'," 1965), pp. 34–58.

[27] B. S. Khorev, "Problemy klassifikatsii i tipologii gorodov," chapter 2 in his *Gorodskie poseleniia SSSR (problemy rosta i ikh izuchenie); ocherki geografii rasseleniia* (M. Izd. "Mysl'," 1968), pp. 33–94.

[28] Iu. G. Saushkin, "Ob izuchenii sistemy gorodov Sovetskogo Soiuza," *Vestnik Moskovskogo universiteta, seriia 5, geografiia*, 1960, no. 1, pp. 23–30.

source and ultimate consumer, and that the final distribution or servicing is market-oriented. Saushkin proposed 29 types of cities in 5 groups: (1) raw material, fuel, and power group; (2) intermediate production; (3) finished industrial production; (4) transportation cities; and (5) non-productive cities (i.e. cities not engaged in material production). This typology is of great assistance in clarifying the principles of industrial location, the territorial movement of goods from resource to market, and the locational nodes for various stages of processing. But only the smaller cities are tied to raw materials. The larger cities at intermediate points or near markets are typically highly complex combinations of many activities not easily handled by this typology.

N. I. Blazhko has proposed the use of freight movements in distinguishing the basic city-forming activities, of input-output relations, and of other quantitative methods in the classification of cities and has provided examples of classifications based on such criteria.[29] These depend on access to special types of data and in part on special mathematical skills in their manipulation.

Other bases of classification of cities, the time of origin, whether in pre-Soviet or Soviet times, or the nature of the settlement before the current thrust of Soviet industrialization, have been used as the primary or supplementary basis of classification by several Soviet authors. L. L. Trube is the leading exponent of genesis as the primary basis of classification: "The disclosure of the most essential traits characterizing the formation and distribution of cities through classification and economic-geographic study is possible not by statistical methods but by historical geographic, or more precisely a genetic approach to them."[30] On this basis he classified in turn the cities of Gor'kiy oblast, the Central

[29] N. I. Blazhko, "K voprosu o metodakh izucheniia kolichestvennykh pokazatelei, neobkhodimykh pri klassifikatsii gorodov," *Trudy konferentsii po voprosam razmeshcheniia promyshlennosti i razvitiia gorodov*, (Vil'nyus: Akademiia nauk Litovskoi SSR, 1963), pp. 57–63; N. I. Blazhko, "Ekonomiko-geograficheskoe matematicheskoe modelirovanie gorodov," *Vestnik Moskovskogo universiteta, seriia 5, geografiia*, 1964, no. 4, pp. 18–27; and N. I. Blazhko, "Kolichestvennye metody izucheniia sistemy gorodskikh poselenii," in *Geografiia naseleniia i naselennykh punktov SSSR* (L. Izd. "Nauka," 1967), pp. 175–214.
[30] L. L. Trube, *Nashi goroda; ekonomiko-geograficheskie ocherki o gorodakh Gor'kovskoi i Arzamasskoi oblastei* (Gor'kiy: Knizhnoe Izd., 1954), p. 10.

Industrial District, and the Volga Region.[31] On a genetic principle, he divides all cities into "old" and "new." Old cities are of 2
types: (a) arising as fortified points and founded up to the 17th
century, or (b) having been transformed in pre-Soviet times from
villages to cities. New cities, i.e. those formed during the Soviet
period, are of 4 types: (a) developing out of factory villages and
settlements, (b) developing out of trade-industrial villages, (c) developing out of suburban villages, or (d) arising in the Soviet
period on "empty spaces," i.e. entirely new settlements. Trube's
scheme aroused considerable criticism but had an important effect
in that many subsequent classifications combined present economic functions with genesis of the city, noting whether cities in
the Soviet period had preserved old functions or radically altered
them.

Konstantinov and Pomus have criticized the use of date of origin.[32] The statistical analysis in Chapter IV of this monograph
confirms the validity of their criticism, since date of origin is not
significantly related to other characteristics of cities utilized in
that analysis.

Furthermore, some of the typologies involving a cross-classification by economic function and size on one hand and by genesis on
the other strike this author as unnecessarily complicated with such
a multitude of types and sub-types as to be confusing. Because of
the tremendous growth of urban population in the last 50 years
virtually all cities have been essentially transformed. Whether the
founding took place in the Soviet period or earlier would appear
to have slight value for a general typology, even if of intense local

[31] L. L. Trube, "Poselki Gor'kovskoi oblasti," *Uchenye zapiski Gor'kovskogo
pedagogicheskogo instituta*, vypusk 20 (1958), pp. 15–33; "Tipy gorodov Tsentral'no-promyshlennogo raiona," *Geografiia v shkole*, 1955, no. 5, pp. 10–14;
"Volzhskie goroda," *Voprosy geografii*, sbornik 45 (M. Geografgiz, 1959),
pp. 89–98.

[32] O. A. Konstantinov, "Tipologiia i klassifikatsiia gorodskikh poselenii v sovetskoi ekonomiko-geograficheskoi nauke," *Materialy po geografii naselenii*,
vypusk 2 (L. Geograficheskoe obshchestvo, Komissiia geografii naseleniia i
gorodov, 1963), pp. 23–30. Comments by M. I. Pomus at the section of urban
geography of the First Inter-Agency Conference on Geography of Population,
Moscow, February 1–2, 1962, as recorded in *Materialy I Mezhduvedomstvennogo soveshchaniia po geografii naseleniia*, vypusk 7 (L. Geograficheskoe obshchestvo SSSR, 1965), p. 152.

or national interest within the Soviet Union. Konstantinov and Knobel'sdorf suggest that paths of development of cities rather than mere date of origin would be a more promising approach. The work of G. M. Lappo for the Moscow area and E. N. Pertsik for the Kuzbas along these lines offer a more meaningful approach, dealing with process and having a future as well as a past.[33]

V. G. Davidovich also focuses on the changes in status, size, or functions rather than on date of juridical recognition as a city. His genetic classification includes old cities, with declining population or slow growth; strongly renovated cities with new industrial or transport establishments and at least a 5-fold growth; and new cities, either those built on "empty" spaces or at the site of existing villages.[34]

Compared to studies in other countries, relatively little attention has been devoted in the Soviet Union to the definition of tributary areas based on trade or services. E. V. Knobel'sdorf is a notable exception as he has made substantial studies of the zones of influence or tributary areas of some cities in the Northwest Regions.[35] Under the terms region-forming or region-organizing roles of cities, work is now beginning on such topics. In recent years V. V. Pokshishevskii and S. A. Kovalev have begun investiga-

[33] G. M. Lappo, "Sovremennoe rasselenie i puti razvitiia gorodov v Moskovskom prigorodnom raione," in *Planirovka i zastroika bol'shikh gorodov* (M. Gosstroiizdat, 1961), pp. 89–104; E. N. Pertsik, "Formirovanie sistemy gorodov Kuzbassa," *Geografiia naseleniia v SSSR; osnovnye problemy* (M-L. Izd. "Nauka," 1964), pp. 183–190.
[34] V. G. Davidovich, "Geneticheskaia klassifikatsiia gorodov," in his "O razvitii seti gorodov SSSR za 40 let," *Voprosy geografii*, sbornik 45, (M. Geografgiz, 1959), pp. 47–50.
[35] E. V. Knobel'sdorf, "Raionoobrazuiushchaia rol' sovetskikh gorodov (na primere nekotorykh gorodov Leningradskogo ekonomicheskogo administrativnogo raiona)," *Materialy po geografii naseleniia*, vypusk 1 (L. Geograficheskoe obshchestvo Soiuza SSR, Otdelenie ekonomicheskoi geografii, 1962), pp. 18–60, and "Zona khoziaistvennogo tiagoteniia Velikikh Luk," *Doklady po geografii naseleniia* (L. Geograficheskoe obshchestvo SSSR, Komissiia geografii naseleniia i gorodov, 1965), pp. 56–82. See also A. Kolotievskii, "O sisteme raionnogorodskikh vzaimosviazei i ikh arealakh," *Voprosy geografii gorodov Pribaltiki, Publikatsii Estonskogo geograficheskogo obshchestva*, 5 (1962), pp. 34-54; and S. Nõmmik, "K voprosu izucheniia khinterlanda goroda," *Voprosy geografii gorodov Pribaltiki, Publikatsii Estonskogo geograficheskogo obshchestva*, 5 (1962), pp. 55-72.

tion of service activities.[36] One type of tributary area possesses great significance in the Soviet Union and its boundaries are easy to ascertain as they are legally established, the political units for which the larger diversified cities serve as administrative centers. The economic-geographic position of cities is universally regarded as important. There are dozens of studies of the role of situation in the development and functions of individual cities. I. M. Maergoiz, V. V. Pokshishevskii, V. S. Varlamov, and V. V. Vorob'ev, for example, have published major studies of the economic-geographic situation of Volgograd, Leningrad, Orenburg, and Irkutsk.[37] But up to the present time the economic-geographic position of cities has not been successfully elaborated, systematized, and utilized in a general classification of cities of the Soviet Union.

Thus of the 5 criteria for classification of cities suggested by Baranskii, that of the functions performed by the city has proved the most fruitful and most widely used, that of size in connection with functions is also very significant, that of time of origin in my judgement has proved to be more complicating than revealing, that of tributary areas useful mainly for administrative centers (in the present state of Soviet research), and that of economic-geographic location relatively undeveloped. Particularly valuable has been the combination of functions performed by the cities with

[36] V. V. Pokshishevskii, "O geografii naseleniia, zaniatogo v SSSR v sfere non-material'nogo proizvodstva i obsluzhivaniia," in *Geografiia naseleniia i naselennykh punktov SSSR* (L. "Nauka," 1967), pp. 103–128; and S. A. Kovalev, "Geografiia potrebleniia i geografiia obsluzhivaniia naseleniia," *Vestnik Moskovskogo universiteta, seriia 5, geografiia,* 1966, no. 2, pp. 3–10 and "Voprosy geografii obsluzhivaniia naseleniia," in *Geografiia naseleniia,* vypusk 1 (M. Geograficheskoe obshchestvo, Moskovskii filial, 1967), pp. 33–37.

[37] I. M. Maergoiz, "Geograficheskoe polozhenie goroda Stalingrada," *Voprosy geografii,* sbornik 2 (M. Geografgiz, 1946), pp. 63–110; V. V. Pokshishevskii, "Nekotorye voprosy ekonomiko-geograficheskogo polozheniia Leningrada," *Voprosy geografii,* sbornik 38 (M. Geografgiz, 1956) pp. 104–130; V. S. Varlamov, "Ob ekonomicheskikh sviaziakh promyshlennosti Orenburga," *Geografiia i khoziaistvo,* sbornik 3–4, 1958, pp. 64–70; V. S. Varlamov, "Ob ekonomiko-geograficheskom polozhenii Orenburga," *Vestnik Moskovskogo universiteta, seriia 5, geografiia,* 1960, vypusk 6, pp. 55–60. V. S. Varlamov, "O kolichestvennoi otsenke ekonomiko-geograficheskogo polozheniia gorodov," *Voprosy geografii,* sbornik 66 (M. Izd. "Mysl'," 1965), pp. 130–140; and V. V. Vorob'ev, "Nekotorye voprosy ekonomiko-geograficheskogo polozheniia goroda Irkutska," *Trudy Vostochno-Sibirskogo filiala Sibirskogo otdeleniia AN SSSR,* vypusk 32, seriia ekonomicheskaia geografiia, 1960, pp. 61–79.

size. Thus some small settlements are unifunctional, lumbering camps, fishing villages, mining settlements, and way stations along railroads but typically even in middle-sized cities many functions are performed although one, especially industry, may be dominant. The larger cities have highly complex combinations of numerous functions including political-administrative, industrial, transport, and cultural activities. Thus detailed classifications in specific regions including all sizes of settlements have many clearcut and specialized types, whereas the classifications of the cities for the entire Soviet Union, limited generally to the larger cities, have fewer types explicitly recognized and these are broad in scope such as complex administrative centers or industrial cities.

Classifications of cities now exist for many parts of the Soviet Union. These are listed in the bibliography at the back of this volume, mainly in the regional section. More than 50 of these have significant value and are worthy of mention.[38] The criteria used in these classifications vary enormously but typically include one

[38] In the Russian Soviet Federated Socialist Republic proceeding from west to east, city classifications have been published for the Northwest Region by E. V. Knobel'sdorf (1962) and G. S. Nevel'shtein (1964); for the Central Industrial Region by A. A. Mints (1957, 1962), by A. A. Mints and B. S. Khorev (1959), and by L. L. Trube (1955), for Moscow Oblast in this region by A. A. Mints (1961) and G. M. Lappo (1958, 1962, and 1964), and for Yaroslavl' and Kostroma oblasts by E. V. Knobel'sdorf (1957); for the Volga-Vyatka Region by B. S. Khorev (1961) and for Gor'kiy Oblast in this region by L. L. Trube (1954, 1958, and 1964) and B. S. Khorev (1962 and 1967) and for the Chuvash ASSR by G. P. Matveev (1959); for the Volga Region by L. L. Trube (1959) and for the Tatar ASSR in this region by M. I. Skliar (1960); for the Kuban' and Black Sea Coast by A. I. Perfil'ev (1957) and for Dagestan ASSR by A. G. Fedorova (1962), both in the North Caucasus; for the Urals by I. V. Komar (1959) and for its Perm' Oblast by M. N. Stepanov (1962) and for its Sverdlovsk Oblast by E. M. Ural'skaia (1966); for Western Siberia by M. I. Pomus (1956) and for its Kuzbas by K. A. Spidchenko (1947) and E. N. Pertsik (1964) and its Altay Kray by A. F. Kurakin (1961 and 1963); for Eastern Siberia by M. I. Pomus (1963) and portions of it by V. V. Vorob'ev (1959) and G. G. Burmantov (1966); and for the Soviet Far East by I. D. Penzin (1965). See bibliography.

For the Ukraine, city classifications have been developed by D. I. Bogorad (1964) and N. I. Blazhko (1965) and for its regions: the Donets Basin by N. I. Blazhko (1963), Donetsk Oblast by E. I. Pitiurenko (1964), Cherkassy Oblast by G. K. Makarenko (1962), Odessa Oblast by D. I. Bogunenko (1958, 1962), Podolia and Northern Bukovina by T. K. Dagaeva and N. G. Ignatenko (1967), the Carpathians by N. I. Blazhko (1964), and the Transcarpathian Oblast by I. I. Bondarenko and R. Ia. Vitebskii (1965).

In the Baltic the cities of Estonia have been classified by T. B. Rea (1959, 1960, 1962, and 1964) and by V. Iu. Tarmisto (1961) and those of part of Lithuania by S. Tarvydas and M. Gudonyte (1962).

or a combination of the following: population, economic functions, genesis, economic ties and place in the territorial division of labor, and economic-geographic position. They also differ sharply in degree of detail and in the provision of the basic data on which they are founded, varying from a mere statement of the different types to elaborate use of quantitative indicators.

The nature of central places and of the interrelated network of settlements of various ranks in the Soviet Union has been examined by V. V. Pokshishevskii.[39] He analyzed the territorial organization of agricultural, woodworking, mining, and transport settlements and identified a functional-economic hierarchy in centers of production. He notes that the hierarchy of settlements with various levels of administrative functions are easy to recognize but cities at each level also have a wide range of cultural, political, transportational, and industrial activities that require study.

E. V. Knobel'sdorf proposed 5 steps in a hierarchy of central places with decreasing size of tributary areas: (1) capital cities or cities of capital type, such as Moscow and Leningrad; (2) major regional centers with tributary areas including a group of oblasts, such as Novosibirsk for Western Siberia or Sverdlovsk for the Urals; (3) oblast centers or former oblast centers which may currently lack administrative functions but which have similar tributary areas, or major intra-oblast economic centers; (4) inter-rayon economic centers with small tributary areas but still extending beyond the rayon in which located; and (5) rayon administrative-economic centers with a tributary area substantially identical with

---

In the cities of Belorussia there are the classifications of V. A. Zhuchkevich, A. Ia. Malyshev, and N. E. Rogozin (1959) and of A. V. Bogdanovich and P. A. Sidorov (1967).

In the Transcaucasus, V. S. Dzhaoshvili has made a whole series of classifications of the cities and towns of Georgia beginning in 1957 and culminating in a substantial monograph in 1968.

The cities of Kazakhstan have been classified by O. R. Nazarevskii (1957) and of its Tselinnyy Kray by E. N. Gladysheva (1965).

The cities of both Kazakhstan and Soviet Middle Asia were classified by O. R. Nazarevskii (1962), of Uzbekistan by N. Faiziev (1965), of the lower Amu-Dar'ya by I. I. Inamov (1963), and of Kirgizia by E. E. Leizerovich (1964).
[39] V. V. Pokshishevskii, "Tipy gorodskikh i sel'skikh poselenii SSSR i teorii 'gorodov-tsentral'nykh mest'," *XIX Mezhdunarodnyi geograficheskii kongress v Stokgol'me* (M. Izd. AN SSSR, 1961), pp. 240–244; "Naselennye punkty — mestnye tsentry i problemy ikh sopodchineniia," *Voprosy geografii*, sbornik 56 (M. Geografgiz, 1962), pp. 30–53; and "V poiskakh 'ierarkhii' gorodov," *Voprosy geografii*, sbornik 45 (M. Geografgiz, 1959), pp. 259–263.

the local rayon.[40] He has also made a general analysis of the region-forming role of cities.[41]

V. G. Davidovich, S. A. Kovalev, and V. V. Pokshishevskii have examined the question of the classification of settlements of all sizes and types; and S. A. Kovalev has made a detailed investigation of the settlements that serve as centers of rayons, the smallest administrative unit in the Soviet Union.[42] He found that on January 1, 1960, there were 3,501 rayon centers; of these 1,201 had the status of a city, 799 the status of a settlement of urban type, and 1,501 the status of a rural settlement. The median size of an urban rayon center was 10 thousand and for a rural rayon center 3 thousand. He analyzed the actual functions performed by rayon centers and noted that the basic employment in such functions ranges from about 250 to 700, broken down as follows:

	Employment
(1) Basic state and party institutions and public organizations	70–150
(2) Cultural institutions (houses of culture, rayon library, cinema, radio and communications, editing and publishing of the rayon newspaper)	20–60
(3) Base secondary school with school boarding house for students from more distant villages of the rayon	60–150
(4) Base establishment for medical, sanitary, and veterinary services of the rayon	50–130
(5) Trade system for the rayon (general store, special shops, transport and communications within the rayon)	20–60

[40] E. V. Knobel'sdorf, "Sovremennye problemy geografii sovetskikh gorodov," *Voprosy geografii gorodov Pribaltiki*, Publikatsii Estonskogo geograficheskogo obshchestva, 5 (Tallin: Izd. AN Estonskoi SSR, 1962), pp. 15–16.
[41] E. V. Knobel'sdorf, "Raionoobrazuiushchaia rol' gorodov i krupnykh sel'skikh poselenii," *Geografiia naseleniia i naselennykh punktov SSSR* (L. Izd. "Nauka," 1967), pp. 69–89.
[42] V. G. Davidovich, S. A. Kovalev, and V. V. Pokshishevskii, "Ob osnovakh klassifikatsii naselennykh punktov SSSR (v sviazi s zadachami ekonomicheskoi geografii)," *Izvestiia AN SSSR, seriia geograficheskaia*, 1959, no. 4, pp. 106–116; and S. A. Kovalev, "Tipy poselenii — raionnykh tsentrov SSSR," *Voprosy geografii*, sbornik 56 (M. Geografgiz, 1962), pp. 54–72.

(6) Basic rayon procurement and supply organizations and their transport · · · 20–100

(7) Establishments of local services and utilities (sewing and repairing workshops and dressmaking and tailoring establishments, hotels, etc.) · · · 10–50

Total · · · 250–700

This represents the lowest rung on the urban central-place administrative hierarchy and a transition from urban to rural. He estimates that this basic employment might support a population of 750 to 2,800. The population of the rayon center depends on what other activities are also carried on in the settlement, whether of industry in some of the cities, or agriculture (as a base for a collective or state farm), or forestry in some of the rural villages. On the basis of combination of administrative functions with other activities he proposed a typology.

SIZE

Soviet geographers and planners have devoted much attention to the questions related to size of cities.

The Soviet literature on optimum size of cities and on the need for limiting the size of the great metropolises is particularly extensive.[43] The best analysis of the relative costs of urban construction in relation to size has been made by V. G. Davidovich.[44] He finds that cities in the size range of 50 to 200 thousand are most efficient in terms of the urban economy, although the optimum size of a city varies by its function. Other authors have pointed out the need to consider also the economies to production that arise from agglomerations for cities of various sizes and different functional types.[45]

---

[43] For a general statement, see B. S. Khorev, "Problemy optimal'noi velichiny gorodov i regulirovanii ikh rosta," chapter 3 in his book, *Gorodskie poseleniia SSSR (problemy rosta i ikh izuchenie); ocherki geografii rasseleniia* (M. Izd. "Mysl'," 1968), pp. 95–138.

[44] V. G. Davidovich, "Opredelenie perspektiv razvitiia gorodov," and "'Optimal'nye velichiny gorodov," in his *Planirovka gorodov i raionov; inzhenerno-ekonomicheskie osnovy* (M. Stroiizdat, 2nd ed. 1964), pp. 22–34, and "Ekonomichnost' planirovochnykh reshenii," *ibid.*, pp. 296–311.

[45] D. I. Bogorad, "Zadachi izucheniia i regulirovaniia rosta gorodskikh aglomeratsii," *Nauchnye problemy geografii naseleniia; materialy ko II Mezhduvedomstvennomu soveshchaniiu po geografii naseleniia* (M. Izd. Moskovskogo

V. I. Perevedentsev asserts that the most efficient city is not where the costs of maintenance of a person are minimal but rather where the difference in what he produces and what is spent on him is the greatest and that the inconveniences and costs of large cities are not inherent in size but result from poor planning.[46]

A frequently suggested solution is the development of satellite cities, which may to some degree combine the lower construction and servicing costs of middle-sized cities with the agglomeration efficiencies of large metropolitan concentrations.

Soviet policy in recent years has been directed toward the development of small and middle-sized cities, partly to utilize the labor reserves of such settlements, which previously had been insufficiently drawn into the industrial life of the country. These small and medium-sized cities are located mainly in the densely settled western parts of the country with a dense transportation network and good location with respect to markets and the population of the country but with relatively modest resources of fuel or mineral raw materials.

The 22nd and 23rd congresses of the Communist Party of the Soviet Union in 1961 and 1966 adopted programs of fostering the growth of small and middle-sized cities. New industrial establishments are to be built primarily in middle-sized and smaller cities.[47] A large number of monographs and articles have recently been devoted to the possibilities and problems of locating industries in small and medium-sized towns, particularly of the western parts of the USSR.[48] S. M. Voskoboinikova has called attention to

universiteta, 1967), pp. 100–112; G. M. Lappo and F. M. Listengurt, "O putiakh razvitiia v SSSR gorodov raznykh tipov," pp. 113–124 in the same volume; and G. M. Lappo and E. Kh. Troitskaia, "Puti razvitiia krupnykh gorodov v SSSR," pp. 125–137 in the same volume.

[46] V. I. Perevedentsev, *Literaturnaia gazeta*, September 20, 1967, No. 38, p. 11, translated in *Current Digest of the Soviet Press*, vol. 19, No. 38 (October 11, 1967), pp. 5–6.

[47] *Pravda* and *Izvestiia*, February 20, 1966.

[48] *Puti razvitiia malykh i srednikh gorodov tsentral'nykh ekonomicheskikh raionov SSSR*, D. G. Khodzhaev, ed. (M. Izd. "Nauka," 1967), 206 p. (Gosplan SSSR. Sovet po izucheniiu proizvodital'nykh sil); B. S. Khorev, "Puti razvitiia nebol'shikh i srednikh gorodov," chapter 5 in his book *Gorodskie poseleniia SSSR (problemy rosta i ikh izuchenie); ocherki geografii rasseleniia* (M. Izd. "Mysl'," 1968), pp. 164–214. E. B. Alaev and B. S. Khorev, "Puti razvitiia malykh i srednikh gorodov SSSR," *Nauchnye problemy geografii naseleniia; materialy ko II Mezhduvedomstvennomu soveshchaniiu po geografii naseleniia* (M. Izd. Moskovskogo universiteta, 1967), pp. 138–150; T. K. Dagaeva and

the possibilities for improving the conditions of life in the small and middle-sized cities.[49]

Soviet geographers are also studying the larger urban agglomerations. Indeed a special volume has been devoted to the great metropolitan concentrations and their suburbs and satellites, and many of its papers were translated into English.[50] V. G. Davidovich, G. M. Lappo, and B. S. Khorev have had a continuing interest in this topic and have published other papers including one with particular attention to the commuting flows to and from the central cities.[51] Davidovich noted that about 415 thousand residents of suburbs and satellite cities are employed in Moscow and

---

N. G. Ignatenko, "Malye i srednie goroda Podol'ia i Severnoi Bukoviny (klassifikatsiia i puti razvitiia)," *Geografiia naseleniia i naselennykh punktov SSSR* (L. Izd. "Nauka," 1967), pp. 157–174. G. M. Lappo, "Problemy malykh gorodov," *Narodonaselenia i ekonomika* (M. Izd. "Ekonomika," 1967), pp. 170–186; F. M. Listengurt and I. M. Smoliar, "O razgranichenii poniatii 'malye' i 'srednie' goroda po materialam izucheniia gorodov Tsentral'nogo ekonomicheskogo raiona," *Vestnik Moskovskogo universiteta, seriia 5, geografiia,* 1965, no. 5, pp. 74–77; F. M. Listengurt and I. M. Smoliar, "Izuchenie nekotorykh predposylok promyshlennogo razvitiia malykh i srednikh gorodov Tsentral'nogo ekonomichskogo raiona," *Izvestiia AN SSSR, seriia geograficheskaia,* 1964, no. 4, pp. 79–90; A. V. Bogdanovich and P. A. Sidorov, "Problemy razvitiia nebol'shikh gorodov Belorussii," *Vestnik Moskovskogo universiteta, seriia 5, geografiia,* 1966, no. 3, pp. 83–85; and F. M. Listengurt, "Perspektivy ekonomicheskogo i territorial'nogo rosta malykh i srednikh gorodov Tsentral'nogo ekonomicheskogo raiona," *Izvestiia AN, seriia geograficheskaia,* 1965, no. 4, pp. 61–69.

[49] S. M. Voskoboinikova, "K voprosu o probleme malykh i srednikh gorodov (na primere gorodov Iaroslavskoi oblasti)," *Trudy konferentsii po voprosam razmeshcheniia promyshlennosti i razvitiia gorodov (Vil'nius, 20–23 avgusta 1962 g.).* (Vil'nyus: An Litovskoi SSR, 1963), pp. 73–79.

[50] *Goroda-sputniki; sbornik statei.* V. G. Davidovich and B. S. Khorev, eds. (M. Geografgiz, 1961) 193 pp. Five of the articles were translated and published in *Soviet Geography: Review and Translation,* vol. 3, no. 3 (March 1962), pp. 3–68.

[51] V. G. Davidovich, "Territorial'nye sistemy rasseleniia v SSSR," *Nauchnye problemy geografii naseleniia; materialy ko II Mezhduvedomstvennomu soveshchaniiu po geografii naseleniia* (M. Izd. Moskovskogo universiteta, 1967), pp. 71–86; V. G. Davidovich, "Gorodskie aglomeratsii v SSSR," in *Materialy k IV s"ezdu Geograficheskogo obshchestva SSSR, Simpozium B, Osnovnye voprosy ekonomicheskoi geografii, Doklady,* chast 1 (L. Geograficheskoe obshchestvo SSSR, 1964), pp. 34–47; V. G. Davidovich and G. M. Lappo, "Voprosy razvitiia gorodskikh aglomeratsii v SSSR," in *Sovremennye problemy geografii; nauchnye soobshcheniia sovetskikh geografov po programme XX Mezhdunarodnogo geograficheskogo kongressa (London, 1964)* (M. "Nauka," 1964), pp. 43–49; and B. S. Khorev, "Razvitie gorodskikh aglomeratsii i problema poselenii—sputnikov," chapter 4 in his book *Gorodskie poseleniia SSSR (problemy rosta i ikh izuchenie); ocherki geografii rasseleniia* (M. Izd. "Mysl'," 1968), pp. 139–163.

that 92 thousand residents of Moscow work in suburban or satellite establishments.[52] Other cities also draw a substantial number of workers from suburbs or satellites: Leningrad, 140 thousand; Khar'kov, 75 thousand; Kiev, 30 thousand; and Baku, 45 thousand. At the opposite extreme in size from the great metropolitan agglomerations are settlements of urban type, which represent smaller and generally more specialized urban settlements. Most are under 10,000 population and the median size in 5,000. Although they numbered 3,460 in 1967, their study has been neglected. L. L. Trube has contended that they should be studied basically in the same manner as cities and has launched such an investigation.[53] B. S. Khorev has made a more recent study of their distribution throughout the Soviet Union and mapped the location of the 385 settlements of urban type of more than 10 thousand population in 1959.[54]

G. M. Lappo studied the settlements transitional between rural and urban in Moscow Oblast.[55]

S. A. Kovalev has written an excellent monograph with a thorough treatment of all aspects of rural settlement in the Soviet Union based on extensive field work and a comprehensive review of the literature.[56]

DISTRIBUTION OF CITIES IN THE URBAN NETWORK

The principal Soviet authors who have devoted themselves to the study of the system of cities for the Soviet Union as a whole are V. G. Davidovich and O. A. Konstantinov. Davidovich with ingenious graphs, statistical indicators, and projections throws light on

[52] V. G. Davidovich, "Gorodskie aglomeratsii v SSSR," cited above, table 2, p. 37.
[53] L. L. Trube, "Ob ekonomiko-geograficheskom izuchenii poselkov gorodskogo tipa," *Geografiia naseleniia v SSSR; osnovnye problemy* (M-L. Izd. "Nauka," 1964), pp. 113–121; L. L. Trube, "Malye goroda i bol'shie poselki i problemy ikh razvitiia (na primere Volgo-Viatskogo raiona)," *Geografiia naseleniia i naselennykh punktov SSSR* (L. Izd. "Nauka," 1967), pp. 144–156.
[54] B. S. Khorev, "Poselki gorodskogo tipa i prochie naselennye punkty kak rezerv popolneniia seti gorodov," chapter 7 in his book *Gorodskie poseleniia SSSR (problemy rosta i ikh izuchenie); ocherki geografii rasseleniia* (M. Izd. "Mysl'," 1968), pp. 238–255.
[55] G. M. Lappo, "Geograficheskoe izuchenie naselennykh punktov, zanimaiushchikh promezhutochnoe polozhenie mezhdu gorodskimi i sel'skimi poseleniiami (na primere Moskovskoi oblasti)," *Geografiia naseleniia v SSSR; osnovnye problemy* (M-L. Izd. "Nauka," 1964), pp. 245–256.
[56] S. A. Kovalev, *Sel'skoe rasselenie (geograficheskoe issledovanie)* (M. Izd. Moskovskogo universiteta, 1963), 370 pp.

the regularities that exist in settlement patterns of the country.[57] O. A. Konstantinov over a period of several decades has studied and reported on the growth of the urban network and has reviewed the literature.[58]

Analysis of the urban network depends on a clear definition of what is urban. In pre-revolutionary Russia there was a wide discrepancy between the juridically recognized cities and the settlements which had an urban function. After the Revolution attempts were made to recognize as cities urban settlements that met 2 criteria: a minimum population (that varies from republic to republic) and a predominantly nonagricultural function. Furthermore a new category was established, settlements of an urban type, typically smaller, dominated by material production (mining or manufacturing) but lacking some of the service activities. Disputes still continue on the proper lower limit in size for urban settlements to be included in comparative analyses.[59]

V. P. Korovitsyn has constructed a map of the development of the urban network.[60]

[57] V. G. Davidovich, "O zakonomernostiakh i tendentsiiakh gorodskogo rasseleniia v SSSR," *Voprosy geografii*, sbornik 66 (M. Izd. "Mysl'," 1965), pp. 6–33; V. G. Davidovich, "Velichina gorodskikh poselenii SSSR (po itogam Vsesoiuznoi perepisi naseleniia 1959 g.," *Voprosy geografii*, sbornik 56 (M. Geografgiz, 1962), pp. 5–29; and V. G. Davidovich, "O razvitii seti gorodov SSSR za 40 let," *Voprosy geografii*, sbornik 45 (M. Geografgiz, 1959), pp. 37–71.

[58] O. A. Konstantinov, "Geograficheskie sdvigi v razmeshchenii bol'shikh gorodov SSSR," *Izvestiia VGO*, vol. 73, no. 1 (1941), pp. 23–30; O. A. Konstantinov, "Izmeneniia v geografii gorodov SSSR za sovetskii period," *Voprosy geografii*, sbornik 6 (M. Geografgiz, 1947), pp. 11–46; O. A. Konstantinov, "Nekotorye vyvody o geografii gorodov i gorodskogo naseleniia SSSR iz itogov perepisi 1959 goda," *Izvestiia AN SSSR, seriia geograficheskaia*, 1959, no. 6, pp. 44–56; and O. A. Konstantinov, "Izuchenie seti gorodskikh poselenii SSSR v sovetskoi ekonomiko-geograficheskoi nauke," *Materialy I Mezhduvedomstvennsogo soveshchaniia po geografii naseleniia*, vypusk 7 (L. Geograficheskoe obshchestvo SSSR, 1965), pp. 72–83.

[59] O. A. Konstantinov, "Neofitsial'nye goroda SSSR," in his "Izuchenie seti gorodskikh poselenii SSSR v sovetskoi ekonomiko-geograficheskoi nauke," cited above, pp. 79–80; O. A. Konstantinov, "Sovremennoe sostoianie deleniia naselennykh punktov SSSR na gorodskie i sel'skie," *Izvestiia AN SSSR, seriia geograficheskaia*, 1958, no. 6, pp. 69–78; V. G. Davidovich, S. A. Kovalev, and V. V. Pokshishevskii, "Ob osnovakh klassifikatsii naselennykh punktov SSSR (v sviazi s zadachami ekonomicheskoi geografii," *Izvestiia AN SSSR, seriia geograficheskaia*, 1959, no. 4, pp. 106–116; and V. G. Davidovich, "Opredelenie poniatii 'goroda' i 'poselki gorodskogo tipa,'" in his "O razvitii seti gorodov SSSR za 40 let," cited above.

[60] V. P. Korovitsyn, "Karta razvitiia seti gorodskikh poselenii SSSR (za 1926–1959 gg.)," *Vestnik Moskovskogo universiteta, seriia 5, geografiia*, 1961, no. 6,

Studies of the network of cities in specific regions are more numerous than for the Soviet Union as a whole. Three studies of particular interest are those of the Donetsk coal basin and industrial district, the most dense network of industrial cities in the USSR, by N. I. Blazhko, of the cities of the Northwest, which contains many old centers, by E. V. Knobel'sdorf, and a comparative study of several regions by N. I. Blazhko, S. M. Voskoboinikova, and B. L. Gurevich.[61]

The new cities which have arisen during the Soviet period are both numerous and in some cases large. They have been the object of attention, both in popular publications and in scholarly studies.[62] Davidovich studied 201 new cities that arose on "empty" spaces and found that 47 per cent of them were engaged in mining or the working of minerals; 37 per cent in manufacturing, 7 per cent were associated with new electricity-generating stations, 6 per cent with transportation, and only 3 per cent with administrative and cultural-political functions.[63]

The cities which became part of the system of Soviet cities by virtue of their incorporation into the Soviet Union as a result of

---

pp. 18–24; V. P. Korovitsyn, "Sdvigi v geografii gorodskikh poselenii SSSR (1926–1959 gg.)," *Izvestiia AN SSSR, seriia geograficheskaia*, 1961, no. 6, pp. 47–68.

[61] N. I. Blazhko, "Donetskaia gorodskaia aglomeratsiia Ukrainskoi SSR," *Materialy po geografii naseleniia*, vypusk 2 (L. Geograficheskoe obshchestvo SSSR, 1963), pp. 54–79; E. V. Knobel'sdorf, "Goroda severo-zapada RSFSR (formirovanie seti gorodov)," *Leningradskii gosudarstvennyi pedagogicheskii institut imeni A. I. Gertsena, Uchenye zapiski*, tom 206 (Leningrad, 1962), pp. 11–44; and N. I. Blazhko, S. M. Voskoboinikova, and B. L. Gurevich, "Sistemy gorodskikh poselenii," *Nauchny problemy geografii naseleniia; materialy ko II Mezhduvedomstvennomu soveshchaniiu po geografii naseleniia* (M. Izd. Moskovskogo universiteta, 1967), pp. 87–99.

[62] V. G. Davidovich, "Razmeshchenie novykh gorodov," and "Prichiny vozniknoveniia novykh gorodov," in his "O razvitii seti gorodov SSSR za 40 let," *Voprosy geografii*, sbornik 45, (M. Geografgiz, 1959), pp. 57–61; Iu. V. Smeile, "Novye goroda SSSR i faktory ikh obrazovaniia," *Materialy I Mezhduvedomstvennogo soveshchaniia po geografii naseleniia*, vypusk 3 (M-L. Geograficheskoe obshchestvo SSSR, 1962), pp. 49–51; B. S. Khorev, "Goroda rozhdennye oktiabrem (ob izmeneniiakh v seti gorodov SSSR za 50 let)," *Geografiia v shkole*, 1967, no. 4, pp. 9–18; and B. S. Khorev, "Rost seti gorodov SSSR za 50 let Sovetskoi vlasti i geografiia novogo gradostroitel'stva," chapter 6 in his book *Gorodskie poseleniia SSSR (problemy rosta i ikh izuchenie); ocherki geografii rasseleniia* (M. Izd. "Mysl'," 1968), pp. 215–237.

[63] V. G. Davidovich, "O razvitii seti gorodov SSSR za 40 let," cited above, table 14, pp. 62–63.

boundary changes during and after World War II have been the subject of a special study by O. A. Konstantinov.[64] Analysis of the forms and densities of individual cities and urban networks has been investigated particularly by V. G. Davidovich.[65]

GROWTH

There have been numerous Soviet studies of the growth of cities during the Soviet period. Many of these are tied specifically to the estimates of a particular year or to earlier censuses. Historically the most extensive study was made by O. A. Konstantinov, reported on briefly in a 1949 article.[66] V. G. Davidovich has also made fundamental studies of the growth of urban population and cities.[67] The most recent general survey of the growth of Soviet cities has been made by B. S. Khorev.[68]

The enormous growth of Soviet cities has been possible only by virtue of gigantic migrations from rural to urban areas, and also by inter-regional movements from densely settled Western areas to pioneer lands with new cities. For long these movements

[64] O. A. Konstantinov, "O seti gorodov na territoriiakh, voshedshikh v sostav SSSR s 1939 g.," *Izvestiia AN SSSR, seriia geograficheskaia*, 1963, no. 4, pp. 23–34.
[65] V. G. Davidovich, "Formy rasseleniia v ugol'nykh basseinakh SSSR," *Voprosy geografii*, sbornik 14 (M. Geografgiz, 1949), pp. 3–28; V. G. Davidovich, "O tipologii rasseleniia v gruppakh gorodov i poselkov SSSR," *Voprosy geografii*, sbornik 38 (M. Geografgiz, 1956), pp. 27–77; V. G. Davidovich, *Rasselenie v promyshlennykh uzlakh* (inzhenerno-ekonomicheskie osnovy) (M. Gosstroiizdat, 1960), 324 pp; V. G. Davidovich, "Goroda i poselki-sputniki v SSSR," in *Goroda-sputniki; sbornik statei* (M. Geografgiz, 1961), pp. 5–39; V. G. Davidovich, "Gorodskie aglomeratsii v SSSR," in *Materialy k IV s"ezdu Geograficheskogo obshchestva SSSR, simpozium B, osnovnye voprosy ekonomicheskoi geografii, doklady*, chast' 1 (L. Geograficheskoe obshchestvo SSSR, 1964), pp. 34–47; V. G. Davidovich, *Planirovka gorodov i raionov; inzhenerno-ekonomicheskie osnovy* (M. Stroiizdat, 1964), 325 pp.; and V. G. Davidovich, "Gorodskie aglomeratsii v SSSR," in *Voprosy gorodskogo rasseleniia* (Kiev: "Budivel'nik," 1964), pp. 16–25.
[66] O. A. Konstantinov, "Tempy rosta gorodov SSSR i kapitalisticheskih stran," *Izvestiia VGO*, 1949, no. 6, pp. 577–583.
[67] V. G. Davidovich, "Rost gorodskogo naseleniia," in his "O razvitii seti gorodov SSSR za 40 let," *Voprosy geografii*, sbornik 45 (M. Geografgiz, 1959), pp. 37–42.
[68] B. S. Khorev, "Osnovnye svedeniia o gorodskikh poseleniiakh SSSR, ikh razvitii i razmeshchenii," chapter 1 in his *Gorodskie poseleniia SSSR (problemy rosta i ikh izuchenie); ocherki geografii rasseleniia* (M. Izd. "Mysl'," 1968), pp. 8–32.

received little attention and basic data needed for their study were poor, but recently an awareness has developed of the importance of the study of migration flows to an understanding of the processes of city growth and to realistic planning for future location of industry and of urban development. V. I. Perevedentsev has been a leading voice in calling for and in defining such studies and V. V. Pokshishevskii, V. V. Vorob'ev, and E. N. Gladysheva have contributed.[69]

[69] V. V. Vorob'ev, E. N. Gladysheva, V. I. Perevedentsev, and V. V. Pokshishevskii, "Ob osnovnykh zakonomernostiakh migratsii," *Materialy k IV s"ezdu Geograficheskogo obshchestva SSSR. Simpozium "B," Osnovnye voprosy ekonomicheskoe geografii SSSR, Doklady*, Chast' 2 (L. Geograficheskoe obshchestvo SSSR, 1964), pp. 32–51; V. V. Pokshishevskii, "Perspektivy migratsii naseleniia v SSSR (voprosy metodiki postroeniia rabochei gipotezy)," in *Geografiia naseleniia Vostochnoi Sibiri* (M. AN SSSR, 1962), pp. 63–81; V. V. Pokshishevskii, "Vnutrennie migratsii naseleniia kak ob"ekt geograficheskogo izucheniia," *Voprosy geografii; sbornik statei dlia XVII Mezhdunarodnogo geograficheskogo kongressa* (M-L. AN SSSR, 1956), pp. 249–260; V. V. Pokshishevskii, *Zaselenie Sibiri; istoriko-geograficheskii ocherk* (Irkutsk: Irkutskoe oblastnoe gosudarstvennoe izd., 1959), 208 pp.; and V. I. Perevedentsev, "Nekotorye voprosy metodiki izucheniia migratsii naseleniia," *Voprosy geografii naseleniia SSSR; sbornik statei k I Mezhduvedomstvennomu soveshchaniiu po geografii naseleniia* (M. Institut geografii AN SSSR, otdel geografii SSSR, 1961), pp. 71–92. Rotaprint.

III.

A Functional Classification of Soviet Cities

A profound scientific analysis of the functions of any city rests upon the necessity for the formation of a statistically based classification of Soviet cities . . . This is the most important problem for the further development of Soviet economic geography.

— E. V. KNOBEL'SDORF
Voprosy geografii gorodov Pribaltiki, 1962, p. 21.

In the definition of the concept of basic types of settlements it is necessary to deal with two major criteria: functions and size (population).

— V. G. DAVIDOVICH, S. A. KOVALEV,
AND V. V. POKSHISHEVSKII
Izvestiia AN SSSR, seriia geograficheskaia, 1959, no. 4, p. 107.

It is especially bad when a functional classification is made without account of the number of inhabitants.

— O. A. KONSTANTINOV
Materialy po geografii naseleniia, vypusk 2, 1963, p. 23.

THERE ARE MANY POSSIBLE BASES for a functional classification of cities. One of the best involves an analysis of the economic base of the city, its employment or occupational structure. But since very large cities also differ substantially from very small ones, even if the proportions in industry and trade might be the same, it is useful to utilize also broad size categories for sub-groups. This chapter examines the statistical basis for a classification of Soviet cities, presents a classification of the 304 cities of more than 50,000 population, and describes the regional associations of these types.

BASIS FOR A FUNCTIONAL CLASSIFICATION OF SOVIET CITIES

The basis of an objective and comparative functional classification of the cities of the Soviet Union is their economic structure. The best general index of economic structure is the proportion of employment in various activities. Ideally, a separation of basic and nonbasic activities (city-forming and city-serving respectively to use the Soviet terminology) in each city would be desirable, but this involves elaborate investigation of individual cases, which is not possible on the bases of available data or field research, although such data are reported to be compiled by project planning institutes of cities in the Soviet Union.[1]

Unfortunately the published volumes for the 1959 census are extremely niggardly with occupational data. The only information published in the census volumes concerns the number of gainfully occupied persons among the total urban population for the Soviet Union as a whole, and for each of the 15 union republics in (1) industry, construction, transportation, and communication as a group; (2) agriculture; (3) trade, eating establishments, procurement, material supplies, and marketing taken together, (4) education, science, art, health, housing and municipal services, domestic services, administration, and finance as a group (or in education, science, art, and health as a sub-group); and (5) in the Soviet Army — a total of 6 figures for the whole urban population.[2] The published census volumes contain no data for individual cities or for urban population by areal units such as oblasts.

Analyses of the published census data do reveal a general pattern of the distribution of proportion of gainfully occupied persons among the urban population in industry, construction, and

[1] B. S. Khorev, "Issledovanie funktsional'noi struktury gorodskikh poselenii SSSR (v sviazi s zadachami ikh ekonomiko-geograficheskoi tipologii), *Voprosy geografii*, sbornik 66 (M. Izd. "Mysl'," 1965), p. 36.

[2] SSSR, Tsentral'noe statisticheskoe upravlenie, *Itogi vsesoiuznoi perepisi naseleniia 1959 goda* (M. Gosstatizdat, 1962–1963), table 33 in each volume.

TABLE 8

PERCENTAGE OF THE GAINFULLY OCCUPIED URBAN PERSONS
IN INDUSTRY, CONSTRUCTION, AND TRANSPORTATION IN
UNION REPUBLICS OF THE USSR, 1959

USSR as a whole	*61.5*
RSFSR	63.9
Ukrainian SSR	59.3
Union republics on western border	
Estonian SSR	61.6
Latvian SSR	58.2
Lithuanian SSR	56.4
Belorussian SSR	54.4
Moldavian SSR	49.2
Kazakhstan and Middle Asia	
Kazakh SSR	60.8
Kirgiz SSR	55.3
Uzbek SSR	53.3
Turkmen SSR	51.0
Tadzhik SSR	50.5
Transcaucasian republics	
Armenian SSR	56.2
Azerbaydzhan SSR	52.9
Georgian SSR	49.6

Source: Calculated from data in SSSR, Tsentral'noe statisticheskoe upravlenie, *Itogi vse-soiuznoi perepisi naseleniia 1959 goda*, table 33, in the volume for each union republic.

transportation as a group (Table 8). The highest proportion occurs in the largest republic, the RSFSR with 63.9 per cent, and a
high proportion also in the Ukraine, the second most populous
republic, with 59.3 per cent, and with regular decreases from
north to south in the republics that lie both along the western
margin of the country and along the eastern margin. Thus in the
republics in the west the percentage of the gainfully occupied
urban population in industry, construction, and transportation
decreases regularly from 61.6 per cent for Estonia to 58.2 for Latvia, 56.4 for Lithuania, 54.4 for Belorussia, to only 49.2 for Moldavia, the lowest percentage of any union republic. Similarly,
from north to south along the eastern border of the Soviet Union
in interior Asia, the corresponding percentages are 60.8 for Kazakhstan, 55.3 for Kirgizia, 53.3 for Uzbekistan, 51.0 for Turkmenia, and 50.5 for Tadzhikistan.

The general decrease from the core outward is even more striking with respect to proportion in industry alone. The RSFSR and
the Ukrainian SSR are above the national urban average of just

over 40 per cent, but the 2 very large but sparsely populated republics of Kazakhstan and Turkmenia have only 30 and 27 per cent, respectively, in industry.[3] The difference between the larger group of industry, construction, and transportation and the smaller group of activities covered by the term industry alone is very striking in these 2 republics, 61 and 30 per cent in Kazakhstan and 51 and 24 per cent in Turkmenia, leaving about 30 and 27 per cent respectively for construction and transportation. Indeed, the percentage of the gainfully occupied in transport alone is higher in Kazakhstan than in any other union republic. Both Kazakhstan and Turkmenistan have enormous areas that require a heavy input of transportation to integrate the economic activities of scattered points.

Fortunately, Khorev has made a tabulation from unpublished data for the 304 cities of more than 50,000 population in 1959 showing the proportion of the gainfully occupied persons in each city (1) in industry (mining and manufacturing), construction, transportation, and communication as a group, and (2) in industry alone, i.e., in mining and manufacturing. His tabulation allocates the cities by 10-per-cent class intervals above or below the average for the urban population for the Soviet Union.[4] Tables 10 and 11, which are rearrangements of his data, provide basic data for the construction of a quantitatively based comparative objective functional classification of the cities of the USSR.

Three features must be noted immediately. First, the cities of the Soviet Union have very high percentages in industry and very low percentages in trade, reflecting the goals of the government and party in emphasizing material production and in assigning a low priority to trade (Table 9). Thus 61.5 per cent of all occupied persons in cities in the Soviet Union are in the combined category of industry, construction, and transportation, about 42.0 per cent in industry alone, 11.5 per cent in construction, 8.0 per cent in transportation, and only 7.8 per cent in trade.[5]

[3] B. S. Khorev, *op. cit.*, p. 39.
[4] *Ibid.*, table 2, pp. 42–43, and B. S. Khorev, *Gorodskie poseleniia SSSR (problemy rosta i ikh izuchenie); ocherki geografii rasseleniia* (M. Izd. "Mysl'," 1968), table 11, pp. 46–51.
[5] *Itogi vsesoiuznoi perepisi naseleniia 1959 goda, SSSR* (svodnyi tom), table 33, p. 106, and projections from analysis of table 44, pp. 146–150 and 152–154; B. S. Khorev, "Issledovanie . . . ," pp. 39, 48, and 49; and B. S. Khorev, *Gorodskie poseleniia SSSR,* table 10, p. 43.

TABLE 9

OCCUPATIONAL STRUCTURE OF THE URBAN POPULATION
OF THE SOVIET UNION, 1959

		Per cent
1. In industry (manufacturing and mining), construction, transportation, and communications		61.5
a. In industry (manufacturing and mining)	42.0	
b. In construction	11.5	
c. In transport and communications	8.0	
2. In agriculture and forestry		4.9
a. In agriculture	4.7	
3. In trade, eating establishments, procurement, material supplies, and marketing		7.8
a. In trade and eating establishments	6.5	
4. In nonmaterial activities		21.4
(housing and municipal services, domestic repairs and services, education, science, art, health, physical culture, social security, finance and credit, government, and social organizations)		
a. In health, physical culture, and social security	5.0	
b. In education	5.6	
c. In government	3.2	
5. Other		4.4
a. In the Soviet army	3.7	
b. Not indicated or not clear	0.3	

Sources: B.S. Khorev, *Gorodskie poseleniia SSSR (problemy rosta i ikh izuchenie)*; *ocherki geografii rasseleniia* (M. izd. "Mysl'," 1968), table 10, p. 43; and SSSR. Tsentral'noe statisticheskoe upravlenie. *Itogi vsesoiuznoi perepisi naseleniia 1959 goda. SSSR (svodnyi tom)* (M. Gosstatizdat, 1962), table 33, p. 106, and table 44, pp. 146–158.

Comparative data are not generally available for urban populations of various countries, but if one takes the total number of gainfully occupied persons in each country in all activities other than agriculture and calculates the percentage in each major activity one gets an approximation to the structure of the urban-type economic activities. This is done with some trepidation because of the variations among countries in methods of collecting and classifying occupational data. A rough comparison, however, shows that among all major countries for which occupational data are available, in activities other than agriculture, the Soviet Union has the highest percentage of its gainfully occupied persons in industry: 40 per cent compared with 33 per cent in the United

States or Japan, or 34 per cent in India.[6] The Soviet Union has by far the lowest percentage in trade: 8.6 per cent compared with 21.2 per cent in the United States, 23.1 per cent in Japan, and 16.8 per cent in India.

Secondly, all large cities are to a degree multifunctional with a diversified and complex combination of many activities. This is particularly true for cities of more than half-a-million population. Most cities of more than 50,000 population are also diversified. For larger cities the classification reveals differences in relative emphasis among the diverse activities of cities rather than unifunctional types. Only small cities are likely to be dominated by a single activity.

Thirdly, more than 70 per cent of the cities of over 50,000 population (222 of 304) had proportions of gainfully occupied persons in industry, construction, and transportation higher than the national urban average (Table 10). About 60 per cent had percentages in industry alone above the national urban average (179 of 304). Since 60 per cent of the urban population of the Soviet Union in 1959 was in cities of more than 50,000 population,[7] one may infer that a large fraction of the smaller cities had percentages occupied in industry well below the national urban average. This point should be stressed heavily since in later discussions of smaller cities we shall be treating mainly those smaller cities that do have specialized industry associated with rapid growth.

As shown by Table 10, 103, or about one third of the 304 cities of over 50,000 population in 1959 had more than 50 per cent of the gainfully occupied persons in industry or at least 10 percentage points above the national urban average of 40 per cent. A similar proportion (113 of 304) had more than 70 per cent in industry-construction-transportation, or more than 10 percentage points above the national urban average for the broader category (60 per cent). Much lower fractions (39 of 304 for industry and 16 of 304 for the broader category) had proportions of occupied persons

---

[6] Data calculated from material in United States, *Demographic Yearbook 1964* (New York: United Nations, 1965), table 12, pp. 378–433, and *Itogi vsesiouznoi perepisi naseleniia 1959 goda, SSSR (svodnyi tom)*, table 33, pp. 104–109, and table 44, pp. 146–158.

[7] *Itogi vsesoiuznoi perepisi naseleniia 1959 goda, SSSR (svodnyi tom)*, table 7, p. 35.

TABLE 10

Number of Soviet Cities of More Than 50,000 Population in 1959 by Groups Based on Percentages Occupied in Certain Activities in 1959

				Percentage of the Gainfully Occupied Persons in Industry (Manufacturing and Mining)				
				Above Urban Average For the USSR			Below Urban Average For the USSR	Totals
Percentage of Occupied Persons in Industry, Construction, Transportation and Communications				Over 60	50–60	40–50	30–40	Under 30	
	Above Urban Average for the USSR	Over 70	30	57	18	5	3	113
		60–70		16	53	34	6	109
								222
	Below Urban Average for the USSR	50–60			5	44	17	66
		Under 50				3	13	16
								82
		Totals	30	73	76	86	39	304
				179			125	304

Source: Based on B. S. Khorev, "Issledovanie funktsional'noi struktury gorodskikh poselenii SSSR (v sviazi s zadachami ikh ekonomiko-geograficheskoi tipologii)," *Voprosy geografii,* sbornik 66 (M. izd. "Mysl'," 1965), table 2, pp. 42–43.

more than 10 percentage points below the national urban average. As shown by Table 10, about a tenth of these cities, 30 of 304, had more than 60 per cent of the gainfully occupied persons in industry alone, or more than 20 percentage points above the national urban average. Gus-Khrustal'nyy, the glass city east of Moscow, had 73.4 per cent in industry.[8]

In general the percentage occupied in the broader category (industry-construction-transportation) among these 304 cities runs about 20 per cent higher than in industry alone (as in the national urban average, which is 61.5 per cent for the broader category and 42.0 per cent for industry alone). Cities in the upper right corner of Table 10 have much larger differences, reaching extremes in 3 cities with more than 70 per cent in the broader category and less than 30 per cent in industry alone, or more than 40 per cent in construction or transportation or some combination of them. Table 10 thus makes possible some differentiation of cities high

[8] B. S. Khorev, "Issledovanie . . . ," p. 41, footnote 1.

in industry, high in construction or transportation, or low in all these categories.

Table 11 lists the 304 individual cities which have been identified as falling into the class intervals of Table 10.[9]

A FUNCTIONAL CLASSIFICATION OF 304 CITIES OF MORE THAN 50,000 POPULATION

The 304 cities of the Soviet Union of more than 50,000 population in 1959 are classified into functional types in Tables 12 and 13 and Figures 7 and 8. This classification is based on Khorev,[10] except that the size groups have been adjusted to 1967 population data, the category of suburbs has been added, other minor modifications made,[11] and all cities in each category have been named.

Nearly 90 per cent of the 304 larger Soviet cities fall into 2 classes: diversified administrative centers and industrial cities, numbering 134 and 136 respectively (Table 12). The overwhelming predominance of these 2 types reflect the nature of the Soviet economy as a command economy, directed by the párty and government apparatus, owned by the state, and administered by government organs with the result that the political administrative structure operated through the urban hierarchy plays a key role in directing and coördinating the entire economic life of the country. It also reflects the focusing of party and government interest, leadership, and investment on the industrial side of the economy, especially on the production of material goods in mines and factories. Only 34 of the 304 cities of this size fall into other classifications.

Diversified Administrative Centers (I)

The 30 largest cities of the Soviet Union are all diversified administrative centers. These and smaller administrative centers

[9] Identification of cities by these categories is based on B. S. Khorev, "Issledovanie . . . ," table 2, pp. 42–43, and B. S. Khorev, *Gorodski poseleniia SSSR*, table 11, pp. 46–51.
[10] "Issledovanie . . . ," table 4, pp. 54–57, and map, pp. 46–47, and *Gorodskie poseleniia SSSR*, table 16, pp. 68–69, figure 1, following p. 64, and text, pp. 63–80.
[11] Based on A. A. Mints and B. S. Khorev, "Opyt ekonomiko-geograficheskoi tipologii sovetskikh gorodov (po materialam Tsentral'no-promyshlennogo raiona)," *Voprosy geografii*, sbornik 45 (M. Geografgiz, 1959), p. 79, and Moscow inset on map following p. 78.

TABLE 11

NAMES OF SOVIET CITIES OF MORE THAN 50,000
POPULATION IN 1959 IN GROUPS BASED ON PERCENTAGES
OCCUPIED IN INDUSTRY, CONSTRUCTION, AND
TRANSPORTATION TAKEN TOGETHER OR IN
INDUSTRY ALONE

The first figures refer to the percentage of the gainfully occupied persons in industry, construction, transportation, and communications taken together as a group.

The second figure refers to the percentage of the gainfully occupied persons in industry alone (including manufacturing and mining).

The third figure is the total number of cities that fall into the stated range of persons occupied in these activities; these figures correspond exactly to those in the corresponding boxes in Table 10.

Thus this table identifies by name all cities that fall within each of the class intervals distinguished in Table 10. A semicolon separates cities of more than 100,000 from those between 50,000 and 99,999. Cities under 50,000 are in parentheses.

Over 70 per cent (in industry, construction, transportation, and communications); and over 60 per cent (in industry alone): 30 cities.
Dzerhinsk, Izhevsk, Serpukhov, Orekhovo-Zuyevo, Podol'sk, Kadiyevka, Kramatorsk, Novoshakhtinsk, Taganrog, Rybinsk; Gus-Khrustal'nyy, Krasnokamsk, Lys'va, Noginsk, Zelenodol'sk, Votkinsk, Konstantinovka, Elektrostal', Zagorsk, Yegor'yevsk, Klin, Pavlovskiy Posad, Vyshniy Volochok, Murom, Kovrov, Pervoural'sk, Revda, Vichuga, Shuya, Severodvinsk.

Over 70 per cent; 50–60 per cent (in industry alone): 57 cities.
Yaroslavl', Shakhty, Tula, Penza, Kuybyshev, Gorlovka, Zhdanov, Makeyevka, Gor'kiy, Rubtsovsk, Noril'sk, Cheremkhovo, Anzhero-Sudzhensk, Kiselevsk, Leninsk-Kuznetskiy, Prokop'yevsk, Kamensk-Ural'skiy, Nizhniy Tagil, Perm', Chelyabinsk, Zlatoust, Kopeysk, Magnitogorsk, Komsomol'sk-na-Amure, Dneprodzershinsk, Zaporozh'ye, Donetsk; Temir-Tau, Leninogorsk, Balkhash, Zyryanovsk, Kineshma, Sumgait, Gukovo, Osinniki, Korkino, Beloretsk, Miass, Krasnyy Luch, Chapayevsk, Chirchik, Chistopol', Sarapul, Artem, Klaypeda, Kremenchug, Yenakiyevo, Torez, Kolomna, Kamensk-Shakhtinskiy, Asbest, Krasnotur'insk, Serov, Sverdlovsk (Lugansk Oblast), Rustavi, Chernogorsk, Margelan.

Over 70 per cent; 40–50 per cent: 18 cities.
Krasnoyarsk, Novosibirsk, Omsk, Novokuznetsk, Belovo, Orsk, Berezniki, Sterlitamak, Krivoy Rog, Novomoskovsk; Mezhdurechensk, Novotroitsk, Kizel, Chusovoy, Salavat, Kamyshin, Kommunarsk, Orsha.

Over 70 per cent; 30–40 per cent: 5 cities.
Angarsk; Cherepovets, Novokuybyshevsk, Angren, Uzlovaya.

Over 70 per cent; under 30 per cent: 3 cities (all under 100,000).
Volzhskiy, Bratsk, Tol'yatti.

60–70 per cent; 50–60 per cent: 16 cities.
Kirov, Barnaul, Lugansk, Ivanovo, Dnepropetrovsk, Nikolayev, Khar'kov, Voronezh, Kazan', Kostroma; Glazov, Berdichev, Berdyansk, Kuznetsk, Balashikha, Tushino[a].

TABLE 11 — Continued

NAMES OF SOVIET CITIES OF MORE THAN 50,000 POPULATION IN 1959 IN GROUPS BASED ON PERCENTAGES OCCUPIED IN INDUSTRY, CONSTRUCTION, AND TRANSPORTATION TAKEN TOGETHER OR IN INDUSTRY ALONE

60–70 per cent; 40–50 per cent: 53 cities (1).

Leningrad, Cheboksary, Biysk, Tomsk, Kemerovo, Sverdlovsk, Ufa, Kutaisi, Karaganda, Semipalatinsk, Bryansk, Leninakan, Gomel', Minsk, Vitebsk, Mogilev, Kaunas, Riga, Tallin, Kherson, Lipetsk, Ul'yanovsk, Saratov, Volgograd, Rostov-na-Donu, Krasnodar, Armavir, Kaluga, Kalinin, Ryazan', Vladimir, Perovo[a], Kuntsevo[a]; Saransk, Yoshkar-Ola, Kungur, Shadrinsk, Yelets, Leninabad, Tiraspol', Vorkuta, Borisov, Bobruysk, Liyepaya, Kerch', Nikopol', Melitopol', Artemovsk (Donets Oblast), Slavyansk, Sumy, Konotop, Lyubertsy, Kansk; (Birobidzhan).

60–70 per cent; 30–40 per cent: 34 cities.

Chimkent, Ulan-Ude, Irkutsk, Orenburg, Kurgan, Tyumen', Ust'-Kamenogorsk, Vladivostok, Orël, Kursk, Petropavlovsk, Murmansk, Vologda, Kaliningrad, Odessa, Syzran', Astrakhan', Arkhangel'sk; Troitsk, Oktyabr'skiy, Velikiye Luki, Novgorod, Baranovichi, Shyaulyay, Daugavpils, Melekess, Novorossiysk, Vol'sk, Bataysk, Engel's, Lyublino[a], Vyborg, Fergana, Nakhodka.

60–70 per cent; under 30 per cent: 6 cities.

Tselinograd; Petropavlovsk-Kamchatskiy, Pavlodar, Belgorod, Kropotkin, Aktyubinsk.

50–60 per cent; 40–50 per cent: 5 cities.

L'vov, Kirovograd, Chernovtsy; Maykop, Yeysk.

50–60 per cent; 30–40 per cent: 44 cities (3).

Moscow, Khabarovsk, Ural'sk, Tbilisi, Ussuriysk, Groznyy, Frunze, Samarkand, Tashkent, Baku, Kirovabad, Yerevan, Kokand, Makhachkala, Ordzhonikidze, Vinnitsa, Zhitomir, Kiev, Sevastopol', Simferopol', Poltava, Tambov, Smolensk, Kishinev, Vil'nyus; Buzuluk, Batumi, Borisoglebsk, Bukhara, Chardzhou, Bel'tsy, Syktyvkar, Pskov, Nal'chik, Grodno, Tartu, Belaya Tserkov, Cherkassy, Chernigov, Novocherkassk, Balashov, Blagoveshchensk, Sovetskaya Gavan', Mytishchi; (Stepanakert), (Cherkessk), (Gorno-Altaysk).

50–60 per cent; under 30 per cent: 17 cities (4).

Chita, Dzhambul, Ashkhabad, Dushanbe, Alma-Ata, Petrozavodsk, Babushkin[a]; Kzyl-Orda, Gur'yev, Abakan, Achinsk, Yuzhno-Sakhalinsk, Osh, Kustanay, Bugul'ma, Brest, Svobodny; (Uzhgorod), (Tashauz), (Mary), (Kokchetav).

Under 50 per cent; 30–40 per cent: 3 cities.

Andizhan; Michurinsk, Pyatigorsk.

Under 50 per cent; under 30 per cent: 13 cities (9).

Namangan, Stavropol'; Yakutsk, Sukhumi, Magadan, Kislovodsk, Lutsk, Yevpatoriya, Rovno, Ternopol', Khmel'nitskiy, Sochi, Ivano-Frankovsk; (Tskhinvali), (Nakhichevan'), (Khorog), (Kyzyl), (Naryn), (Termez), (Urgench), (Nukus), (Elista).

Source: B. S. Khorev, *Gorodskie poseleniia SSR (problemy rosta i ikh izuchenie); ocherki geografii rasseleniia* (M. Izd. "Mysl'," 1968), table 11, pp. 46–51.
[a] Cities incorporated into Moscow since 1959.

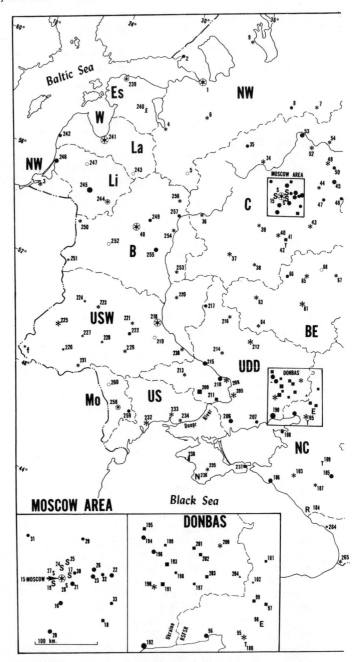

Fig. 7 Functional types of cities (economic types): western part of the USSR. For identification of regions and cities, see Table 13.

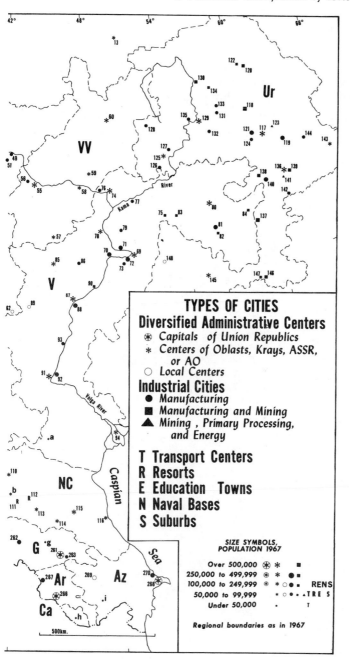

TYPES OF CITIES
Diversified Administrative Centers
⊛ *Capitals of Union Republics*
∗ *Centers of Oblasts, Krays, ASSR,*
  or AO
○ *Local Centers*
Industrial Cities
● *Manufacturing*
■ *Manufacturing and Mining*
▲ *Mining , Primary Processing,*
  and Energy

T Transport Centers
R Resorts
E Education Towns
N Naval Bases
S Suburbs

SIZE SYMBOLS,
POPULATION 1967

Over 500,000	⊛ ∗	■
250,000 to 499,999	⊛ ∗	● ●
100,000 to 249,999	⊛ ∗ ○ ● ■	RENS
50,000 to 99,999	∗ ○ ● ▲	TRE S
Under 50,000	●	T

Regional boundaries as in 1967

500km.

have complex functions and a broad spectrum of economic activities including both those of material production, such as manufacturing, construction, transportation, and trade, and nonmaterial activities such as administration and finance, education, science, health, art, publishing, and cultural activities.

The administrative centers represent, of course, central-place types, each with a legally determined tributary area for political

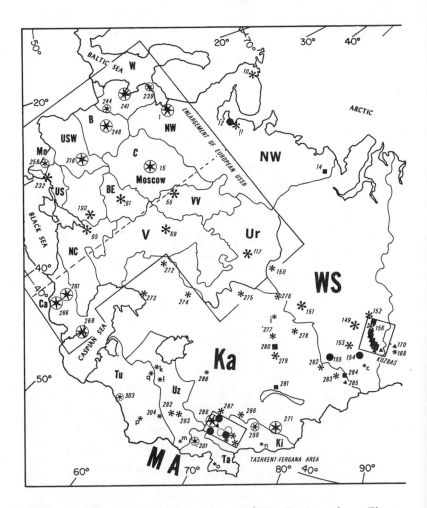

Fig. 8 Functional types of cities: rest of USSR. For legend, see Figure 7. For identification of regions and cities, see Table 13.

and administrative functions. They tend thus to be evenly spaced over the ecumene of the Soviet Union (Figures 7 and 8). As is regularly the case in other countries, the central places of equal rank are larger in densely populated areas and smaller in sparsely populated areas. These larger central places in more densely settled industrial areas also have a more complex economic profile with a higher proportion of workers in the city in industry.

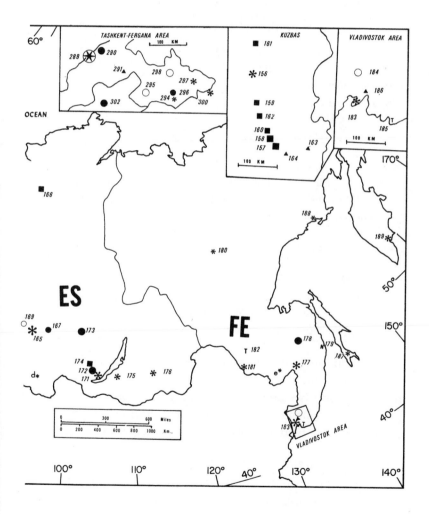

TABLE 12

FUNCTIONAL CLASSIFICATION OF CITIES OF THE USSR
Number in Each Category

I. Diversified Administrative Centers			134
A. Capitals of Union Republics		16	
(1) With population over 500,000	10		
(2) With population 250,000–499,999	6		
B. Centers of oblasts or similar units		118	
(1) With population over 500,000	21		
(2) With population 250,000–499,999	27		
(3) With population 100,000–249,999	57		
(4) With population 50,000–99,999	13		
(5) With population under 50,000	(17)		
II. Local Centers			15
III. Industrial Cities			136
A. Manufacturing		82	
(1) With population over 100,000	42		
(2) With population 50,000–99,999	40		
B. Manufacturing and mining		44	
(1) With population over 100,000	29		
(2) With population 50,000–99,999	15		
C. Mining, primary processing, and energy	10	10	
IV. Transport Centers			5
V. Resorts			4
VI. Education and Research Cities			2
VII. Naval Bases			2
VIII. Suburbs			6
Total Cities over 50,000 Population in 1959			304
Administrative Centers under 50,000 Population in 1959			17
Total Number of Cities Classified			321

The administrative centers are separated into sub-categories of capitals of the union republics or centers of oblasts, including similar administrative units, such as krays, autonomous republics (ASSR), or autonomous oblasts (AO). In addition each of these 2 sub-categories is further broken down by size groups.

Capitals of Union Republics (1A)

In the administrative hierarchy of the Soviet Union the highest ranks are accorded to the capitals of the 15 constituent union republics (Table 13). They have major administrative-political,

TABLE 13

FUNCTIONAL CLASSIFICATION OF CITIES OF THE USSR
Name, Location, Population, and Occupational Data
of Cities in Each Category

This classification includes all 304 cities of more than 50,000 population at the time the 1959 census was taken, plus 17 administrative centers then of smaller size. Numbers and letters correspond to the maps (Figures 7 and 8). Order of numbering is generally from north to south and west to east by major regions first for the RSFSR and then for the other union republics. Within each oblast or comparable unit cities are numbered in order of size in 1967.

REGIONS AND NUMBER OF CITIES

(Numbers in parentheses refer to cities of less than 50,000 population in 1959)

Abbre-viation	Republic Region	Numbers on Map	Number of Cities Classified	
	RSFSR	1–189	189	
NW	Northwest	1–14	14	
C	Center	15–54	40	
VV	Volga-Vyatka	55–60	6	
BE	Black-Earth Center	61–68	8	
V	Volga	69–94	26	(1)
NC	North Caucasus	95–116	22	(1)
Ur	Urals	117–148	32	
WS	Western Siberia	149–164	16	(1)
ES	Eastern Siberia	165–176	12	(1)
FE	Far East	177–189	13	(1)
U	Ukrainian SSR	190–238	49	
UDD	Donets-Dnepr	190–217	28	
USW	Southwest	218–231	14	(1)
US	South	232–238	7	
W	Western (Baltic)	239–247	9	
Es	Estonian SSR	239–240	2	
La	Latvian SSR	241–243	3	
Li	Lithuanian SSR	244–247	4	
B	Belorussian SSR	248–257	10	
Mo	Moldavian SSR	258–260	3	
Ca	Caucasus	261–270	10	
G	Georgian SSR	261–265	5	(1)
Ar	Armenian SSR	266–267	2	
Az	Azerbaydzhan SSR	268–270	3	(2)
Ka	Kazakh SSR	271–288	18	(1)
MA	Middle Asia	289–304	16	
Uz	Uzbek SSR	289–298	10	(3)
Ki	Kirgiz SSR	299–300	2	(1)
Ta	Tadzhik SSR	301–302	2	(1)
Tu	Turkmen SSR	303–304	2	(2)
Total		1–304	304	
Under 50,000		a–q		(17)

TABLE 13 — Continued

FUNCTIONAL CLASSIFICATION OF CITIES OF THE USSR

No. on Map	City	Region	Political Unit (Oblast unless noted)	Population in 1967 (thousands)	Percentage of Gainfully Occupied in: Industry, Building, Transport	Industry Alone
I. Diversified Administrative Centers						
A. Capitals of Union Republics						
(1) With over 500,000 population (10)					50–70	25–50
15	Moscow	C	RSFSR, USSR	6,507	50–60	35
1	Leningrad[1]	NW		3,706	60–70	45
218	Kiev	USW	Ukrainian SSR	1,413	50–60	30–40
241	Riga	W	Latvian SSR	680	60–70	40–50
248	Minsk	B	Belorussian SSR	772	60–70	40–50
261	Tbilisi	Ca	Georgian SSR	842	50–60	30–40
266	Yerevan	Ca	Armenian SSR	665	50–60	30–40
268	Baku	Ca	Azerbaydzhan SSR	1,196	50–60	30–40
271	Alma-Ata	Ka	Kazakh SSR	652	50–60	under 30
289	Tashkent	MA	Uzbek SSR	1,239	50–60	38.8
(2) With 250,000–499,999 population (6)						
239	Tallin	W	Estonian SSR	340	60–70	40–50
244	Vil'nyus	W	Lithuanian SSR	316	50–60	30–40
258	Kishinëv	Mo	Moldavian SSR	302	50–60	30–40
299	Frunze	MA	Kirgiz SSR	396	50–60	30–40
301	Dushanbe	MA	Tadzhik SSR	333	50–60	under 30
303	Ashkhabad[2]	MA	Turkmen SSR	238	50–60	under 30
B. Centers of oblasts or similar units						
(1) With over 500,000 population (21)					60–80	40–60
55	Gor'kiy	VV	Gor'kiy	1,120	70–80	50–60
61	Voronezh	BE	Voronezh	611	60–70	50–60
69	Kuybyshev	V	Kuybyshev	992	70–80	50–60
74	Kazan'	V	Tatar ASSR	821	60–70	50–60
80	Ufa	V	Bashkir ASSR	704	60–70	40–50
87	Saratov	V	Saratov	720	60–70	40–50
91	Volgograd	V	Volgograd	743	60–70	40–50
95	Rostov-na-Donu	NC	Rostov	757	60–70	40–50
117	Sverdlovsk	Ur	Sverdlovsk	961	60–70	40–50
129	Perm'	Ur	Perm'	796	70–80	50–60
136	Chelyabinsk	Ur	Chelyabinsk	836	70–80	50–60
149	Novosibirsk	WS	Novosibirsk	1,064	70–80	40–50
151	Omsk	WS	Omsk	774	70–80	40–50
165	Krasnoyarsk	ES	Krasnoyarsk Kray	576	70–80	40–50
190	Donetsk	UDD	Donetsk	840	70–80	50–60
205	Zaporozh'ye	UDD	Zaporozh'ye	595	70–80	50–60
208	Dnepropetrovsk	UDD	Dnepropetrovsk	816	60–70	50–60
212	Khar'kov	UDD	Khar'kov	1,125	60–70	50–60
225	L'vov[3]	USW	L'vov	512	50–60	40–50

TABLE 13 — Continued

FUNCTIONAL CLASSIFICATION OF CITIES OF THE USSR

No. on Map	City	Region	Political Unit (Oblast unless noted)	Population in 1967 (thousands)	Percentage of Gainfully Occupied in: Industry, Building, Transport	Industry Alone
232	Odessa[4]	US	Odessa	776	60–70	30–40
279	Karaganda[2]	Ka	Karaganda	498	60–70	40–50
	(2) With population 250,000–499,999 (27)				60–80	30–60
3	Kaliningrad	NW	Kaliningrad	270	60–70	30–40
10	Murmansk	NW	Murmansk	287	60–70	30–40
11	Arkhangel'sk[4]	NW	Arkhangel'sk	310	60–70	30–40
34	Kalinin	C	Kalinin	318	60–70	40–50
37	Bryansk	C	Bryansk	288	60–70	40–50
40	Tula	C	Tula	377	70–80	50–60
43	Ryazan'	C	Ryazan'	311	60–70	40–50
48	Ivanovo	C	Ivanovo	407	60–70	50–60
52	Yaroslavl'	C	Yaroslavl'	498	70–80	50–60
60	Kirov	VV	Kirov	309	60–70	50–60
63	Kursk	BE	Kursk	255	60–70	30–40
65	Lipetsk	BE	Lipetsk	253	60–70	40–50
78	Ul'yanovsk	V	Ul'yanovsk	294	60–70	40–50
85	Penza	V	Penza	333	70–80	50–60
94	Astrakhan'	V	Astrakhan'	368	60–70	30–40
103	Krasnodar	NC	Krasnodar Kray	407	60–70	40–50
115	Groznyy[3]	NC	Chechen-Ingush ASSR	331	50–60	30–40
125	Izhevsk[5]	Ur	Udmurt ASSR	376	70–80	60–70
145	Orenburg	Ur	Orenburg	326	60–70	30–40
152	Tomsk	WS	Tomsk	324	60–70	40–50
153	Barnaul	WS	Altay Kray	407	60–70	50–60
156	Kemerovo	WS	Kemerovo	364	60–70	40–50
171	Irkutsk	ES	Irkutsk	420	60–70	34.7
177	Khabarovsk[3]	FE	Khabarovsk Kray	435	50–60	30–40
183	Vladivostok[4]	FE	Maritime Kray	397	60–70	30–40
200	Lugansk	UDD	Lugansk	352	60–70	50–60
233	Nikolayev	US	Nikolayev	300	60–70	50–60
	(3) With population 100,000–249,999 (57)				50–70	Under 50
9	Petrozavodsk	NW	Karelian ASSR	171	50–60	less than 30
4	Pskov	NW	Pskov	112	50–60	30–40
6	Novgorod	NW	Novgorod	109	60–70	30–40
7	Vologda	NW	Vologda	170	60–70	30–40
13	Syktyvkar	NW	Komi ASSR	102	50–60	30–40
36	Smolensk	C	Smolensk	196	50–60	30–40
38	Orël	C	Orël	209	60–70	30–40
39	Kaluga	C	Kaluga	179	60–70	40–50
44	Vladimir	C	Vladimir	211	60–70	40–50

TABLE 13 — Continued

FUNCTIONAL CLASSIFICATION OF CITIES OF THE USSR

No. on Map	City	Region	Political Unit (Oblast unless noted)	Population in 1967 (thousands)	Percentage of Gainfully Occupied in: Industry, Building, Transport	Industry Alone
54	Kostroma[5]	C	Kostroma	209	60–70	50–60
57	Saransk	VV	Mordov ASSR	154	60–70	40–50
58	Cheboksary	VV	Chuvash ASSR	178	60–70	40–50
59	Yoshkar-Ola	VV	Mari ASSR	137	60–70	40–50
64	Belgorod[8]	BE	Belgorod	129	60–70	under 30
67	Tambov	BE	Tambov	211	50–60	30–40
107	Maykop	NC	Adygey AO	106	50–60	40–50
110	Stavropol'[3]	NC	Stavropol' Kray	177	under 50	under 30
113	Nal'chik	NC	Kabardinobalkar ASSR	119	50–60	30–40
114	Ordzhonikidze	NC	N. Oset ASSR	219	50–60	30–40
116	Makhachkala	NC	Dagestan ASSR	165	50–60	30–40
143	Kurgan	Ur	Kurgan	215	60–70	30–40
150	Tyumen'	WS	Tyumen'	240	60–70	30–40
175	Ulan-Ude	ES	Buryat ASSR	227	60–70	38.3
176	Chita	ES	Chita	203	50–60	27
181	Blagoveshchensk	FE	Amur	121	50–60	30–40
189	Petropavlovsk-Kamchatskiy[8]	FE	Kamchatka	123	60–70	under 30
213	Kirovograd	UDD	Kirovograd	168	50–60	40–50
214	Poltava	UDD	Poltava	184	50–60	30–40
216	Sumy	UDD	Sumy	140	60–70	40–50
220	Chernigov	USW	Chernigov	134	50–60	30–40
221	Zhitomir	USW	Zhitomir	141	50–60	30–40
223	Rovno[3]	USW	Rovno	100	under 50	under 30
229	Vinnitsa	USW	Vinnitsa	163	50–60	30–40
230	Cherkassy	USW	Cherkassy	128	50–60	30–40
231	Chernovtsy	USW	Chernovtsy	178	50–60	40–50
234	Kherson	US	Kherson	235	60–70	40–50
235	Simferopol'	US	Crimea	223	50–60	30–40
250	Grodno	B	Grodno	111	50–60	30–40
253	Gomel'	B	Gomel'	237	60–70	40–50
254	Mogilëv	B	Mogilëv	176	60–70	40–50
256	Vitebsk	B	Vitebsk	203	60–70	40–50
265	Batumi	Ca	Adzhar ASSR-G	100	50–60	33.3
272	Ural'sk	Ka	Ural'sk	123	50–60	30–40
273	Gur'yev	Ka	Gur'yev	101	50–60	under 30
274	Aktyubinsk[4]	Ka	Aktyubinsk	135	60–70	under 30
275	Kustanay[8]	Ka	Kustanay	118	50–60	under 30
276	Petropavlovsk	Ka	N. Kazakhstan	166	60–70	30–40
277	Tselinograd[4]	Ka	Tselinograd	176	60–70	under 30
278	Pavlodar[8]	Ka	Pavlodar	154	60–70	under 30
282	Semipalatinsk	Ka	Semipalatinsk	204	60–70	40–50
283	Ust'-Kamenogorsk	Ka	E. Kazakhstan	212	60–70	30–40

TABLE 13 — Continued

FUNCTIONAL CLASSIFICATION OF CITIES OF THE USSR

No. on Map	City	Region	Political Unit (Oblast unless noted)	Population in 1967 (thousands)	Percentage of Gainfully Occupied in: Industry, Building, Transport	Industry Alone
286	Dzhambul	Ka	Dzhambul	158	50–60	under 30
287	Chimkent	Ka	Chimkent	219	60–70	30–40
292	Bukhara	MA	Bukhara-Uz	102	50–60	30–40
293	Samarkand	MA	Samarkand-Uz	248	50–60	30–40
297	Andizhan[7, 3]	MA	Andizhan-Uz	169	under 50	30–40
300	Osh	MA	Osh-Ki	119	50–60	under 30
	(4) With population 50,000–99,999 (13)				Under 60	Under 40
168	Abakan[4]	ES	Khakass AO	78	50–60	21.3
180	Yakutsk	FE	Yakut ASSR	95	under 50	14
187	Yuzhno-Sakhalinsk	FE	Sakhalin	92	50–60	under 30
188	Magadan	FE	Magadan	82	under 50	under 30
224	Lutsk	USW	Volyn	82	under 50	under 30
226	Ivano-Frankovsk	USW	Ivano-Frankovsk	92	under 50	under 30
227	Ternopol'	USW	Ternopol'	72	under 50	under 30
228	Khmel'nitskiy	USW	Khmel'nitskiy	87	under 50	under 30
251	Brest[4]	B	Brest	96	50–60	under 30
264	Sukhumi	Ca	Abkhaz ASSR-G	88	under 50	under 30
288	Kzyl-Orda[4]	Ka	Kzyl-Orda	91	50–60	under 30
294	Fergana[6]	MA	Fergana-Uz	93	60–70	30–40
304	Chardzhou	MA	Chardzhou[10]–Tu	88	50–60	30–40
	(5) With populations under 50,000 in 1959 (17)				Under 60	Under 40
a	Elista[7]	V	Kalmyk ASSR	43	under 50	9
b	Cherkessk[11]	NC	Karachayevo-Cherkess AO	57	50–60	30–40
c	Gorno-Altaysk	WS	Gorno-Altaysk AO	32	50–60	30–40
d	Kyzyl	ES	Tuva ASSR	47	under 50	15.1
e	Birobidzhan[5, 6]	FE	Hebrew AO	46	60–70	40–50
f	Uzhgorod[11]	USW	Transcarpathia	61	50–60	under 30
g	Tskhinvali	Ca	S. Oset AO-G	27	under 50	under 30
h	Nakhichevan'	Ca	Nakhichevan' ASSR-Az	29	under 50	under 30
i	Stepanakert	Ca	Nagorno-Karabakh AO-Az	28	50–60	30–40
j	Kokchetav[11]	Ka	Kokchetav	76	50–60	under 30
k	Nukus[11]	MA	Kara-Kalpak ASSR-Uz	56	under 50	under 30
l	Urgench[11]	MA	Khorezm-Uz	65	under 50	under 30
m	Termez	MA	Surkhandar'ya-Uz	30	under 50	under 30
n	Naryn	MA	Tyan'-Shan'[10]-Ki	20	under 50	under 30

TABLE 13 — Continued

FUNCTIONAL CLASSIFICATION OF CITIES OF THE USSR

No. on Map	City	Region	Political Unit (Oblast unless noted)	Population in 1967 (thousands)	Percentage of Gainfully Occupied in: Industry, Building, Transport	Industry Alone
o	Khorog[7]	MA	Gorno-Badakhshan AO-Ta	12	under 50	7
p	Mary[11]	MA	Mary[10]-Tu	59	50–60	under 30
q	Tashauz[11]	MA	Tashauz[10]-Tu	60	50–60	under 30

II. *Local Centers*

Population mostly under 100,000 (15) — Under 70 — Under 40

No. on Map	City	Region	Political Unit	Population	Ind/B/T	Industry Alone
5	Velikiye Luki[6, 12]	NW	Pskov	80	60–70	30–40
62	Borisoglebsk	BE	Voronezh	62	50–60	30–40
68	Michurinsk	BE	Tambov	91	under 50	30–40
89	Balashov[4, 12]	V	Saratov	71	50–60	30–40
148	Buzuluk	Ur	Orenburg	63	50–60	30–40
169	Achinsk[12]	ES	Krasnoyarsk Kray	69	50–60	under 30
184	Ussuriysk[12]	FE	Maritime Kray	124	50–60	30–40
219	Belaya Tserkov	USW	Kiev	92	50–60	30–40
243	Daugavpils	W	Latvian SSR	89	60–70	30–40
247	Shyaulyay	W	Lithuanian SSR	82	60–70	30–40
252	Baranovichi[12]	B	Brest	85	60–70	30–40
260	Bel'tsy	M	Moldavian SSR	87	50–60	30–40
269	Kirovabad[12]	Ca	Azerbaydzhan SSR	174	50–60	30–40
295	Kokand[12]	MA	Fergana-Uz	131	50–60	30–40
298	Namangan[7, 12]	MA	Andizhan-Uz	158	under 50	under 30

III. *Industrial Cities* — 60–80
A. *Manufacturing* — (mainly
(1) With population over 100,000 (42) — 70–80) — Over 40

No. on Map	City	Region	Political Unit	Population	Ind/B/T	Industry Alone
8	Cherepovets[8, 12]	NW	Vologda	165	70–80	30–40
12	Severodvinsk	NW	Arkhangel'sk	121	70–80	60–70
16	Podol'sk	C	Moscow	163	70–80	60–70
20	Serpukhov	C	Moscow	121	70–80	60–70
21	Lyubertsy	C	Moscow	120	60–70	40–50
22	Orekhovo-Zuyevo	C	Moscow	117	70–80	60–70
23	Elektrostal'	C	Moscow	117	70–80	60–70
26	Noginsk	C	Moscow	102	70–80	60–70
45	Kovrov	C	Vladimir	116	70–80	60–70
53	Rybinsk	C	Yaroslavl'	212	70–80	60–70
56	Dzerzhinsk	VV	Gor'kiy	201	70–80	60–70
70	Syzran'[4]	V	Kuybyshev	169	60–70	30–40
71	Tol'yatti[8]	V	Kuybyshev	143	70–80	under 30
72	Novokuybyshevsk[8]	V	Kuybyshev	107	70–80	under 30
81	Sterlitamak[8]	V	Bashkir ASSR	162	70–80	40–50
88	Engel's[9]	V	Saratov	122	60–70	30–40
92	Volzhskiy[8]	V	Volgograd	114	70–80	under 30

TABLE 13 — Continued

FUNCTIONAL CLASSIFICATION OF CITIES OF THE USSR

No. on Map	City	Region	Political Unit (*Oblast unless noted*)	*Population in 1967 (thousands)*	Percentage of Gainfully Occupied in: Industry, Building, Transport	Industry Alone
96	Taganrog	NC	Rostov	245	70–80	60–70
105	Armavir	NC	Krasnodar Kray	139	60–70	40–50
106	Novorossiysk[4, 9]	NC	Krasnodar Kray	123	60–70	30–40
119	Kamensk-Ural'skiy	Ur	Sverdlovsk	161	70–80	50–60
121	Pervoural'sk	Ur	Sverdlovsk	110	70–80	60–70
140	Miass	Ur	Chelyabinsk	122	70–80	60–70
154	Biysk[8]	WS	Altay Kray	181	60–70	40–50
155	Rubtsovsk	WS	Altay Kray	142	70–80	50–60
172	Angarsk[8]	ES	Irkutsk	183	70–80	30–40
173	Bratsk[8]	ES	Irkutsk	122	70–80	under 30
178	Komsomol'sk-na-Amure	FE	Khabarovsk	209	70–80	50–60
192	Zhdanov	UDD	Donetsk	385	70–80	50–60
194	Kramatorsk	UDD	Donetsk	141	70–80	60–70
196	Konstantinovka	UDD	Donetsk	103	70–80	60–70
206	Melitopol'	UDD	Zaporozh'ye	119	60–70	40–50
210	Dneprodzerzhinsk	UDD	Dnepropetrovsk	224	70–80	50–60
215	Kremenchug	UDD	Poltava	136	70–80	50–60
245	Kaunas	W	Lithuanian SSR	284	60–70	40–50
246	Klaypeda	W	Lithuanian SSR	131	70–80	50–60
255	Bobruysk	B	Mogilev	120	60–70	40–50
262	Kutaisi	Ca	Georgian SSR	159	60–70	40–50
267	Leninakan	Ca	Armenian SSR	133	60–70	40–50
270	Sumgait[8]	Ca	Azerbaydzhan	104	Over 80	50–60
290	Chirchik	MA	Tashkent-Uz	100	70–80	50–60
302	Leninabad	MA	Tadzhik SSR	100	60–70	40–50
	(2) With population 50,000–99,999 (40)				60–80	Over 40
2	Vyborg[9]	NW	Leningrad	65	60–70	30–40
29	Zagorsk	C	Moscow	85	70–80	60–70
30	Balashikha	C	Moscow	74	60–70	50–60
31	Klin	C	Moscow	69	70–80	60–70
32	Pavlovskiy Posad	C	Moscow	65	70–80	60–70
33	Yegor'yevsk	C	Moscow	64	70–80	60–70
35	Vyshniy Volochek	C	Kalinin	73	70–80	60–70
46	Murom	C	Vladimir	96	70–80	60–70
47	Gus'-Khrustal'nyy	C	Vladimir	63	over 80	73.4
49	Kineshma	C	Ivanovo	94	70–80	50–60
50	Shuya	C	Ivanovo	69	70–80	60–70
51	Vichuga	C	Ivanovo	53	70–80	60–70
66	Yelets	BE	Lipetsk	96	60–70	40–50
73	Chapayevsk	V	Kuybyshev	87	70–80	50–60

TABLE 13 — Continued

FUNCTIONAL CLASSIFICATION OF CITIES OF THE USSR

No. on Map	City	Region	Political Unit (Oblast unless noted)	Population in 1967 (thousands)	Industry, Building, Transport	Industry Alone
76	Zelenodol'sk	V	Tatar ASSR	72	70–80	60–70
77	Chistopol'	V	Tatar ASSR	61	70–80	50–60
79	Melekess[8]	V	Ul'yanovsk	75	60–70	30–40
86	Kuznetsk	V	Penza	75	60–70	50–60
93	Kamyshin	V	Volgograd	93	70–80	40–50
108	Yeysk[3]	NC	Krasnodar Kray	68	50–60	40–50
124	Revda	Ur	Sverdlovsk	57	70–80	60–70
126	Sarapul	Ur	Udmurt ASSR	91	70–80	50–60
127	Votkinsk	Ur	Udmurt ASSR	72	70–80	60–70
128	Glazov	Ur	Udmurt ASSR	65	60–70	50–60
131	Lys'va	Ur	Perm'	79	70–80	60–70
132	Kungur	Ur	Perm'	70	60–70	40–50
133	Chusovoy	Ur	Perm'	63	70–80	40–50
135	Krasnokamsk	Ur	Perm'	55	70–80	60–70
142	Troitsk[4, 9]	Ur	Chelyabinsk	86	60–70	30–40
144	Shadrinsk	Ur	Kurgan	65	60–70	40–50
167	Kansk	ES	Krasnoyarsk Kray	91	60–70	40–50
207	Berdyansk	UDD	Zaporozh'ye	37	60–70	50–60
217	Konotop	UDD	Sumy	61	60–70	40–50
222	Berdichev	USW	Zhitomir	60	60–70	50–60
242	Liyepaya	W	Latvian SSR	86	60–70	40–50
249	Borisov	B	Minsk	74	60–70	40–50
257	Orsha	B	Vitebsk	89	70–80	40–50
259	Tiraspol'	M	Moldavian SSR	91	60–70	40–50
263	Rustavi	Ca	Georgian SSR	95	70–80	50–60
296	Margelan	MA	Fergana-Uz	89	over 70	over 40
	B. *Manufacturing and Mining*					
	(1) With population over 100,000 (29)				60–80	Over 40
18	Kolomna	C	Moscow	131	70–80	50–60
41	Novomoskovsk	C	Tula	126	70–80	40–50
97	Shakhty	NC	Rostov	209	70–80	50–60
99	Novoshakhtinsk	NC	Rostov	107	70–80	60–70
118	Nizhniy Tagil	Ur	Sverdlovsk	377	70–80	50–60
120	Serov	Ur	Sverdlovsk	104	70–80	50–60
130	Berezniki[8]	Ur	Perm'	134	70–80	40–50
137	Magnitogorsk	Ur	Chelyabinsk	357	70–80	50–60
138	Zlatoust	Ur	Chelyabinsk	178	70–80	50–60
139	Kopeysk	Ur	Chelyabinsk	166	70–80	50–60
146	Orsk	Ur	Orenburg	215	70–80	40–50
157	Novokuznetsk	WS	Kemerovo	493	70–80	40–50
158	Prokop'yevsk	WS	Kemerovo	290	70–80	50–60
159	Leninsk-Kuznetskiy	WS	Kemerovo	138	70–80	50–60

TABLE 13 — Continued

FUNCTIONAL CLASSIFICATION OF CITIES OF THE USSR

No. on Map	City	Region	Political Unit (Oblast unless noted)	Population in 1967 (thousands)	Percentage of Gainfully Occupied in: Industry, Building, Transport	Industry Alone
160	Kiselevsk	WS	Kemerovo	138	70–80	50–60
161	Anzhero-Sudzhensk	WS	Kemerovo	116	70–80	50–60
162	Belovo	WS	Kemerovo	116	70–80	40–50
166	Noril'sk	ES	Krasnoyarsk Kray	129	70–80	50–60
174	Cheremkhovo	ES	Irkutsk	109	70–80	50–60
191	Makeyevka	UDD	Donetsk	414	70–80	50–60
193	Gorlovka	UDD	Donetsk	343	70–80	50–60
195	Slavyansk	UDD	Donetsk	113	60–70	40–50
201	Kadiyevka	UDD	Lugansk	139	70–80	60–70
202	Kommunarsk[8]	UDD	Lugansk	124	70–80	40–50
203	Krasnyy Luch	UDD	Lugansk	102	70–80	50–60
209	Krivoy Rog	UDD	Dnepropetrovsk	510	70–80	40–50
211	Nikopol'	UDD	Dnepropetrovsk	110	60–70	40–50
237	Kerch	US	Crimea	118	60–70	40–50
280	Temirtau	Ka	Karaganda	150	70–80	50–60
(2) With population 50,000–99,999 (15)						
14	Vorkuta	NW	Komi ASSR	65	60–70	40–50
75	Bugul'ma[3, 9]	V	Tatar ASSR	74	50–60	under 30
82	Salavat[8]	V	Bashkir ASSR	98	70–80	40–50
83	Oktyabr'skiy[8, 9]	V	Bashkir ASSR	79	60–70	30–40
84	Beloretsk	V	Bashkir ASSR	64	70–80	50–60
90	Vol'sk[9]	V	Saratov	70	60-70	30–40
101	Kamensk-Shakhtinskiy	NC	Rostov	71	70–80	50–60
122	Krasnotur'insk	Ur	Sverdlovsk	61	70–80	50–60
134	Kizel	Ur	Perm'	55	70–80	40–50
147	Novotroitsk[8]	Ur	Orenburg	82	70–80	40–50
197	Torez	UDD	Donetsk	95	70–80	50–60
198	Yenakiyevo	UDD	Donetsk	94	70–80	50–60
199	Artëmovsk	UDD	Donetsk	77	60–70	40–50
281	Balkhash	Ka	Karaganda	75	70–80	50–60
284	Leninogorsk	Ka	E. Kazakhstan	70	70–80	50–60
C. Mining, Primary Processing, and Energy Population under 100,000 (10)					60–80	Over 40
102	Gukovo[8]	NC	Rostov	68	over 80	50–60
123	Asbest	Ur	Sverdlovsk	74	70–80	50–60
141	Korkino	Ur	Chelyabinsk	83	70–80	50–60
163	Mezhdurechensk[8]	WS	Kemerovo	79	70–80	40–50
164	Osinniki	WS	Kemerovo	69	70–80	50–60
170	Chernogorsk	ES	Krasnoyarsk Kray	61	70–80	50–60

TABLE 13 — Continued

FUNCTIONAL CLASSIFICATION OF CITIES OF THE USSR

No. on Map	City	*Region*	Political Unit (*Oblast unless* noted)	*Population in 1967 (thousands)*	Percentage of Gainfully Occupied in: Industry, Building, Transport	Industry Alone
186	Artëm	FE	Maritime Kray	65	70–80	50–60
204	Sverdlovsk	UDD	Lugansk	73	70–80	50–60
285	Zyryanovsk	Ka	E. Kazakhstan	57	70–80	50–60
291	Angren[8]	MA	Tashkent-Uz	74	70–80	30–40
	IV. *Transport Centers*					
	Population under 100,000 (5)				Over 50	Under 40
	(More than 20 per cent in transportation)					
42	Uzlovaya	C	Tula	52	70–80	under 30
100	Bataysk	NC	Rostov	85	60–70	30–40
109	Kropotkin	NC	Krasnodar Kray	62	60–70	under 30
182	Svodobnyy	FE	Amur	62	50–60	under 30
185	Nakhodka	FE	Maritime Kray	96	60–70	30–40
	V. *Resorts*					
	Population mostly under 100,000 (4)				Under 50	Under 40
	(More than 10 per cent in health services)					
104	Sochi	NC	Krasnodar Kray	188	under 50	under 30
111	Kislovodsk	NC	Stavropol' Kray	84	under 50	under 30
112	Pyatigorsk	NC	Stavropol' Kray	81	under 50	30–40
238	Yevpatoriya	US	Crimea	70	under 50	under 30
	VI. *Centers of Education and Research* (2)				Under 60	Under 40
98	Novocherkassk	NC	Rostov	161	50–60	30–40
240	Tartu	W	Estonian SSR	85	50–60	30–40
	VII. *Naval Bases* (2)					
179	Sovetskaya Gavan'	FE	Khaborovsk Kray	26	50–60	30–40
236	Sevastopol'	US	Crimea	209	50–60	30–40
	VIII. *Suburbs*					
	Population under 150,000 (6)				Highly variable	
17	Perovo[13]	C	Moscow	143	60–70	40–50
19	Kuntsevo[13]	C	Moscow	129	60–70	40–50 less
24	Babushkin[13]	C	Moscow	112	50–60	than 30
27	Tushino[13]	C	Moscow	90	60–70	50–60
28	Lyublino[13]	C	Moscow	86	60–70	30–40
25	Mytishchi	C	Moscow	112	50–60	30–40

Source: Based on data in B. S. Khorev, "Issledovanie funktsional'noe struktury gorodskikh poselenii SSSR (v sviazi s zadachami ikh ekonomiko-geograficheskoi tipologii)," *Voprosy geografii*, sbornik 66 (M. Izd. "Mysl'," 1965), table 2, pp. 42–43, map on pp. 46–47, table 4, pp. 54–57; and B. S. Khorev, *Gorodskie poselenie SSSR (problemy rosta i ikh*

cultural, and educational activities. Moscow stands at the head of the hierarchy serving simultaneously as capital of the entire Soviet Union, capital of its largest republic, the RSFSR, and center of an oblast. Leningrad, which for more than 200 years served as capital of Russia (1712–1918), has many of the characteristics of a capital city, with numerous governmental installations, though not presently a capital, and is here classified with capital cities (just as Moscow might well have been during the period that St. Petersburg was capital).

Several observations may be made about these capitals of union republics.

First, they are invariably the largest cities within their respective republics and thus generally large, 5 of them having over a million, another 5 more than half a million, and another 5 over a quarter million (Table 13). Moscow with 6.5 million and Leningrad with 3.7 million are, of course, the largest cities in the country, but Kiev, capital of the Ukraine has 1.4 million; Baku, capital of the Azerbaydzhan SSR in the Transcaucasus, has 1.2 million; and so does Tashkent, capital of the Uzbek SSR in Soviet Middle Asia. Capitals of union republics with more than half a million population include Riga of the Latvian SSR in the Baltic republics, Minsk of the Belorussian SSR, Tbilisi of the Georgian SSR, and Yerevan of the Armenian SSR both in the Transcaucasus, and Alma-Ata of the Kazakh SSR, between Western Siberia

---

izuchenie); ocherki geografii rasseleniia (M. Izd. "Mysl'," 1968), figure 1, following p. 64, table 16, pp. 68–69, and pp. 39–80.

[1] Leningrad is classified with the capital cities, since for more than 200 years it was the capital of the Russian Empire and it retains many functions characteristic of such cities, although not now a capital.

[2] Population slightly under the minimum for this size category.

[3] City with percentage in industry-construction-transportation below typical range for this category.

[4] Cities with more than 15 per cent in transportation.

[5] City with percentage in industry above the typical range for this category.

[6] City with percentage in industry-construction-transportation above the typical range for this category.

[7] City with significant percentage occupied in agriculture.

[8] Cities with major construction in 1959 at the time of the census; high percentages in industry-construction-transportation but relatively lower percentages in industry alone. Percentage in construction more than 20.

[9] City with percentage in industry alone below the typical range for this category.

[10] Chardzhou, Mary, and Tashauz oblasts in the Turkmen SSR were abolished as separate oblasts in January, 1963. Tyan'-Shan' Oblast in the Kirgiz SSR was also abolished at about the same time.

[11] Oblast centers with population under 50 thousand in 1959 but more than 50 thousand in 1967.

[12] Formerly an administrative center of an oblast, guberniya, or comparable unit.

[13] 1959 population.

and Soviet Middle Asia. Capitals with over a quarter million include 3 in the west, Tallin of the Estonian SSR, Vil'nyus of the Lithuanian SSR, and Kishinëv of the Moldavian SSR, and 2 in Soviet Middle Asia, Frunze of the Kirgiz SSR and Dushanbe of the Tadzhik SSR. The remaining capital of a republic, Ashkhabad, with 238,000, is the smallest. It is the capital of the Turkmen SSR, with the second smallest population of any union republic and the lowest density of population of any republic, only 3 persons per square kilometer. Ashkhabad stands in splendid isolation in the Middle Asiatic deserts, distant from other cities or oases.

Second, aside from Moscow, the capitals of union republics are located on the western and southern margins of the Soviet Union, since they are centers for major non-Russian ethnic groups incorporated into the Russian Empire by the expansion of the Russian state outward from the core area of Russian settlement around Moscow (Figure 8). There are no such centers on the northern or eastern margins of the country in the Soviet Far North or in Siberia or the Soviet Far East because there were no such densely settled areas with major ethnic groups incorporated by expansion of the Russian Empire in these directions, except for the various groups at the bend of the Volga River. These are distant from the external boundaries of the Soviet Union and thus do not qualify for status as a union republic, which requires independent direct access to areas lying outside the Soviet Union.

Third, unlike the largest oblast centers, they have relatively low proportions of occupied workers in industry. Except for Leningrad, not currently a capital, and for Tallin in Estonia, Riga in Latvia, and Minsk in Belorussia, all in the long-settled and relatively well-developed western borderland of the country, all the capitals of union republics have proportions of gainfully occupied persons in industry alone or in the combination of industry, construction, and transportation below the urban average for the Soviet Union (Table 13, type IA). Two factors may be involved in this relatively low proportion in industry: (1) the cities as capitals of union republics have large numbers engaged in fulfilling complex and important administrative, political, cultural, and educational roles, and (2) since they are the capitals of political units defined on the basis of non-Russian ethnic groups, except for Moscow and Leningrad, they are located in peripheral areas with a lesser average level of industrial development than in the core Russian areas, in which industry first developed in the country.

Fourth, the capitals of the union republics have shown accelerating rates of comparative growth. Omitting Moscow and Leningrad, (capital and former capital of the entire country), the aggregate population of the 14 capitals of union republics showed a slower rate of increase than the urban population of the country as a whole before 1959 but a more rapid rate since then. These large capital cities and regional centers of major non-Russian ethnic groups grew on the average at about 60 per cent the rate of other cities in the period 1926–1939, at about 90 per cent the rate of other cities for the period 1939–1959, but about 15 per cent faster than other cities for 1959–1967. The lower earlier rates are doubtless related to the low proportions of their occupied persons in industry, which has been the major growth sector of the economy, although administrative functions have also increased rapidly.

Centers of Oblasts or Similar Units (IB)

The administrative centers of oblasts or similar units range in size about a hundred fold from 1,125,000 to only 12,000 (Table 13). A great centrally located administrative and industrial metropolis of more than a million is very different in many characteristics from a small isolated center of a sparsely populated and remote mountainous area. Since many features of cities are related to size, the 135 administrative centers of oblasts are classified into 5 sub-groups in relation to size (Tables 12 and 13): (1) over half a million (21 cities), (2) from a quarter to half a million (27 cities), (3) from 100,000 to 249,999 (57 cities), (4) from 50,000 to 99,999 (13 cities), and (5) less than 50,000 (17 cities).

The 17 oblast centers with less than 50,000 population in 1959 do not come into our functional classification of 304 cities of more than 50,000, but since they form part of an exactly defined system and since data for them are available, they have been included to round out the picture of the administrative network of cities of this level. Of the 17 such centers with less than 50,000 popu-

lation in 1959 (category IB-5), 7 had already reached more than
50,000 population by 1967, leaving only 10 of the smallest size
category for that year.

There is a close association of size of the administrative
centers of oblasts or similar units and the degree of development
of industry. As one goes down the size gradations among administrative centers of oblasts, one finds generally lower and lower
proportions of the gainfully occupied persons in industry-con-
struction-transport or in industry alone. Thus the range is 60–80
per cent of gainfully occupied persons in industry-construction-
transport for size groups 1 and 2 (250,000 to 1,120,000), 50–70 per
cent for size group 3 (100,000–249,999), and under 60 per cent for
size groups 4 and 5 (under 100,000). Similarly percentage of gainfully occupied persons in industry alone range 40–60 per cent for
the largest size (over 500,000), 30–60 for size group 2 (250,000–
499,999), under 50 per cent for size group 3, and under 40 per
cent for size groups 4 and 5. This remarkably regular increase
of per cent of gainfully occupied persons in industry with size is
one of the key characteristics of larger Soviet cities that are oblast
centers. It may reflect: (1) Cities in industrial areas are larger because they serve a more densely populated tributary area and
thus a larger total population in the subordinate political unit.
(2) The industrial component of a city affects its size for if the
administrative functions of a city serving a particular oblast require that the city be a given size, it is clear that the more industrial employment adds to the administrative employment, the
larger the city will be. In such cases, the size of a city would bear
a direct relationship to the percentage in industry.

Another evidence of the role of industry in size of administrative centers is the proportion of such centers that have a
markedly industrial character as measured by having more than
70 per cent of the gainfully occupied persons in industry, construction, and transportation, i.e., more than 10 percentage points
above the national urban average. It is significant that all 13
oblast centers with such an industrial emphasis have populations
of more than 250,000. Stated another way, 9 of the 21 oblast centers (43 per cent) with more than half a million population have
this degree of industrialization, 4 of 27 oblast centers (15 per

cent) with between a quarter and a half million, but none of the 87 oblast centers with less than a quarter million. This is a remarkable witness to the weight of industry and related activities.

Oblast Centers with More Than 500,000 Population (IB-1)

The 21 oblast centers with more than a half million population are great regional and industrial and transport centers. They reveal both a characteristic location pattern and economic structure.

Nineteen of the 21 giant oblast centers are located in an industrial core of the Soviet Union. The heart of this core stretches from the Dnepr River and the Donets-Dnepr Region of the Ukraine eastward through the Volga Region and the Urals to Western Siberia. Each of these 4 regions has more than one such city. Four cities in the Donets-Dnepr Region are Khar'kov, the largest city in this group with 1,125,000, Donetsk, center of the Donbas coalfield and industrial district, and Dnepropetrovsk and Zaporozh'ye oblast centers and industrial cities on the Dnepr River. The adjoining Volga Region of the RSFSR has 5 such cities, from north to south, Kazan', capital of the Tatar ASSR, Kuybyshev, Ufa, capital of the Bashkir ASSR, Saratov, and Volgograd. Except for Ufa these are Volga River cities. The Urals have 3 oblast centers of this size, Sverdlovsk, Perm', and Chelyabinsk. Western Siberia has 2 such cities, Novosibirsk and Omsk. On the periphery of this core are 5 other such cities, Gor'kiy in the Volga-Vyatka Region on the Volga River upstream from the main Volga Region, Voronezh in the Black-Earth Center adjacent to the Donets-Dnepr and Volga regions, Rostov-na-Donu in the North Caucasus between the Donets-Dnepr and Volga regions, Karaganda, in Kazakhstan just south of Western Siberia, and Krasnoyarsk on the Yenisey River in Eastern Siberia near the boundary with Western Siberia. Only 2 such large oblast centers lie outside this interior core, Odessa and L'vov in the Ukraine, both old regional centers near the western boundary of the Soviet Union.

In economic structure most of these very large oblast centers have very high percentages of gainfully occupied persons in industry, construction, and transportation. For example, Gor'kiy,

Kuybyshev, Perm', Chelyabinsk, Novosibirsk, Omsk, Krasnoyarsk, Donetsk, and Zaporozh'ye have more than 70 per cent of their gainfully occupied persons in these activities, or more than 10 percentage points above the national urban average. Furthermore, they constitute 9 of the 13 oblast centers in the Soviet Union with this high a percentage in this group of activities. Transportation is relatively important, particularly in the Siberian cities of Novosibirsk, Omsk, and Krasnoyarsk, all located on the Trans-Siberian Railway at major river crossings, the Ob', Irtysh, and the Yenisey, respectively. Industry is relatively important in Kazan', Voronezh, Dnepropetrovsk, and Khar'kov; all have more than 50 per cent of gainfully occupied persons in industry, or more than 10 percentage points above the national urban average. Sverdlovsk, center of the great Ural Region, Rostov-na-Donu, center of the North Caucasus, and Ufa (capital of the Bashkir ASSR), Saratov, and Volgograd in the Volga Region, and Karaganda, center of a large mining and industrial region of Kazakhstan, have somewhat lower percentages in industry and related activities, although still well above the national urban average.

The western cities of L'vov and Odessa, falling outside the industrial core of the country, have a lesser industrial component in their economic structure, L'vov falling below the national urban average for employment in industry, construction, and transportation taken together, but being above average for industry alone, and Odessa falling below the national urban average for industry alone but having above average employment in the larger group by virtue of its important transportation functions.

Oblast Centers with 250,000–499,999 Population (IB-2)

The 27 oblast centers with between a quarter and a half million inhabitants show a wide distribution over the Soviet Union and a wide range of degree of industrial development.

Twenty-five of the 27 cities of this group lie within the RSFSR but within this republic they extend all the way from the western to the eastern borders. The Industrial Center alone has 6 such cities: Yaroslavl', the largest in this group, and Ivanovo, major industrial cities northeast of Moscow, Tula, an old industrial city south of Moscow, and Kalinin, Bryansk, and Ryazan'. The

Northwest Region has 3, Murmansk and Arkhangel'sk, Arctic ports, and Kaliningrad, the Baltic port. Two are Volga River cities, Ul'yanovsk and Astrakhan'. Three lie in the southeast corner of Western Siberia, Tomsk, Kemerovo, and Barnaul. Farther east are Irkutsk, center of Eastern Siberia, and Khabarovsk and Vladivostok, twin centers of the Soviet Far East. The other 8 cities in the RSFSR are widely distributed: Kirov in the northern part of the Volga-Vyatka Region, Kursk and Lipetsk in the Black-Earth Center, Penza in the western part of the Volga Region, Krasnodar and Groznyy in the North Caucasus, Izhevsk and Orenburg on the fringes of the Ural Region. Only 2 lie outside the RSFSR, both in the Ukraine, Lugansk, center of the eastern part of the Donbas coalfield, and Nikolayev, port on the Black Sea.

In economic structure this group of oblast centers ranges from strong to weak development of industry.

The 4 oblast centers in this size group with more than 70 per cent of gainfully occupied persons in industry, construction, and transportation may serve as examples of industrial cities diversified by administrative functions.

Izhevsk, capital of the Udmurt ASSR on the northwest flanks of the Urals, ranks highest among oblast centers in percentage in industry alone, more than 60 per cent, or more than 20 percentage points above the national urban average. The other 29 cities with such a high proportion in industry alone are all classified as industrial cities, mainly manufacturing cities (Type IIIA). With administrative functions added only during the Soviet period, Izhevsk is essentially an industrial city, founded in 1760 around an iron works (later also guns). It was a factory village called Izhevskiy Zavod, "Izhevsk Factory," and did not become a city until 1917.

Other oblast cities with high proportions in industrial and related activities are Yaroslavl', Tula, and Penza. Yaroslavl', the oldest Russian city on the Volga River, was an early center of a principality that rivalled Moscow. It developed as a textile center but has recently shifted more to machinery and chemicals. Tula, one of the oldest Russian industrial cities, producing arms in the 17th century, has modern metallurgical and machinery works. Penza is a diversified industrial and administrative center. Four other oblast centers of this size are also characterized by a heavy industrial emphasis, as evidenced by having more than 50 per cent of their gainfully occupied persons in industry alone, more than 10 percentage points above the national average: Ivanovo, the textile city in the Central Industrial Region northeast of Moscow; Kirov, farther to the northeast in the Volga-Vyatka Region; Lugansk, the oblast center for the eastern part of the Donbas coalfield and industrial district; and Barnaul, center of Altay Kray in Western Siberia.

At the other extreme are Khabarovsk on the Amur River in the Soviet Far East and Groznyy, the old Russian fortress in the Caucasus, now center of the Chechen-Ingush ASSR in the North Caucasus and of an oil-producing district. In both of them the proportion of gainfully occupied persons in industry, construction, and transport, or in industry alone are below the national urban average. They thus fit more closely into the traditional picture of an administrative and regional center.

Of the 27 oblast centers in this size category all except Khabarovsk and Groznyy have percentages gainfully occupied in industry, construction, and transportation as a group above the national urban average but 9 of the 27 have percentages occupied in industry alone below the national urban average. These 9 are all located away from the main industrial districts and have important transportation functions, either as ports, Kaliningrad on the Baltic Sea, Murmansk and Arkhangel'sk on the Arctic Ocean, Astrakhan' on the lower Volga River, Khabarovsk on the Amur River, and Vladivostok on the Sea of Japan; or as railroad junctions, servicing points or gateways, Kursk, a railroad junction in the Black-Earth Center, Orenburg on the Ural River, the gateway from Europe to Kazakhstan and Soviet Middle Asia, which served as the capital of Kazakhstan from 1920 to 1926,[12] and Irkutsk and Khabarovsk on the Trans-Siberian Railway.

Oblast Centers with 100,000–249,999 Population (IB-3)

The 57 oblast centers with populations between one hundred thousand and a quarter million may be considered the most typi-

---

[12] V. S. Varlamov, "Ob ekonomiko-geograficheskom polozhenii Orenburga," *Vestnik Moskovskogo Universiteta, Seriia 5, Geografiia*, 1960, vypusk 6, pp. 55–60.

cal expression of the oblast administrative center. This is the most numerous group with 57 of the 135 oblast centers, or 42 per cent of such centers.

Unlike the larger oblast centers, which lie mainly in the RSFSR, this size group is widely distributed, extending to all parts of the Soviet Union, with 26 in the RSFSR and 31 in other republics.

In economic structure these cities tend to cluster around the national urban average of 60 per cent in industry, construction, and transportation and 40 per cent in industry alone, with more below than above the national average. They are thus not pronouncedly industrial, as are larger oblast centers, although as in most Soviet cities, industries play a considerable role. Very commonly these cities have a rather wide spread between the percentage in industry, construction, and transportation taken together and the percentage in industry alone revealing major transportation functions or construction activities at the time of the census. Cities that fit this special type of oblast centers with important transportation functions include a group of cities along the Trans-Siberian Railway, Kurgan and Tyumen', just east of the Urals, Petropavlovsk in Northern Kazakhstan, and Ulan-Ude and Chita in Eastern Siberia. Kazakhstan, with the highest percentage of its gainfully occupied persons in transportation of any republic, has many oblast centers that have major transportation functions: Gur'yev, Aktyubinsk, Tselinograd, Pavlodar, Kustanay, and Semipalatinsk. The port Petropavlovsk-Kamchatskiy on Kamchatka also has important transportation activities.

Oblast Centers with 50,000–99,999 Population (IB-4)

The 20 smaller oblast centers with populations between 50 and 100 thousand in 1967 lie mostly outside the RSFSR and have weak development of industry. These include the 13 shown in category IB(4) in Table 13 and 7 in category IB(5) that had less than 50 thousand in 1959 but had reached this size by 1967. Only 5 lie in the RSFSR and these are centers of small ethnic minorities or lie in the Soviet Far East. The 15 in other union republics lie particularly in the Western Ukraine (5), where there are many small oblasts, or in Soviet Middle Asia (6). Three of these oblasts in Soviet Middle Asia, all in the Turkmen SSR, have been disestablished since 1959 and thus 3 of these smaller cities have lost their administrative functions as oblast centers. The small size of these oblast centers is explained in part by the small populations of their tributary oblasts and in part by the lack of industrial development. All of the 20 oblast centers of this group have proportions of gainfully occupied persons in industry below the national urban average, 16 of them at least 10 percentage points below the national urban average, that is, they have less than 30 per cent in industry. These are thus local and regional centers of small or sparsely populated oblasts, usually on the periphery of the Soviet Union, in the west, southeast, or east.

Oblast Centers with Less Than 50,000 Population (IB-5)

The 10 oblast centers with under 50,000 population in 1967 are mainly centers of small ethnic minorities with very little industrial development. Eight of the 10 are centers of autonomous republics (ASSR) or of autonomous oblasts (AO). Naryn was the center of the former Tyan'-Shan' Oblast in the mountainous part of the Kirgiz SSR. Also 8 of the 10 have less than 30 per cent of the gainfully occupied persons in industry, that is more than 10 percentage points below the national urban average. In this group only Birobidzhan, capital of the Yevreyskaya (Hebrew) Autonomous Oblast in the Soviet Far East, has more than the national urban average in industry or in industry, construction, and transportation. Khorog, capital of the Gorno-Badakhshan Autonomous Oblast in the mountainous Pamir eastern section of the Tadzhik SSR in the Soviet Middle Asia, and Elista, capital of the Kalmyk ASSR, west of the mouth of the Volga River, have extremely low percentages occupied in industry, only 7 and 9 per cent respectively.

Local Centers (II)

The 15 local centers of more than 50,000 population in 1959 are characterized by small size, wide distribution in the well-settled parts of the Soviet Union, and a low level of industrial development (Table 13 and Figures 7 and 8). Mostly they have less than 100,000 population, though 4 are slightly larger. They are widely spaced one from another within the ecumene. The only regions of the Soviet Union with more than one such center are the Black-Earth Center with Borisoglebsk and Michurinsk, the Western Region with Daugavpils in Latvia and Shyaulyay in Lithuania, and Soviet Middle Asia with 2 in the ancient and densely settled Fergana Basin, Kokand and Namangan. If they had substantial industrial development, they would be classified as industrial cities. All have less than the national urban average of gainfully occupied persons in industry. Only one, Velikiye Luki, in the Northwest Region has more than the national average in the combined group of industry, construction, and transportation. It is a railroad center of some importance and thus might be classified as a local and transport center.

They are similar to the smaller administrative centers in being central places. They are also similar in that at one time or another more than half of them have been centers of oblasts or similar administrative units: Velikiye Luki, Balashov, Ussuriysk, Baranovichi, and Namangan of oblasts, Achinsk of an okrug, Kokand of an uyezd, and Kirovabad of a guberniya (Yelisavetpol', its former name, in Tsarist times). But their administrative units have been discontinued and their territories amalgamated with adjoining oblasts.

During the periods 1897–1926, 1926–1939, and 1939–1959 the population in this group of cities increased at only about half the average rate for cities of the country, but since 1959 their population growth has kept pace with the average, reflecting in part perhaps the new emphasis on small and middle-sized cities and the utilization of labor reserves.

These are all old cities. Kirovabad in the Transcaucasus dates back to the 7th century and Kokand in Soviet Middle Asia to the 10th century. Other cities in this group arose from the 11th to the 18th century, except for Ussuriysk that is just over a century old. None arose in the Soviet period.

Industrial Cities (III)

Industrial cities are the most numerous among the functional types of Soviet cities, including 136 of the 304 cities of more than 50,000 population (Table 12). They are also the most distinctive type of Soviet city, expressing the urgent and powerful Soviet drive for industrial development. They are divided into 3 types, manufacturing cities, cities that combine mining and manufacturing, and cities devoted mainly to mining, to primary processing of mineral products, or to the production of energy.

The first 2 of these types are further subdivided by size into those of more than 100,000 population and those with less. Manufacturing cities and cities that combine mining and manufacturing are similar to administrative centers in that they are most numerous in the size category 100,000–249,999 in population but cities that are primarily in mining are smaller, all under 100,000.

Only 9 of the industrial cities exceed 250,000 population in size (Table 13). The very largest, the mining and manufacturing center of Krivoy Rog, attains a half a million population and thus is exceeded in size by only the 30 largest administrative centers. Any industrial city that grows to this size is likely to be given administrative functions also.

Administrative cities tend to be widely spaced from one another, but industrial cities show patterns of sharp localization and clustering, particularly near sources of energy, on coalfields such as the Donbas or Kuzbas; in oilfields such as the Volga-Urals; near hydroelectric projects as along the Volga River; near mineral deposits, particularly metalliferous ores, as in the Urals; or in industrial areas of good location and transportation. Some have historically evolved from early handicraft and textile industries to complex combinations of machinery, chemical, and other industries.

Manufacturing Cities (IIIA) with
More Than 100,000 Population (IIIA-1)

The 42 manufacturing cities without significant mining and with more than 100,000 population form the largest group of industrial cities. About half the cities of this category are located in only 3 of the 19 major economic regions: the Industrial Center with 8 such cities, the Volga Region with 6, and the Donets-Dnepr Region of the Ukraine with 6 (Table 13 and Figure 7). The adjacent North Caucasus and Urals regions each have 3 such cities. This category of city is absent from 5 of the 19 major economic regions. Thus the main concentration of these larger manufacturing cities lies in the European industrial core of the Soviet Union from Moscow east to the Urals and south to the Black Sea and the North Caucasus.

The category of manufacturing includes an enormous range of processes and materials appropriate for a separate treatise. In the very broadest terms we may say that the most characteristic feature of Soviet manufacturing cities is their association with machinery production and metal-working. Machines are the tools of further industrialization. Expansion of machinery production has been a major and generally successful aim of Soviet economic policy. Machinery production characterizes virtually all larger Soviet manufacturing cities. The 3 major clusters of manufacturing cities of more than 100,000 population have major machinery production: all 9 cities of this class in the Industrial Center, 6 of 7 cities in the Volga Region, and 5 of 6 cities in the Donets-Dnepr Region.

In associated manufacturing these 3 great industrial clusters, however, show a sharp differentiation. In the Industrial Center, 5 of the 9 manufacturing cities of this class have important textile industries, in the Volga Region all 6 cities have chemical industries (typically associated with petroleum), and in the Donets-Dnepr Region, 4 of 6 cities have major iron and steel works. Thus textiles are associated with the historical handicrafts of the Industrial Center, chemicals with the great oil deposits of the Volga, and ferrous metallurgy with the coking coal and iron ore desposits of the Donets-Dnepr Region. Of course, none of these industries is the exclusive prerogative of any of these districts. The chemical industry in particular, although highly developed in the Volga Region, is also present in 3 of the 8 manufacturing cities of this size in the Industrial Center and in 4 of the 6 similar cities of the Donets-Dnepr.

For the Industrial Center typical textile manufacturing cities are Serpukhov (cotton textiles and synthetic fibers), Orekhovo-Zuyevo (cotton textiles), Noginsk (an old center of cotton, wool, and silk textiles), and Kovrov (cotton textiles); each also has machinery industries and some have chemical industries. Also the large oblast cities of the Industrial Center, Ivanovo and Yaroslavl', have important textile industries.

For the Volga Region typical chemical cities are Syzran' (petrochemicals), Tol'yatti (synthetic rubber and nitrogen fertilizers), Novokuybyshevsk (petrochemicals and plastics), Sterlitamak (synthetic rubber and heavy chemicals such as soda and chlorine), Engel's (synthetic fibers), and Volzhskiy (synthetic fibers and synthetic rubber). Except for Novokuybyshevsk each of these also has machinery industries. The large administrative centers of the Volga Region, Kuybyshev, Kazan', Ufa, Saratov, and Volgograd, all also have substantial chemical industries.

Typical manufacturing cities in the Donets-Donbas Region with iron and steel works are Zhdanov, Kramatorsk, Konstantinovka, and Dneprodzerzhinsk; these usually have associated machinery and chemical industries. Great metallurgical works are also located in the large oblast centers, Donetsk, Dnepropetrovsk, and Zaporozh'ye, and of course, also in some cities that combine mining and manufacturing such as Krivoy Rog on the orefield and Makeyevka on the coalfield.

The Ural cluster is characterized, like that of the Donets-Dnepr, by metallurgy, both iron and steel and nonferrous, and machinery production.

Outside these major clusters individual manufacturing cities usually have substantial machinery industries. Some have metallurgical works, as Cherepovets in the Northwest (iron and steel), Bratsk in Eastern Siberia (aluminum), Komsomol'sk-na-Amure in the Far East (iron and steel), and Sumgait in Azerbaydzhan in the Transcaucasus (aluminum). Some have chemical industries as Bratsk (wood chemicals, especially viscose fibers for tires), Komsomol'sk-na-Amure (oil refining), Bobruysk in Belorussia (rubber goods and tires), Kutaisi in Georgia in the Transcaucasus, Sumgait (synthetic rubber, superphosphates, and ammonia), and Chirchik near Tashkent in Soviet Middle Asia (nitrate fertilizers). Others have a textile industry as Biysk in Western Siberia (linen), Kaunas and Klaypeda in Lithuania, Kutaisi and Leninakan in the Transcaucasus, and Leninabad in the Fergana Valley of Soviet Middle Asia.

In terms of size only 2 of these 42 manufacturing cities have more than 250,000 population, Zhdanov, formerly Mariupol', on the Sea of Azov in the Donets-Dnepr Region with 385,000 and Kaunas, former capital of Lithuania, with 284,000. Larger cities with a heavy industrial component in their economic structure have become centers of oblasts or comparable units and thus have been classified as diversified administrative centers.

Manufacturing Cities with 50,000–99,999 Population (IIIA-2)

The smaller manufacturing cities are also very numerous, 40 with populations between 50 and 100 thousand. They also show a high degree of areal concentration, two-thirds in just 3 adjacent regions, the Industrial Center with 11 such cities, the Volga with 6, and the Urals with 10.

Industries vary with region and city. As in larger manufacturing cities, machinery and metal working are the most widespread industrial activity, being of major importance in two-thirds of the manufacturing cities of this smaller size. Textiles are a leading industry in 12 of the cities, especially of those in the Industrial Center but also in individual cities in regions to the west as in Vyborg in the Northwest Region and in Orsha in Belorussia, or in regions to the east as Melekess and Kamyshin in the Volga Region, or in the famous silk factory of Margelan in the Fergana Basin of Soviet Middle Asia. Wood-working industries are particularly common in cities along the northern fringe of the ecumene adjacent to or within the forest belt. Food industries are widespread in southern cities in the main agricultural belt. Iron and steel works are found in relatively few manufacturing cities of this size: Revda, Lys'va, and Chusovoy in the Urals and Rustavi in Georgia. Large integrated iron and steel works with associated activities typically give rise to cities that exceed 100 thousand inhabitants in size.

Gus'-Khrustal'nyy, "crystal goose," in the Industrial Center, is an excellent example of a highly specialized manufacturing city, both in its concentration on a single product, glass, and in having one of the very highest proportions (more than 80 per cent) of its gainfully occupied persons in industry, construction, and transportation, and 73.4 per cent in industry alone, nearly double the national urban average. The percentage of occupied persons in activities other than industry and related activities is less than half the national urban average.

Some of these industrial cities also serve as sub-oblast non-administrative regional, trade, and transportation centers, such as the Baltic ports of Vyborg (the Finnish Viipuri) now in Leningrad Oblast and Liyepaya in Latvia, Yelets in the Black-Earth Center, Kungur in the northwest Urals, Troitsk and Shadrinsk east of the Urals, and Tiraspol', which served as capital of the Moldavian ASSR, 1924–1940, before the expansion of the republic and its elevation to the status of a union republic. In economic structure these approach the smaller oblast centers, Type IB-4, or the local centers, Type II. Yeysk in the North Caucasus on the Sea of Azov is also a health resort.

Manufacturing and Mining Cities (IIIB)
with More Than 100,000 Population (IIIB-1)

The 29 manufacturing and mining cities with more than 100,000 population include some very large industrial cities and show sharp localization.

Seven of these cities have more than a quarter million inhabitants and one more than half a million; they are all associated with mining and with the processing of steel. Four are on coal deposits, Makeyevka and Gorlovka in the Donbas and Novokuznetsk and Prokop'yevsk in the Kuzbas, and 3 are on iron-ore deposits, Krivoy Rog in the western part of the Donets-Dnepr Region and Nizhniy Tagil and Magnitogorsk in the northern and southern Urals. The climax expression of this type includes large mining operations, an integrated iron and steel works, machinery production, and coke-oven byproduct chemical industries. Novokuznetsk in the Kuzbas and Nizhniy Tagil and Magnitogorsk in the Urals have this full combination. Krivoy Rog with 510,000 population, the largest city, alone lacks a large chemical industry, and Makeyevka alone lacks a large machinery and metal-working industry. Gorlovka and Prokop'yevsk have all the elements of the syndrome except blast furnaces.

More than 80 per cent of the cities in this group (24 of 29) are associated with 3 great industrial districts, the Donets-Dnepr, the

Urals, and the Kuzbas (Figures 7 and 8). Altogether 11 such large mining and manufacturing cities of more than 100,000 population are associated with the Donets-Dnepr cluster, 6 with the Kuzbas, and 7 with the Urals. The Donets-Dnepr cluster includes the core cities on the coalfield, Makeyevka and Gorlovka, already mentioned, plus Kadiyevka, Kommunarsk, and Krasnyy Luch in the Ukrainian part of the Donbas and Shakhty and Novoshakhtinsk on the eastern extension of this coalfield into Rostov Oblast in the RSFSR. This cluster also includes 3 ore-mining cities physically separate from the coalfield but economically integrated into its industrial complex: Krivoy Rog, the iron-mining center to the west, Nikopol', the manganese-mining center, also to the west, and Kerch, the iron-ore mining city to the south in the Crimea. Slavyansk on the northern edge of the Donbas coalfield has salt mining. These cities typically have some combination of mining with ferrous metallurgy as at Kadiyevka, Kommunarsk, Nikopol', and Shakhty, or machinery production as in most of them, or with chemical processing, especially at Slavyansk and Novoshakhtinsk.

The Kuzbas cluster of 6 cities in this category, Novokuznetsk, Prokop'yevsk, Leninsk-Kuznetskiy, Kiselevsk, Anzhero-Sudzhensk, and Belovo, is similar to the Donbas group in its combination of coal mining with machinery production in 5 of the cities and the chemical industry in 5. It also has nonferrous metallurgy with aluminum at Novokuznetsk and zinc at Belovo.

The Ural cluster of 7 cities in this category differs in that the mining of metalliferous ores predominates over coal. Four of the cities have important iron-ore mines, Nizhniy Tagil, Serov, Magnitogorsk, and Zlatoust. The other 3 are diverse: Berezniki with salt, Kopeysk with lignite, and Orsk with nickel. The smelting and processing of minerals is particularly characteristic of these cities with integrated iron and steel works at Nizhniy Tagil, Serov, and Magnitogorsk, with steel furnaces at Zlatoust, and with the smelting of magnesium at Berezniki and of nickel at Orsk. Thus in this group only the lignite-mining city of Kopeysk lacks a metallurgical industry. Machinery production is also found in most of the cities. The chemical industry is associated with the steel industry in Nizhniy Tagil and Magnitogorsk, with common salt and potash in the production of fertilizers at Berezniki, and with oil refining at Orsk.

Of the 5 other manufacturing and mining cities in this class, 4 are engaged in the mining of coal, either bituminous or lignite: Novomoskovsk in the Moscow coal basin south of Moscow, Temirtau in the Karaganda coal basin in Kazakhstan, Cheremkhovo in the coal basin of this name west of Irkutsk in Eastern Siberia, and Noril'sk in the Far North of Krasnoyarsk Kray in Eastern Siberia. Kolomna near Moscow produces limestone utilized in the cement industry of the city. Noril'sk also mines nickel and copper smelted in the city. Temirtau has a large integrated iron and steel works. Again machinery production is found in several of the cities, especially at Kolomna with railroad equipment. The chemical industry occurs in Novomoskovsk (fertilizers) and Temirtau (synthetic rubber).

Mining and Manufacturing with 50,000–99,999 Population (IIIB-2)

The 15 smaller cities with both mining and manufacturing fall into 3 main groups: coal-mining towns with machinery and metal-working industries, centers of oil production, and cities which mine and smelt metalliferous ores.

To the first group of 6 coal cities belong Vorkuta in the isolated and recently developed coalfield at the northeastern corner of the European USSR, Torez, renamed after Maurice Thorez, former French communist leader, Yenakiyevo, Artëmovsk, and Kamensk-Shakhtinskiy all in the Donbas, and Kizel in the northwest Urals.

The second group includes 3 centers of the oil industry in the Volga-Ural district: Bugul'ma and Oktyabr'skiy with associated machinery industries and Salavat with associated oil refining and a nitrogen-fertilizer plant.

The 5 mining and smelting centers for metalliferous ores are typically highly specialized: Krasnotur'insk in the north Urals with aluminum, Beloretsk in the middle Urals (but in the Bashkir ASSR) with mining of manganese and ferrous metallurgy, Novotroitsk in the south Urals with iron and steel, Leninogorsk in East Kazakhstan with lead, and Balkhash on Lake Balkhash in central Kazakhstan with copper. The remaining city of this category, Vol'sk on the Volga, utilizes local limestone and clay deposits for the production of cement.

Mining Cities (IIIC)

Cities devoted primarily to mining and thus without other major economic activities such as manufacturing, transportation, trade, or administration are mostly much smaller (Table 13). Ten mining cities in the Soviet Union have more than 50,000 population, none more than 100,000. Of the 10 cities in this group 8 are coal-mining towns, Sverdlovsk and Gukovo in the Donbas, Korkino in the Chelyabinsk lignite basin of the Urals, Mezhdurechensk and Osinniki in the Kuzbas, Chernogorsk in the Minusinsk coal basin of Eastern Siberia on the upper Yenisey River, Artëm in the lignite basin near Vladivostok in the Soviet Far East, and Angren in the lignite basin just east of Tashkent in Soviet Middle Asia. The other 2 mining cities are Asbest in the Urals near Sverdlovsk which mines asbestos and Zyryanovsk in East Kazakhstan, a mining center for lead, zinc, and silver ores.

These 10 mining towns are all relatively new. Most did not exist in 1926. Their combined population then was only about 15,000. Most were established during the early Five-Year Plans and their combined population reached 180,000 by 1939. Their principal growth came during the period 1939–1959 as they increased 233 per cent or nearly 4 times as rapidly as the average urban population of the country. But having reached an effective size for the exploitation of their respective deposits and not having developed diversifying manufacturing activities of importance, their growth slowed down for the period 1959–1967 to an aggregate increase of only 17 per cent, only about two-thirds the average rate for the urban population in this period.

Construction Cities (IIID)

Cities in which construction workers constitute a high proportion of the gainfully occupied persons represent a temporary phase in the creation, growth, or reconstruction of cities. They are thus not separately identified in Tables 12 and 13 or Figures 7 and 8. Twenty-five cities had over 20 per cent of workers engaged in construction, nearly double the national urban average of 11.5 per cent.[13] Ten of these were manufacturing cities, 7 combined manufacturing with mining, 3 were primarily mining towns, and 5 were oblast centers. Thus large construction projects are primarily associated with industrial cities.

The 4 most striking cities of this group are Bratsk, Volzhskiy, Angarsk, and Tol'yatti. Bratsk and Volzhskiy at the time of the 1959 census had 59.4 and 55 per cent of all gainfully occupied persons in construction. Both were the sites for the building of huge dams for hydroelectric projects. Bratsk lies in Eastern Siberia, north-northwest of Irkutsk on the Angara River, which has a large volume of water and relatively regular regimen, thanks to the regulating effect of Lake Baykal on its flow, and a very high head of water as the stream tumbles down the Middle Siberian Plateau toward the Yenisey River and the West Siberian Lowland. Construction began in 1955 and the present stage for generation of hydroelectric energy was completed in 1966. It might be expected that the population of the city would decline once the 127-meter high dam (420 feet) and generating equipment (4.1 million kw. capacity although an ultimate capacity of 5.0 million is envisaged) was completed but the population grew from 51,000 in 1959 to 122,000 in 1967 as the wood chemical, aluminum, and other energy-intensive industries were developed at this site of very cheap electric power.

Volzhskiy is the site of the large Volga Hydroelectric Station named for the 22nd Party Congress just upstream from Volgograd. Construction began in 1951 and the last unit of the hydroelectric station was installed in 1962, bringing the project up to 2,563,000 kw. capacity. As in Bratsk the chemical industry has been developed at the power site, and completion of construction and a presumed sharp drop in number of construction workers did not result in a corresponding decline in population. Rather the population increased rapidly from 67,000 in 1959 to 114,000 in 1967 as chemical industries, synthetic fiber and synthetic rubber, were developed using the adjacent hydroelectric power and feedstocks from the Volgograd petroleum refinery across the river.

[13] Occupation data in this section from B. S. Khorev, "Issledovanie . . . ," p. 48.

The 2 other outstanding construction cities of 1959 were near hydroelectric projects but were based mainly on the chemical industry. Tol'yatti and Angarsk in the same 2 regions, the Volga and Eastern Siberia, had 46.3 and 42.3 per cent of their gainfully occupied persons in construction in 1959. Tol'yatti, formerly Stavropol' but renamed in 1964 after the Italian communist leader Palmiro Togliatti, lies on the Volga River just above Kuybyshev and near the site of the large dam that backs up the Volga for 500 km. in a long lake and the Volga Hydroelectric Station named after Lenin, with 2.3 million kw capacity, built mainly 1951–1957. A series of huge chemical works were then built in the city to produce synthetic rubber, synthetic fiber, nitrogen fertilizers, and various chemical intermediates. It, too, grew rapidly from 61,000 in 1959 to 143,000 in 1967. Angarsk on the Angara River is near the Irkutsk Hydroelectric Station but the major construction here in 1959 was on the large Angarsk Oil Refinery, the first unit of which was put into operation in 1961, and on the planned city itself.

Other manufacturing cities with more than 100,000 population in 1967, Type 3A-1, with at least 20 per cent gainfully occupied persons in construction were Sumgait (27 per cent in construction) north of Baku in Azerbaydzhan on the west shore of the Caspian Sea with rapidly expanding chemical industries and aluminum production; Novokuybyshevsk, near Kuybyshev in the Volga Region, also with a developing chemical industry; Sterlitamak in the Volga-Ural Oilfield south of Ufa also with a chemical industry; Cherepovets in the Northwest Region at the northern tip of the Rybinsk Reservoir north of Moscow with a large new integrated iron and steel works; and Biysk in the Altay Kray of Western Siberia with diversified industries. Only one manufacturing city of less than 100,000 population, Melekess, Type IIIA-2, had a high proportion of workers in construction; on an eastern arm of the new reservoir on the Volga River north of Kuybyshevsk, it had a new port and atomic power plant.

Seven cities that combined manufacturing and mining had also had substantial construction in 1959. Three are centers of an iron and steel industry and mining: Krivoy Rog in the Ukraine and Novotroitsk in the south Urals with nearby iron ore mines, and Kommunarsk in the Donbas with coal mines. Three are centers of oil production in the Volga-Urals district, Bugul'ma (22.3 per cent in construction), Oktyabr'skiy, and Salavat, the last named having an oil refinery. Berezniki in the northwest Urals on the Kama River is an expanding chemical center with nearby mines of salt and potash.

The 3 mining cities with high proportions in construction are all coal-mining towns, Gukovo in the eastern extension of the Donbas (24 per cent in construction), Mezhdurechensk in the Kuzbas, and Angren in Soviet Middle Asia just southeast of Tashkent.

Five oblast centers also had relatively high proportions of workers in construction, Pavlodar (27.3 per cent) and Kustanay (22.7 per cent) were both centers for the opening up of new agricultural lands under the Virgin Lands Program in northern Kazakhstan, Ust'-Kamenogorsk in East Kazakhstan had an expansion of non-ferrous metallurgy and machinery. Belgorod and Petropavlovsk-Kamchatskiy, old centers in the Black-Earth Center and Kamchatka, have diverse expanding industries.

The areal distribution of these cities, with higher proportions in construction, shows a marked concentration on the Volga Region with 8 such cities, and a belt extending eastward through the Urals (2), West Siberia (2), East Siberia (2), and Kazakhstan (3). The other 8 construction cities are scattered around the periphery of this core.

Transport Centers (IV)

Although all large cities have transportation activities, centers which have transportation as the leading activity are usually small. Only 5 have more than 50,000 population and none of them has more than 100,000. Of course, the great ports, such as Leningrad and Odessa, have very large numbers of people engaged in transport but they also have many other activities, such as manufacturing, administration, education, and science, that contribute to their size. The typical railroad junction with railroad employees predominant is very much smaller.

In the absence of published occupational data by cities for transportation alone, one may compile for investigation a list of cities with percentages occupied in industry, construction, and transportation higher than the national average but in industry alone, below the national average. These cities with an inferred high proportion in construction and transportation fall into the upper right quadrant of Table 10; they are listed in Table 11.

Five of these are clearly mainly transport centers (T on Figures 7 and 8). Uzlovaya, whose name means "junction," with more than 70 per cent occupied in industry, construction, and transport, or more than 10 percentage points above the national urban average and with less than 30 per cent in industry alone, or more than 10 percentage points below the national urban average, that is with more than 40 per cent in construction and transportation, or more than double the national urban average. Uzlovaya is a railroad junction in the Moscow coalfield southeast of Tula; it also has coal mining and machinery industries, but transportation plays a leading role.

Kropotkin in the North Caucasus is the Soviet city of more than 50,000 population with the highest proportion of the gainfully occupied persons in transportation alone, 30.1 per cent, or 4 times the national urban average of 8.0 per cent.[14] It has railroad shops and is located where the main line from Rostov to Baku crosses the Kuban' River and where branch lines diverge to Krasnodar on the west and Stavropol' on the east, both kray centers. Another transport center in the North Caucasus is Bataysk, just south of Rostov-na-Donu, a rail junction with railroad shops and freight yards. Two transport centers are located in the Soviet Far East: Svobodnyy with railroad shops on the Trans-Siberian (including car repair works) and also an operation and repair base for the ship fleet of the Amur River, though the city itself is located on its tributary the Zeya River; and Nakhodka, the Soviet port on the Sea of Japan, just east of Vladivostok.

These 5 cities all have more than 20 per cent of the gainfully occupied persons in transportation, or more than two and a half times the national urban average. It must be emphasized again that there are numerous small cities and towns which are specialized railroad centers and which perform the service of binding together the huge territory of the Soviet Union.

Three cities given other classifications also have important transport activities, as evidenced by their having more than 20

[14] Occupation data in this section from *ibid.*, pp. 48–49.

per cent of the gainfully occupied persons in transportation. Brest with 22.4 per cent in transportation is a railroad junction and river port on the border between the Soviet Union and Poland. Tselinograd is a major railroad junction at the crossing of east-west and north-south lines in the heart of the grain-shipping areas of the New and Virgin Lands. Both Brest and Tselinograd are examples of oblast centers with important transportation functions. Troitsk in the southeast Urals south of Chelyabinsk is also a rail junction which may be considered an industry-transport city.

Eight other cities also have proportion of gainfully occupied persons in transportation of 15–20 per cent, about double the national urban average. Five are administrative centers (Type I), one is a local center (Type II), and 2 are industrial cities (Type III). The 2 largest cities are ports and oblast centers, Vladivostok, main Soviet port on the Sea of Japan and thus for the Pacific Ocean, and Arkhangel'sk, main Soviet port on the White Sea and thus for the Arctic Ocean. Two are oblast centers on the Middle Asiatic Railroad that joins the European USSR with Soviet Middle Asia through the vast stretches of western and southern Kazakhstan: Aktyubinsk and Kzyl-Orda. Abakan is a railroad junction and river port on the upper Yenisey River in the Minusinsk Basin of Eastern Siberia and political center of the Khakass Autonomous Oblast; it was once the end of a branch line to the south from the Trans-Siberian but now lies on a more southern east-west mountainous line at its crossing of the Yenisey. Balashov is a local center in western Saratov Oblast in the Volga Region and a railroad junction. The 2 industrial cities with substantial transportation employment are Novorossiysk, a port on the northeast shore of the Black Sea in the North Caucasus and Syzran', an important railroad junction and river station on the Volga River just below Kuybyshev.

Resorts (V)

The 4 resorts in the Soviet Union of more than 50,000 population are all in the southern part of the country, 3 in the North Caucasus on the flanks of the great Caucasus mountains and one in the Crimea (R on Figure 7). Sochi, the largest, is a center of many sanitaria, rest homes, tourist bases, and camps; it has mineral baths, a warm climate, and bathing beaches on the northeast coast of the Black Sea. Kislovodsk, "sour water," and Pyatigorsk, "5 mountains" (since one can see 5 peaks from the city), are both mineral springs and health resorts in the sunny and warm North Caucasus. Yevpatoriya on the west coast of the Crimea is a health resort with sea bathing, a good climate, and also some mud baths. In Kislovodsk 23.0 per cent of the gainfully occupied persons are engaged in health care, and in Yevpatoriya 22.1 per cent, or more than 4 times as high as the urban average of 5.0 per cent.[15]

Centers of Education and Research (VI)

All large cities have institutions of education and research but specialized cities in which education plays a leading role are relatively scarce in the Soviet Union. Most Soviet universities, for example, are in administrative centers. Among cities of more than 50,000 population examples of major educational centers or the university city are Tartu in the Estonian SSR and Novocherkassk, the old center of the Don Cossacks northeast of Rostov, which has 10 scientific research institutes (Figure 7). They have 9.5 and 12.7 per cent respectively of their gainfully occupied workers in education, compared to a national urban average of 5.6 per cent, or more than double the average.[16] Both also have other activities, such as the manufacture of electric locomotives at Novocherkassk.

Among smaller cities dominated by research activities and thus well-known in the scientific community are Akademgorodok near Novosibirsk, the site of many institutes of the Siberian Branch of the Academy of Sciences of the USSR; Dubna north of Moscow, site of atomic research; Obninsk south of Moscow with an atomic electric station, and Zernograd near Rostov, site of agricultural institutes.

Naval Bases (VII)

Two Soviet naval bases had more than 50,000 population in 1959: Sevastopol', the famous city on the Black Sea in the Crimea, that figured both in the Crimean War of the mid-19th century

---

[15] *Ibid.*, p. 49.
[16] *Ibid.*, p. 44, footnote 1.

and World War II of the mid-20th century, and Sovetskaya Gavan' in the Soviet Far East on the Tatar Strait between the Sea of Japan and the Okhotsk Sea. The reported population of Sovetskaya Gavan', however, dropped from 50,000 in 1959 to only 26,000 in 1967, so that on the basis of the 1967 population it would not have been included in our classification.

Other cities also serve as naval bases. Kronshtadt, the naval base of the Baltic fleet, with about 40,000 population, played a key role in the October Revolution of 1917 and in the defense of Leningrad in World War II. It is politically subordinate to Leningrad. Vladivostok, although classified as a diversified administrative center, also has functions as a naval base.

Suburbs (VIII)

The 6 cities with more than 50,000 population in 1959 classified as suburbs, Perovo, Kuntsevo, Babushkin, Tushino, Lyublino, and Mytishchi are all located in Moscow Oblast (inset on Figure 7). As is often the fate of suburbs, 5 of them have since lost their separate status, being incorporated into a larger Moscow metropolis on August 18, 1960. Many cities have suburbs, of course, although in the Soviet Union few independent cities that are clearly suburbs reach a population of 50,000. Lesser suburban development in the Soviet Union than in the United States probably reflects the greater administrative flexibility in the Soviet Union in expanding municipal boundaries and the lesser use of private automobiles, which encourages suburban development. As in other countries some suburbs are primarily industrial, others residential.[17] Tushino falls in the first category with more than 50 per cent of its gainfully occupied persons in industry. Babushkin is in the second category with less than 30 per cent in industry. The other suburbs are intermediate in type.

Agricultural Towns (IX)

In the cities of the Soviet Union 4.7 per cent of gainfully occupied persons are engaged in agriculture. The proportion is lowest in the RSFSR, only 2.9 per cent, and highest in Moldavia,

[17] cf. Chauncy D. Harris, "Suburbs," *American Journal of Sociology,* vol. 49, no. 1 (July, 1943), pp. 1–13.

13.0 per cent, but runs relatively high in the union republics in the southwest, south, and southeast, about 8 per cent for Belorussia and the Ukraine, the 3 republics of the Transcaucasus, and the 4 republics of Soviet Middle Asia (a little higher in Tadzhikistan, 10.7 per cent).[18]

The densely populated irrigated oasis of the Fergana Basin provides two exceptional cases in Andizhan Oblast of the Uzbek SSR. Andizhan, the oblast center with 169,000 population, has 18.5 per cent of the occupied persons in agriculture and Namangan, a local center with 158,000 population, has 22.3 per cent in agriculture.[19] Both are centers of cotton and silk production. Both have more persons occupied in industry than in agriculture.

Two smaller administrative centers, Elista of the Kalymk ASSR on the west side of the mouth of the Volga, and Khorog, center of the Gorno-Badakhshan Autonomous Oblast in the eastern part of the Tadzhik SSR in the Pamir Mountains (Type IB-5), are both small, 43 and 12 thousand inhabitants respectively, and in both agriculture takes first place in number of occupied persons, 21.8 and 19.5 per cent respectively. They are agricultural towns and centers with mixed functions as home for farmers and as central places with administrative, trade, and cultural services for the closely associated rural tributary areas.

Agricultural towns are not recognized as a separate type in Tables 12 and 13 and Figures 7 and 8.

CITIES OF LESS THAN 50,000 POPULATION

The above classification includes only the 304 cities of more than 50,000 population. What of the 1,375 juridical cities of the Soviet Union of less than 50,000 population? Their types are summarized in Table 14.

Occupational data for 1959 were tabulated by the Central Statistical Office for the 444 cities with between 20 and 50 thousand population. These data were utilized by Khorev to classify the cities in this size category.[20] The great majority of cities of this

---

[18] *Itogi vsesoiuznoi perepisi naseleniia 1959 goda,* calculated from table 33 in each volume.
[19] B. S. Khorev, "Issledovanie . . . ," p. 49.
[20] B. S. Khorev, *Gorodskie poseleniia SSSR,* pp. 67-80.

size, 310 of 444 or 70 per cent, are classed as industrial. Relatively few of the diversified administrative centers are small enough to fall into this size category, only 14, compared with the 134 that are of larger size. On the other hand the 61 transport cities with populations between 20 and 50 thousand form 14 per cent of all cities of this size in the Soviet Union. Local inter-rayon intra-oblast centers number 40, or 9 per cent of the cities of this size category.

With respect to yet smaller cities, exact numbers cannot be given for the 443 cities between 10 and 20 thousand, because of the absence of any tabulation of occupational data. This size category includes primarily 2 types of cities: industrial cities and local centers; the latter includes the smaller inter-rayon intra-oblast centers and the larger rayon centers.

The 488 cities under 10 thousand in population are largely local centers, predominantly centers of rayons. Soviet industrial establishments typically have a scale of employment resulting in larger cities.

F. M. Listengurt and I. M. Smoliar studied 162 small and medium-sized cities of the Central Region plotting population on one axis and proportion occupied in industry and construction on the other.[21] The diagram revealed clear clustering of types, recognized as (1) industrial centers, with proportion in industry and construction lying between 50 and 70 per cent and populations ranging from 10,000 up to 100,000 (the largest size included); (2) industrial-administrative and economic centers of surrounding agricultural regions with 30–50 per cent in industry and construction and populations ranging from 5,000 to 20,000; (3) administrative-cultural and economic centers for surrounding rural agricultural areas with 10–30 per cent in industry and construction and populations ranging from less than 3,000 up to 10,000; (4) transport cities with 10–35 per cent in industry and construction and populations ranging from just under 10,000 to 35,000; and (5) scientific and experimental centers with 20–50 per cent in industry and populations ranging from 15,000 to 50,000. Of these

[21] F. M. Listengurt and I. M. Smoliar, "Izuchenie nekotorykh predposylok promyshlennogo razvitiia malykh i srednikh gorodov Tsentral'nogo ekonomicheskogo raiona," *Izvestiia AN SSSR, seriia geograficheskaia,* 1964, no. 4, pp. 79–82, figures 1 and 2.

TABLE 14

FUNCTIONAL TYPES OF SOVIET CITIES IN
RELATION TO SIZE

	Population (in thousands) 1959			
	Over 50	20–49	10–19	Under 10
I. Diversified Administrative Centers	134	14	3	–
II. Local Centers: (a) inter-rayon	15	40	many	few
(b) rayon	–	–	many	very many
III. Industrial Cities	136	310	many	few
IV. Transport Cities	5	61	some	some
V. Resorts	4	1	some	some
VI. Centers of Education and Research	2	3	some	some
VII. Others, including unclassified	8	15	some	some
	304	444	443	488

Sources: B. S. Khorev, *Gorodskie poseleniia SSSR (problemy rosta i ikh izuchenie); ocherki geografii rasseleniia* (M. Izd. "Mysl'," 1968), table 16, pp. 68–69, and SSSR, Tsentral'noe statisticheskoe upravlenie, *Itogi vsesoiuznoi perepisi naseleniia 1959 goda: SSSR (svodnyi tom)* (M. Gosstatizdat, 1962), table 7, p. 35.

This table is limited to the 1,679 cities juridically recognized as such at the time of the publication of the 1959 census. It excludes the 2,940 settlements of urban type that existed at that time, 2,555 of which had less than 10,000 population, 355 had 10,000–19,000 and 30, 20,000–50,000 population.

small and medium-sized cities classified, 53 per cent were industrial centers, 21 per cent mixed industrial-administrative, 16 per cent administrative and local centers with virtually no industry, 7 per cent transport towns, and 3 per cent scientific experimental centers. Studies of the proportion in industry and construction by size revealed that the smaller cities had very much lower proportions in industry, the average falling from about 55 per cent for cities of more than 30,000 to 35 per cent for cities of 10,000 and 15 per cent for cities of 5,000.

REGIONAL PATTERNS OF CITIES OF MORE THAN 50,000 POPULATION BY TYPE

The 304 larger cities of the Soviet Union, those of more than 50,000 population in 1959, may be considered also on a regional basis. We shall discuss the patterns of distribution of the various types of cities region by region proceeding west to east across the RSFSR and then from northwest to southeast for the other union republics (Figures 7 and 8).

The Northwest. The 14 larger cities of the Northwest are mainly administrative centers of the central-place type with Leningrad, a former capital of the whole country, as the great regional center and also an industrial center of significance. From west to east the other oblast and regional centers are Kaliningrad, Pskov, Novgorod, Vologda, Petrozavodsk, Murmansk, Arkhangel'sk, and Syktyvkar (Figures 7 and 8). In addition Velikiye Luki, now classed as a local center, is a former oblast center, and Cherepovets, now classed as an industrial city, is a former guberniya center. Vyborg has long been a regional and trading center, although now classed as an industrial city. Vorkuta, a manufacturing and mining town, is also the center of a series of coal-mining towns of the Pechora Basin. The other city is virtually a suburb of Arkhangel'sk. In addition 6 of these cities also serve as seaports of some significance, Kaliningrad, Vyborg, and Leningrad on the Baltic Sea, Murmansk on the Barents Sea, and Arkhangel'sk and Severodvinsk on the White Sea.

The Center. The 40 larger cities of the Industrial Center present a sharp contrast to the Northwest in that they combine a pattern of dispersion of 12 central places with a clustering of 28 cities of other types (Figure 7). In number of cities of more than 50,000 population the Center exceeds any other region of the country. The center of this region and of the country is the great metropolis of Moscow. The other oblast administrative centers in a counter-clockwise direction are Kalinin, Smolensk, Bryansk, Orël, Kaluga, Tula, Ryazan', Vladimir, Ivanovo, Yaroslavl', and Kostroma. As in the Northwest Region, the oblast centers are of intermediate size, between 100,000 and 500,000 in population.

The 21 industrial cities of the Center are clustered around Moscow (inset in Figure 7), lie to the south in the Moscow Coal Basin near Tula, or cluster in larger numbers to the east and northeast in the early developed Central Industrial District, which arose on the basis of handicrafts and the textile industry but is now highly diversified. They are particularly centers of machinery, textile, and chemical industries. The one transport center lies in the Moscow Coal Basin.

The remaining 6 cities are part of a ring of suburbs around metropolitan Moscow.

The Volga-Vyatka Region. The 6 larger cities of the Volga-Vyatka Region are predominantly administrative centers. Gor'kiy is the regional center as well as an industrial city. The other administrative centers are Saransk, Cheboksary, Yoshkar-Ola, and Kirov; the first 3 are each the center of an autonomous republic (ASSR), giving recognition to an ethnic minority. The only city classified as industrial is really a suburb of Gor'kiy.

Black-Earth Center. The 8 larger cities of the Black-Earth Center are almost entirely central-place types. Voronezh is the center for the region. Other oblast administrative centers are Kursk, Belgorod, Lipetsk, and Tambov. Local centers of more than 50,000 population include Borisoglebsk and Michurinsk. The region has only one industrial city.

The Volga Region. The 26 larger cities of the Volga Region combine very large diversified administrative centers with small industrial cities. The 9 central-place cities include 5 administrative centers of more than half a million population: Kuybyshev, Kazan' (Tatar ASSR), Ufa (Bashkir ASSR), Saratov, and Volgograd, and 3 administrative cities of more than a quarter million, Ul'yanovsk, Penza, and Astrakhan', and one smaller local center, Balashov. The Volga River artery seems to have occasioned the rise of very large administrative, transport, and industrial centers.

Ten of the 12 manufacturing cities are also closely associated with the Volga or its navigable tributaries, and with the petrochemical industry.

However, of the 5 cities that combine manufacturing and mining, 4, all associated with the Volga-Urals oilfields, lie away from the Volga River at petroleum deposits, and only Vol'sk lies on the river, where limestone makes possible cement production.

The North Caucasus. The 22 larger cities of the North Caucasus represent the greatest variety of types of those in any region of the Soviet Union: 8 administrative centers, 8 industrial centers with manufacturing and mining or some combination of them, and 6 cities of special types (2 transport centers, 3 resorts, and 1 educational center). Rostov-na-Donu is the major regional center. Other administrative centers are Krasnodar and Stavropol', centers of krays, Nal'chik, Ordzhonikidze, Groznyy, and Makhach-Kala, each the center of an autonomous republic

(ASSR), and Maykop, center of an autonomous oblast. This diversity of types of political units reflects the nature of the North Caucasus as the refuge and home of many ethnic minorities. The 8 industrial cities include 4 primarily engaged in manufacturing, 3 that combine manufacturing and mining, and one mining town. Three of the 4 manufacturing cities are also ports located on the coast. All 4 cities in which mining is important lie on the eastern extension of the Donbas and thus reflect a marked cluster pattern. The 2 transport towns are both railroad junctions. The 3 resorts are located at the foot of the mighty Caucasus Mountains, 2 at mineral springs and one on the Black Sea coast. The educational center was an old administrative-political center.

The Urals. In number of cities of more than 50,000 population the Urals with 32 is second only to the Industrial Center. But its cities are more predominantly industrial for 25 are classed as manufacturing or mining cities and only 7 as central-place types. Three of the oblast centers in the core of the Urals have more than half a million population, Sverdlovsk, center for the whole region, Perm', and Chelyabinsk. The other administrative centers are Izhevsk, Kurgan, and Orenburg, all on the outer edges of the Urals. One, Buzuluk, is a local center.

Of the 25 industrial cities, 13 are manufacturing cities, 10 combine manufacturing with mining, and 2 are primarily mining towns. Typical of these cities are Nizhniy Tagil, an old center of iron-ore mining and ferrous metallurgy, and Magnitogorsk, a new center of both. Most of the cities are engaged in the mining of ores, the working of metals, or the production of machinery made of metals, although individual cities mine other products such as coal, salt, or asbestos.

Western Siberia. The 16 larger cities of Western Siberia show 2 very different patterns, 6 dispersed administrative centers and 10 industrial cities, mostly sharply localized mining and manufacturing cities in the Kuzbas (Figure 8). Novosibirsk is the major regional center. Other administrative centers are Omsk, Tomsk, Kemerovo, Barnaul, and Tyumen', the last formerly grouped with the Urals but now considered in West Siberia. The great cluster of cities in the Kuzbas coal basin and industrial district are so closely packed together as to require an inset on Figure 8; they are made up of the oblast center, Kemerovo, 6 cities that combine mining and manufacturing, at the head of which stands Novokuznetsk, and 2 mining towns. All 9 of these Kuzbas cities have coal mines. The 2 manufacturing cities ouside the Kuzbas have diversified industries.

Eastern Siberia. The 12 larger cities of Eastern Siberia are evenly split, 6 of central-place type, and 6 industrial. The administrative centers show a great range in size from large cities, such as Krasnoyarsk and Irkutsk, to medium-sized cities, such as Ulan-Ude and Chita, to relatively small centers, such as Abakan. The local center, Achinsk, was once also an administrative center. Five of these 6 central-place cities are strung like beads along the artery of the Trans-Siberian Railway. The other, Abakan, recognizes an ethnic minority in the mountains to the south.

Of the 6 industrial cities 3 are engaged primarily in manufacturing, 2 in mining and manufacturing, and one primarily in mining. Of these, 3 lie along the Trans-Siberian but 3 tied to localized resources lie off it: Noril'sk to the north and Chernogorsk to the south at mines, and Bratsk to the north at the site of water-power development.

The Far East. The 13 larger cities of the Soviet Far East show great variety but generally weak industrial development. Eight are central-place types, one a manufacturing city, one a mining city, 2 transport centers, and one a naval base. The administrative centers include Khabarovsk and Vladivostok, the twin centers of the region, and other widely spaced centers, Yakutsk, Blagoveshchensk, Yuzhno-Sakhalinsk, Magadan, and Petropavlovsk—Kamchatskiy. Komsomol'sk-na-Amure, the single manufacturing city, stands as an isolated iron and steel center amid the forests of the lower Amur River. Near Vladivostok the crowding of cities of different types requires an inset, with a local center, a coal-mining town, and a transport center. Along the Trans-Siberian there is a specialized railroad town, and on the coast is a naval base.

The Donets-Dnepr Region of the Ukraine. The 28 larger cities
of the Donets-Dnepr Region include the densest large cluster of
mining and industrial cities in the Soviet Union, combining some
of the characteristics of the Urals and the Kuzbas.

Eight cities are diversified administrative centers and 20 are
industrial (Figure 7). The 8 oblast centers include 4 particularly
large ones, all of more than half a million population, Donetsk,
Dnepropetrovsk, Zaporozh'ye, and Khar'kov, and 4 somewhat
smaller ones, Lugansk, Kirovograd, Poltava, and Sumy.

The 20 industrial cities include 8 devoted mainly to manufacturing and 12 in which mining plays a major role. The *leit-
motiv* of these cities is the mining of coal or iron ore, the iron
and steel industry, and the making of machinery. The 8 manufacturing cities are well distributed throughout the region, on
the outer edge of the Donbas, along the Dnepr River, and elsewhere. But the distinguishing type of city is the manufacturing
and mining city, of which there are 11 in this region, 9 of them
in the Donbas, 7 of them with coal mining and 2 with salt mining.
The 2 mining and manufacturing cities outside the Donbas are
Krivoy Rog, the iron-ore and iron and steel center with 510,000
population, the largest city in the Soviet Union in which mining
is a major activity, and Nikopol', the manganese city. In the
Donbas Makeyevka and Gorlovka are particularly large coal-
mining and manufacturing cities. Only one city of more than
50,000 population is devoted primarily to coal mining, evidence
of the excellent central location of the district which encourages
the rise of manufacturing, even in cities engaged in coal mining.
The southeast of the region with the great cluster of the Donbas
mining and manufacturing towns stands in contrast to the northwest with its more widely dispersed predominantly administrative centers.

The Southwest of the Ukraine. The Southwest Region of the
Ukraine is the land of central-place cities. All 14 of the larger
cities could be considered as central-place types. Berdichev, although classified as an industrial center, is an old commercial and
regional center. Belaya Tserkov, "white church," a local center
without current administrative functions, is an old commercial

center. All other 12 cities are oblast centers. Two of them are large, Kiev, the capital of the Ukraine, and L'vov, the ancient regional center for Galicia and now for the western Ukraine. The other 10 oblast centers, Chernigov, Zhitomir, Rovno, Lutsk, Ivano-Frankovsk, Ternopol', Khmel'nitskiy, Vinnitsa, Cherkassy, and Chernovtsy, are characterized by small size, 6 a bit over 100,000 and 4 under 100,000 in population, and by rather close spacing. They are classical central-place foci for densely settled rich agricultural regions. Christaller could have developed his central-place typology here perhaps as well as in Southern Germany.

The South of the Ukraine and Moldavia. These 2 regions are conveniently treated together. Their 10 larger cities fall predominantly into the central-place type, except for a touch of diversity in the Crimea. The major administrative centers are Odessa, the regional center, Nikolayev, Kherson, Simferopol', and Kishinëv. The other 2 cities of Moldavia, Bel'tsy, classified as a local center, and Tiraspol', classified as an industrial center, are also old regional centers. In the Crimea are 3 special and very different cities, Sevastopol', the famous naval base, Yevpatoriya, the resort, and Kerch, a mining and industrial city.

The Baltic. The 9 larger cities of the 3 Baltic republics include 3 capitals of union republics, Riga, the major center and capital of Latvia, Tallin, capital of Estonia, and Vil'nyus, capital of Lithuania, 2 local centers, 3 industrial cities, and one educational center. In their spacing, however, they do not show clustering but rather a central-place type distribution, as though some of the regional and local centers had developed diversifying economic activities more than others rather than having been predominantly industrial in origin.

Belorussia. The 10 larger cities of Belorussia are similar to those of the Baltic. They include 6 oblast centers, Minsk, also capital of the republic, Grodno, Brest, Gomel', Mogilëv, and Vitebsk, one local center, Baranovichi, formerly an oblast center, and 3 industrial cities, one of which, Bobruysk, was also formerly an oblast center. Thus, 8 of 10 of the larger cities of Belorussia are present or former oblast centers.

The Caucasus. The 10 larger cities of the Transcaucasian republics include 5 administrative centers, one local center, and 4 industrial cities. The administrative centers are made up of the 3 capitals of the union republics, Tbilisi of Georgia, Yerevan of Armenia, and Baku of Azerbaydzhan, all of more than half a million population and each very much larger than other cities within its republic. Sukhumi and Batumi are centers of autonomous republics (ASSR) within Georgia. The local center, Kirovabad, is the regional center for the western Azerbaydzhan and was formerly the center of a large guberniya. Kutaisi, although classified as an industrial center, is similar to Kirovabad in having been a guberniya center in Tsarist Russia and in currently serving as a regional center of western Georgia. Of the other 3 industrial cities, one dates from the 19th century, Leninabad, and 2 are entirely new cities built around giant metallurgical and chemical works, Rustavi and Sumgait.

Kazakhstan. The 18 larger cities of Kazakhstan fall into 2 distinct classes, 14 oblast centers, and 4 industrial cities associated with mining (Figure 8). The oblast centers are remarkably uniform in size. Except for 2 large administrative centers, Alma-Ata, the capital of the republic, and Karaganda, both of the half-million population category, and one small oblast center, Kzyl-Orda with less than 100 thousand in a river oasis, all oblast centers fall in the size category between 100 thousand and a quarter million: Ural'sk, Gur'yev, and Aktyubinsk in the western part of Kazakhstan, Kustanay, Petropavlovsk, Tselinograd, and Pavlodar in the northern part of the republic, Semipalatinsk and Ust'-Kamenogorsk in the eastern part, and Dzhambul and Chimkent in the southern part. Three mining centers also have major manufacturing, Temir-Tau, Balkhash, and Leninogorsk, and one is dominated by mining alone, Zyryanovsk.

Soviet Middle Asia. The 16 cities of Soviet Middle Asia fall into 2 categories, 12 central places and 4 industrial cities. The administrative centers include 4 capitals of union republics, Tashkent of the Uzbek SSR, which serves also as a regional center for the whole of Middle Asia, and Frunze of the Kirgiz SSR, Dushanbe of the Tadzhik SSR, and Ashkhabad of the Turkmen SSR. The 6 oblast centers include Bukhara, Samarkand, Fergana, Andizhan, Osh, and Chardzhou. Kokand and Namangan, now classified as local centers are also former oblast centers. The 4 industrial cities lie near Tashkent or in the adjacent Fergana Basin, Chirchik, Leninabad, and Margelan, manufacturing cities, and Angren, the mining town (inset on Figure 8).

IV.

Principal Components Analysis

The application of mathematics is opening up new horizons in the geography of population.

— Iu. V. Medvedkov,
*Nauchnye problemy
geografii naseleniia,*
1967, p. 237.

THE COVARIATION AMONG 30 CHARACTERISTICS of 1,247 Soviet cities and towns is analyzed in this chapter. The 1,247 urban settlements are those of more than 10,000 population which are listed in the published volumes of the 1959 census. These include 633 cities and settlements of urban type in the Russian Soviet Federated Socialist Republic (RSFSR) and 614 from the other 14 union republics. The Soviet Union actually had 1,576 urban units of more than 10,000 population in 1959, but unfortunately the published census volume for the RSFSR, unlike the volumes for all other republics, contains data only for cities and towns of more than 15,000 population. Thus the settlements in the RSFSR with populations between 10,000 and 14,999 are excluded.

On the basis of an intense investigation, data on characteristics of Soviet cities were assembled from such diverse sources as the census publications for 1959, 1926, and 1897, statistical yearbooks, administrative handbooks, encyclopedias, gazetteers, atlases, oblast maps, and scholarly publications on Soviet urban geography. On the basis of these data, or of measurements or calculations based on them, information was tabulated on 61 characteristics of each of the 1,247 cities or settlements of urban type.

It was decided to make an inductive investigation of the properties that seemed to be most critical in the description of variations among Soviet cities. A very useful mathematical approach to the description of the commonalities among a large number of variables is provided by principal components analysis. This method can handle effectively only variables that are scalar in nature, if its strict assumptions are to be satisfied.

Of the 61 characteristics tabulated, only 30 were scalar in nature and thus only these could be subjected to components analysis to determine whether groups existed among these variables. The groups were defined by high correlation within groups and low correlations with other groups.

The 30 variables utilized in this analysis had to be tested also for normality. Many data were reverse-J shape, but could usually be transformed to a normal distribution by using the logarithm of the number rather than the number itself. Of the 30 variables, 23 were actually transformed to give characteristics of skew and kurtosis better satisfying the assumptions of components analysis.

These 30 variables were then subjected to principal components analysis. Three independent components were found to be highly significant in that they measured a high proportion of the variation for the 30 analyzed characteristics (Table 15). These components were rotated to a normal varimax position to approximate "simple structure" (each characteristic correlating with just one factor).

The first factor to be extracted in the principal components analysis of the 30 variables (35.9 per cent of the variation) showed the highest association with the logarithm of the population of 1959. It is called the *size factor* (Table 15).

The second factor (24.6 per cent of the variation) exhibited the highest association with the logarithm of the urban population potential within particular economic regions. It is named the *density factor*.

The third factor (19.0 per cent of the variation) revealed the highest association with the percentage increase in population for the period 1926–1959. It is called the *growth factor*.

These 3 components together accounted for about four-fifths (79.5 per cent) of the variation among the 30 variables. Only 2 characteristics showed no significant variation common to other variables: (1) age as measured by the year of legal recognition as a city or settlement of urban type and (2) latitude.

TABLE 15

Principal Components Analysis of 30 Characteristics of 1,247 Soviet Cities

Factor Number and Name	1 (Size)	2 (Density)	3 (Growth)
Sum of Squares (Eigenvalue)	6.002	4.110	3.187
Per cent of the total variance	35.9	60.5	79.5
Per cent of the variance explained by three factors	45.1	76.0	100.0

No.	Variable	Communality*	Factor Loadings**		
1.	Latitude	0.028	0.085	0.099	−0.103
2.	Manufacturing: relative size	0.644	0.746	−0.103	−0.277
3.	No. of rail lines	0.279	0.406	0.134	−0.310
4.	No. of roads	0.526	0.471	−0.037	−0.550
5.	Percentage Growth 1897–1926	0.139	−0.268	0.132	0.222
6.	Percentage Growth 1926–1939	0.514	−0.094	0.089	0.705
7.	Percentage Growth 1926–1959	0.789	−0.080	0.058	0.883
8.	Log of size rank within oblast	0.713	−0.668	0.466	0.225
9.	Log of longitude	0.483	0.108	−0.399	0.559
10.	Log of population 1897	0.114	0.319	0.108	−0.021
11.	Log of population 1926	0.366	0.571	0.035	−0.198
12.	Log of population 1939	0.658	0.787	0.084	−0.179
13.	Log of population 1959	0.909	0.944	0.129	−0.005
14.	Log of percentage growth 1939–1959	0.347	−0.069	−0.071	0.581
15.	Log of distance to nearest railroad station	0.130	−0.228	−0.182	0.212
16.	Log of no. of gas pipelines	0.157	0.360	0.136	−0.095
17.	Log of no. of oil pipelines	0.066	0.253	0.014	0.049
18.	Log of no. of water routes	0.079	0.269	−0.081	−0.023
19.	Log of no. of air lines	0.503	0.706	−0.028	0.064
20.	Log of distance to nearest neighbor	0.597	0.183	−0.721	−0.209
21.	Log of distance to nearest larger neighbor	−0.758	0.627	−0.585	−0.154
22.	Log of no. of administrative functions	0.467	0.517	−0.237	−0.379
23.	Log of no. of branches of manufacturing	0.609	0.671	−0.161	−0.366

TABLE 15 — Continued

PRINCIPAL COMPONENTS ANALYSIS OF 30 CHARACTERISTICS
OF 1,247 SOVIET CITIES

No.	Variable	Communality*	Factor Loadings**		
24.	Log of distance to Moscow	0.550	0.048	–0.648	0.358
25.	Log of distance to center of major economic region	0.388	–0.151	–0.601	0.067
26.	Log of distance to center of oblast	0.428	–0.611	–0.231	0.030
27.	Log of urban population potential within major economic region	0.923	0.252	0.926	0.028
28.	Log of urban population potential within oblast	0.877	0.368	0.837	0.203
29.	Log of urban population potential within major economic region but outside oblast	0.255	–0.078	0.476	–0.149
30.	Log of reciprocal of year of establishment or juridical recognition as city or settlement of urban type	0.004	–0.036	0.037	0.029

Number of rotations for normal varimax convergence: 8
* Proportion of variance explained by 3-factor solution
** Correlations of variables with factors

Sources of data for the 30 characteristics of Soviet cities included in this table:
Glavnoe Upravlenie Geodezii i Kartografii, *Atlas SSSR*, A. N. Baranov, chairman of the editorial board; S. N. Teplova, responsible editor (Moscow: GUGK, 1962), which includes the following information: Relative size of manufacturing (by symbol); number of branches of manufacturing supplemented by other sources such as encyclopedias and special atlases; number of railroad lines supplemented by Glavnoe Upravlenie Geodezii i Kartografii, *Atlas Skhem Zheleznykh Dorog SSSR*, (Moscow: GUGK, 1961); number of roads (supplemented by oblast maps); number of gas pipelines; number of oil pipelines; number of water routes; and number of airlines.
Glavnoe Upravlenie Geodezii i Kartografii, *Soiuz Sovetskikh Sotsialisticheskikh Respublik, politicheskaia-administrativnaia karta*, 1:4,000,000 (in 4 sheets) (Moscow: GUGK, 1962), which was the base for measurement of distance to nearest neighbor (within the 1,247 cities included in this study; base for measurement of distance to nearest larger neighbor.
SSSR. Administrativno-Territorial'noe Delenie Soiuznykh Respublik na 1 aprelia 1963 goda (Moscow: Izd. "Izvestiia Sovetov Deputatov Trudiashchikhsia SSSR," 1963), which contains data on: number of administrative functions; year of establishment as a city or settlement of urban type; distance to nearest railroad station.
U. S. Board on Geographic Names, *Gazetteer No. 42. U.S.S.R. and Certain Neighboring Areas* (Washington: Government Printing Office, 1959). 7 vols., which provides information on latitude and longitude.
Population in 1897, 1926, 1939, and 1959 were taken from the census reports: Russia, Tsentral'nyi statisticheskii komitet, *Pervaia vseobshchaia perepis' naseleniia Rossiiskoi imperii 1897 g.* (S.-Peterburg, 1899–1905), 89 vols.; SSSR, Tsentral'noe statisticheskoe upravlenie, *Vsesoiuznaia perepis' naseleniia 1926 g.* (M. 1928–1933), 56 vols.; and SSSR, Tsentral'noe statisticheskoe upravlenie, *Itogi vsesoiuznoi perepisi naseleniia 1959 goda* (M. 1962–1963), 16 vols.
Percentage growth 1897–1926, 1926–1939, and 1926–1959 were calculated from population data. Growth 1939–1959 was taken from the 1959 census.
Size rank within oblast was taken from the 1959 census.
Distance to Moscow, distance to center of major economic region, and distance to center of oblast were calculated from latitude and longitude.
Urban population potential within each major economic region, urban population potential within each oblast, and urban population potential within each major economic region but outside the oblast for which computations were being made were all calculated from data on population of each urban settlement included in this study and within the specified area and from distances calculated from latitude and longitude.

THE SIZE FACTOR OF SOVIET CITIES

Sixteen variables highly correlated among themselves show a high degree of communality with size of the 1,247 cities in the Soviet Union (Table 16).

TABLE 16

CORRELATION OF VARIABLES WITH THE SIZE FACTOR

Variable	Correlation with the Size Factor
Size	
Population, 1959	0.944
Population, 1939	0.787
Population, 1926	0.571
Population, 1897	0.319
Rank in size within oblast	−0.668
Functions	
Size of manufacturing output	0.746
No. of branches of manufacturing	0.671
No. of administrative functions	0.517
Transport Facilities	
No. of air lines	0.706
No. of railroad lines	0.406
No. of roads	0.471
No. of gas pipelines	0.360
No. of oil pipelines	0.253
No. of navigable water routes	0.269
Spacing	
Distance to nearest largest neighbor	0.627
Distance from center of oblast	−0.611

Population in 1959 proved to be the best single indicator of this factor with a loading of 0.944 (ie., 94.4 per cent of the variation in population in 1959 was associated with the common variation of the group of features).[1] The assertion of O. A. Konstantinov that size should be one of the principal criteria for the classification of cities is thus statistically confirmed.[2] Size of cities at the times of previous censuses also shows significant association with this factor but with increasing weakness with more remote time (0.787 in 1939; 0.571 in 1926; and 0.319 in 1897). There is

[1] An index of 1.00 would indicate complete identity of variation and an index of 0.00 complete independence.
[2] O. A. Konstantinov, "Tipologiia i klassifikatsiia gorodskikh poselenii v sovetskoi ekonomiko-geograficheskoi nauke," *Materialy po geografii naseleniia*, vypusk 2 (L. Geograficheskoe obshchestvo SSSR, 1963), p. 7.

also a high inverse relationship between the size factor and size rank of a city within its oblast (index –0.668).[3]

A second group of characteristics associated with the size factor measures of functions served by the cities, especially in manufacturing and administration. A measure of manufacturing output (quantity) shows an index of association of 0.746 with the size factor. The diversity (range) of manufacturing as measured by number of branches represented also shows a high index (0.671). A measure of number of administrative functions shows a somewhat lower but still quite significant index of 0.517.

A third group of characteristics closely associated with the size factor are transport facilities. The number of air lines shows a very high degree of relationship (0.706) with lesser but still significant relationships for number of railroad lines (0.406)[4] and of roads (0.471). Three other transport facilities also show some association: gas pipelines, oil pipelines, and water transport; they tend to be mainly available in the larger cities but not in all large cities.

A fourth group of characteristics associated with the size factor concern spacing. The larger the city the greater the distance to the next larger city (index 0.627), and the less the distance from the center of the oblast (index –0.611).

These 4 groups of characteristics primarily associated with the size factor include 16 of the 30 variables studied.[5]

Each of the 1,247 cities was given a "score" on each component as part of the analysis. Those cities with high scores on the size

[3] It might be thought initially that the relationship between size of city and its rank (in size) within an oblast would be even higher, but in very populous oblasts there are large cities that have only moderate ranks in size and in oblasts of small population even a city of modest size may have the highest rank.

[4] Lewis and Rowland also found a relationship between number of railroad lines and size of city. (Robert A. Lewis and Richard H. Rowland, "Urbanization in Russia and the USSR: 1897–1966," *Annals of the Association of American Geographers*, vol. 59, no. 4 (December, 1969), table 11, p. 792.

[5] Six other variables, associated with the density factor or the growth factor, also show a weak association with the size factor. Since these 3 factors have been statistically rotated to be independent of one another, the 6 variables are demonstrated to have a weak independent association with the size factor.

Thus the size factor is also positively associated with the market potential of the oblast in which a city is located (0.368), with the market potential of the economic region in which the city is located (0.252), and with the distance to the nearest neighbor (0.183), i.e., the larger the city the greater the distance to the nearest neighbor, partly perhaps because cities large in population are

factor tend to be relatively large, to be the larger cities within their administrative unit, to have been the larger cities for some time, to have important manufacturing and administrative functions, to be centers of transportation networks, and to be widely separated in space from similar cities.

That these characteristics are also attributes of high-order central places is indicated by numerous studies of geographers, economists, sociologists, and planners.[6] Variation in this cluster of features therefore may help in the construction of a hierarchy of central places in the Soviet Union. Since countrywide data on volume or structure of trade and on tributary areas for trade are lacking in the Soviet literature and in statistical sources and since it is not feasible for a foreigner (or for any one person) to cover all the cities of the entire Soviet Union by personal field research, we need to find some other measure of central-place functions. Since the Soviet economy is largely a "command economy" directed by governmental administrative organs rather than a "market economy," one would expect that an economic and political administrative hierarchy would be a close approximation to a comprehensive central-place hierarchy, and to the component scores of Soviet cities on the size factor. A more detailed examination of the structure of administrative centers of the Soviet Union in relation to the variables associated with the size factor is given in Chapter V, in which scores on the size factor for individual cities are analyzed.

THE DENSITY FACTOR OF SOVIET CITIES

After size variations were eliminated from the data by the extraction of factor one (the size factor), another type of variation was

---

also large in area covered. The size factor is negatively associated with distance to a railroad (−0.228), i.e., smaller cities tend to be farther from a railroad; and with distance from the center of an economic region (−0.151), i.e., larger cities tend to be nearer the center of an economic region. The size factor is also negatively associated with the rate of growth for the period 1897–1926 (−0.268), i.e., the large cities of 1959 grew relatively slowly in that earlier period.

[6] Brian J. L. Berry and Allan Pred, *Central place studies: a bibliography of theory and applications* (Philadelphia: Regional Science Research Institute, 1961), "Bibliography Series No. 1," supplement through 1964 by H. Gardiner Barnum, Roger Kasperson, and Shinzo Kiuchi (1962), and Brian J. L. Berry and Chauncy D. Harris, "Central Place," *International encyclopedia of the social sciences* (New York: Macmillan and the Free Press, 1968), vol. 2, pp. 365–370.

identified as associated with a second factor, called the density factor. Nine variables show a significant association with the density factor (Table 17). These measure urban population potential and spacing characteristics.

TABLE 17

CORRELATION OF VARIABLES WITH THE DENSITY FACTOR

Variable	Correlation with the Density Factor
Population Potential	
Urban Population Potential within the major economic region	0.926
Urban Population Potential within the oblast	0.837
Urban Population Potential outside oblast but within region	0.476
Spacing	
Distance to nearest neighbor	−0.721
Distance to nearest larger neighbor	−0.585
Distance from Moscow	−0.648
Distance from center of major economic region	−0.601
Distance from center of oblast	−0.231
Longitude	−0.399

Urban population potential within the major economic region proves to be the best single indicator of the density factor (0.926), i.e., 92.6 per cent of the variation in urban population potential within economic regions was associated with the common variation in the density factor, the cluster of characteristics associated with density. The second best indicator was urban population potential within the oblast (0.837). It is noteworthy that urban population potential by economic regions gave a substantially higher figure than urban population potential by oblasts; this suggests that the clustering of urban settlements is not an intra-oblast phenomenon but rather a phenomenon of major economic regions. Thus the great clustering of settlements in both the Central Industrial Area near Moscow and in the Donets-Dnepr Industrial Area extend over many oblasts. Oblast boundaries indeed cut through continuous areas of clustered settlements. As a check, the urban population potential for that portion of the economic region lying outside the oblast in which a settlement was located was also included in the calculations and it, too, showed a high association with the density factor (0.476). But the urban population potential for the whole economic region, including both the oblast in which a settlement is located and all other oblasts of the economic region, had the highest statistical association with the density factor.

The urban population potential of any city is calculated as a summation of the population of all urban settlements included within some specified area as divided by their distance from the given city.

$$P = \Sigma \frac{p}{d}$$

where $P =$ urban population potential of any point, $p =$ the population of each urban settlement within a specified area such as an oblast or economic region, and $d =$ the distance of each settlement from the point for which potential is being calculated. It measures accessibility or potential interaction of the people in any city with the urban population of the oblast or economic region within which the city is located. Assuming that each person is an equal consumer, it also gives a measure of the urban market potential.[7] Since trade is channeled through urban centers, it also gives an approximation to total market potential.

Another measure of density of settlements is distances between settlements. The distance to the nearest neighbor (i.e., the nearest urban settlement included in this study) showed a high negative association with the density factor (-0.721), as did also the distance to the nearest larger neighbor (-0.585).[8]

Other measures of distance are also highly associated negatively with the density factor: distance from Moscow (-0.648), the center from which political and economic organization of the country has proceeded, i.e., the greater the distance from Moscow,

[7] Capacity of the computer did not permit the calculation of urban population potential based on individual cities for the Soviet Union as a whole (this would have involved a matrix of 1,247 × 1,247 calculations). Published Soviet population data for total population or rural population are given only as totals by oblasts and thus do not permit the distribution of this population within the oblast. Therefore, calculation of total population potential or rural population potential within oblasts is not possible.

[8] Distance to nearest larger neighbor showed a high negative correlation with the density factor (-0.585) and a high positive correlation with the size factor (0.627). Central places are removed a maximum distance from competing central places but clustered settlements are near other larger settlements.

the less the density factor; distance from the center of the economic region, in which a city is located (–0.601), i.e., the greater the distance from the center of the economic region, the less the density factor; and much more weakly the distance from the center of the oblast (–0.231), i.e., the greater the distance from the center of the oblast, the less the density factor. Thus high development of clustering of settlements, of agglomeration, of satellite and suburban cities tends to occur near Moscow, near centers of economic regions, and near centers of oblasts and is weakly developed far from such centers. There is also a negative relationship of longitude and the density factor (–0.399), i.e., the higher the longitude, that is the farther east a settlement, the less likely it is to be a part of a cluster. This is as would be expected since settlement has proceeded from west to east and for historical and other reasons the clusters are mainly in the western part of the country. But distance from Moscow (–0.648) is a more significant element than longitude (–0.399).[9]

Density patterns, clustering, and population potential characteristics of Soviet cities are investigated in further detail in Chapter VI.

THE GROWTH FACTOR OF SOVIET CITIES

A third principal component has been called the growth factor. It is most closely associated with the percentage increase in population for the period 1926–1959 (0.883) (Table 18). It is essentially the factor of development during the Soviet period, since urban growth from 1917 to 1926 was relatively slight. The 1926 level of urban population barely recovered the level of 1913 after the damage of World War I and the Civil War had been repaired. The variable of growth for the shorter period between the censuses of 1926 and 1939 (0.705) is more highly associated than the growth for the later intercensal period 1939–1959 (0.581). At first

---

[9] Two other associations of moderate level may be mentioned. Size position within an oblast has an association of 0.466 with the cluster factor; only oblasts with clusters of many cities have large numbers of urban settlements and therefore cities with a high ordinal position within the oblast. Number of administrative functions shows a negative association with clustering (—0.237). In areas of dense clustering of settlements, a lower proportion can have regional administrative functions since there are more settlements per unit area or per administrative unit.

TABLE 18

CORRELATIONS OF VARIABLES WITH THE GROWTH FACTOR

Variable	*Correlation with the Growth Factor*
Population Increase	
Increase in Population 1926–1959	0.883
Increase in Population 1926–1939	0.705
Increase in Population 1939–1959	0.581
Increase in Population 1897–1926	0.222
Reflecting Location in Pioneer or Peripheral Eastern Regions	
Longitude	0.559
Distance from Moscow	0.358
Distance from railroad	0.212
Number of roads	−0.550
Number of railroads	−0.310
Reflecting Clustering	
Distance to nearest neighbor	−0.209
Population potential within oblast	0.203
Size position in oblast	0.225
Number of administrative functions	−0.379

this might seem puzzling until one recalls the terrible destruction in cities in the western part of the Soviet Union during World War II and other dislocations of the wartime period. Association with the rate of growth for the essentially pre-Soviet period, 1897 to 1926, is markedly lower (0.222).

The location variables have an interesting positive association with the growth factor. High association with longitude (0.559) reveals more rapid growth in eastern than in western parts of the Soviet Union, a reflection of the pioneer character of settlement in parts of Siberia, the rapid growth of cities in distant and previously little developed areas, and also the relatively slow growth in the western parts of the Union which suffered heavy damage in World War II. Association with distance from Moscow, although weaker (0.358), also reflects the more rapid growth of peripheral regions including both areas of new settlement and areas long settled but previously not participating fully in the urban and industrial revolutions that have spread out from the central regions like an innovation wave or a classical case of cultural diffusion.

The interpretation of more rapid growth in cities in the eastern more remote regions is confirmed by 3 measures of transportation: a weak association of the growth factor with distance from a railroad (0.212), since only in the eastern, newer region are there any substantial number of urban settlements at large distances from railroads; a strong negative association with number of roads (–0.550) and number of railroads (–0.310) also suggests that more rapid growth has taken place beyond the core of well-developed transportation networks; it also reflects in part the relative stagnation of many cities and towns in areas of abundant transportation facilities in the West resulting from (1) heavy damage during World War II, (2) declining rural population in those areas, which has reduced the base for old-established trading centers, and (3) the decreasing role of trade in comparison with industry in Soviet cities.

Four relatively weak associations also suggest that, other things being equal, most rapid growth has taken place in concentrated clusters of settlements. A negative association with distance to nearest neighbor (–0.209) indicates that the closer a settlement is to other settlements the faster will be its growth. A positive association with the population potential of the oblast (0.203) also reveals that clustered dense settlements are associated with more rapid growth. A positive association with size rank (position) in the oblast (0.225) also indicates that growth is more rapid in oblasts with many settlements, since only in them can cities or towns have a high rank number, i.e., in oblasts with few cities all have a low number in the rank by size. Finally, the low negative association of the growth factor with number of administrative functions (–0.379) suggests that growth has been rapid not so much in the dispersed central-place administrative hierarchy as in the non-administrative settlements, which for the most part are clustered industrial cities and towns.[10]

Rapidity of growth is thus positively associated both with eastward position in the country and with proximity to other settle-

---

[10] Low negative association of the growth factor with relative size of manufacturing (—0.277) and number of reported branches of manufacturing (—0.366) may well reflect the severe limitations of the source material available to the author. For example, the *Atlas SSSR* provides only a rather crude measure of industry in cartographic form, probably with inadequate representation of size or variety of manufacturing in the smaller towns, especially in dense clusters, and probably with a time lag in recognition of industry. This source probably also overrepresents the oblast centers and larger cities.

ments, even though these 2 are negatively associated with each other: the correlation coefficient of distance to nearest neighbor with longitude is 0.294. It takes relatively refined statistical manipulation, such as that of factor matrices in principal components analysis, to clarify such correlations.

Our empirical manipulation of the data on 30 characteristics of 1,247 Soviet cities thus revealed 3 underlying qualities that are basic to any description of the features of Soviet cities: size, spacing (density), and growth. Aspects of these 3 features is treated in turn in the following chapters. The size factor leads us into an attempt to construct a central-place hierarchy of the Soviet Union (Chapter V). The density factor incites us to investigate the clustering patterns and to analyze interrelations among networks of industrial cities (Chapter VI). Growth patterns call for further study in chapters VII and VIII.

V.

Size Relations, Central Places,
and the Administrative Hierarchy

> Cities are like the command staff of a country
> organizing it in all its relations, economic,
> political-administrative, and cultural. As in
> a command staff, cities have their hierarchy.
> — N. N. BARANSKII,
> *Voprosy geografii,*
> sbornik 2, 1946, p. 22.

AS REVEALED BY THE PRINCIPAL COMPONENTS analysis in Chapter IV
and as suggested by O. A. Konstantinov, the Soviet urban and economic geographer, size is a key characteristic basic to any classification or understanding of Soviet cities. Let us turn, therefore,
first to a consideration of the patterns of size relationships among
Soviet cities, and then to some of the central-place administrative
characteristics closely associated with the size factor.

RANK-SIZE RELATIONSHIPS AND URBAN SYSTEMS

Zipf observed many years ago a regularity in city-size distributions
which he called the rank-size rule.[1] If the cities of a country or
region are arrayed in order of size, in general the second largest
city will have about half the population of the largest city, the
third city about a third the population of the largest city, and so

---

[1] G. K. Zipf, *National Unity and Disunity: The Nation as a Bio-Social Organism,* (Bloomington: The Principia Press, Inc., 1941).

on.[2] The population of a city multiplied by its rank in size typically is approximately equal to the population of the largest city. If on double log graph paper the population of cities in a group is plotted on one axis and their rank on the other axis, the distribution will tend to be a straight line at an angle of $-45°$ or a slope of -1.00. If the cities of various regions are so plotted, departures from "normal" distributions are graphically revealed.

The rank-size rule is not a law of necessary behavior but is a statistical regularity which appears when large numbers of cases are considered.

Figure 9 shows a series of expected rank-size relations among urban settlements. A-1, A-2, A-3, . . . A-10 defines a typical size relationship among 10 cities of more than 10,000 population in which the rank of the city in size in the region times its population equals a constant. Thus a typical largest city in this case would have a rank of one and a population of about 100,000. The second largest city would have a population of 50,000; the fourth largest, 25,000, and so on to the tenth largest city with a population of about 10,000.

If 3 entirely independent 10-member regional systems without significant interrelationships among their urban networks were mechanically joined, one would expect the rank-size distribution shown by a series of 10 steps, A1–C1–C10, with 3 cities of about 100,000 population, 3 of approximately 50,000, 3 of roughly 25,000, in a total of 30 cities with more than 10,000 population. If 10 such regions were mechanically assembled, one might expect 10 cities of about 100,000 population, A1–J1, and 90 other cities arranged in a step-like series, i.e., about 10 of 50,000 population, 10 of 25,000 population, etc. Because of random variations in size of cities in each step, the distribution might even assume a relatively smooth line, J1–J10, or some intermediate patterns with steps or partial steps. The upper part of the line would have a slope of 0.00 (A1–J1) and the lower part of the diagram might approach a slope of -1.00. The sharp break in slope at point J1 sug-

---

[2] This is a special case of the statement of $P_1 = P_1 r^{-q}$, in which $q = 1$, or simply $P_1 = \dfrac{P_1}{r}$, where P_1 is the population of any given city, P_1 the population of city of rank 1, r the rank of the given city, and q the slope of the line joining cities of various sizes arrayed in rank order on double logarithmic paper.

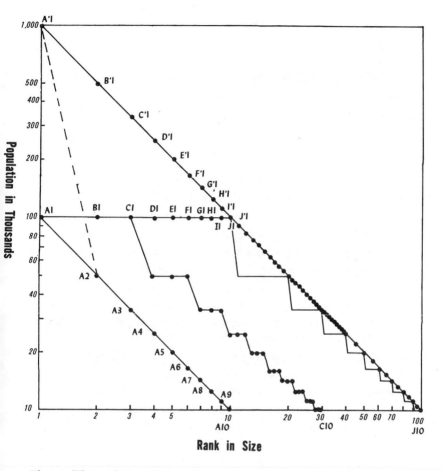

Fig. 9 Theoretical rank-size distributions of groups of cities of more than 10,000 population.

gests a lack of interrelationship among the cities and hints that the 100 cities of more than 10,000 here plotted represent in actuality not one but 10 different urban systems, each of which has its independent rank-size distribution. Of course the evidence should be not simply at the top, but also in steps all the way down the distribution.

Now if 10 regions were fully integrated into a single functionally co-ordinated and interacting urban system, one would expect to find the distribution of the 100 cities as in line A′1–J′1–J10, with the whole cluster of cities showing a slope of −1.00 and with the largest city of this expanded region with a rank of 1 and a population of about a million, a city of rank 2 (B′) with a population of about half a million, a city of rank 4 (D′) with a population of about a quarter million, and so on. City A′1 would serve not only as the regional center of its own immediate cluster of about 10 cities of more than 10,000 population but also as a higher-order center for a much larger area encompassing the 100 cities of all 10 of the smaller regions of 10 cities each. Cities of rank 1, 2, and 3 might also be centers of intermediate-sized regions each including 3 or so small regions. Thus there is a hierarchy of centers.

Variations in physical sizes, populations, numbers of cities in actual regions on the earth's surface, and historical differentiation of growth, transportation facilities, and activities in the regional centers account for random variations in size so as to produce a relatively smooth line of size distributions in the integrated region. Otherwise the rank-size distribution might have a step-like distribution of cities in a rigid urban hierarchy.

Thus a "normal" rank-size distribution may suggest that the universe of cities plotted represents an integrated urban system or a region. A distribution with a flat top (such as A1–J1) and several "steps" down the line warns that the cities plotted may represent several relatively independent regions with little functional integration. A distribution such as A′1–A2–A10 with a very steep slope between a city of rank 1 and a city of rank 2 hints that the largest city may serve a much larger area than is encompassed by the cities included in the plotted distribution. In Figure 9 city A′1 does indeed serve as the primary regional center for the cluster of cities A2–A10, but it also serves as a higher-order center for 9 other similar regions.

The analysis of rank-size distributions thus may be a device to suggest interesting intellectual problems in the analysis of urban systems. Irregular slopes, either unusually steep ones or very gentle ones pose questions. Answers to such questions may involve consideration of the historical evolution of the cities of an area, the geographic structure of settlement, transportation facilities, the territorial division of labor, political and administrative factors in definition of areas subordinate to cities, specialized industrial development, and commercial factors in the shaping of tributary areas. It must be emphasized that the method is suggestive, not definitive. There are many factors other than mere size proportions which enter into the regional relationships among urban systems. But the rank-size rule is a point of entry into a study of the size characteristics of cities.

Studies have been made of size distributions of the 1,576 Soviet cities of more than 10,000 population in 1959.[3] On the basis of the rank-size rule, one would expect that the largest city of any given region would have a population approximately equal to 10,000 times the number of cities of at least this size.[4] Thus an area with 10 cities of more than 10,000 population would be expected to have a largest city with about 100,000 population. An area with 100 cities of more than 10,000 population might have a largest city of about 1,000,000 population, and an area with 1,000 such cities, a largest city of about 10,000,000. This model is now compared with a number of actual distributions.

An example of a rank-size distribution with a low slope among the larger cities is provided by the Komi ASSR in the sparsely settled northeastern corner of Europe (Figure 10). The largest city and capital, Syktyvkar, has less than half the population that would be suggested by the size of the network of urban settlements with more than 10,000 population. The 14 such settlements would typically be headed by a primate city with a population of about 140,000, but Syktyvkar has only 64 thousand (1959). It is not located on the main rail line to other urban centers of the Komi ASSR, but lies far to the east of the rail line and is connected by the Severnaya Dvina River or by a recently constructed (1962) branch rail line. The 3 next largest cities of the Komi ASSR — Vorkuta with a population of 56 thousand, built during World War II to utilize the remote Pechora Coal Basin, Inta with a population of 45 thousand, another coal-mining center also built during World War II, and Ukhta with a population of 36 thousand and the center of an oil field — are separated from Syktyvkar, and

---

[3] In rank-size analyses the cities between 10,000 and 15,000 population in the RSFSR are included since the 1959 census volume for the RSFSR does report the number of urban settlements of more than 10,000 population, although it lists population figures for individual settlements of more than 15,000 only.
[4] If one accepts a rank-size model with $q = 1.0$, and only in this special case.

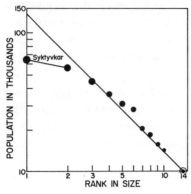 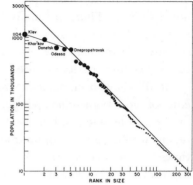

Fig. 10 Rank-size distribution: cities of the Komi ASSR.

Fig. 11 Rank-size distribution: Kiev and cities of the Ukrainian SSR.

from each other, by hundreds of miles of northern coniferous forests devoid of urban settlements. Each of these 3 next largest cities is in effect the center of a small urban cluster with little interaction with Syktyvkar, the capital and largest city, and possibly with

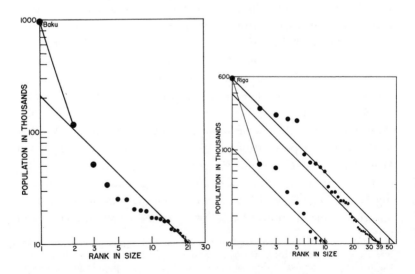

Fig. 12 Rank-size distribution: Baku and cities of the Azerbaydzhan SSR.

Fig. 13 Rank-size distribution: Riga and cities of the Latvian SSR and of the Baltic Region.

relatively little interrelationship with one another. Only for a number of administrative functions is Syktyvkar the center for the whole region.

Kiev, capital of the Ukrainian SSR with a population of 1,104,000 (1959), is only about a third as large as would be expected from the network of 301 cities and towns of more than 10,000 population in the Ukraine (Figure 11). The 5 largest cities in the Ukraine show small differences in size with a slope on double log paper of only –o.32 in contrast to the cities of ranks number 6 to number 301 which follow closely the rank-size distribution with a "normal" slope of a –1.00. The rank-size analysis suggests that the Ukraine, established on ethnic principles, may not be a single urban economic unit but rather that it may be composed of as many as 5 urban network regions. There are also 5 or so semi-steps down the distribution line in Figure 11.

An example of the opposite type, a primate city with a very steep slope to the other urban centers of its region is provided by Baku just south of the Caucasus and near the west shore of the Caspian Sea. This long-dominant oil city is more than 4 times as large as would be expected from the scale of the urban network of the Azerbaydzhan SSR, of which it is the capital (Figure 12). Its size reflects not only its regional services within the Azerbaydzhan SSR but also possibly a wider role in the Transcaucasus and particularly its function as center of a major petroleum producing area, which historically has served most of the Soviet Union, has provided exports, and has been the basis of related chemical and other industries.

Riga, the port on the Baltic Sea and capital of the Latvian SSR, has a population 5 times as large as would be predicted from the urban network of the Latvian SSR (lowest line in Figure 13). The size appears to reflect in part the port functions which it serves for a much wider area including much of the western part of the Soviet Union. The size also seems to suggest a possible role of Riga as regional center for a larger area including the Baltic republics of Latvia, Estonia, and Lithuania, and also Kaliningrad Oblast. The upper line in Figure 13, which includes the urban centers of the whole Baltic, tends to confirm this last suggestion for the rank-size relations are about what would be expected among the 10 largest cities. The middle line shows the distributions expected from the number of cities of more than 10,000 population in the entire Baltic; it fits the distribution of the cities below rank 20 reasonably well. Intermediate size cities (rank 11–18) fall in between. The existence of several steps in the distribution of cities in the Baltic suggests that integration of the combined urban network with Riga is less than complete. An alternative hypothesis is that the slope through the cities other than Riga is greater than 1 (i.e., $q > 1$) and that Riga is smaller than projected for a fully integrated Baltic urban system.

Tashkent in Soviet Middle Asia with a population of about 912,000 is 6 times as large as would be predicted from the size of the urban network of Tashkent Oblast alone (Figure 14) and more than double the size that would be expected from the urban network of the Uzbek SSR, of which it is the capital, but of almost exactly the size that would be suggested from the urban network of the whole of Soviet Middle Asia, which includes 4 union republics, the Uzbek, the Kirgiz, the Tadzhik, and the Turkmen.

Tashkent also illustrates the nesting principle of regional centers. It serves simultaneously as (1) the regional center for the whole of Soviet Middle Asia, (2) as one of 4 capitals of union republics within this area, and (3) as one of 8 centers of oblasts (or units of comparable rank) within the Uzbek SSR. The urban networks within each of these 3 areas depicted on Figure 14 roughly follow the rank-size distribution except that Tashkent is anoma-

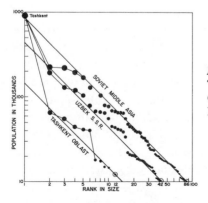

Fig. 14 Rank-size distribution: Tashkent and cities of Tashkent Oblast, the Uzbek SSR, and Soviet Middle Asia.

lously large if considered solely with respect to the urban networks of its own oblast or its own republic.

The cities of the entire Soviet Union are plotted on Figure 15. The hundred largest cities are plotted individually, then every fifth city to the 300th city (with a population of just over 50,000), then at intervals of 5,000 population to city number 1,576 with 10,000 population.

Cities from number 22 (Riga) down to number 1,576 have a slope near the "normal" of −1.00, that is they follow closely the rank-size formula. But between city number 3 (Kiev) and city number 22 (Riga), the slope is only about −0.33 or about one third

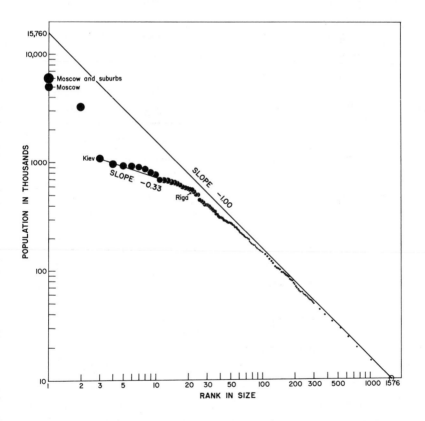

Fig. 15 Rank-size distribution: 1,576 cities of more than 10,000 population in 1959 for the entire Soviet Union.

as much as expected. The question may be raised whether there is some difference in this group of cities. One possible explanation may lie in the extraordinary size of the Soviet Union, which is a country of continental dimensions (22.4 million square kilometers or 8.65 million square miles). Each of its major regions is large enough to be an ordinary country. The larger cities may well be the centers of loosely connected regions and thus not distributed in a single rank-size scale characteristic of a fully integrated territory of more modest size. The friction of space over the enormous expanses of the Soviet Union may have tended toward the relative independence of distant regions and thus to the lack of the emergence of interregional centers of a size suggested by "normal" distribution for the total number and size of cities for the entire country.

The existence of 2 or several large cities of more nearly the same size than might be expected by the rank-size rule in several smaller countries is suggestive of residual regionalization or lack of full spatial integration as in Italy with Rome, Milan, and Naples, in Spain with Madrid and Barcelona, in Australia with Sydney and Melbourne, in India with Calcutta and Bombay, in Brazil with Rio de Janeiro and São Paulo, and in Canada with Montreal and Toronto. In most of these countries historical regionalism or external orientations are factors. The present and former capitals of the Soviet Union, Moscow and Leningrad (formerly St. Petersburg), are substantially smaller than expected for the urban network of the country as a whole. They do not dominate the country as strongly as do such capitals of the smaller West European unitary states as London and Paris. Regionalism in the Soviet Union is reflected not only in the federal structure of the country, which is composed of 15 union republics, but also in the existence of widely separated centers of major economic regions within the largest of these republics, the Russian Soviet Federated Socialist Republic (RSFSR).

On the basis of rank-size distributions of population and the number of cities of more than 10,000 population for the entire Soviet Union (1,576), a population of Moscow might be predicted of about 15,760,000, or about the population of the New York Metropolitan Area. But Moscow was only 32 per cent of this population (boundaries of 1959) or 38 per cent (boundaries of 1961).

Peter Hall notes that metropolitan Moscow included a much lower percentage of the population of its country than any of the 7 world cities he studied, only 3.8 per cent (1959), compared with 22.5 per cent for London, 16.8 per cent for Paris, 33.1 per cent for Randstad, 19.3 per cent for Rhine-Ruhr, 14.6 per cent for Tokyo-Yokohama, and 8.2 per cent for New York at about the same time.[5] That size of country, either in population or area or both, may be inversely related to the proportion of its population in its largest city is suggested by the relatively low percentage which New York includes of the population of the United States (8.2 per cent). Although more than double the Moscow proportion of the Soviet Union, New York has only a half to a third of the proportions which London, Paris, and Tokyo have for their respective countries.

If one hypothesizes that the size of the Soviet Union results in the existence of several sub-groups of city systems somewhat separated from one another and made semi-independent by the operation of space friction, one may proceed to try to define them. If one takes the more compact territory of the European part of the Russian Soviet Federated Socialist Republic only, Moscow comes out almost exactly the predicted size for the network of its 599 cities of more than 10,000 population in this area (Figure 16). This close relationship is suggestive but must not be taken as conclusive for Moscow does serve many functions for even the most distant corners of the Soviet Union, although apparently fewer than if they were nearer at hand. The size relationships hold very nicely within the urban system for the European part of the RSFSR with major regional centers at Leningrad, Moscow (as regional center as well as primate city), Gor'kiy, Voronezh, Kuybyshev, and Rostov.

Moscow serves simultaneously as: (1) capital for the entire country, for which it is smaller than predicted (Figure 15); (2) super-regional center for the European part of the Russian SFSR, for which it is almost exactly the projected size (Figure 16); (3) center for the Central Major Economic Region, which might be expected to have a center of about 2 million population, were it not also the center of a larger area (Figure 17); (4) the center for

[5] Peter Hall, *The World Cities* (London: Weidenfeld and Nicolson and New York: McGraw-Hill, 1966), table 4, p. 23.

the Moscow Industrial-Management Region, which might have a center of a little over a million population, were it not simultaneously a central place of several higher ranks; and (5) the center of the highly urbanized and densely populated Moscow Oblast. In all 3 of the rank-size distributions plotted on Figure 17, the smaller centers follow the expected rank-size rule closely but the larger centers seem to stand in the shadow of Moscow and thus to be smaller than would be expected.

The larger cities in the Asiatic part of the Soviet Union appear to be centers of relatively independent networks of cities, i.e., of regions with weak connections with other regions. Novosibirsk in Western Siberia (Figure 18), Irkutsk in Eastern Siberia (Figure 19), Vladivostok in the Soviet Far East (Figure 20), and Tashkent

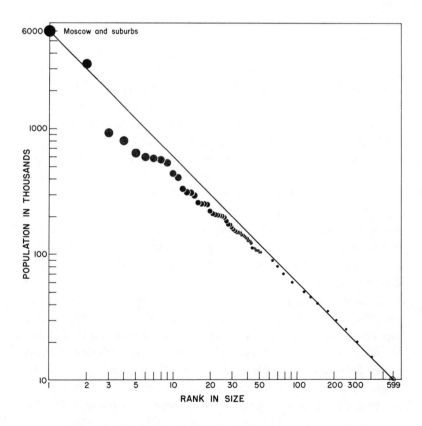

Fig. 16 Rank-size distribution: Moscow and 599 cities of the European RSFSR.

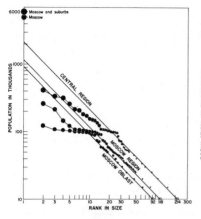

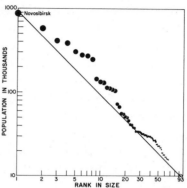

Fig. 17 Rank-size distribution: Moscow and cities of Moscow Oblast, the Moscow industrial-management (*Sovnarkhoz*) region, and the central major economic region.

Fig. 18 Rank-size distribution: Novosibirsk and 93 cities of Western Siberia.

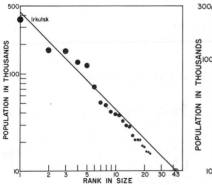

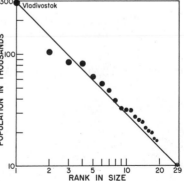

Fig. 19 Rank-size distribution: Irkutsk and 43 cities of Eastern Siberia.

Fig. 20 Rank-size distribution: Vladivostok and 29 cities of the Soviet Far East.

in Soviet Middle Asia (Figure 14) appear to be centers of systems of cities that approximate the predicted distributions of rank-size. None of these centers with its subordinate system of lesser cities clearly falls within the sphere of any larger city in terms of expected characteristics of city size distributions, neither under another city within the Asiatic part of the Soviet Union nor under distant Moscow in the European part. These cities may be centers of relatively independent city systems, probably more independent than the city systems of the relatively small separate countries of Western Europe. After all, the Asiatic portion of the Soviet Union is more than 500 times the size of either the Netherlands or Belgium or more than 15 times the size of the combined area of the United Kingdom, France, the Federal Republic of Germany, and Italy. Each of the urban systems in the Asiatic part of the Soviet Union is separated from each of the other systems by enormous distances and often by lofty mountains (the Caucasus), by vast deserts (Soviet Middle Asia), and by great stretches of forests (Siberia and the Soviet Far East).

A tentative set of urban regions for the Soviet Union based solely on the size relationships of cities, particularly on the size of the largest city in relation to the number of cities of more than 10,000 population within its presumed tributary area has been constructed (Table 19 and Figure 21). As already suggested, the 6

TABLE 19

Possible Urban Regions Based Solely on Size Relationships of Cities (Size of Largest City in Relation to Number of Cities of More Than 10,000 Population within Its Region)

City	Region	Primate City Population (Thousands)	Number of Cities Over 10,000 In Region	Projected Size of Center	Ratio of Actual to Projected Size of Center
	CORE AREA: EUROPEAN R.S.F.S.R.				
MOSCOW	European RSFSR[a][b][d]	6,008	599	5,990	1.0
1. Leningrad	Northwest RSFSR[b]	3,321	110	1,100	(3.0)
2. Moscow	Central Region	(6,008)	214	2,140	(2.8)
3. Gor'kiy	Volga-Vyatka Region[c]	942	68	680	1.4
4. Voronezh	Central Chernozem Region	448	40	400	1.1

TABLE 19 — Continued
POSSIBLE URBAN REGIONS BASED SOLELY ON SIZE RELATIONSHIPS OF CITIES (SIZE OF LARGEST CITY IN RELATION TO NUMBER OF CITIES OF MORE THAN 10,000 POPULATION WITHIN ITS REGION)

City	Region	Primate City Population (Thousands)	Number of Cities Over 10,0000 In Region	Projected Size of Center	Ratio of Actual to Projected Size of Center
5. Kuybyshev	Volga Region[cd]	806	94	940	0.9
6. Rostov	North Caucasus[a]	599	73	730	0.8
URALS, SIBERIA, AND THE FAR EAST					
7. Sverdlovsk	Middle Urals	788	61	610	1.3
8. Chelyabinsk	South Urals	689	56	560	1.2
9. Perm'	West Urals	629	42	420	1.5
10. Novosibirsk	West Siberia[e]	886	93	930	1.0
11. Irkutsk	East Siberia[ef]	366	43	430	0.9
12. Khabarovsk	Amur and Northeast	322	20	200	1.6
13. Vladivostok	Far Eastern Region	290	29	290	1.0
THE CAUCASUS, SOVIET MIDDLE ASIA, AND KAZAKHSTAN[d]					
14. Baku	Caucasus and NE	971	94	940	1.0
(or Tbilisi)	N. Caucasus[a]	694			(0.7)
15. Tashkent	Middle Asia	911	86	860	1.1
16. Alma Ata	Eastern and Southern Kazakhstan	456	34	340	1.3
17. Karaganda	Central Kazakhstan	387	34	340	1.1
EUROPEAN U.S.S.R. OUTSIDE THE R.S.F.S.R.					
18. Riga	Baltic[b]	580	39	390	1.5
19. Minsk	Belorussia	509	32	320	1.6
20. Kiev	Southwest Ukraine	1,104	84	840	1.3
21. Odessa	Southern Ukraine and Moldavia	667	46	460	1.4
22. Khar'kov	Northeastern Dnepr-Donets	934	86	860	1.1
23. Donetsk	Donetsk Oblast	699	57	570	1.2
24. Dnepropetrovsk	Dnepr	660	41	410	1.6

[a] Four autonomous republics in the Northeast Caucasus (Dagestan, Kabardino-Balkar, North Oset, and Chechen-Inguish ASSR) with 19 cities of more than 10,000 population are not here attached to the North Caucasus centered on Rostov and thus the European RSFSR but rather to the Caucasus and Northeast Caucasus with a center at Baku.

[b] Kaliningrad Oblast with 5 cities of more than 10,000 population (part of old East Prussia) is here attached to the Baltic with center at Riga rather than to the Northwest RSFSR from which it is physically separated.

[c] The Tatar ASSR with 17 cities of more than 10,000 population is here attached to Gor'kiy and the Volga-Vyatka Region rather than Kuybyshev and the Volga Region.

[d] The oblasts of West Kazakhstan Kray with 18 cities of more than 10,000 population are here placed within the urban system of Kuybyshev and the Volga and thus included with the figures for the European RSFSR.

[e] Krasnoyarsk Kray with 24 cities of more than 10,000 population is here included in the urban system of Novosibirsk.

[f] The Yakut ASSR with 3 cities of more than 10,000 population is here attached to Irkutsk.

regions of the European Russia (RSFSR) appear to be clearly subordinate to Moscow, but the Asiatic centers of Novosibirsk, Irkutsk, Vladivostok, and Tashkent, as already discussed, appear to be centers of relatively independent urban regional systems.

The cities of the Urals, which on a small-scale map look close enough together to be a single system, are in reality separated also by long distances. The rank-size analysis suggests that Sverdlovsk, Chelyabinsk, and Perm' are heads of relatively separate regional urban systems (Figure 21). Farther east Khabarovsk on the Amur River shares with Vladivostok, the port, dominion over a segment of the cities of the Soviet Far East. In the Transcaucasus, Baku and Tbilisi vie for leadership. Within city limits proper Tbilisi is larger, but if one includes nearby urban settlements politically subordinate to the city council Baku is larger.

The cities of Kazakhstan present some complexities since they do not clearly all fall within the orbit of the capital of the republic, Alma-Ata, which has a peripheral location far from many parts of the Kazakh SSR, the second largest in area among the 15 union republics of the Soviet Union. Alma-Ata in the southeast and Karaganda in the center give very good rank-size distributions within their separate regions. The cities of Western Kazakhstan, remote from either of these cities, seem to fall naturally into the sphere of Kuybyshev in the RSFSR, which is both nearer and larger than the 2 largest cities within the Kazakh SSR. The boundaries of the republic were established on the basis of ethnic distribution, not economic ties.

Along the western and southwestern borders of the Soviet Union are a series of non-Russian union republics. From the viewpoint of systems of cities they fall into a number of regions, the Baltic with Riga as regional center, Belorussia with Minsk as center, and within the Ukraine and Moldavia as many as 5 regions centered on Kiev, on Odessa, and possibly on Khar'kov, Donetsk, and Dnepropetrovsk.

In 13 out of the 20 autonomous soviet socialist republics (ASSR), the capital is substantially larger than expected from the number of other cities (of more than 10,000 population) within these political units. Perhaps the capital acts as a focus of economic and cultural contact between a minority cultural group

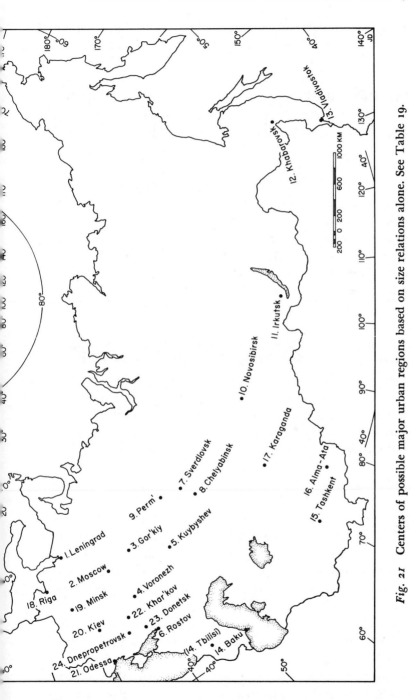

Fig. 21 Centers of possible major urban regions based on size relations alone. See Table 19.

recognized in the creation of this ethnic political unit on the one hand and a wider cultural area (usually Russian) on the other, as for example, in Kazan' (Tatar ASSR), Yoshkar-Ola (Mari ASSR), Cheboksary (Chuvash ASSR), and Saransk (Mordov ASSR) near the bend of the Volga. In at least one case, the capital of such a unit, Groznyy, the oil town in the Chechen-Ingush ASSR in the North Caucasus, has economic relations far beyond the local unit.

A substantial number of oblast centers connected with transportation arteries or junctions in areas of frontier or sparse settlement are much larger than anticipated merely from the number and size of other cities in the immediate hinterland: Astrakhan' near the mouth of the Volga River in the Caspian Sea in a narrow strip of settlement in a desert area; Petropavlovsk-Kamchatskiy, the port for remote and thinly peopled Kamchatka; and a series of railroad towns at river crossings near the frontiers of agricultural settlement, e.g., Petropavlovsk (in North Kazakhstan), Omsk on the Irtysh, and Tomsk on the Tom' (all 3 on the Trans-Siberian Railroad), Ural'sk at the crossing of the Ural River by the rail line from European Russia to Soviet Middle Asia, and Semipalatinsk at the crossing of the Irtysh River by the Turk-Sib railroad joining Turkestan (Soviet Middle Asia) with Siberia.

Another type of city larger than expected from present tributary areas is represented by cities near the boundary of the Soviet Union which now cuts off segments of former hinterlands, e.g., Kaliningrad (Königsberg), formerly the center of a larger East Prussia, or Chernovtsy (Cernăuţi), formerly the center of a larger Bukovina.

POPULATION AND THE SIZE FACTOR

The rank-size relationships suggest the importance of population (size) in the hierarchy of Soviet cities, but an analysis of the size factor as defined in Chapter IV suggests that elements other than mere size are also involved. It will be recalled from the statistical analysis that the size factor though closely related to population (size) also reflects the number of functions served by the city, transportation facilities of the city, and the spacing of the city in relation to other settlements. If the larger cities in the Soviet Union are arrayed in order according to the size factor and also according to population in 1959, variations in relative rank suggest some differentiation of type. A number of cities ranking much higher on the size factor than on population (Khabarovsk, Irkutsk, and Rostov) obviously have important regional central-place functions. Cities ranking much lower on the size factor than on population include some major industrial centers (Khar'kov, Donetsk, Dnepropetrovsk) in which manufacturing activities are important and central-place functions relatively less important. Of course, all of the larger cities in the Soviet Union are both regional centers and industrial centers but the relative weight of each function varies from city to city. Since it appears that the size factor may be a more sensitive indicator of regional leadership and central-place functions than mere population alone, we must now turn to an analysis of the relationship of the size factor, defined statistically in Chapter IV, to the central-place hierarchy of the Soviet Union.

In the Soviet Union none of the other features associated with the size factor is more important than administrative functions. The governmental and party apparatus with a high degree of centralization direct the Soviet economy as well as political and cultural affairs. The administrative hierarchy which has been evolved through repeated experimentation reflects a complex of numerous factors and is based on informed judgement and discussion by involved participants at each level. Under the Soviet system it provides a legal, administrative, and functional definition of the central-place hierarchy.

HIGH-ORDER ADMINISTRATIVE HIERARCHY: REGIONAL AND OBLAST CENTERS

The Soviet Union was administratively divided into 15 union republics, 149 oblasts (or comparable units),[6] and 2,959 rayons (as of July 1967). The first-level administrative organization into 15

---

[6] The 149 administrative units areally comparable to oblasts consist of 20 autonomous soviet socialist republics (ASSR), 8 autonomous oblasts (AO), 6 krays, 105 oblasts, and 10 of the smaller union republics (SSR) which have areas not divided into oblasts and thus are territorially similar to oblasts. *(SSSR, Administrativno-territorial'noe delenie soiuznykh respublik, na 1, iiulia 1967, goda, p. xix.)* All 10 national okrugs are subordinate to oblasts or krays and thus are not counted as units comparable to oblasts. Located in the Far North or in Siberia, though sometimes large in area, they are small in population and have few cities, only 4 of which are large enough to be in our study group.

union republics based on distribution of ethnic groups is highly asymmetric with one republic, the Russian Soviet Federated Socialist Republic (RSFSR), having about three-fourths of the total area, 60 per cent of the cities of more than 10,000 population, over half the population, and over half of the administrative units of lesser level.

The other union republics are the Estonian SSR (Soviet Socialist Republic), Latvian SSR, Lithuanian SSR, Belorussian SSR, Ukrainian SSR (the second largest in population), and Moldavian SSR on the western edge of the country from the Baltic Sea to the Black Sea; the Georgian SSR, Armenian SSR and Azerbaydzhan SSR in the Caucasus between the Black and Caspian Seas; and the Kazakh SSR (the second largest in area), Turkmen SSR, Uzbek SSR, Kirgiz SSR, and Tadzhik SSR, east of the Caspian Sea in Soviet Middle Asia or Turkestan. Each of these other union republics is organized to give recognition to a major non-Russian ethnic group, indicated by the name of the republic. Each is located on the external boundary of the Soviet Union and has the theoretical right to withdraw from the USSR (Union of Soviet Socialist Republics) if it wishes. The boundaries of each are drawn on the basis of the distribution of the ethnic group which it recognizes.[7] The tremendous range in size and population among the union republics tends to invalidate the use of their capitals as central places of the same rank except for certain specific political-administrative functions which they perform.

A possible hierarchy of cities and associated regions at more nearly comparable levels is suggested by the division of the Soviet Union into 18 major economic regions, 50 industrial-management (Sovnarkhoz) regions, and 146 oblast or similar administrative units as of 1962–1963 (Table 20).

The major economic regions were established in May 1961 after long investigation and recommendations by planners, economists, and geographers, and by planning agencies, universities, research institutes, and other bodies.[8] The 17 major economic re-

---

[7] Some administrative units of lower order are also based on recognition of ethnic groups: autonomous soviet socialist republics (ASSR) and autonomous oblasts (AO) comparable to oblasts, and national okrugs of lower rank, not here analyzed.

[8] *Ekonomicheskaia Gazeta,* May 28, 1961, p. 2.

TABLE 20
A Possible Hierarchy of Central Places for the Soviet Union Based on Major Economic Regions, Industrial-Management Regions, and Oblasts of 1963

18 Centers of major economic regions.[1]
50 Centers of industrial-management (Sovnakhoz) regions.[2]
146 Centers of oblasts or similiar administrative units.[3]

		Size Factor	Density Factor
1–4–9	I. Leningrad (Northwest Region)	5.27	2.43
	A. Leningrad	x	x
	1. Leningrad (city)	x	x
	2. Leningrad (oblast)	x	x
	3. Pskov	1.21	–0.16
	4. Novgorod	1.29	–0.05
	5. Vologda	1.53	–0.10
	B. Arkhangel'sk (Northwest Region)	2.32	–0.26[b]
	1. Arkhangel'sk	x	x
	2. Petrozavodsk (Karelian ASSR)	1.98	–0.20
	C. Murmansk	1.90	0.01
	1. Murmansk	x	x
	D. Syktyvkar (Komi ASSR)	1.66	–1.44
	1. Syktyvkar (Komi ASSR)	x	x
1–4–13	II. Moscow (Central Region)	5.08	4.70
	A. Moscow (city)	x	x
	1. Moscow (city)	x	x
	B. Moscow (region)	x	x
	1. Moscow (oblast)	x	x
	2. Ryazan'	2.27	0.74
	3. Kalinin	2.12	0.91
	4. Smolensk	1.59	0.31
	C. Ivanovo (Upper Volga Region)	2.71	1.20
	1. Ivanovo	x	x
	2. Kostroma	1.90	0.45
	3. Yaroslavl'	2.70	0.94
	4. Vladimir	1.33	0.81
	D. Tula (Oka Region)	2.38	1.53
	1. Tula	x	x
	2. Kaluga	1.52	0.77
	3. Bryansk	2.38	0.61
	4. Orël	2.11	0.05
1–1–5	III. Gor'kiy (Volga-Vyatka Region)	4.45	1.73
	A. Gor'kiy	x	x
	1. Gor'kiy	x	x
	2. Kirov	2.44	0.16
	3. Yoshkar-Ola (Mari ASSR)	0.90[a]	–0.39
	4. Cheboksary (Chuvash ASSR)	1.49	–0.29
	5. Saransk (Mordov ASSR)	1.33	–0.04
1–1–5	IV. Voronezh (Central Chernozëm Region)	3.51	1.01
	A. Voronezh	x	x

TABLE 20 — Continued

A POSSIBLE HIERARCHY OF CENTRAL PLACES FOR THE SOVIET UNION BASED ON MAJOR ECONOMIC REGIONS, INDUSTRIAL-MANAGEMENT REGIONS, AND OBLASTS OF 1963

18 Centers of major economic regions.[1]
50 Centers of industrial-management (Sovnakhoz) regions.[2]
146 Centers of oblasts or similar administrative units.[3]

		Size Factor	Density Factor
	1. Voronezh	x	x
	2. Belgorod	1.23	−0.27
	3. Kursk	2.48	0.16
	4. Lipetsk	1.49	0.20
	5. Tambov	2.07	0.24
1–3–9	V. Kuybyshev (Volga Region)	4.31	1.35
	A. Kuybyshev (Middle Volga Region)	x	x
	1. Kuybyshev	x	x
	2. Kazan' (Tatar ASSR)	3.70	0.80
	3. Ufa (Bashkir ASSR)	3.84	0.21
	B. Saratov (Volga Region)	3.97	0.77
	1. Saratov	x	x
	2. Ul'yanovsk	2.46	−0.01
	3. Penza	2.91	0.33
	C. Volgograd (Lower Volga Region)	3.92	0.58
	1. Volgograd	x	x
	2. Astrakhan'	2.93	−0.55
	3. Elista (Kalmyk ASSR)	0.38[a]	−1.34
1–1–7	VI. Rostov-on-Don (North Caucasus Region)	4.06	1.62
	A. Rostov-na-Donu	x	x
	1. Rostov	x	x
	2. Krasnodar	3.27	0.54
	3. Stavropol'	2.08	−0.08
	4. Nal'chik (Kabardino-Balkar ASSR)	0.95[a]	−0.51
	5. Ordzhonikidze (North Oset ASSR)	1.46	−0.07
	6. Groznyy (Chechen-Ingush ASSR)	2.65	−0.05
	7. Makhachkala (Dagestan ASSR)	1.95	−0.32
1–3–7	VII. Sverdlovsk (Ural Region)	3.97	1.32
	A. Sverdlovsk (Middle Ural Region)	x	x
	1. Sverdlovsk	x	x
	2. Tyumen'	2.23	−0.51
	B. Chelyabinsk (South Ural Region)	3.75	0.83
	1. Chelyabinsk	x	x
	2. Orenburg	2.64	−0.27
	3. Kurgan	1.98	−0.52
	C. Perm' (West Urals Region)	3.43	0.45
	1. Perm'	x	x
	2. Izhevsk (Udmurt ASSR)	2.31	0.11
1–2–5	VIII. Novosibirsk (West Siberian Region)	4.33	0.77
	A. Novosibirsk (West Siberia)	x	x
	1. Novosibirsk	x	x

TABLE 20 — Continued
A POSSIBLE HIERARCHY OF CENTRAL PLACES FOR THE SOVIET UNION BASED ON MAJOR ECONOMIC REGIONS, INDUSTRIAL-MANAGEMENT REGIONS, AND OBLASTS OF 1963

18 Centers of major economic regions.[1]
50 Centers of industrial-management (Sovnakhoz) regions.[2]
146 Centers of oblasts or similar administrative units.[3]

		Size Factor	Density Factor
	2. Tomsk	2.27	−0.25
	3. Omsk	3.78	−0.25
	B. Kemerovo (Kuzbas)	2.69	−0.13[b]
	1. Kemerovo	x	x
	2. Barnaul (Altay Kray)	2.64	0.11
1–2–5	IX. Irkutsk (East Siberian Region)	3.60	0.07
	A. Irkutsk (East Siberia)	x	x
	1. Irkutsk	x	x
	2. Ulan-Ude (Buryat ASSR)	2.42	−0.95
	3. Chita	2.34	−1.33
	B. Krasnoyarsk	3.43	−0.83
	1. Krasnoyarsk	x	x
	2. Kyzyl (Tuva ASSR)	0.90[a]	−2.17
1–3–7	X. Khabarovsk (Far Eastern Region)	3.63	−0.58
	A. Khabarovsk	x	x
	1. Khabarovsk	x	x
	2. Blagoveshchensk (Amur)	2.04	−1.62
	B. Vladivostok (Far East)	2.38	−0.92
	1. Vladivostok (Maritime Kray)	x	x
	2. Yuzhno-Sakhalinsk (Sakhalin)	1.74	−1.37
	3. Petropavlovsk-Kamchatskiy (Kamchatka)	1.22	−2.78
	C. Magadan (Northeast Region)	1.81	−2.76[b]
	1. Magadan	x	x
	2. Yakutsk (Yakut ASSR)	1.94	−2.73
1–3–8	XI. Donetsk (Donets-Dnepr Region)	3.39	1.87
	A. Donetsk	x	x
	1. Donetsk	x	x
	2. Lugansk	2.40	1.17
	B. Khar'kov	3.83	1.18
	1. Khar'kov	x	x
	2. Poltava	1.68	0.36
	3. Sumy	1.22	0.00
	C. Dnepropetrovsk (Dnepr)	3.41	1.28
	1. Dnepropetrovsk	x	x
	2. Zaporozh'ye	2.96	0.95
	3. Kirovograd	1.42	0.00
1–3–14	XII. Kiev (Southwest Region)	4.47	1.67
	A. Kiev	x	x
	1. Kiev (city)	x	x
	2. Kiev (oblast)	x	x
	3. Chernigov	1.46	−0.03

TABLE 20 — Continued
A POSSIBLE HIERARCHY OF CENTRAL PLACES FOR THE SOVIET UNION BASED ON MAJOR ECONOMIC REGIONS, INDUSTRIAL-MANAGEMENT REGIONS, AND OBLASTS OF 1963

18 Centers of major economic regions.[1]
50 Centers of industrial-management (Sovnakhoz) regions.[2]
146 Centers of oblasts or similar administrative units.[3]

			Size Factor	Density Factor
		4. Cherkassy	1.20	0.03
		5. Zhitomir	1.50	0.37
	B.	L'vov	3.28	0.38
		1. L'vov	x	x
		2. Uzhgorod (Transcarpathian Oblast')	0.44[a]	−0.49
		3. Lutsk (Volyn Oblast')	0.68[a]	−0.35
		4. Rovno	0.80[a]	0.03
		5. Ivano-Frankovsk	0.97[a]	−0.70
	C.	Vinnitsa (Podolian Region)	1.52	0.11
		1. Vinnitsa	x	x
		2. Ternopol'	0.97[a]	−0.17
		3. Khmel'nitskiy	1.00	−0.12
		4. Chernovtsy	1.69	−0.01
1–1–4	XIII.	Odessa (Southern Region)	3.52	1.10
	A.	Odessa (Black Sea Region)	x	x
		1. Odessa	x	x
		2. Simferopol' (Crimea)	2.26	−0.12
		3. Kherson	2.14	0.35
		4. Nikolayev	1.84	0.50
1–3–4	XIV.	Riga (Western Region)	3.57	1.16
	A.	Riga (Latvia)	x	x
		1. Riga	x	x
	B.	Tallin (Estonia)	2.53	0.10
		1. Tallin	x	x
	C.	Vil'nyus (Lithuania)	2.62	0.10
		1. Vil'nyus (Lithuania)	x	x
		2. Kaliningrad (in RSFSR)	1.70	−0.04
1–1–6	XV.	Minsk (Belorussia)	3.55	1.05
	A.	Minsk	x	x
		1. Minsk	x	x
		2. Brest	1.56	−0.59
		3. Vitebsk	1.70	−0.09
		4. Gomel'	1.88	0.05
		5. Grodno	1.31	−0.55
		6. Mogilëv	1.76	0.02
1–3–6	XVI.	Tbilisi (Transcaucasian Region)	3.89	1.20
	A.	Tbilisi (Georgia)	x	x
		1. Tbilisi (Georgian SSR except special units)	x	x
		2. Sukhumi (Abkhaz ASSR)	1.23	−0.58
		3. Batumi (Adzhar ASSR)	1.38	−0.32
	B.	Baku (Azerbaydzhan)	3.69	0.17

TABLE 20 — Continued
A POSSIBLE HIERARCHY OF CENTRAL PLACES FOR THE
SOVIET UNION BASED ON MAJOR ECONOMIC REGIONS,
INDUSTRIAL-MANAGEMENT REGIONS, AND OBLASTS OF 1963

18 Centers of major economic regions.[1]
50 Centers of industrial-management (Sovnakhoz) regions.[2]
146 Centers of oblasts or similar administrative units.[3]

			Size Factor	Density Factor
		1. Baku (Azerbaydzhan SSR except special units)	x	x
		2. Nakhichevan' (ASSR)	0.14[a]	−0.97
	C.	Yerevan (Armenia)	2.85	0.44
		1. Yerevan	x	x
1–4–16	XVII.	Tashkent (Middle Asiatic Region)	4.18	1.09
	A.	Tashkent (Uzbekistan)	x	x
		1. Tashkent	x	x
		2. Andizhan	1.69	−0.16
		3. Bukhara	1.19	−0.42
		4. Samarkand	1.98	−0.18
		5. Termez (Surkhandar'ya Oblast')	0.24[a]	−1.62
		6. Fergana	1.12	−0.20
		7. Urgench (Khorezm Oblast')	1.19	−1.09
		8. Nukus (Kara-Kalpak ASSR)	1.10	−1.10
	B.	Frunze (Kirgizia)	2.18	−0.44
		1. Frunze (Kirgiz SSR except special units)	x	x
		2. Osh	0.78[a]	−0.49
		3. Naryn (Tyan'shan' Oblast')	0.39[a]	−1.91
	C.	Dushanbe (Tadzhikistan)	2.13	−0.20
		1. Dushanbe	x	x
	D.	Ashkhabad (Turkmenistan)	2.25	−1.23[b]
		1. Ashkhabad (Turkmen SSR except special units)	x	x
		2. Mary	0.78[a]	−1.19
		3. Tashauz	0.83[a]	−1.04
		4. Chardzhou	1.46	−1.05
1–7–15	XVIII.	Alma Ata (Kazakhstan)	3.43	0.14
	A.	Alma Ata	x	x
		1. Alma Ata	x	x
	B.	Ust'-Kamenogorsk (East Kazakhstan Oblast)	2.17	−0.75
		1. Ust'-Kamenogorsk	x	x
	C.	Semipalatinsk	1.93	−1.09
		1. Semipalatinsk	x	x
	D.	Chimkent (South Kazakhstan Kray)	2.05	−0.73
		1. Chimkent	x	x
		2. Kzyl-Orda	0.76[a]	−1.39
		3. Dzhambul	1.73	−0.91
	E.	Tselinograd (Tselinnyy Kray) (Virgin Lands)	1.97	−1.05[b]
		1. Tselinograd	x	x

TABLE 20 — Continued

A POSSIBLE HIERARCHY OF CENTRAL PLACES FOR THE
SOVIET UNION BASED ON MAJOR ECONOMIC REGIONS,
INDUSTRIAL-MANAGEMENT REGIONS, AND OBLASTS OF 1963

18 Centers of major economic regions.[1]
50 Centers of industrial-management (Sovnakhoz) regions.[2]
146 Centers of oblasts or similar administrative units.[3]

			Size Factor	Density Factor
	2. Kokchetav		1.16	−0.99
	3. Kustanay		1.77	−1.04
	4. Pavlodar		1.91	−1.38
	5. Petropavlovsk (North Kazakhstan Oblast')		2.17	−0.92
	F. Aktyubinsk (West Kazakhstan Kray)		2.12	−1.15[b]
	1. Aktyubinsk		x	x
	2. Ural'sk		1.41	−1.19
	3. Gur'yev		1.87	−0.97
	G. Karaganda		2.62	−0.26
	1. Karaganda		x	x
0–1–1	XIX. Kishinëv (Moldavia) (Not a major economic region but not within any other major economic region)		2.51	−0.10
	A. Kishinëv		x	x
	1. Kishinëv		x	x
18–50–146				

x — Center of this unit is also center of a higher-order unit.
a — Low index discussed in text in the section "Disparities: Administrative Centers with Low Scores on the Size Factor."
b — Low index discussed in text in the section "The Size Factor and the Density Factor."
[1] *Ekonomicheskaia gazeta*, May 28, 1961, p. 2, and October 19, 1963, pp. 12–13 (also given in *Soviet geography: review and translation*, vol. 2, no. 8 [October 1961], pp. 84–88, and vol. 4, no. 9 [November 1963], pp. 58–61) and *Narodnoe khoziaistvo SSSR v 1963 g. statisticheskii ezhegodnik*, pp. 715–716.
[2] *Ekonomicheskaia gazeta*, February 16, 1963, p. 13, and October 19, 1963, pp. 12–13, (also given in *Soviet geography: review and translation*, vol. 4, no. 3 [March 1963], pp. 49–52 and vol. 4, no. 9 [November 1963], pp. 58–61.) The former Middle Asiatic Industrial Management Region, established February 3, 1963, was split into four industrial management regions, corresponding to the four union republics, Uzbek, Kirgiz, Turkmen, and Tadzhik in late 1964 (*New York Times*, December 24, 1964).
[3] *Narodnoe khoziaistvo SSSR v 1963 godu: statisticheskii ezhegodnik*, pp. 715–716; Tsentral'noe statisticheskoe upravlenie: *Itogi vsesoiuznoi perepisi naseleniia 1959 goda*, (Moskva: Gosstatizdat, 1963–1965) 16 volumes; and *SSSR: Administrativno-territorial'noe delenie soiuznykh respublik* (Moskva: Izdatel'stvo "Izvestiia Sovetov Deputatov Trudiashchikhsia SSSR"), 11th ed. (for January 1, 1962), pp. 7–14; 12th ed. (for April 1, 1963), pp. 7–18; and 13th ed. (for January 1965), pp. 8–14. Neither the 8 autonomous oblasts nor the 10 national okrugs are included in the category of oblasts or similar administrative units; all are subordinate to krays or oblasts in the RSFSR or to small republics without regular divisions into oblasts.

gions established on that date (increased to 18 in October 1963) (Figure 22)[9] replaced an earlier system of 13 regions, that with variations over time go back to the early days of Soviet planning

[9] *Ekonomicheskaia Gazeta*, October 19, 1963, pp. 12–13.

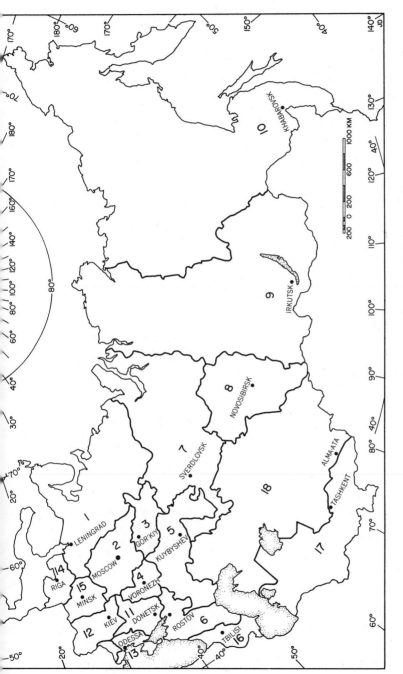

Fig. 22 Major economic regions of 1963 and their centers.

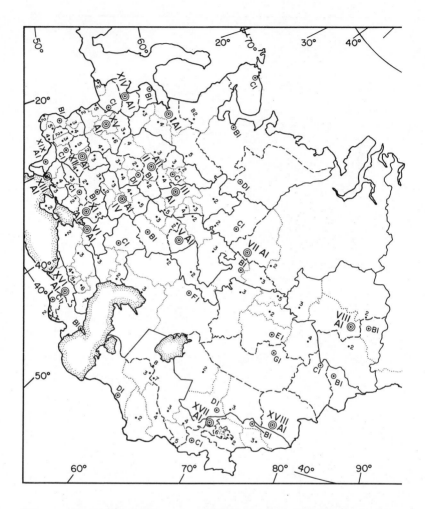

Fig. 23 Central-place hierarchy and tributary areas based on planning and administrative regions of 1963. Boundaries and centers of major economic regions, industrial-management (*Sovnarkhoz*) regions, and oblasts or similar administrative units. Numbers correspond to those in Table 20.

after the Revolution of 1917. These major regions are utilized for long-range planning of resource utilization and economic development. They are not primarily administrative regions. They represent an attempt to divide the country into areal units that have somewhat similar problems and potentialities, some degree of

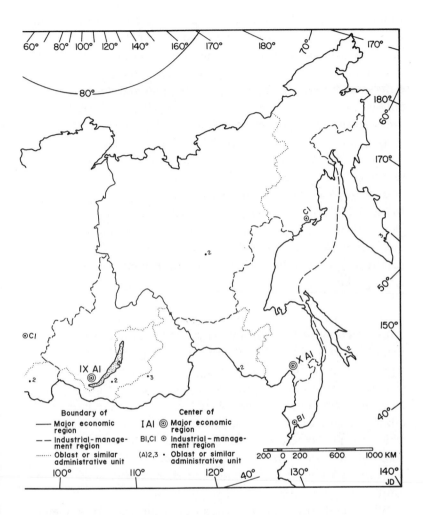

economic unity, and are roughly co-ordinate in scale. In other words they are primarily economic planning units rather than ethnic or political-administrative units.

The 50 industrial-management regions have been the subject of considerable experimentation in their size, numbers, and management functions (Table 20 and Figure 23). Their creation in 1957 was a radical change from the previous practice of administration of manufacturing establishments throughout the entire country by branches of industry to a regional principle of general administration of many diverse types of factories within some specified area. Our concern here is not with the so-called branch versus the regional principle of administration but rather with the recognition of some tendencies toward regional organization of units smaller than 18 major economic regions and larger than 146 oblasts. The industrial-management regions first numbered 104 on their creation in 1957, corresponding to oblasts in the RSFSR and with groups of oblasts in the Ukrainian, Kazakh, and Uzbek union republics, or with entire republics for some of the smaller republics. These were reduced to 47 in December 1962 but increased to 50 in late 1964 by the splitting of the Middle Asiatic Industrial-Management Region (the only one including in a single economic administrative region enterprises located in several union republics) into 4 regions corresponding to the 4 Middle Asiatic union republics. These regions were abolished on October 2, 1965. They obviously were unstable in both time and areal extent.

The 146 oblasts or similar administrative units are generally those which existed during 1962–1963 at the time of the publication of the 1959 census and for which city populations were then reported (Table 20 and Figure 23). These include 110 oblasts proper, 6 krays (which are similar to oblasts but include typically some subordinate ethnic units such as autonomous oblasts or national okrugs), 20 autonomous soviet socialist republics (ASSR), which are similar to oblasts in size and population but are based on ethnic minorities and 10 smaller union republics that are not generally subdivided into oblasts and thus each is in some ways similar to an oblast in size and population.

We hypothesize that the centers of these 3 levels of regions form an approach to a hierarchy of economic-administrative central places of decreasing rank and successively smaller tributary areas, and that these centers are "nested" so that centers of a higher order have within their tributary areas several centers of the next lower order, which in turn have several centers of the next lower, and so on. Each higher-order center serves also the functions of lower-order centers but for much smaller areas. It is to be realized that the process of historical development and the diversity of natural resources and natural conditions make for great variations in density of population and in degree and type of economic development from place to place and thus make the size and spacing of central places of similar rank somewhat irregular.

The size factor revealed by the principal components analysis of 30 characteristics of Soviet cities (Chapter IV) appears to be closely associated with central-place functions. In order to study the association of this factor and the administrative hierarchy (and thus to a possible central-place hierarchy), we have arrayed the score on the size factor for the 1,247 cities studied. The mean score is zero (0) and the standard deviation 1.00. All cities with factor scores of above 1.00 on this scale thus have a concentration of the variables associated with the size factor of more than one standard deviation above the average of Soviet cities.

The 153 Soviet cities (out of 1,247) that have a plus deviation of more than 1.00 by the above criterion show a remarkably close relationship to the 3 levels of economic-administrative centers as defined above. The higher the score on the size factor, the higher the position of the city on this economic-administrative hierarchy.

Because of the enormous variations in density of population over the Soviet Union, the scores on the size factor for cities of equal rank in the hierarchy vary from area to area, being higher in the densely settled areas, especially near Moscow, and much lower in the sparsely settled parts of Siberia.

Nevertheless, the 8 cities with indices of more than 4.00 are all centers of major economic regions and all 18 centers of major economic regions have indices on the size factor of 3.39 or higher. Of the 153 cities with an index of 1.00 or more, 127 are centers of oblasts or comparable units and 26 are not such centers. Most of the latter have indices just barely over 1.00 (Table 22 below). Only 16 oblast centers do not have an index of more than 1.00; they are centers of smaller oblasts.[10]

The hierarchy of central places based on the 3 levels of economic or administrative regions together with the scores on the size factor are given in Table 20. The location of the administra-

[10] For the 146 oblasts and similar administrative units there are 143 centers. Moscow, Leningrad, and Kiev are each the center of 2 units (the cities themselves constitute units in addition to the surrounding oblasts).

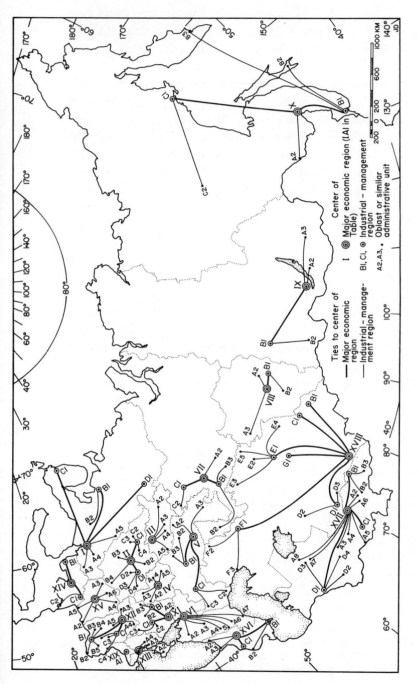

Fig. 24 Lines of subordination of second and third-order central cities based on planning and administrative regions. Numbers correspond to those in Table 20.

tive centers and of their tributary areas are shown on Figure 23. The lines of subordination of administrative centers is depicted in Figure 24.

A comparison of the central places of the major economic regions (Table 20 and Figure 22), which have been determined by political-administrative and planning considerations, with the centers of urban systems determined solely on the basis of relationships with the network of urban places (Table 19 and Figure 21) demonstrates a remarkable similarity (Figure 25).

The 6 major regional centers for the European RSFSR are identical: Moscow, Leningrad, Gor'kiy, Voronezh, Kuybyshev, and Rostov-on-Don (Tables 19 and 20 and Figures 21, 22, and 25). Also identical are the regional centers for Siberia (Novosibirsk and Irkutsk) for Soviet Middle Asia (Tashkent), for the Baltic (Riga), for Belorussia (Minsk), for the Southwestern Ukraine (Kiev), and for the Southern Ukraine (Odessa). For the Caucasus both systems are ambivalent with either Baku or Tbilisi a possible center. Thus in 14 out of 18 major economic regions the determination of the regional center and the identity of the region are essentially the same, whether by Soviet political decision on administrative regions or by a statistical analysis of urban systems based on rank-size distributions.

In 4 major economic regions, however, the urban systems analysis suggests further subdivision into a total of 10 urban systems.

The Soviet Far East (center Khabarovsk) seems to have 2 urban systems centered on Khabarovsk and Vladivostok. Of the 18 major economic regions this is the largest in physical area and the smallest in population, a most remarkable combination. It is thus not surprising that although treated as one region for planning purposes, the tremendous distances in the Soviet Far East lead to 2 urban systems in this area.

The Kazakh SSR, the largest union republic other than the RSFSR and indeed larger than the 13 remaining union republics put together, is administratively considered as one major economic region centered on the capital Alma-Ata. However, analysis of the urban systems shows centrifugal tendencies. These reflect in part the peripheral position of Alma-Ata on the far eastern side of this enormous Asiatic republic. The cities in the western part

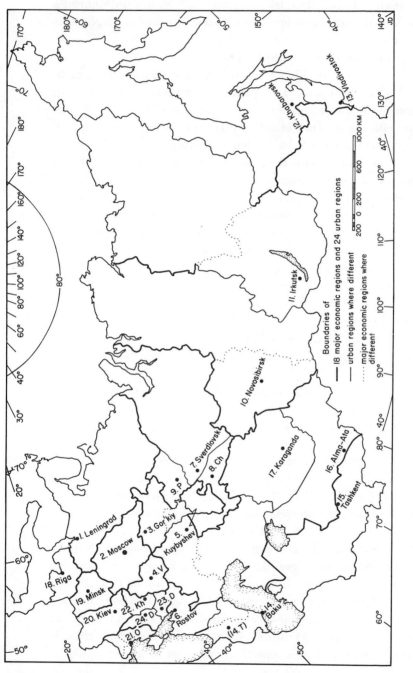

Fig. 25 Comparison of centers and boundaries of 24 urban regions based on size relationships alone and 18 major economic regions administratively defined for planning purposes.
O: Odessa. D(24): Dnepropetrovsk. D(23): Donetsk. Kh: Khar'kov. V: Voronezh. T: Tbilisi. P: Perm'. Ch: Chelyabinsk.

of Kazakhstan are closer to *all* the cities of the European part of the Soviet Union than to the capital of their own republic. Cities in the southern parts of Kazakhstan are much closer to Tashkent in Soviet Middle Asia than to Alma-Ata. There appear to be at least 2 major urban systems within Kazakhstan subordinate in terms of size relations to Alma-Ata and to Karaganda and with peripheral areas in the west and possibly also in the south with close relations to cities outside the Kazakh SSR.

In the Ural major economic region centered on Sverdlovsk there are 3 subdivisions in the administrative hierarchy tributary to Sverdlovsk, Chelyabinsk, and Perm'. By virtue of the great concentration of industrial cities in the Urals, these 3 administrative subregions show up in the urban systems analysis as separate regions.

Similarly the highly industrialized and urbanized Donets-Dnepr Major Economic Region of the Eastern Ukraine has 3 administrative subregions centered on Khar'kov, Donetsk, and Dnepropetrovsk. The urban systems analysis reflects the intense concentration of urban centers in the area by elevating all 3 to full major urban regions (possibly with some boundary modifications).

Thus 2 entirely independent approaches to a hierarchy of central places in the Soviet Union, one administrative and the other statistical, show a remarkable similarity. The 4 areas in which the urban analysis suggests possible further subdivision of planning regions (the Donets-Dnepr, Urals, Kazakhstan, and Soviet Far East major economic regions) are characterized by large populations (in the first 2) or very large physical size (in the last 2).

The Moscow Major Economic Region may be taken as an illustration of the nature of the administrative and urban hierarchy in the Soviet Union (Table 20, region II and Figure 26, sketch A). Moscow itself with an index of 5.08 on the size factor is a center for the entire country, but is also one of 18 centers of major economic regions. The Moscow Major Economic Region contains 4 industrial-management (Sovnarkhoz) regions with centers at Moscow (for 2 units Moscow Region and Moscow City, which is itself a region of this rank), at Ivanovo (the Upper Volga Region) with an index of 2.71, and at Tula (Oka Region) with an index of 2.38 (Table 20). Each of these industrial-management regions in turn contains several oblasts. The Moscow Industrial-Management Region contains 4 oblasts with centers at Moscow itself, at Ryazan', Kalinin, and Smolensk. The Upper Volga Industrial-Management Region (center Ivanovo) contains oblast centers at Ivanovo itself and at Yaroslavl', Kostroma, and Vladimir. The Tula Industrial-Management Region contains oblast centers at Tula itself and at Bryansk, Orël, and Kaluga. In 2 cases other oblast centers with long historical and administrative importance have indices nearly the same as that of the center of the industrial-management region; Yaroslavl' nearly matches Ivanovo and Bryansk matches Tula. In these 2 cases the subordination is not as clear as is typical. Indeed Yaroslavl' is considerably larger than Ivanovo, though not as central in this region; Yaroslavl' is much larger than would be expected from the urban network of its own oblast and about the size that would fit the region. Rank-size analysis would suggest Yaroslavl' as the center.

The Volga Major Economic Region may be taken as another example of the nature of the hierarchies (Table 20, region V, and Figure 26, sketch B). Kuybyshev, the center for the major economic region has an index of 4.31; centers of 3 industrial-management regions lie within its sphere: Kuybyshev as center of the Middle Volga, Saratov (3.97) as center of the Volga, and Volgograd (3.92) as center of the Lower Volga industrial-management regions. These centers, in turn, have lesser centers within their spheres. Kuybyshev as center of the Middle Volga Industrial-Management Region has 3 oblast-level centers subordinate to it: Kuybyshev itself, Kazan' (3.70), and Ufa (3.84). Kazan' and Ufa have unusually high indices for oblast level centers; they are capitals of the 2 most populous autonomous soviet socialist republics in the USSR: the Tatar and Bashkir ASSR respectively. Saratov, as center of the Volga Industrial-Management Region might be considered to have 3 oblast centers subordinate to it: Saratov itself, Penza, and Ul'yanovsk (though Ul'yanovsk could perhaps better be grouped with Kuybyshev). Volgograd, as center of the Lower Volga Industrial-Management region also has 3 oblast-level centers subordinate to it: Volgograd itself, Astrakhan' and Elista (Kalmyk ASSR). The very low figure for Elista reveals its small size and the extremely sparse population of its political unit in the

HIERARCHY OF CENTRAL PLACES IN SELECTED MAJOR ECONOMIC REGIONS

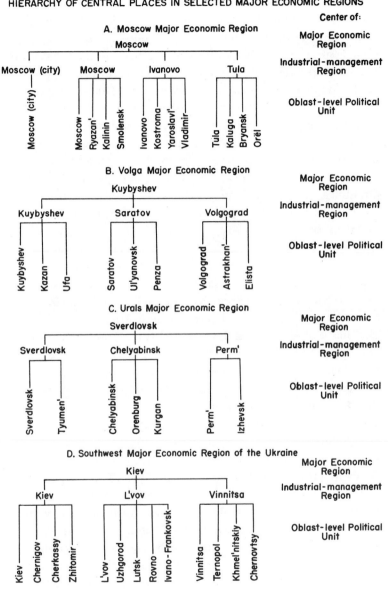

Fig. 26   Hierarchy of central places in selected major economic regions.

arid country west of the mouth of the Volga River, which was organized to give recognition to a small ethnic minority, the Kalmyks. On the other hand, relatively high indices of the other oblast centers reveals strong regional dominance of them within their respective oblasts (or units of comparable level) associated with their positions along the great waterway of the Volga River.

In the Urals a similar hierarchy exists (Table 20, region VII, and Figure 26, sketch C) with Sverdlovsk (3.97) as the center of the Major Economic Region and with 3 centers of industrial-management regions (Sverdlovsk, Chelyabinsk, and Perm'). These in turn have subordinate oblast-level administrative centers: Sverdlovsk with Sverdlovsk and Tyumen'; Chelyabinsk with Chelyabinsk, Orenburg, and Kurgan; and Perm' with Perm' and Izhevsk.

The Southwest Major Economic Region in the Ukraine may be taken as yet another example (Table 20, region XII, and Figure 26, sketch D). Kiev (4.47) is the center; it contains 3 industrial-management regions with centers at Kiev itself, at L'vov, and at Vinnitsa. The Kiev Industrial-Management Region has 4 oblast centers: Kiev itself (for Kiev city and for Kiev oblast), Chernigov, Cherkassy, and Zhitomir. The L'vov Industrial-Management Region has 5 oblast centers: L'vov itself, Ivano-Frankovsk (formerly Stanislav), Lutsk, Rovno, and Uzhgorod. Here L'vov (3.28) is a very dominant regional center and the oblast centers have low indices as the oblasts are relatively small. Vinnitsa, the center of the Podolian Industrial-Management Region has 4 oblast centers: Vinnitsa itself, Chernovtsy, Khmel'nitskiy, and Ternopol'.

The matching of size gradations among cities from the urban systems analysis (Table 19) and the arraying of indices on the size factor in the principal components analysis (Table 20) with the 3-level hierarchy of administrative regional centers in the Soviet Union reveals a few anomalies, i.e., cases in which the largest city is not also the administrative center (Table 20). In the 18 major economic regions there are only 3 such cases, in the 50 industrial-management regions only 6, and in the 146 oblasts only 2. The pairs of centers and larger cities in question are Donetsk-Khar'kov, Tbilisi-Baku, and Irkutsk-Krasnoyarsk in the major economic regions; Ivanovo-Yaroslavl', Kemerovo-Barnaul, Magadan-Yakutsk, Vinnitsa-Chernovtsy, Tselinograd-Petropavlovsk, and Aktyubinsk-Ural'sk in the industrial-management regions; and Kemerovo-

Novokuznetsk and Fergana-Kokand at the oblast level. These will now be discussed in turn.

Donetsk, center of the Donbas coalfield and industrial area in the Ukraine, has been named center of the Donets-Dnepr Major Economic Region in place of Khar'kov, the earlier designated center of this region, even though Khar'kov has a higher index (Table 20, Region XI), and is much larger (Table 19, lines 22 and 23). Dnepropetrovsk also has a slightly higher score on the size factor. This seeming anomaly will be discussed later when the combination of the size and density factors is examined.

In the Caucasus region (Table 20, Region XVI) although Tbilisi has the highest score on the size factor, Baku is much the larger city if administratively subordinate satellite settlements of urban type are included. It is the suggested center based on rank-size analysis (Table 19, line 14). This duality will also be discussed later as an interesting case of interplay of size and density factors.

In the East Siberian Major Economic Region (Table 20, Region IX), Irkutsk, the center, although not as large as Krasnoyarsk, has a higher score on the size factor. It also has a central rather than a peripheral position for the region.

In the Upper Volga Industrial-Management Region (Region II-C), Ivanovo had been designated the center although Yaroslavl' is larger. The 2 cities have about the same index on the size factor. Ivanovo has a somewhat more central location within the region.

In the Kuzbas Industrial-Management Region (Region VIII-B), Kemerovo has been designated the center even though Barnaul (Altay Kray) is slightly larger. On the other hand, Kemerovo is more centrally located with respect to the cluster of mining and industrial cities of the Kuznetsk Basin and also has a slightly higher index on the size factor.

In the Northeast Industrial-Management Region of the Far Eastern Major Economic Region (Region X-C), Magadan on the Okhotsk Sea has been officially designated as center though Yakutsk, capital of the Yakut ASSR, is both larger and has a higher score on the size factor. This region is somewhat artificial as Yakutsk is possibly more tributary to Irkutsk.

Chernovtsy in the Podolian Industrial-Management Region in the southwestern part of the Ukraine is larger and has a higher score on the size factor than Vinnitsa, the center of the region

(Region XII-C). Chernovtsy (formerly Cernăuţi), ancient economic center of Moldavia, capital of Austrian Bukowina (1775–1918) and later of Rumanian Cernăuţi (1918–1940, 1941–1944), remains a strong regional center of Bukovina, but it has a peripheral position with respect to the whole Podolian Industrial-Management Region, both historically and geographically.

In the Virgin Lands Industrial-Management Region (Tselinnyy Kray) of Kazakhstan, Tselinograd has been made the regional center, although Petropavlovsk, on the Trans-Siberian Railroad is larger (Region XVIII-E). The immense governmental agricultural development program associated with the expansion of cultivated area focused attention on Tselinograd, which means virgin-land city (formerly Akmolinsk) and that may be one reason it was designated as the administrative center.

In West Kazakhstan Kray (Region XVIII-F), Aktyubinsk, the center, is a little smaller than Ural'sk but has a much higher score on the size factor; it also has a somewhat more central position since Ural'sk is on the edge of the region and of Kazakhstan.

At the oblast level there are only 2 exceptions to the rule of the largest city serving as the oblast center.

In Kemerovo Oblast, which includes the Kuznetsk coal basin and industrial district, Kemerovo is now exceeded in size by 2 other cities in the oblast, Novokuznetsk (formerly Stalinsk) and Prokop'yevsk, although all 3 are engaged in coal mining and heavy industry. Kemerovo developed central-place functions as the terminal in the region of a pre-revolutionary branch from the Trans-Siberian Railroad, but new rail lines have been built during the Soviet period to the newer, more southern, part of the coalfield where Novokuznetsk and Prokop'yevsk are located.

In Fergana Oblast of the Uzbek SSR in Soviet Middle Asia, Fergana, the oblast center, is smaller than Kokand, the largest city (80 thousand compared with 105 thousand in 1959). Kokand in the lower, western part of the Fergana Basin is the ancient center, mentioned as early as the 10th century; it served as center of the Kokand khanate from the end of the 18th century until the Russian conquest of 1876. In that year the Russians founded Fergana, some distance away in the higher southeastern part of the valley, then called Novyy Margelan (New Margelan), to distinguish it from the then-larger nearby old Margelan. By the time of the 1897 census Kokand was still much larger (81,354 compared with only 8,928 for Novyy Margelan), but Fergana has about doubled its population between each of the succeeding censuses (1926, 1939, and 1959), whereas Kokand has stagnated, declining to 69,324 in 1926, reaching its 1897 population again by 1939 and increasing modestly to 1959. The newer Fergana is more important both administratively and industrially than the older Kokand and is symbolic of external innovations and relations rather than internal traditions.

In spite of numerous individual exceptions, there appears to be some tendency in these major regions toward a ratio of about 3 smaller regions within each larger one. There are 18 major economic regions and 50 industrial-management regions or an average of about 3. The 50 industrial management regions include 146 oblast-level administrative regions, or also an average of about 3 each, although 12 have only a single oblast. In cases in which a higher-order region has only a single lower-order region, special factors are involved and the system may be regarded as atypical; furthermore, it is likely to be somewhat unstable and subject to modification whenever the regions are reorganized.

All three of these levels of economic-administrative regionalization have been the subject of much experimentation and modification through time. Indeed, the second level, the industrial-management regions, had official administrative status only from 1957 to 1965. In contrast, the first and third levels have had almost continuous existence, although with changing boundaries and numbers.

It should be recognized that these factor scores on the city characteristics associated with size are based on a limited number of variables (16 of which were significant for this factor) for which data could be gathered by the author for the whole universe of 1,247 cities studied. In actual decisions within the Soviet Union on administrative organization and reorganization, the planners doubtless have an enormous body of far more refined data for many more relevant characteristics and considerations; this is doubtless especially the situation in individual cases that may be subject to special study.

LOW-ORDER REGIONAL CENTERS: SUB-OBLAST INTER-RAYON CENTERS AND RAYON CENTERS

Within each of the 146 oblast or similar administrative units a hierarchy of lesser centers also exists. Between the 2,959 rayon centers and the 146 oblast centers there typically are a number of intra-oblast inter-rayon centers serving a number of rayons. They do not have legal or official administrative status but in history and in trade they have served as regional centers at the sub-oblast level. Their investigation would make a series of interesting projects. Unfortunately, illustration of the type of centers must suffice here. E. V. Knobel'sdorf and G. S. Nevel'shtein, both of Leningrad, have studied the role of this type of city in the Northwest Region, of which Leningrad is the center.[11] Following Nevel'shtein (with minor modifications), 47 sub-oblast regional centers are recognized in the Northwest Region (Table 21 and Figures 27 and 28). Each of these could be the subject of a fruitful individual study of the historical and geographical factors in its rise and of the activities which serve the respective tributary areas.

Within the Northwest Region, there are thus one great center for the entire major economic region (Leningrad), 4 centers of industrial-management (Sovnarkhoz) regions (Leningrad, Arkhangel'sk, Murmansk, and Syktyvkar), 8 centers of oblasts, 47 centers of sub-oblast inter-rayon regions, and 118 centers of rayons (Figure 27). The ratios of numbers of each center to the next higher order of center for the Northwest Region thus are 4.0, 2.0, 5.9, and 2.5. The individual numbers are unstable because the administrative status of an individual center may change in the future, as it has so often in the past. At this point it may be useful to note the similar ratios for the Soviet Union as a whole: 2.5, 3.1, 4.3, and 4.3.

[11] E. V. Knobel'sdorf, "Raionoobrazuiushchaia rol' gorodov v SSSR (na primere nekotorykh gorodov Leningradskogo ekonomicheskogo raiona)," *Materialy po geografii naseleniia,* vypusk 1 (L. Geograficheskoe obshchestvo SSSR, 1962), pp. 18–60; E. V. Knobel'sdorf, "Goroda Severo-Zapada RSFSR (formirovanie seti gorodov)," in Voprosy ekonomiko-geograficheskogo izucheniia raionov i gorodov SSSR, *Leningradskii gosudarstvennyi pedagogicheskii institut imeni A. I. Gertsena, Uchenye zapiski,* tom 206, (L. 1962) pp. 11–44; G. S. Nevel'shtein, "Naselenie," *Severo-Zapad RSFSR; ekonomiko-geograficheskaia kharakteristika* (M. Izd. "Mysl'," 1964), pp. 135–155. (Akademiia nauk SSSR, Institut geografii, and Leningradskii gosudarstvennyi universitet, Geografo-ekonomicheskii nauchno-issledovatel'skii institut).

The last 2 numbers are only rough approximations, since no country-wide investigation has been made of the sub-oblast regional centers, and it has been assumed for the purpose of approximating the ratios that the ratio from oblast center to sub-oblast center and then from sub-oblast center to rayon center would be about the same. The typical ratios of increasing numbers with decreasing rank in the regional hierarchy thus vary from about 2 to about 6 for each step with some clustering around 3 to 4. The variations in historical development, in geographical structure of the country, and in administrative policy make for a wide range in such ratios and for their very considerable departure from theoretical patterns based on developments under uniform conditions.

The hierarchy of regional centers in the Northwest Region shows a regular gradation both in population and in the size factor, each lower-order center having a smaller population and a lower index on the size factor than the higher-order center to which it is subordinate but a larger population and a higher index than the next lower-order centers which are subordinate to it. Of course, there are some sizable cities which do not fall into the central-place administrative network. Good examples are Severodvinsk, with a population of 78,657 in 1959, virtually a twin city with Arkhangel'sk (Archangel) at the mouths of the Severnaya Dvina River; or Severomorsk (32,234 in 1959) an outport for Murmansk; or Gornyatskiy, a settlement of urban type (28,457 in 1959) which is a coal-mining suburb of Vorkuta. Cherepovets (92,356 in 1959), the iron and steel center at the northern end of the Rybinsk Reservoir, is the largest inter-rayon center and the largest city in the region which is not an oblast center. It is of interest that Cherepovets was a guberniya center from 1918 to 1927, i.e., before the establishment of the present system of oblasts, the construction of the Rybinsk Reservoir on which it is located, or the construction of the modern steel mill which has stimulated its recent growth. It also has the highest score on the size factor (1.22) of any inter-rayon center in the Northwest Region.

Rayon centers, the lowest administrative rank for cities and settlements of urban type in the Soviet Union, are administrative entities legally established with definite well-recognized functions primarily for surrounding rural areas. Their number for the

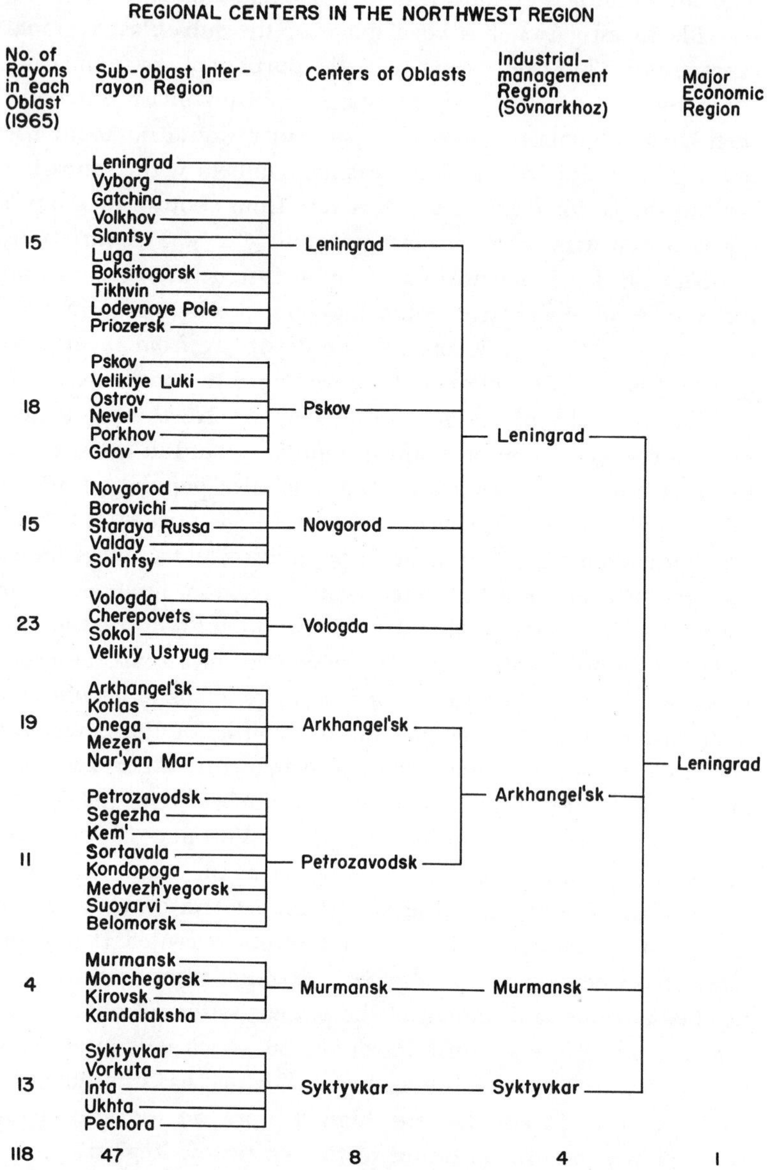

REGIONAL CENTERS IN THE NORTHWEST REGION

No. of Rayons in each Oblast (1965)	Sub-oblast Inter-rayon Region	Centers of Oblasts	Industrial-management Region (Sovnarkhoz)	Major Economic Region
15	Leningrad, Vyborg, Gatchina, Volkhov, Slantsy, Luga, Boksitogorsk, Tikhvin, Lodeynoye Pole, Priozersk	Leningrad		
18	Pskov, Velikiye Luki, Ostrov, Nevel', Porkhov, Gdov	Pskov	Leningrad	
15	Novgorod, Borovichi, Staraya Russa, Valday, Sol'ntsy	Novgorod		
23	Vologda, Cherepovets, Sokol, Velikiy Ustyug	Vologda		
19	Arkhangel'sk, Kotlas, Onega, Mezen', Nar'yan Mar	Arkhangel'sk		Leningrad
11	Petrozavodsk, Segezha, Kem', Sortavala, Kondopoga, Medvezh'yegorsk, Suoyarvi, Belomorsk	Petrozavodsk	Arkhangel'sk	
4	Murmansk, Monchegorsk, Kirovsk, Kandalaksha	Murmansk	Murmansk	
13	Syktyvkar, Vorkuta, Inta, Ukhta, Pechora	Syktyvkar	Syktyvkar	
118	47	8	4	1

Fig. 27 Regional centers in the Northwest Region. Based in part on G. S. Nevel'shtein, "Naselenie" in *Severo-zapad RSFSR; ekonomiko-geograficheskaia kharakteristika* (M. Izd. "Mysl'," 1964), table on p. 143 and map facing p. 141.

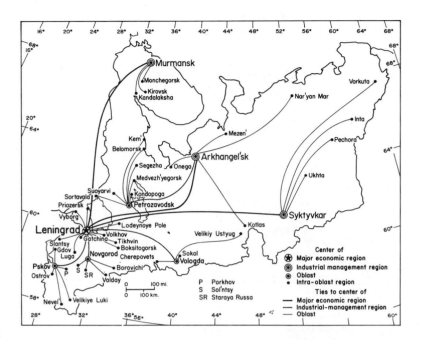

Fig. 28 Lines of suggested subordination of second, third, and fourth-order central places in the Northwest Region. Based in part on G. S. Nevel'shtein, *op. cit.*

TABLE 21

Regional Centers in the Northwest Region

Centers of: Major Economic Region Industrial-Management Region Oblast Sub-Oblast Inter-Rayon Region	Population 1959	Size Factor Score
Leningrad	3,321,196	5.27
Leningrad	x	x
Leningrad[e]	x	x
Vyborg	51,088	0.65
Gatchina	36,752	0.32
Volkhov	36,630	0.38
Slantsy	35,303	0.03
Luga	25,540	−0.12
Boksitogorsk	20,394	−0.33
Tikhvin	18,412	−0.47
Lodeynoye Pole	17,485	−0.51
Priozersk	(15,000)[d]	−

TABLE 21 — Continued

REGIONAL CENTERS IN THE NORTHWEST REGION

Centers of: *Major Economic Region* *Industrial-Management Region* *Oblast* *Sub-Oblast Inter-Rayon Region*	*Population* *1959*	*Size* *Factor* *Score*
Pskov	81,073	1.21
Velikiye Luki[a][b]	58,939	0.18
Ostrov	17,646	−0.69
Nevel'	−	−
Porkhov	−	−
Gdov	−	−
Novgorod[c]	60,669	1.29
Borovichi[b]	44,123	0.02
Staraya Russa	25,409	−0.17
Valday	−	−
Sol'tsy	−	−
Vologda[c]	139,137	1.53
Cherepovets[a][b]	92,356	1.22
Sokol	41,709	−0.02
Velikiy Ustyug	37,026	−0.13
Arkhangel'sk	256,309	2.32
Arkhangel'sk[c]	x	x
Kotlas[b]	39,162	0.27
Onega	21,306	−0.61
Mezen'	−	−
Nar'yan-Mar	(15,000)[d]	−
Petrozavodsk[c]	136,294	1.98
Segezha	19,708	−0.11
Kem'	18,127	−0.69
Sortavala	17,611	−0.63
Kondopoga	16,060	−0.43
Medvezh'yegorsk	15,824	−0.54
Suoyarvi	−	−
Belomorsk	(16,000)[d]	−
Murmansk	221,874	1.90
Murmansk	x	x
Monchegorsk	45,523	0.14
Kirovsk	39,047	−0.03
Kandalaksha	37,045	−0.25
Syktyvkar	64,461	1.66
Syktyvkar[c]	x	x
Vorkuta	55,668	0.94
Inta	45,136	0.15
Ukhta	36,154	0.65
Pechora	30,586	0.59

[a] Former centers of oblasts or guberniyas that have been abolished by consolidation.
[b] Cities considered by Nevel'shtein to be regional centers of near oblast scale.
[c] Also center of inter-rayon region
[d] Estimated population 1965
Source: Based on G. S. Nevel'shtein, "Naselenie" in *Severo-zapad RSFSR; ekonomiko-geograficheskaia kharakteristika* (M. Izd. "Mysl'," 1964), table on p. 143 and map facing p. 141.

country as a whole has changed sharply over time from 1,641 in 1927, reaching a maximum of 4,368 in 1954 as a result of successive subdivisions, falling back sharply to 1,833 on April 1, 1963, as a result of a wave of consolidations, and then rising again to 2,959 on July 1, 1967, as the stringent conditions of consolidation were relaxed.[12] The majority of rayon centers are too small to be included in our group of 1,247 cities and towns of more than 10,000 population; indeed many of them do not achieve the rank of a city or a settlement of urban type.

DISPARITIES: ADMINISTRATIVE CENTERS
WITH LOW SCORES ON THE SIZE FACTOR

Sixteen of the administrative centers of oblasts or comparable administrative units are distinguished by low scores on the size factor (less than 1.00) (Table 20 and Figure 29). All but one have positive scores on the size factor, thus falling above the average for all cities in the Soviet Union even though their scores are unusually low for administrative centers. All had less than 100,000 population in 1959. Furthermore their scores on the density factor are all below zero, i.e., below the average for all cities of the Soviet Union. This suggests that they are located in regions of low density of urban population or in peripheral locations or both. Analysis of the cities confirms this suggestion. Most of these 16 centers lie on the southern or western periphery of the country outside the core area of Russian language. All of them are located in political units that give official recognition to non-Russian ethnic groups. They fall into 3 categories: (a) centers of autonomous republics (ASSR), the principle for the establishment of which was the recognition of an ethnic minority group of relatively small size; (b) centers of oblasts in the Western Ukraine which before World War II were in Poland or Czechoslovakia; these oblasts are unusually small in size, reflecting historical factors; and (c) centers of oblasts in the deserts or mountains of Soviet Middle Asia, sometimes enormous in area but small in population and very low in population density.

Five cities are centers of administrative units organized specifically to give administrative recognition to small ethnic groups.

[12]*SSSR, Administrativno-territorial'noe delenie Soiuznykh Respublik,* ianvar' 1965 goda, p. xix.

Three are in the Caucasus area. Nal'chik, nestled on the northern slopes of the Great Caucasus, is the center of the Kabardino-Balkar ASSR, which as the name indicates includes an area of settlement by two groups: the Kabardinians, one of the numerous but small Caucasian ethnic groups that live in the foothills, and the Balkars, a Turkic group that occupies the high mountain valleys and slopes. Elista, located in the arid eastern part of the North Caucasus region, is the center of the Kalmyk ASSR, home of the remnants of the Kalmyks, a Mongol-speaking group that migrated from Chinese Turkestan in the mid-17th century to the dry steppes west of the mouth of the Volga River. Most of this group attempted to return to China in the 18th century and some were deported to Siberia during World War II. Farther south in the

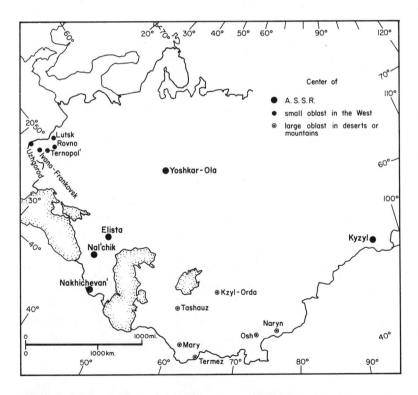

Fig. 29 Oblast centers with low scores on the size factor and the density factor.

Lesser Caucasus, Nakhichevan' is the center of the Nakhichevan' ASSR, a western outlier of the Turkic-speaking Azerbaydzhans set inside the Armenian SSR. Kyzyl, in Eastern Siberia near the border of the Soviet Union and the Mongolian People's Republic in the headwaters of the Yenisey River, beyond the Sayany mountains, is the capital of the Tuva ASSR, the home of the Tuvinians, a small group speaking a Turkic language. The location of the mountain border between the Russian Empire and the Chinese Empire was uncertain in this peripheral and isolated area with the result that political status shifted over time from Chinese sovereignty, to Russian protection, to independence, and then to incorporation into the Soviet Union. And finally there is Yoshkar-Ola, capital of the Mari ASSR, far from the external boundaries of the country, well within the RSFSR, but near the northeastern edge of continuous agricultural settlement in the European part of the Soviet Union. Here live the Mari, a small ethnic group that speaks a Finnic language, a relic of the Finnic people who once occupied much of the northeastern part of Europe before the northeastern wave of settlement by Slavs. All 5 of these relatively small cities have been given special political roles as centers for administrative units of small size and population but of a special type (ASSR) in order to give recognition to small ethnic minorities.

A group of 5 oblast centers in the western part of the Ukrainian SSR that became part of the Soviet Union during World War II reflects the historical persistence or modification of administrative units somewhat smaller than the typical oblast of the USSR. They are centers of 5 of the 6 smallest present oblasts of the Ukrainian SSR. Lutsk (Polish: Łuck) and Rovno (Polish: Równe) although within the boundaries of the old Russian Empire were part of Poland from 1921 to 1939. Ivano-Frankovsk, formerly Stanislav (Polish: Stanisławów) and Ternopol' (Polish: Tarnopol) were in Austrian Galicia to 1918, then in Poland until 1939. Uzhgorod (Czech: Užhorod; Hungarian: Ungvár) was in Austria-Hungary to 1920, in Czechoslovakia, 1920–1938, and in Hungary, 1938–1945.

A group of another 6 oblast centers reflect neither a small localized minority ethnic group nor small administrative regions in territories recently incorporated into the Soviet Union but rather very sparse population in the deserts or mountains of Soviet Middle Asia. Located in irrigated oases amid vast deserts are Kzyl-Orda on the Syr-Dar'ya (river) in southern Kazakhstan, Termez on the Amu-Dar'ya in extreme southern Uzbekistan on the border of Afghanistan, Tashauz near the lower Amu-Dar'ya in extreme northern Turkmenistan, and Mary on the lower Murgab River in Southeastern Turkmenistan. Two, both in the Kirgiz SSR, lie amid high mountains: Osh at the eastern end of the mountain-girt Fergana valley and Naryn in the heart of the majestic Tyan'-Shan (mountains). Three of these oblasts were recently abolished.

Thus all 16 of the administrative centers with low scores on the size factor (and also on the density factor) reflect special circumstances of small size of administrative unit (recognizing small ethnic minorities or historical associations) or small populations (as in areas of very low density of population in desert and mountain regions), or both.

DISPARITIES: CITIES WITH HIGH SCORES ON THE SIZE FACTOR BUT LACKING MAJOR ADMINISTRATIVE FUNCTIONS

Cities without major administrative functions generally have substantially lower scores on the size factor than centers of oblasts or higher-order centers. Of the approximately 1,100 cities and settlements of urban type without major administrative roles included in this study, however, 26 do have scores above 1.00 on the size factor (Table 22 and Figure 30).

Eight of these cities have a score of more than 1.50. Especially noteworthy are 5 industrial centers associated with the steel industry: Magnitogorsk, Novokuznetsk, Nizhniy Tagil, Komsomol'sk-na-Amure, and Krivoy Rog. Magnitogorsk (2.17) on the Ural River in the southern Urals in Chelyabinsk Oblast with a 1959 population of 311,000 was built in 1929–1931 during the First Five-Year Plan as an entirely new city on the empty steppes to utilize the rich local iron-ore deposits. Today it is one of the largest iron and steel centers not only of the Soviet Union but also of the entire world. For long it was the terminus of a branch railroad only and was thus in a relatively isolated position. It may be taken

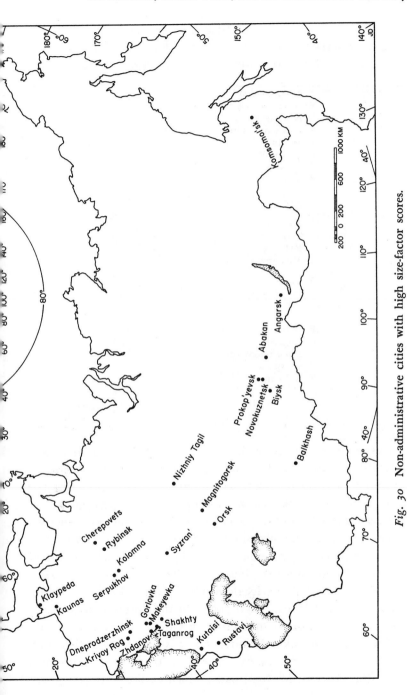

Fig. 30 Non-administrative cities with high size-factor scores.

TABLE 22
CITIES WITH SCORES ON THE SIZE FACTOR ABOVE 1.00
THAT ARE NOT ADMINISTRATIVE CENTERS FOR OBLASTS

1.	Magnitogorsk	2.17
2.	Novokuznetsk	1.86
3.	Nizhniy Tagil	1.77
4.	Komsomol'sk-na-Amure	1.66
5.	Syzran'	1.65
6.	Krivoy Rog	1.59
7.	Gorlovka	1.52
8.	Kutaisi	1.52
9.	Orsk	1.48
10.	Taganrog	1.46
11.	Kaunas	1.40
12.	Zhdanov	1.38
13.	Rybinsk	1.37
14.	Makeyevka	1.25
15.	Cherepovets	1.22
16.	Serpukhov	1.22
17.	Biysk	1.21
18.	Prokop'yevsk	1.18
19.	Balkhash	1.16
20.	Angarsk	1.15
21.	Dneprodzerzhinsk	1.13
22.	Klaypeda	1.12
23.	Kolomna	1.11
24.	Shakhty	1.10
25.	Rustavi	1.08
26.	Abakan	1.05

as a type case of a large modern industrial city founded to utilize a localized resource rather than to serve as a central place for a surrounding rural territory. Novokuznetsk (1.86) (formerly Stalinsk) in the Kuznetsk coal basin (Kuzbas) in Western Siberia (at the eastern terminus of the Ural-Kuznetsk Combine) in Kemerovo Oblast is actually the biggest city in its oblast with a 1959 population of 377,000. It, too, is an industrial city with a large iron and steel plant and associated industries, dating also from the First Five-Year Plan, but the localized resource is coking coal rather than iron ore. Nizhniy Tagil (1.77), in the northern part of the Ural industrial district in Sverdlovsk Oblast, is also a large city (338,500 in 1959); like Magnitogorsk it is located on a rich iron-ore deposit but in contrast by virtue of the presence of local forests (and thus charcoal for fuel) had a much earlier start (1725). Although important in the production of iron and steel from local ore, it has a much more mature industrial development with relatively large steel-using industries such as machinery and railroad cars. Komsomol'sk-na-Amure (1.66) in the Soviet Far East on the lower Amur River is a new city, built in the 1930s for the production of iron and steel and machinery. Krivoy Rog (1.59) in the Ukraine west of Dnepropetrovsk is one of the world's great centers for the mining of iron ore (dating from 1881), with associated iron and steel mills and machinery works. It is the source of iron ore that supplies many blast furnaces in other centers not only in the Donets Basin in the Ukraine but also in the people's democracies (Poland and the German Democratic Republic). The other 3 non-administrative cities with high scores on the size factor are Syzran', Gorlovka, and Kutaisi, 3 very different types of cities. Syzran' (1.65) on the Volga River, below and west of Kuybyshev, the oblast center, is an old Volga River station but has become a large city since the development of the Volga-Ural oilfields (dating from 1936) and of associated chemical and machinery industries. Gorlovka (1.52) in the Donets coal basin northeast of Donetsk is also an industrial city, with coal mining, production of machinery for the mining industry, and for the processing of chemicals derived from coal. Kutaisi (1.52) is an ancient city and old regional and transportation center for the western part of the Georgian SSR (of which it is the second city) with modern industry, especially the production of automobile trucks. The Georgian SSR is not divided into oblasts; if it were, Kutaisi would make an appropriate center for the western part of the republic.

Six other cities not centers of oblasts have scores on the size factor between 1.25 and 1.49. Three are industrial centers in the Donets coal basin (Donbas) or on the shores of the Sea of Azov to the south: Makeyevka the coal-mining and iron and steel center just northeast of Donetsk, the center of the oblast; Zhdanov (formerly Mariupol'), a railroad terminus and port on the Sea of Azov for the Donetsk coal basin with a position between Donets coal and Kerch iron ore, also with a large steel works; and in Taganrog in Rostov Oblast, on the Sea of Azov and also a steel center. Orsk in Orenburg Oblast, in the southern Urals at the bend of the Ural River, is an industrial center with a large non-ferrous metallurgical combine based on nearby ores, oil refining (from the Emba oil-field), and machinery. Rybinsk in Yaroslavl' Oblast on the upper Volga River at the Rybinsk Reservoir, north of Moscow, is a very different sort of city. An old river port on the Volga, it became the junction of river and canal routes eastward down the Volga, south to Moscow, and northwest to Leningrad: thus it became a center of shipping and diversified industries. The last city of this group, Kaunas, in the Lithuanian SSR, is an old and important regional, industrial, and commercial center, having served as the capital of Lithuania from 1918 to 1940, and rivalling the present capital, Vil'nyus, in size and industrial and commercial importance, because of Kaunas' more central location.

Cities with high scores on the size factor are typically central places with functions of a high-order rank in the administrative hierarchy. Aside from Kutaisi and Kaunas most of the group of non-administrative centers with high scores on the size factor represent a different type of city, not central places widely spaced, but rather industrial towns localized by specific raw materials (such as iron ore, coal, or petroleum) or by industrial location factors associated with high accessibility to market or to skilled labor. Unlike the diffuse pattern of central places they tend to have a cluster pattern around specific resources and within historically evolved industrial districts. They suggest the need to examine more closely the density factor, the second of the characteristics revealed by the principal components analysis in Chapter IV.

THE SIZE FACTOR AND THE DENSITY FACTOR

The size factor and the density factor are defined through the varimax rotation of axes produced by the components analysis to be independent of one another and to certain mutually exclusive sets of city characteristics. The size factor is characterized by sharp differences within each region (typically in a rank-size gradation) and only moderate interregional differences, whereas the density factor shows very marked variations between regions but only modest gradations within a region. It is all the more remarkable, therefore, that the centers of the 18 major economic regions show high scores on both size and density factors. Indeed in all cases the centers of the major economic regions have the highest scores within their regions on the density factor (Table 20 and Figure 31). On the diagram the center of each major economic region is like the head of a comet with a tail of centers of industrial-management regions or oblasts with lower scores on both size and density factors. Of course, centers of major economic regions with low densities of population and thus small total population in large

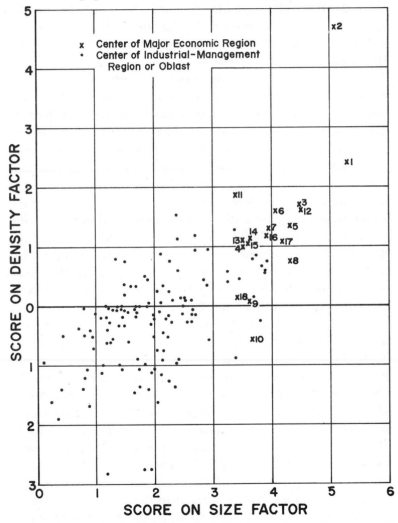

Fig. 31 Scores on the size factor and the density factor for centers of major economic regions and centers of industrial-management regions or oblasts. For identification of cities, see Table 20.

areas have lower scores on size and density factors than the centers of the other major economic regions and even of a few of the larger centers of other densely populated regions of lower rank. Typical of these are Irkutsk, Khabarovsk, and Alma-Ata, the centers of Eastern Siberia, the Soviet Far East, and Kazakhstan (Numbers 9, 10, and 18 in Figure 31).

In the Donets-Dnepr Major Economic Region (Table 20, Region XI), although Donetsk clearly has the highest score on the density factor, Khar'kov has a higher score on the size factor and Dnepropetrovsk has about the same score on the size factor. This duality is reflected in some uncertainty as to which city should be designated as the center for this major economic region, for Khar'-kov and Donetsk have each been reported at different dates to have been chosen for that role. Khar'kov is clearly the larger city and indeed for the years 1917–1934 was the capital of the entire Ukrainian SSR, which includes 3 major economic regions. It is also a transportation center, one of the major railroad centers of the entire USSR. But Donetsk has the key central position in the large and dense agglomeration of coal-mining and manufacturing cities of the Donets Basin, as evidenced by its high score on the density factor, the highest of any city in the Ukraine and the third highest among centers of major economic regions in the entire Soviet Union, exceeded only by Moscow and Leningrad (Table 20, Numbers I, II and XI and Figure 31, Numbers 1, 2 and 11).

The only other case of somewhat equivocal leadership of a major economic region is in the Caucasus (Table 20, Region XVI). Tbilisi easily leads in the score on the density factor but Baku with a somewhat peripheral location challenges it on the size factor. Baku is the fourth largest city of the entire Soviet Union, if its administratively dependent oilfield settlements are included. Initially in 1961 Baku was designated as the center of Caucasus Major Economic Region, but Tbilisi in a more central location was later designated as the center.

Of the 50 centers of industrial-management regions, 44 have higher scores on the density factor than the centers of any of the subordinate oblasts. In 6 cases, however, other centers of oblasts (or comparable units) have higher scores on the density factor than the center of the industrial-management region. In these cases the other centers have more accessible locations with respect to areas of dense settlement outside the industrial-management region (as in Petrozavodsk, Barnaul, Yakutsk, Gur'yev, and Petropavlovsk) or to oases within the region (as in the oblast centers of the Turkmen SSR). In the Northwest, Petrozavodsk, capital of the Karelian ASSR, is slightly higher than Arkhangel'sk, which lies off center in an isolated position in the Far North on the White Sea (Table 20, Region I-B). For many purposes Petrozavodsk surely looks directly to Leningrad, which is nearer and much more accessible than Arkhangel'sk. In Western Siberia Barnaul, center of Altay Kray, has a higher score than Kemerovo center for the Kuzbas and again it probably looks directly to Novosibirsk, which is closer and more accessible (Region VIII-B). In the Soviet Far East Yakutsk has a slightly higher score than Magadan and in any case it probably faces more toward Irkutsk (Region X-2). In West Kazakhstan Gur'yev has a slightly higher score than Aktyubinsk but there are strong peripheral pulls on both (Region XVIII-F). In Central Kazakhstan Tselinograd, the center of the industrial-management region for the Virgin Lands, has lower scores on both the size factor and the density factor than Petropavlovsk, an older center (Region XVIII-E). The last case is the most striking of all, for Ashkhabad, capital of the Turkmen SSR, has a lower density score than any of the centers of the 3 oblasts in the republic (Region XVII-D). It stands in splendid isolation in the desert; separate oblasts have been formed in the republic only where there are oases with several urban settlements. Thus the subordinate oblast centers have higher scores on the density factor than the capital of the Turkmen republic.

It is now time to turn to a more detailed analysis of the density factor itself.

VI.

Density of Urban Settlements

The degree of development of the urban system depends on the level of industrialization of the region.

— N. I. BLAZHKO,
*Vestnik Moskovskogo universiteta,
seriia 5, geografiia,* 1963, no. 6,
p. 24.

CITIES ARE HUMAN ARTIFACTS through which large numbers of people can be brought near one another in order to be able to combine their efforts in production, trade, and social organization. The essence of the city is people in contact with each other. Increasing the accessibility of people to other people is a major role of a city. Potential accessibility is a function of density. The empirical analysis of the characteristics of Soviet urban settlements in Chapter IV revealed that density was the second major underlying pattern of these cities.

POPULATION POTENTIAL FOR THE ENTIRE COUNTRY

What are significant measures of the density and accessibility characteristics of urban systems? Possibly the most valuable single index is the population potential as measured by the formula

$$P = \Sigma \frac{p}{d}$$

where P is the population potential of a point, p is the population of each unit within the area for which the potential is being calculated, and d is the distance of each unit from the point for which population potential is being calculated. Since accessibility among people is a function of the total numbers involved divided by some measure of the distances which separate them, population potential is a measure of the potential interaction or contact among people. It is not a measure of actual contacts in any specific activity but is a highly generalized abstract mathematical statement of the *potential;* for the social sciences it may be a measure as basic as similar measures of gravitational or electrical fields are for the physical sciences. For large populations spread over widespread areas, it may summarize relative accessibility of various points to the people of the whole area better than any other single measure yet devised. Furthermore, insofar as each person represents a consumer, this formula also gives a measure of the market potential for consumer-oriented goods.[1]

Thus, the map of population potential of the USSR is a generalized representation of the relative accessibility of each part of the Soviet Union to the population of the entire Soviet Union (Figure 32).[2]

[1] Chauncy D. Harris, "The Market as a Factor in the Localization of Industry in the United States," *Annals of the Association of American Geographers,* Vol. 44, No. 4 (December, 1954), pp. 315–348.

[2] Data are compiled from the 1959 census of population by oblasts or similar administrative units, the smallest areal units for which populations are published for the entire Soviet Union. Distances are calculated as direct airline distances between points on the globe located at the geographical coordinates of the oblast centers, at which the entire population of the oblast is considered concentrated, except for the home oblast, in which the distance is considered the average distance to points within the oblast.

The calculation of the self potential of the point or oblast from which calculations are being made merits special attention for the over-all results can be substantially affected by the formula used; if the distance from a point to the home oblast were put at zero (i.e., from the oblast center to itself), the potential of the oblast would be infinity and thus mask all other calculations. In some huge oblasts of the Far North, Siberia, or the Far East, in which most of the population is concentrated in a small area, sparsely populated remote sections have been excluded from the area of the oblast or kray used in the calculation of the self potential.

The self potentials of all oblasts were calculated to check their portion of the total population potential, urban population potential, and rural population potential for each unit. For Moscow Oblast, which had the highest population potential in the Soviet Union, 42 per cent of the total was accounted for by Moscow Oblast itself with 10.9 million persons densely congregated in 47 thousand square kilometers. Moscow Oblast also had the highest urban population potential in the Soviet Union; 55 per cent of its total urban potential

As expected, population potential reaches its highest peak at Moscow, the capital and largest city of the country and the focus of the Central Region (Figure 32). The Central Region has about 25 million population of which about 11 million are in Moscow Oblast itself. Furthermore, Moscow is relatively accessible to all parts of the country, especially the areas of denser settlement in Europe. From Moscow outward the population potential declines regularly and steeply toward the relatively empty Far North of the European USSR, somewhat more gradually eastward toward the Urals or westward toward long-settled and densely populated lands, and most gradually of all southward through the Moscow Coal Basin (around Tula) and toward the greatest center of heavy industry in the Soviet Union, the Donets-Dnepr area, and the area of densest rural settlement, the Ukraine.

Two major peaks, one minor peak, and one notable prolongation modify the regularity of this outward decline of population potential from Moscow.

The most important secondary peak of population potential occurs in the Eastern Ukraine in the highly urbanized and densely populated Donbas coalfield and industrial area and in nearby industrial areas between the coalfield and Dnepropetrovsk on the Dnepr River in the west and Khar'kov in the north. This peak occurs in the coalfield and industrial area but it is also relatively near the areas of highest rural population density (to the north and west) and it lies in an area that is relatively accessible to other parts of the European USSR.

Another major secondary peak rises in Soviet Middle Asia extending from Tashkent, the great regional center, eastward through the densely settled fertile intermontane Fergana Basin. A small secondary peak occurs in the irrigated oases of the lower Amu-Dar'ya just south of the Aral Sea.

---

was the self potential within the oblast, which in 1961 boundaries had 8.8 million urban dwellers (6.0 in Moscow itself and 2.8 in other cities of the oblast). In the oblast with the highest rural population potential, Belgorod oblast, however, only 11 per cent was accounted for by self potential. Rural population is highly dispersed within each oblast just as it is relatively evenly distributed over the agricultural regions of the Soviet Union, whereas urban population is both highly concentrated within each oblast and within urbanized areas in the country as a whole.

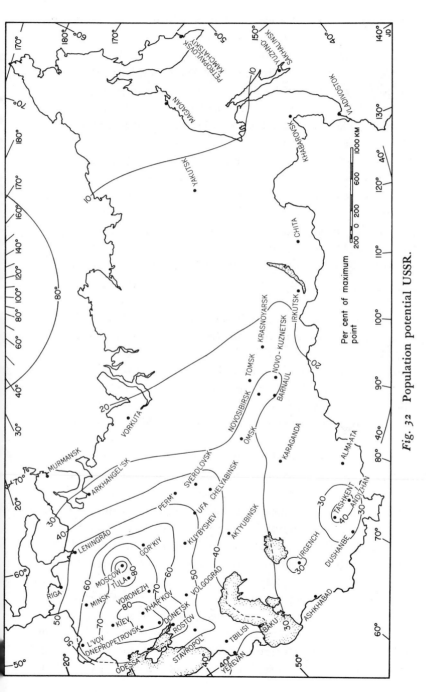

Fig. 32 Population potential USSR.

A prolongation of areas of high population potential extends from Moscow eastward through the Volga oilfields to the Ural industrial areas, the agricultural lands of the Trans-Siberian routeway along the southern edge of Western Siberia and Northern Kazakhstan, and the industrial area of the Kuzbas (Kuznetsk coalfield). This prolongation encompasses 3 major industrial areas: the Central Industrial District (mainly north and east of Moscow), the Urals, and the Kuzbas. Most of Siberia, Soviet Middle Asia, and the Soviet Far East have population potentials considerably less than 30 per cent that of Moscow.

Thus the areas of greatest accessibility to the population of the Soviet Union as a whole clearly lie within the central European part of the country with the axis of maximum accessibility running from Moscow south to the eastern Ukraine. The Central Urals on the eastern edge of Europe have a population potential only 40 per cent that of Moscow. Murmansk or Vorkuta on the northwestern and northeastern edges of Europe have potentials less than a quarter that of Moscow. On the other hand Riga or L'vov on the western margins of the European Soviet Union have population potentials within the Soviet Union of more than half that of Moscow. Their population potentials would be much higher, of course, if nearby lands outside the Soviet Union were also included. Eastern Siberia generally has potentials less than 20 per cent that of Moscow and Northeast Siberia less than 10 per cent.

Population potential reflects a combination of location with respect to nearby concentrations and more general accessibility to the more-distant general distribution of population of the country. By definition the nearer a unit of population the greater its contribution to the potential of a point. For the city of Moscow, for example, the immediate oblast in which the city is located (including the city which is an independent political unit) contains 5 per cent of the population of the country and contributes 42 per cent of the population potential of the city. Other parts of the Central Region with just under 7 per cent of the population of the country contribute an additional 15 per cent of the potential of Moscow city, whereas all other parts of the Soviet Union with 88 per cent of the total population of the country contribute only 43 per cent of the population potential of Moscow city. A small city in the agricultural heart of the country would draw only a modest part of its potential from the immediate oblast or region but would have a high potential because of central location within the more densely populated parts of the country. On the other hand, a large city amid the oases of Soviet Middle Asia might draw a high proportion of its total potential from the densely settled nearby regions and only a small fraction from the relatively distant other parts of the Soviet Union.

The population potential is broken down into 2 very different segments, the rural population potential and the urban population potential.

The potential of rural population reveals a very different pattern from that for total population (Figure 33). The area of highest potential is not near Moscow, but rather in the agricultural heartland extending from Ternopol' and Vinnitsa in the Western Ukraine eastward past Kiev to Khar'kov and Sumy in the Eastern Ukraine and across the border of the RSFSR to Kursk and to Belgorod, where it actually reaches its highest value. From this high area the potential of rural population declines regularly in all directions. Prolongations of relatively high values extend northeastward into the European RSFSR through the Central Black-Earth (Chernozem) Region to the Volga-Vyatka Region and into the Trans-Siberian belt of the southern part of Western Siberia. A smaller prolongation extends southeastward to the North Caucasus. An outlying peak of high values occurs at Andizhan in the Fergana Valley of Soviet Middle Asia, which is separated from the main European area of high rural potential by the broad deserts of Middle Asia (Figure 33). A minor rise occurs in the oasis of the lower Amu Dar'ya south of the Aral Sea.

The urban population potential shows a sharper peak than the total of rural potential, and a sharper gradient outward (Figure 34). Within a few miles in all directions from Moscow the potential drops at least 30 per cent. Adjacent industrial oblasts of the Central Region to the north, east, west, and south lie within the Moscow area of high potential (i.e., at least 60 per cent that of Moscow), but only Tula in the south falls within the area having at least 70 per cent of the Moscow figure.

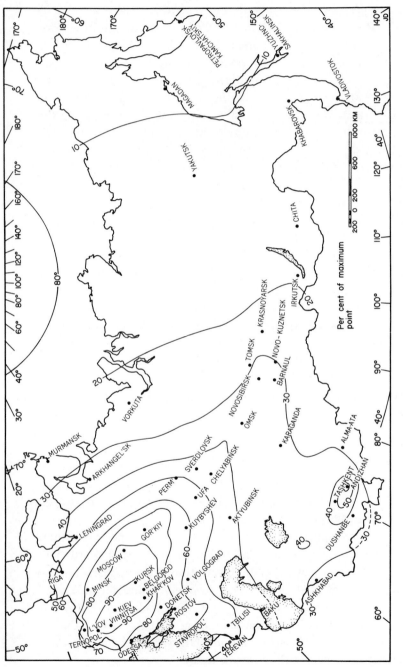

Fig. 33 Population potential for the rural population USSR.

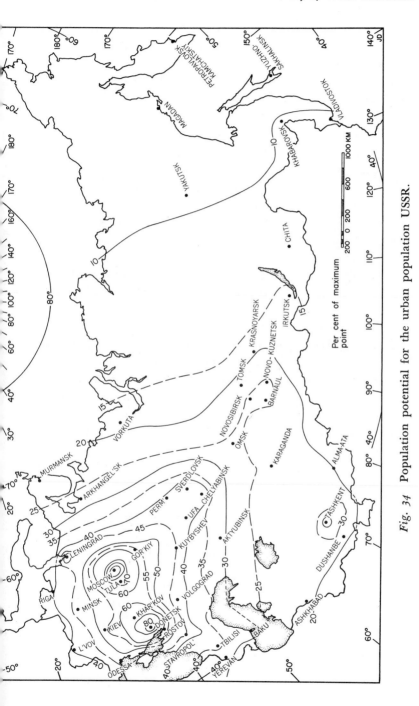

Fig. 34 Population potential for the urban population USSR.

The notable separate peak in the Donetsk Basin at Donbas coalfield and industrial area of the eastern Ukraine attains 83 per cent of the Moscow level. Indeed, this district has the second highest urban potential of any oblast in the entire Soviet Union. The whole Donbas has urban potentials more than 70 per cent of the Moscow level. The black-earth rural agricultural area occupies a saddle between the highs of the Moscow Area and the Central Region on the north and the Donets-Dnepr-Khar'kov industrial area of the eastern Ukraine on the south.

As in total potential, a band of higher potential extends eastward through the Volga petroleum district and the Ural industrial district, reaching the Kuzbas industrial and urban concentration in western Siberia. Secondary small peaks occur around Leningrad in the Northwest and around Tashkent in Soviet Middle Asia.

This is a highly significant pattern since it shows the potentialities for interaction among cities and among urban activities such as industry, trade, and culture. Insofar as trade is concentrated in cities, urban population potential may serve as an indicator of the market potential. On the other hand, since complex industries depend upon other industries for processed raw materials and parts and since industries are distributed in correspondence to urban population, urban population potential is a generalized approximation of the potential relative availability of processed parts and materials for industry for the entire country. Urban population potential is also an abstract measure of the potential intensity of availability of industrial labor. It thus measures on a country-wide basis and in a highly generalized and abstract form many elements of industrial location: market, labor, industrial materials for complex industries, and of the interaccessibility of such elements. However, it does not measure in this form the specifics of an individual industry or of regional or local market.

URBAN POPULATION POTENTIAL WITHIN
MAJOR ECONOMIC REGIONS AND OBLASTS

The data and maps on population potential for the entire Soviet Union reveal the pattern of distribution for the country as a whole. More detailed analysis by smaller regional units is also desirable. For example, the statistical analysis discussed in Chapter IV revealed that the urban population potential for each urban settlement within its own major economic region was the most significant single component in the cluster of characteristics called the density factor, i.e., urban population potential within major economic regions was more significant than within the smaller areal units, the oblasts. For many activities and many urban settlements the principal relationships are not with the entire Soviet Union but rather within the region in which they are located. By the use of data for each urban settlement within each region it is possible to obtain a much finer computational grid and therefore a pattern of greater areal detail, since there are 1,247 data points for urban settlements and only 157 for oblasts or similar administrative units. It was not possible to use urban settlements in calculations for the entire Soviet Union since the complex computations exceeded the capacity of the computer utilized. Nor was it possible to use total population by any units smaller than the oblasts since such data simply are not published. For the finest areal breakdown we are thus forced to utilize population data for the urban settlements alone. In any case, the use of urban settlements for the finer grid of computational points has some theoretical justification in analysis of the interrelations among the network of urban centers.

In the calculations of urban population potential a special problem is posed by the self potential of each city. For the calculations in this study, the population of each city was regarded as being an average of 5 kilometers from the center of the city. The actual values given on the map are in thousands of persons per kilometer of distance. The self potential of a city is thus its population in thousands divided by 5. The internal distance for the larger cities would reduce the height of the peaks of the very large cities on the maps but would not change the pattern in any other way.

On the basis of theory one would expect to find 2 contrasting types of general patterns of distribution of urban population potential, one associated with widely dispersed central-place settlements in rural areas, and the second associated with clusters of specialized-function cities in industrial areas. In the first case, of central-place type cities, much of the urban population potential of each city comes from its own population, since the cities are relatively far apart and there is a rapid distance decay in the contribution of the population of other cities. Especially the major regional centers, which often contain a high proportion of the total urban population of a region, are likely to stand out as isolated peaks of high population potential in a general area of low potential. They may be compared to Fujiyama in their towering prominence. The subregional centers are likely to be isolated lower peaks of intermediate population potential. In the second case of specialized-function cities in industrial areas, the clustering of urban settlements means that many nearby cities and towns enter significantly into the population potential of one another. Plateaus and ridges of relatively high population potential extend over wide areas, above which moderate peaks of somewhat higher population potential rise at the larger cities.

Figure 35, Urban Population Potential of the Three Major Economic Regions of the Ukraine and of Moldavia, reveals both

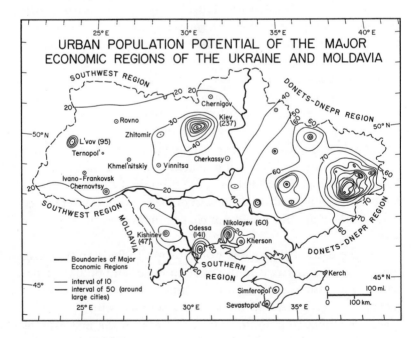

Fig. 35 Urban population potential of the major economic regions of the Ukraine and Moldavia.

types of patterns. The Southwest Major Economic Region, particularly in its western part, is typical of the first type. In the west L'vov stands as a high peak with a population potential of 95, or more than 4 times as great as in nearby areas; and in the east Kiev stands out with a value of 237, 6 times as high as areas outside the zone of immediate metropolitan influence. Lesser regional centers typically rise with values of only 10 or so above the prevailing regional base: Chernovtsy, Ivano-Frankovsk, Ternopol', Khmel'nitskiy, and Rovno in the western part and Vinnitsa, Zhitomir, Cherkassy, and Chernigov in the eastern part.

A similar pattern characterizes the Southern Major Economic Region with Odessa as the great regional center and peak of urban population potential and with Nikolayev, Kherson, Simferopol', Sevastopol', and Kerch as lesser centers. In Moldavia only Kishinëv stands out.

The Donets-Dnepr Major Economic Region (Figures 36 and 37) illustrates the second type of pattern of distribution of urban population potential — that associated with massive clusters of specialized urban industrial settlements and therefore with widespread plateaus and ranges of high population potential. The highest urban population potential not only of this economic region but also of the entire Ukraine is reached in Donetsk (Number 5 in Figure 36), which is far from the largest city of the region or the Ukraine but which is located near the tremendous concentrations of urban settlements associated with coal mining and manufacturing in the Donbas. The peak of urban population potential for the city itself rises from a very high base that extends northeastward from Donetsk to Gorlovka and beyond that to Kadiyevka (Figure 37). Lugansk, the oblast center of Lugansk Oblast, which includes the eastern part of the Donbas, stands somewhat aside from the area of highest potentials but as a moderate peak on its eastern flank. Nearly a hundred closely spaced urban settlements of more than 10,000 population each contribute to this large area of very high population potentials. Khar'kov in the northern part of the Donets-Dnepr Major Economic Region stands on a fairly high base but primarily is a single peak of very high potential reflecting its own large size (Number 1 in Figure 36). Dnepropetrovsk and Zaporozh'ye (Numbers 2 and 3 in Figure 36) along the Dnepr River are major centers of an intermedi-

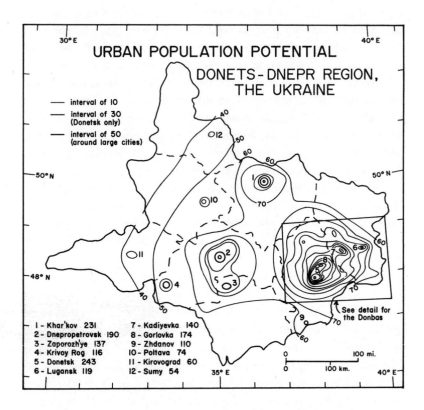

URBAN POPULATION POTENTIAL

DONETS-DNEPR REGION, THE UKRAINE

—— interval of 10

—— interval of 30 (Donetsk only)

—— interval of 50 (around large cities)

See detail for the Donbas

1 - Khar'kov 231
2 - Dnepropetrovsk 190
3 - Zaporozh'ye 137
4 - Krivoy Rog 116
5 - Donetsk 243
6 - Lugansk 119
7 - Kadiyevka 140
8 - Gorlovka 174
9 - Zhdanov 110
10 - Poltava 74
11 - Kirovograd 60
12 - Sumy 54

Fig. 36 Urban population potential of the Donets-Dnepr Region.

ate type, for they are part of a cluster of cities along the river, less numerous and widespread than those of the Donbas but far exceeding any clustering of the Southwestern or Southern regions. Furthermore, like Khar'kov, they rise from a fairly high regional base. To the west stands Krivoy Rog, in an iron-ore district, clearly dominating the lesser mining towns. To the south Zhdanov rises as a peak on the shore of the Sea of Azov.

Another example of the first type of distribution of urban population potential rising to separate and isolated peaks in regional centers is found in the Caucasus (Figure 38). Here the great regional centers and capitals of the three republics of the Transcaucasus, Tbilisi of Georgia, Baku of Azerbaydzhan, and Yerevan of Armenia stand out as lofty peaks of high potential. The oilfield

URBAN POPULATION POTENTIAL
DONETS-DNEPR REGION, UKRAINE

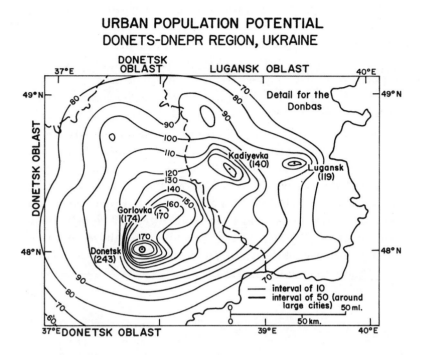

Fig. 37 Urban population potential for the Donets-Dnepr Region: detail for the Donbas.

towns of the Apsheron Peninsula, which juts eastward into the Caspian Sea, are dominated by the great size of Baku. Lesser regional centers are Kutaisi, Sukhumi, and Batumi in Georgia, Leninakan in Armenia, and Kirovabad in the western part of Azerbaydzhan.

Another example of the second type of distribution of urban population potential, of plateaus and ranges in clusters of specialized settlements, is found, as would be expected, in the Kuzbas coal-mining and industrial district of Western Siberia (Figure 39). Novosibirsk, the great regional center for Western Siberia, stands as a single peak of high potential as does, to a lesser height, Barnaul, the center of the Altay Kray. Even Kemerovo, the administrative center of Kemerovo Oblast, which includes the Kuzbas, rises as a somewhat separate peak. The range of high urban population potential extends north-south along the axis of the coalfield and industrial area reaching a peak at Novokuznetsk, with sharp gradients to the east and west but with only a gradual decline northward to Leninsk-Kuznetskiy. A relatively low plateau extends farther northward to Anzhero-Sudzhensk. From the centers of Novosibirsk, Tomsk, Barnaul, and the cluster of the Kuzbas, values drop off in all directions toward the sparsely settled areas of Siberia and Kazakhstan or the boundary of the Soviet Union.

The urban population potential of the Center Major Economic Region is dominated by the massive concentration of population of the city of Moscow. The city itself has over 6 million people, or more than the total population of any other oblast and more than some of the major economic regions. The urban population potential of Moscow city itself towers far above the figures for any other part of the country and dominates much of the Central Region, as is shown in Figure 40. Oblast centers, particularly in the west, rise as individual points — Kalinin, Smolensk, Kaluga,

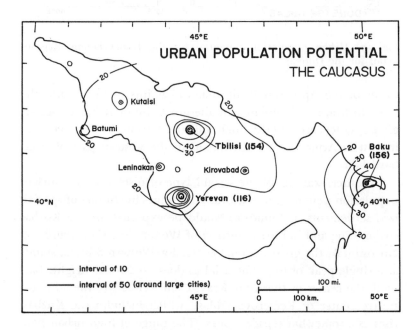

Fig. 38 Urban population potential of the Caucasus.

and Bryansk. On the other hand, plateaus or ridges extend the concentric rings of declining potential outward both south and northeast to encompass other concentrations of urban population, i.e., toward Tula and the Moscow lignite basin in the south and toward Vladimir, Ivanovo, and Yaroslavl', and their industrial concentrations in the northeast.

The dominance of Moscow makes it necessary to break the Central Region down into oblast segments to study patterns of dis-

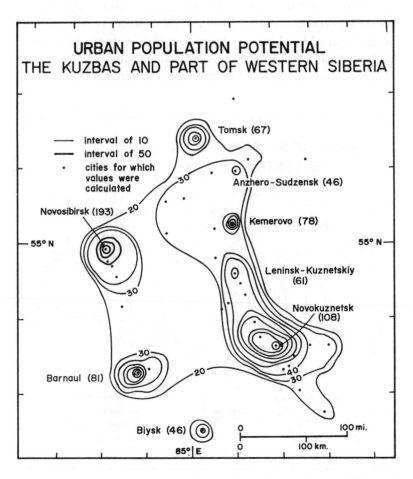

Fig. 39 Urban population potential of the Kuzbas and part of Western Siberia.

tribution of urban population potential. Moscow Oblast (Figure 41) is overwhelmingly dominated by the city of Moscow and the pattern of potential would not differ substantially within the oblast whether calculated for the country as a whole, the European RSFSR, the Central Region, or merely the oblast itself.

The distributions of urban population potential within each of the other individual oblasts in the Central Region are plotted on Figure 42. Two different patterns stand out clearly: (1) the central-place type of widely spaced urban centers distributed more or less regularly over a territory and (2) the clustered pattern of specialized-function cities within industrial districts. The first pattern is typified by oblast centers and other cities to the west, south, and southeast: Kalinin, Smolensk, Kaluga, Bryansk, Orël, and Ryazan', and to the farther northeast, Kostroma, with widely

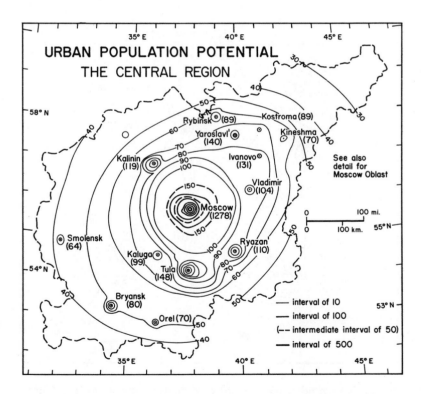

Fig. 40 Urban population potential of the Central Region.

spaced points of high urban potential rising above a plain of low potential. On the other hand, industrial clusters with extensive areas of high urban population potential, each with numerous urban settlements, occur in the south in the Tula industrial and lignite mining region, and in the east and northeast in the old textile manufacturing areas now developed into diversified manufacturing districts in Vladimir, Ivanovo, and Yaroslavl' oblasts.

The Urals present another example of the clustering of specialized industrial towns to produce extensive areas of high urban

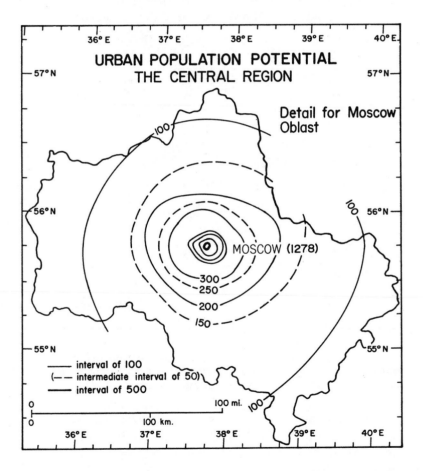

Fig. 41 Urban population potential of the Central Region. Detail for Moscow Oblast.

population potential (Figure 43). An axis of high potential extends north-south on the eastern flank of the Urals from Serov (the metallurgical center) on the north southward through Nizhiny Tagil (metallurgical works and railroad cars) to high peaks at Sverdlovsk and Chelyabinsk, greatly diversified industrial cities and regional centers. An arm extends westward from Chelyabinsk

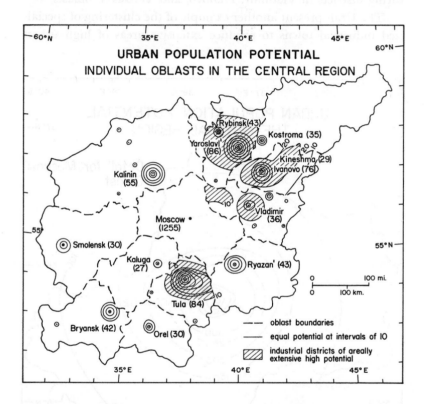

Fig. 42 Urban population potential of individual oblasts in the Central Region. On this map Moscow Oblast has been left blank in order that the other patterns will stand out more clearly.

through and past Zlatoust, the metallurgical and machinery center. On the northwestern flank of the Urals mining and industrial towns are the basis of a similar axis from Solikamsk and Berezniki (the salt, potash, and magnesium towns in a lignite basin) southward through the coal town of Kizel to Lys'va, a metallurgical cen-

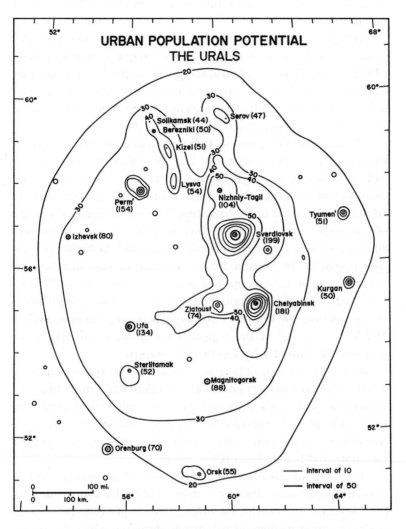

Fig. 43 Urban population potential for the Urals.

ter for quality steels. From these Ural axes the potential drops off sharply in all directions but with individual outlying peaks of high potential at large cities, typically oblast or republic centers, such as Perm', Izhevsk, Ufa, Orenburg, Kurgan, and Tyumen', but including also industrial nodes such as Sterlitamak (oil), Orsk (nonferrous metals), and especially Magnitogorsk, the great iron-ore mining town and steel center which, however, is located in an isolated position.

An analysis of the distribution of urban population potential reveals that the seat of each of the 18 major economic regions (Table 20 in Chapter V) is also the point at which the urban population potential within the region reaches its highest point, with only 2 exceptions: in the Caucasus and in Eastern Siberia. In the Caucasus the urban population potential within the region reaches a very slightly higher point at Baku, the former seat of the region, than at Tbilisi, the present seat, but the difference is not statistically significant (Figure 38). Baku with its oilfield suburbs is larger than Tbilisi but has a less central position. In Eastern Siberia, Irkutsk with a good central position has been designated the seat of the major economic region but Krasnoyarsk near its western edge is a slightly larger city and thus has a slightly higher population potential. In Eastern Siberia because of vast distances between cities, the urban population potential for each city is made up mainly of its own self potential and is thus closely proportional to its own size. In the other 16 major economic regions, and in Moldavia, the seat of the region is the point of highest urban potential and usually by a very wide margin.

In 137 of the 145 oblasts or similar administrative units for which urban population potential was calculated both within the boundaries of major economic regions as a whole and within the boundaries of each individual oblast alone, the oblast administrative center was the point within each oblast where urban population potential reached its highest value.

The 8 exceptions illustrate some types of distribution of urban population potential. Parts of 2 oblasts fall under strong influence of a very large city outside the oblast, namely Moscow. In 3 oblasts coalfield concentrations of urban population produce higher urban population potentials on the coalfields than at the administrative center of the oblast or similar administrative unit. In 3 oblasts the administrative center has a peripheral location on the external boundary of the Soviet Union, the economic region, and the oblast; in each case smaller cities with more central position within the oblast and nearer other parts of the major economic region have higher urban population potentials.

In the Central Major Economic Region in both Kaluga and Vladimir oblasts the cities of these names, which are the oblast centers, stand as small peaks of high potential that do not, however, reach values as high as cities in the parts of the oblast that lie adjacent to Moscow Oblast and thus have high values because of proximity to the great urban agglomeration of Moscow and other cities of that oblast (Figure 40). If the urban population potential is calculated solely within each oblast rather than for the entire major economic region (and thus the population of Moscow and other oblasts outside Kaluga and Vladimir oblasts themselves are excluded), the pattern is reversed and the administrative centers of the oblasts are the points of highest urban potential (Figure 42).

In three coalfields urban population potentials rise above values for the administrative centers of the oblasts. In the Donets-Dnepr Major Economic Region, Lugansk does not attain as high an urban population potential as do several smaller cities in the western part of Lugansk Oblast adjacent to Donetsk Oblast (Figure 37). In this case, however, if the urban population potential is restricted to that internal to Lugansk Oblast, Lugansk, the largest city and administrative center, still has a potential below that of Kadiyevka and some other cities in the great urban concentration on the Donbas coalfield in the western part of the oblast.

The same pattern is repeated in Kemerovo Oblast in Western Siberia, where Kemerovo, the administrative center of the oblast, has a lower urban population potential than Novokuznetsk, which is itself a larger city and also has a more central position with respect to the Kuzbas coalfield urban agglomerations (Figure 39). If the urban population potential is taken not for the major economic region as a whole but only for the oblast, the same relationship remains. In the Komi ASSR, in the northeast part of the European RSFSR, the highest urban population potentials (calculated either for the major economic region or just within the Komi ASSR) occur in the northeast in the Vorkuta coal basin opened during World War II rather than in Syktyvkar, the capital, in the southwest corner of the republic (Figure 48A below).

Three cities have peripheral locations on international boundaries of the Soviet Union. In the Ukraine in the Transcarpathian

Oblast (Zakarpatskaya Oblast), the territory beyond the Carpathian Mountains in the Danube drainage basin, Uzhgorod, the administrative center is located on the edge of the oblast near the international boundary with Czechoslovakia and Hungary; Mukachevo with about the same population and a more central position has a higher urban population potential whether taken for the economic region as a whole (the Southwest Ukraine) or limited to the oblast itself (Figure 48G below). Similarly in the Uzbek SSR and the Middle Asiatic Major Economic Region, Termez on the Amu-Dar'ya River lies on the international boundary with Afghanistan and thus on the edge of its oblast (Surkhandar'ya Oblast) (Figure 48 below). Thus although Termez is the largest city and administrative center of the oblast, it has a lower urban population potential than Karshi nearer other urban centers. This is true whether calculated for the entire economic region or only the oblast. Brest on the Polish boundary has a peripheral location within its own oblast and within the Belorussian SSR and thus has a lower urban population potential within the major economic region (the Belorussian SSR) than Baranovichi located in the eastern part of the oblast and nearer other parts of Belorussia (Figure 48F). However, if calculations are limited to the territory of Brest Oblast itself, Brest, the largest city, has the highest urban population potential within the oblast.

TRANSPORT EFFORT TO REACH THE ENTIRE POPULATION OF THE COUNTRY

The same data utilized in the calculation of population potential make possible a generalized calculation of the theoretical transportation effort needed to reach the entire population, according to the formula

$$T = \Sigma\, pd,$$

where T is the total transportation effort needed to reach the entire population of an area from any given point, p is the population of each constituent unit of this area, and d is the distance of the unit from the point for which transport effort is being calculated. These calculations involve some severe generalizing assumptions, namely that the transport effort is directly proportional to distance and that a perfect transport system exists with all points connected directly by airline distances with all other points. Actual transport effort follows routes by rail, road, water, or air, but calculations by individual transport lines would involve an enormous expenditure of time and would be complex.

The total theoretical transport effort to reach the entire Soviet population from all oblast centers in the Soviet Union according to these calculations and assumptions is depicted on Figure 44. A central area with least transport effort needed to reach the entire country extends from Moscow eastward to the Volga, including Gor'kiy on the Upper Volga and Saratov on the Middle Volga, and southward through the fertile black-earth agricultural belt to the northeastern boundary of the Ukraine, reaching its lowest values in this belt in Tambov, Lipetsk, Voronezh, and Penza oblasts. All this favorably situated area has theoretical transport effort values of less than 5 per cent above the minimum. From this central area values increase regularly in all directions, reaching values 400 per cent higher in the extreme northeast of the country.

Transport effort differs from population potential in being relatively strongly affected by distant populations in the reaching of which a large transport effort is required. The effect of nearby populations is very slight.

Areas of low transport effort have, of course, superb positions for the location of any industrial enterprises which produce directly for the entire population of the whole country. The area of relatively low transport effort (less than 10 per cent above the minimum) includes the Central Industrial District northeast of Moscow, part of the Volga oilfields in the area of Kazan' and Kuybyshev, and part of the Donbas coalfield and industrial area. All points within this rather large area have excellent locations for the all-Union market or for supplying industries serving the entire country. If the experience of other countries is relevant, this is an area in which many industries can be located in small and middle-sized towns, because all such settlements in this area are relatively accessible to one another and thus may produce goods utilized by other factories, which in turn may supply still different factories or be distributed to the entire country. However, the development of smaller towns and cities in the core black-earth agricultural

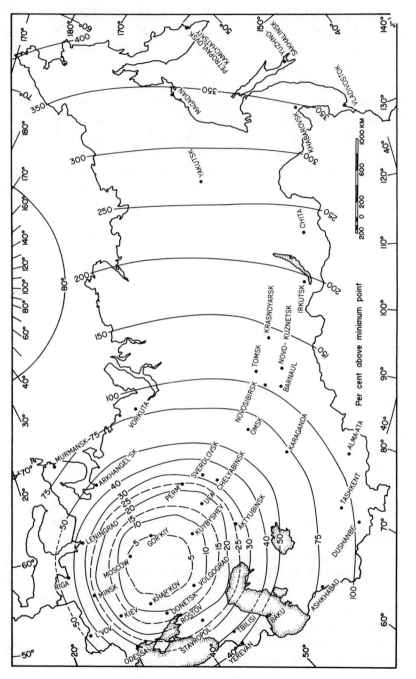

Fig. 44 Transport effort to reach the total population of the Soviet Union.

belt has lagged, although such towns have developed in dense networks in the Central Industrial District on the northern edge of this area, in the oilfields and towns along the Volga in the northeast, and in the Donbas coalfield and industrial district on the southern edge of this area.

TRANSPORT EFFORT TO REACH THE URBAN POPULATION WITHIN SEPARATE MAJOR ECONOMIC REGIONS AND OBLASTS

Since relatively few transport movements extend over the entire Soviet Union it is important to break down the theoretical calculations of transport effort into major economic regions, oblasts, or even smaller regional units. The maps of distribution of transport effort can be considered to represent the total cumulative travel distance from each point within the area to reach the total urban population of that area by rail or road movement, assuming a dense network of railroads or roads that make possible fairly direct movement.

Since the measure of transport effort is strongly affected by the large expenditures of time, labor, fuel, and facilities needed to reach the more distant points within any area, maps of the distribution of theoretical transport effort tend to show low values near the centers of any given area and increasingly higher values toward the outer edge. In areas in which the largest city and regional center is located peripherally, the point of theoretical least transport effort may not occur at the actual center of established transportation facilities.

The point of least transport movement to reach the entire population of any given area is also the center of population, the point at which the area would be balanced on a fulcrum if each person in the area weighed the same and were to stand in his relative position on a giant platform the size and shape of the whole area or on a scale reduction.

It will be recalled that since population figures are not published for units smaller than oblasts we have utilized the distribution of urban population by cities for which data are given (cities of more than 15,000 in the RSFSR and cities of more than 10,000 for other parts of the Soviet Union) to secure the urban population potential of the separate major economic regions and oblasts.

Whereas urban population potential with rare exceptions clearly reaches a towering peak at the seat of a major economic region or an oblast, the point of lowest theoretical transport effort to reach the urban population often is located some distance from the regional or oblast center and largest city. Indeed in 10 of the 18 major economic regions, the point of lowest transport effort to reach the urban population occurs at points other than at the administrative seat or largest city.

Kazakhstan (Figure 45) is a good example of this situation, since the location of the point of least transport effort lies at a considerable distance from the capital of the Kazakh SSR or the seat of the Kazakhstan Major Economic Region. Alma-Ata, the capital, has a peripheral location near the southeastern boundary of the republic and region and indeed not very far from the international boundary of the Soviet Union with the People's Republic of China. Most movements of goods or people have to go in one direction to reach the population of Kazakhstan since there is very little population within the region to the south or east of Alma-Ata. Obviously total movement is minimized if a point of departure is found in which there is a rough balance of movement in all

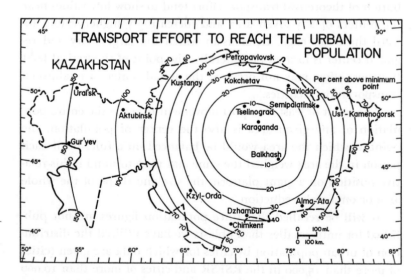

Fig. 45 Transport effort to reach the urban population of Kazakhstan.

directions. In Kazakhstan the point of calculated minimum transport movement to reach the urban population (in the 45 cities and towns of more than 10,000 population and under the rigorous limiting assumptions of direct airline movement) lies at Karaganda, a large urban concentration with a central location. This point lies nearly 900 kilometers (more than 500 miles) to the north-northwest of Alma-Ata. From Karaganda outward all points have higher calculated values of transport effort; the farther away, the higher the value. The central area of low values, less than 10 per cent above Karaganda extends northward to Tselinograd, a railroad junction, and southward to Balkhash, the industrial city on Lake Balkhash. Petropavlovsk, on the northern periphery, Chimkent on the southern edge, and Ust' Kamenogorsk near the eastern edge, all have values only slightly above the figure for Alma-Ata.

Kiev has a somewhat peripheral location for the Southwest Major Economic Region in the Ukraine, but by virtue of its very large size plays a substantial role in transport costs to urban centers from any other part of the region (Figure 46). Thus the area of calculated least transport effort for this region lies in Zhitomir Oblast, although Kiev and Vinnitsa also have relatively low values, less than 10 per cent higher. From this central area values increase regularly in all directions.

Rostov, the seat of the North Caucasus Major Economic Region, also has an off-center location, but like Kiev, by virtue of its own very large relative size, plays a major role in the region (Figure 47). The point of calculated least transport effort lies in the area between Rostov, Stavropol', and Krasnodar. Values rise in all directions to reach very high levels in the Dagestan ASSR in Makhach-Kala and Derbent, which lie at very great distances indeed.

In other major economic regions, the point of lowest transport effort to the region lies near but not at the seat. For the Volga Region it lies just west of Kuybyshev but within Kuybyshev Oblast. For the Urals Region it lies just west of Sverdlovsk but within Sverdlovsk Oblast. For the Western Siberian Region it lies just southeast of Novosibirsk (toward the Kuzbas) but within Novosibirsk Oblast. For the Eastern Siberian Region it lies northwest of Irkutsk but within Irkutsk Oblast. For the Donets-Dnepr

Major Economic Region it lies northwest of Donetsk but within Donetsk Oblast. For the Caucasus it lies southeast of Tbilisi but still within the Georgian SSR. For Soviet Middle Asia it lies south of Tashkent but still within Tashkent Oblast.

In the other 8 major economic regions the point of calculated lowest transport effort to reach the urban population of the region, and thus also the center of population for the region, lies in the administrative seat of the region, which in each case is also the largest city: Leningrad in the Northwest Region, Moscow in the Central Region, Gor'kiy in the Volga-Vyatka Region, Voronezh in the Central Black-Earth Region, Khabarovsk in the Far Eastern Region, Odessa in the Southern Region in the Ukraine, Riga in the Baltic Region, and Minsk in Belorussia. In Moldavia, not included in any major economic region, Kishinëv, the capital and largest city, is also at the point of least transport effort and the center of population.

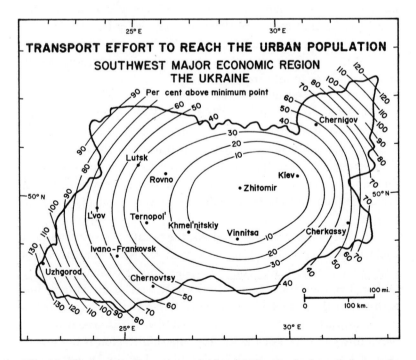

Fig. 46 Transport effort to reach the urban population of the southwest major economic region of the Ukraine.

Of the 145 oblasts or comparable units for which analyses were
made of the distribution of theoretical transport effort to the urban population within each unit (under the limiting conditions
and assumptions already stated), 129, or the overwhelming majority, were characterized by a symmetrical pattern in which the
administrative center was the point of lowest transport effort to
reach the urban population of the unit, reflecting both central location and size primacy of the administrative center. Indeed, in
many cases the boundaries of the oblasts have developed around a
leading city, roughly halfway between it and other similar cities;
thus it might be more accurate to say not that the administrative
seat of an oblast is located centrally within a given oblast but

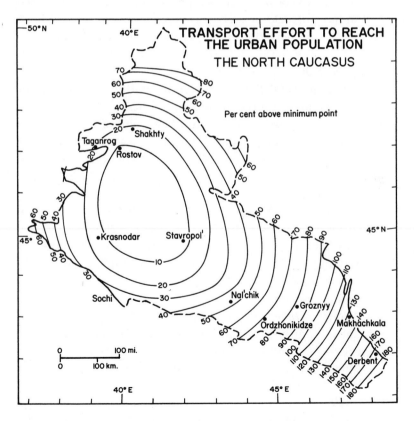

Fig. 47 Transport effort to reach the urban population of the North
Caucasus.

rather that an oblast has evolved historically and administratively around a given center.

In 16 cases, however, the administrative center of an oblast or comparable administrative unit is not at the point of theoretical lowest transport effort to reach the urban population of the unit (again according to the rigorous conditions stated) and thus not at the center of urban population (Figure 48).[3] In all these cases the administrative seats occupy not a central position but a peripheral location, often on a bounding river or coast, at a gateway from outside the area, or at a point of other site advantage which occasioned the historical development of the administrative center as the leading city of the region. Points of theoretical least transport effort lie between such cities and more central positions within the oblasts or between such positions and clusters of settlements in new coalfields, resort areas, or oases. In many cases, however, actual transportation networks focus on the administrative center and a calculation of movement by existing travel routes would yield a different picture.

In the Komi ASSR (Figure 48A) in the northeastern European part of the country, Syktyvkar, the capital lies near the southeast corner and, as already noted, Vorkuta, the point of highest urban potential, is in a coalfield in the northeast corner; the point of least transport effort for the republic lies between them in a more central position at Pechora, where the single long rail line crosses the Pechora River·

In Kemerovo Oblast (Figure 48M) in Western Siberia the point of lowest transport effort occurs not in Kemerovo but farther south in Kiselevsk in a central position in the cluster of industrial and mining towns in the Kuzbas coalfield just northwest from Novokuznetsk, where the highest urban potential is developed.

In Donetsk Oblast (Figure 48K) in the Eastern Ukraine, Donetsk, the administrative center, lies on the southwestern edge of the great cluster of mining and manufacturing cities of the Donbas coalfield. Consequently, the point of lowest transport effort

---

[3] The point of least transport effort lies in settlements of urban type that are suburbs of the administrative center in Krasnodar Kray in the North Caucasus in Pashkovskiy, an eastern suburb of the city of Krasnodar; and in Dnepropetrovsk Oblast in Taromskoye, a western suburb of Dnepropetrovsk.

(and center of population) of the oblast lies somewhat to the northeast between Makeyevka, the second largest city in the oblast, and Yasinovataya.

In the adjoining oblast on the east (Figure 48L), Lugansk, the administrative center, as has already been pointed out, lies east of the coalfield concentration of mining and manufacturing towns, and thus the point of least transport effort and the center of population lie in the city of Kommunarsk in the western part of the oblast in the Donbas coalfield.

In Irkutsk Oblast (Figure 48B) in Eastern Siberia the point of lowest transport effort is located not in Irkutsk but in Angarsk, a little to the northwest toward the other urban settlements and coalfield towns strung along the Trans-Siberian Railroad. Irkutsk lies in the extreme southeast near Lake Baykal, which is the boundary of the administrative unit.

In the Maritime (Primorskiy) Kray (Figure 48D), the point of least transport effort occurs not at Vladivostok, the kray center, but a little to the north in Artëm (a coal-mining town), toward the other settlements in the kray; the port of Vladivostok lies at the southern edge of the administrative unit on the Sea of Japan.

In Stavropol' Kray (Figure 48N) in the North Caucasus the point of lowest transport effort lies not in Stavropol', the kray center, which has a gateway but peripheral position near the northwest corner of the more densely settled parts of the kray but in a cluster of urban settlements and mineral spas, Yessentuki, Pyatigorsk, Kislovodsk, and Mineral'nyye Vody in the south-central part of the kray on the edge of the Caucasus Mountains.

In the Transcarpathian (Zakarpatskaya) Oblast (Figure 48G) in the Western Ukraine, the point of lowest transport effort, as the point of highest urban potential, lies in Mukachevo, which has a more central position than Uzhgorod, the administrative center, near the border with Czechoslovakia and Hungary.

In Brest Oblast (Figure 48F) in Belorussia, Brest, the administrative center, lies on the Polish boundary on the western edge of the oblast and thus the point of least transport effort lies to the east in a more central position at Kobrin.

As already pointed out in the case of urban population potential in Surkhandar'ya Oblast (Figure 48-O) in Soviet Middle Asia, Termez, the administrative center, lies on the southern edge (on

218

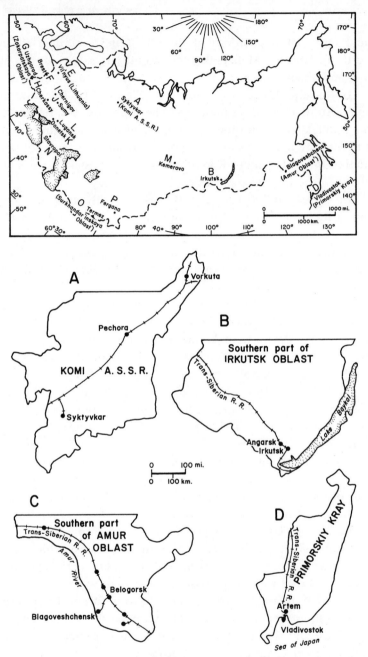

Fig. 48 Oblasts or comparable administrative units in which centers are not at point of least transport effort to reach the urban population of the oblast.

the border with Afghanistan); the point of lowest transport effort thus occurs between Karshi and Shakhrisyabz, in the north of the oblast where more of the population is concentrated.

In Lithuania (Figure 48E), Vil'nyus, the capital, has a peripheral position and thus the point of lowest transport effort of the republic lies in Kaunas, the former capital, in a more central location.

In Soviet Middle Asia in Fergana Oblast (Figure 48P) in the beautiful mountain-girt Fergana basin, Fergana, the administrative center of the oblast, has a peripheral position on the southern edge of the basin and thus the point of lowest transport effort lies in Margelan somewhat to the north in a more central location.

In Cherkassy Oblast (Figure 48H) in the Central Ukraine, Cherkassy, the administrative center lies on a reservoir on the Dnepr River but most of the oblast extends southwestward from the river and thus the point of lowest calculated transport effort lies to the southwest in a more central position between Smela and Gorodishche.

In Amur Oblast (Figure 48C) in the Far East Blagoveshchensk has a peripheral position on the Amur River, so the point of least transport effort lies to the north in a central position at Belogorsk, the rail junction for the branch line to Blagoveshchensk from the main Trans-Siberian Railroad along which most of the urban settlements of the oblast are strung to the northwest or the southeast.

Finally, in the northern part of the Ukraine in Sumy Oblast (Figure 48J) the point of least transport effort lies between Belopol'ye and Vorozhba, to the northwest of Sumy, the administrative center of the oblast. Chernigov, the administrative center of adjacent Chernigov Oblast (Figure 48I) lies in the western part of its administrative unit and thus the point of least transport effort occurs at Nezhin, to the southeast in a more central position.

EFFECT OF ASSOCIATION WITH THE
EUROPEAN PEOPLE'S DEMOCRACIES

Substantial economic flows between the Soviet Union and the European people's democracies, that is the countries of the Council for Mutual Economic Assistance (CMEA, also called Comecon), lead to the interesting question as to what would be the effect of the economic integration of the Soviet Union and 6 countries of CMEA (Poland, the German Democratic Republic, Czechoslovakia, Hungary, Romania, and Bulgaria).

Figure 49 depicts the population potential for the combined area of the Soviet Union and these 6 countries of CMEA. The highest figures for population potential occur not within the Soviet Union but in Silesia (Śląsk) of Poland (around Katowice), in Saxony in the German Democratic Republic (around Leipzig), and around Budapest in Hungary, reflecting the large and dense populations of these western areas (Figure 50). A belt of maximum potential extends from Saxony in the west through Silesia in the center, to the Ukraine and the Donets coalfield and industrial district in the southeast and then to the central black-earth belt of dense agricultural settlement in the northeast, i.e., to Belgorod in the RSFSR (Figure 49). Moscow and the Central Industrial Region of the RSFSR rise as a smaller but sharp peak with the highest figure in the USSR, about 85 per cent the market potential of the maximum in Silesia but not quite attaining the same heights as the Leipzig and Budapest peaks. Tashkent in Soviet Middle Asia is the principal interruption to the regular decline in the level of market potential eastward, northeastward, and southeastward.

The economic integration of the Soviet Union with the European countries of CMEA also tends to exert a westward pull on the points of low transport effort to reach the entire unified market (Figure 51). Within the Soviet Union alone the tremendous distances to the Eastern regions exert a powerful eastward component to the point of lowest transport effort, which occurs at Tambov 400 kilometers southeast of Moscow (Figure 44). The people's democracies to the west, although not as distant, have relatively large populations and thus impart a strong westward pull on the point of lowest transport effort, which for the combined area occurs in the northern Ukraine near the border with Belorussia and the RSFSR in the oblasts of Chernigov and Sumy, some 600 kilometers southwest of Moscow, and just to the northeast of Kiev, the capital of the Ukraine (Figure 51). Kiev, the mother of Russian cities, thus once again occupies a central position, which it had in the eastern Slavic realms before the conquest by the Mongols in

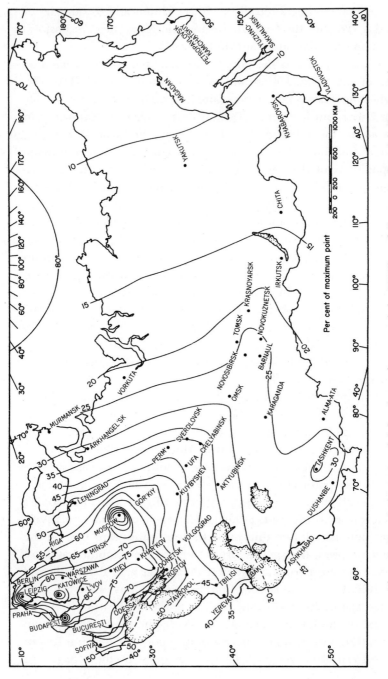

Fig. 49 Population potential for the entire area of the USSR and European People's Democracies.

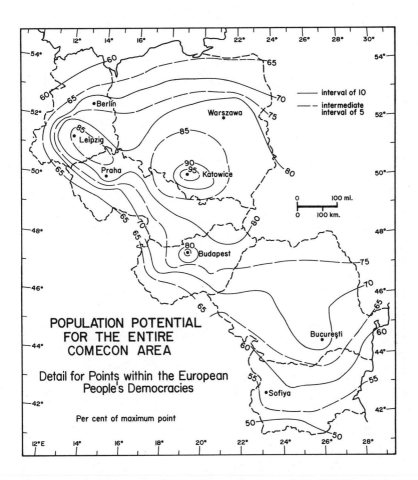

Fig. 50 Population potential for the entire area of the USSR and the European People's Democracies: detail for points within the European People's Democracies.

1240. The relations of the Soviet Union and the European countries of Comecon is reciprocal. On the one hand, the tremendous total size and population of the Soviet Union make possible its dominant role in the associated planning area. On the other hand, the people's democracies in Europe though small in area have a large combined population at high density that exerts a strong westward pull on the location of any industrial enterprise designed to serve the entire Comecon area. The area of relatively

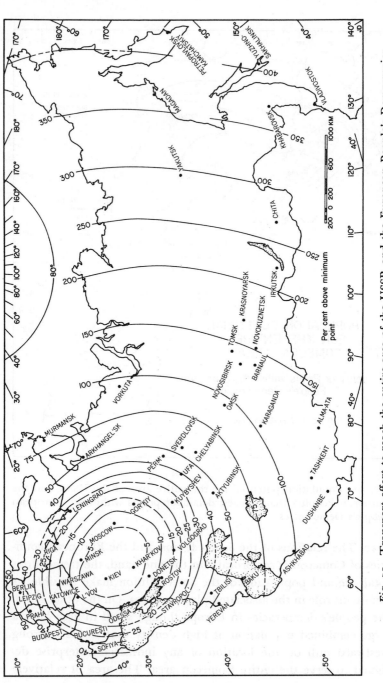

Fig. 51 Transport effort to reach the entire area of the USSR and the European People's Democracies.

low transport effort to reach the entire combined area is itself rather large and includes the Ukraine and Belorussia and extends northeastward to Moscow and the Central Industrial District. But to reach this combined gigantic market area takes no more transport effort from Warsaw than from Gor'kiy, or from Budapest than from Kuybyshev, or from Leipzig than from Ufa. To reach the population of this combined area from the Urals requires more transport effort than from any point in the people's democracies of Europe.

VII.

Growth of Cities: Long-Range Trends

Considering the fact that serfdom was abolished only in 1861, and that the era of industrialism scarcely opened before the seventies, it is to be expected that the growth of the urban population [in Russia] has been comparatively recent.

— A. F. WEBER,
The growth of cities in the nineteenth century: a study in statistics, 1899, p. 106.

The last half century of Tsarist rule saw not only the spectacular growth of particular cities but also the rapid multiplication of the numbers of sizeable cities on the map of Russia. Whereas there were estimated to be only 15 cities of over 50,000 in the Russian Empire in 1870, there were a hundred such cities by the eve of the First World War.

— DAVID J. M. HOOSON
in *Urbanization and its problems: essays presented to E. W. Gilbert,* edited by R. P. Beckinsale and J. M. Houston, 1968, p. 259.

THE MOST ANCIENT URBAN SETTLEMENTS in the present territory of the Soviet Union were non-Slavic centers along the dry southern margins of the country, such as the oasis towns in Middle Asia, the mountain towns of Transcaucasia, and the Greek cities along the northern shore of the Black Sea.[1]

---

[1] See A. L. Mongait, *Arkheologiia v SSSR* (M. Izd. AN SSSR, 1955), or conveniently in English as *Archeology in the U.S.S.R.* (Harmondsworth, Middlesex: Penguin Books, 1961), translated and adapted by M. W. Thompson.

The first Slavic towns appeared about the 9th century A.D. on river routeways in the wooded western part of the country.[2] More than a score of these cities are mentioned in the chronicles of the period, including Novgorod, Smolensk, and Kiev on the key Baltic-Black Sea water route via the Volkhov, Lovat', and Dnepr rivers, and Pskov and Chernigov on nearby streams, and Murom and Rostov, farther east between the Oka and Volga rivers.

Kiev near the edge of the wooded steppe and on the Dnepr River became the capital of Rus, its leading city, and the "mother of Russian cities." Its primacy, however, was dealt a decisive blow through its destruction in 1240 by the steppe-based Mongols.

The Slavic cities farther to the north in the mixed forest zone were better protected from raids by the nomadic steppe dwellers. The northwestern group of cities fell under the strong leadership of Novgorod (called Novgorod Velikiy, or Novgorod the Great, during this period). An eastern group of cities in the wooded lands between the Volga and Oka rivers were divided among a number of small principalities, no one of which was dominant in the early period. None lay on a major river route comparable at that time to the one through Novgorod and Kiev. Each town was the center of a local district only. Rostov, Suzdal', Vladimir, Ryazan', and Murom were major early centers.

Moscow was first mentioned in 1147, when it lay within the realm of Rostov-Suzdal' with its 2 parallel centers. It had a superb combination of defensive site with central location for river routeways. It also had aggressive leadership. In 1328 it superseded Vladimir as the chief seat of sovereignty for at this time it gained the right to collect from the other principalities the tribute for the Mongols (the Golden Horde). The seat of the church was transferred to Moscow. The city took the lead in the expanding unified Russian state, capturing the lands of Novgorod the Great to the west and north in the 1470s, throwing off the Mongol yoke in 1480, conquering Kazan' and Astrakhan' to the east in the 1550s, and thus opening the way for rapid expansion to the Urals, Siberia,

[2] See M. N. Tikhomirov, *Drevnerusskie goroda*, 2nd ed. (M. Gospolizdat, 1956), available in English as *The towns of ancient Rus* (M. Foreign Language Publishing House, 1959). For subsequent periods see W. H. Parker, *An historical geography of Russia* (London: University of London Press, 1968), pp. 62–64 (1200), 74–76 (1400), 91–92, 95–97 (1600) and 129–136 (1725).

and the Far East. During this period cities were primarily administrative and military centers with associated trade and handicrafts.

Peter the Great transferred the capital from Moscow to St. Petersburg in 1713 and for 2 centuries St. Petersburg played the central political-administrative role, though Moscow, more centrally located, continued to play a special role.

Peter also greatly accelerated the development of industrial towns.[3] Tula, south of Moscow, was already a metal-working center, but the establishment of a government arsenal there by Peter stimulated its industrial development and growth. A whole series of new industrial settlements arose in the Urals based on mining of metalliferous ores, smelting (with charcoal from uncleared forests that provided a much better fuel supply than the nearly exhausted forests near Tula), metal working, and gun manufacturing. Yekaterinburg (now Sverdlovsk) with its mint became the main center for this district. St. Petersburg itself became an entry point for foreign workers, foreign raw materials, and new ideas and industries. The Moscow area became the Central Industrial District with the rise of textile manufacturing in Moscow itself, and in Vladimir, Yaroslavl', and Ivanovo.

In the latter part of the 19th century new industrial towns arose in two districts at sources of fuel supply. In the Donets Basin (Donbas) in the south, coalfields began to be exploited with the rise of new methods of smelting pig iron by the use of coke and with the building of railroads that consumed enormous quantities of iron and later of steel and transported coal long distances. The petroleum deposits around Baku on the western shore of the Caspian Sea made the region for a time the world's leading producer. Foreign capital played an important role in making possible the rapid rate of development of industries and cities in these districts.

We shall now examine in more detail the trends in growth of cities over the last century and a half noting (1) trends of urban growth 1811–1967, (2) the 20 largest cities at approximately half-

---

[3] See P. I. Liashchenko, *Istoriia narodnogo khoziaistva SSSR* (M. 1939), 2nd ed. (M. Gospolitizdat, 1947–1948), 2 vol.; 3rd ed., 1952, 3 vols.; 4th ed., 1956. First edition in English as Peter I. Lyashchenko, *History of the national economy of Russia to the 1917 Revolution* (New York: Macmillan, 1949).

century intervals: 1811, 1867, 1915, and 1967, (3) the growth pattern of individual cities during the last century 1867–1967, and (4) regional contrasts in growth of urban population and in degree of urbanization in the period between the first census of 1897 and the last one of 1959. The burgeoning of urban settlements in the Soviet period is treated in Chapter VIII.

GROWTH OF URBAN POPULATION 1811–1967
AND FORECAST 1967–1980

Urban population increased at moderate rates in the first half of the 19th century and then began to accelerate in the second half with the building of railroads (as in Khar'kov), the development of a massive grain-export trade (as in Odessa), the development of coal mining and an iron and steel industry based on coking coal (as in Yuzovka, later Stalino, now Donetsk in the Donbas), the expansion of the textile industries in the cities and industrial villages of the Central Industrial District northeast of Moscow, and the rise of Baku as an oil center. Urban growth was at high rates on the eve of World War I. Then came the terrible destruction of World War I and the Civil War and cities suffered sharp losses in population. Recovery in the 1920s was followed by a series of Five-Year Plans of industrialization which resulted in record rates of urban growth during the intercensal period 1926–1939 particularly for centers of heavy industry. Industrial giants such as Magnitogorsk were created in the empty steppe. Then came the heavy destruction of World War II, which reduced the rate of urban growth, particularly in the western areas that were occupied. The post-war era has witnessed renewed rapid urban growth.

The urban population of the Soviet Union has increased from about 2.8 million to 128.0 million over the last century and a half (from 1811 to 1967) (Tables 23 and 24 and Figure 52).[4] This is a 46-fold increase.

---

[4] See A. G. Rashin, "Dinamika chislennosti i protsessy formirovanniia gorodskogo naseleniia Rossii v XIX i nachale XX vv.," razdel 2 in his *Naselenie Rossii za 100 let (1811–1913 gg.); statisticheskie ocherki* (M. Gosstatizdat, 1956), pp. 85–148. For accounts of individual cities and of geographical factors in the rise of cities in this period see W. H. Parker, *An historical geography of Russia*, pp. 198–208 (1800), 261–265 (1861), 314–318 (1914), and 343–345 (Soviet period), and David J. M. Hooson, "The growth of cities in pre-Soviet Russia," chapter X in *Urbanization and its problems: essays in honour of E. W. Gilbert*, R. P. Beckinsale and J. M. Houston, eds. (Oxford: Basil Blackwell, 1968), pp. 254–276.

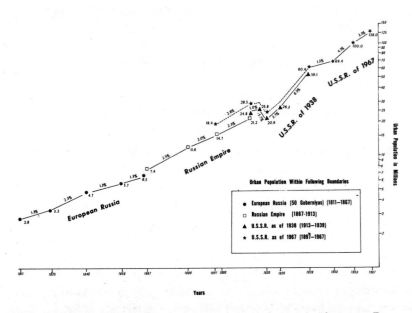

Fig. 52 Urban population and average annual per cent increase, Russia and the Soviet Union, 1811–1967. See tables 23–25.

Analysis of the process of this growth is complicated because of the fluctuating boundaries of the country, the irregular periods between dates of censuses or estimates, and variations in the definition of "urban."

TABLE 23

URBAN POPULATION, EUROPEAN RUSSIA
(50 Guberniyas excluding Poland and Finland),
1811–1867

Year	(Thousands)
1811	2,765
1825	3,329
1840	4,666
1856	5,684
1867	6,543

Source: 1811, 1825, 1840, and 1856: A. G. Rashin, *Naselenie Rossii za 100 let (1811–1913 gg.): statisticheskie ocherki* (M. Gosstatizdat, 1956), p. 86. And 1867: Russia. Tsentral'nyi Statisticheskii Komitet. *Statisticheskii Vremennik Rossiiskoi Imperii*, seriia 2, vypusk 1. (Sanktpeterburg, 1871), p. 30.

Figure 52 shows 4 different series based on 4 different areal delimitations of the country. A serious effort has been made to make the figures within each of these 4 series comparable. From 1811 to 1867 the data refer to European Russia, i.e., the 50 traditional guberniyas of Russia, excluding Poland and Finland, which had special statuses within the Russian Empire. From 1867 to 1913 the data cover the entire Russian Empire, including the Caucasus, Middle Asia, Siberia, and the Far East, but exclude again Poland (the ten Vistula Provinces) and the Grand Duchy of Finland. The first series for the Soviet Union covers the years 1917 to 1939 within the boundaries of the Soviet Union as of 1938 (or up to September 17, 1939), before the beginning of the Soviet territorial expansion of World War II. An estimate for 1913 for this same territory has been included. The fourth series is for the Soviet Union in its present boundaries and covers the years 1939–1967 with estimates for 1897 and 1913 for the corresponding territory.

The Soviet Union has not had decennial censuses or even regular censuses. There have been only 4 published general censuses covering the entire country: 1897, 1926, 1939, and 1959, separated respectively by intervals of nearly 30 years, just over 12 years (the 1926 census was in December), and 20 years. Earlier, intermediate, and later years are covered by estimates (Table 24). In order to facilitate comparisons over these irregular years percentage increase figures have been calculated not only for the individual periods but also per decade and per annum (Table 25 and Figure 52).

Finally there are variations in definition of urban. During the Tsarist period many large industrial settlements did not have urban status. During the Soviet period these were made cities or settlements of urban type. Thus the 1897 figures for the present territory of the Soviet Union (and the present urban definition) are much higher than the 1897 figure for the then territory of the Russian Empire but with the urban definition as of that date.

In general, over this century and a half the growth of urban population has accelerated, not only in absolute numbers but also, more significantly, in percentage increase per annum (Figure 52 and Table 25). Thus the average annual rate of increase in urban population in the first half century (1811–1867) was about 1.5 per cent; in the second half-century (1867–1913), about 2.3 per cent; in the last half-century (1917–1967), about 2.8 per cent.

TABLE 24
URBAN, RURAL, AND TOTAL POPULATION,
RUSSIAN EMPIRE AND SOVIET UNION, 1867–1967

Year	Date	Boundaries	Urban	Rural	Total	Per Cent Urban
1811		European Russia	2,765,000	39,040,600	41,805,600	7
1867		Russian Empire*	7,395,051	66,801,396	74,196,447	10
1885		Russian Empire*	11,630,747	87,019,763	98,650,510	12
1897	Jan. 28	Russian Empire*	14,669,733	101,568,035	116,237,768	13
		Soviet Union of 1967	18,400,000	106,200,000	124,600,000	15
1913	Jan. 1	Russian Empire*	21,248,400	137,694,000	158,942,400	13
		Soviet Union of 1938	24,819,600	114,493,100	139,312,700	18
		Soviet Union of 1967	28,451,700	130,701,300	159,153,000	18
1917		Soviet Union of 1938	25,800,000	117,700,000	143,500,000	18
1920	Aug. 28	Soviet Union of 1938	20,885,000	115,925,000	136,810,000	15
1926	Dec. 17	Soviet Union of 1938	26,314,114	120,713,801	147,027,915	18
1939	Jan. 17	Soviet Union of 1938	56,125,139	114,431,954	170,557,093	33
		Soviet Union of 1967	60,409,216	130,268,674	190,677,890	32
1950	Jan. 1	Soviet Union of 1967	69,400,000	109,100,000	178,500,000	39
1959	Jan. 15	Soviet Union of 1967	99,977,695	108,848,955	208,826,650	48
1967	Jan. 1	Soviet Union of 1967	128,000,000	106,400,000	234,400,000	55
1969	Jan. 1	Soviet Union of 1967	134,200,000	104,700,000	238,900,000	56

* Data on the Russian Empire exclude the 10 Vistula Provinces (Poland) and the Grand Duchy of Finland.
Sources:

TABLE 24 – Continued

1811. A. G. Rashin, *Naselenie Rossii za 100 let (1811–1913 gg.); statisticheskie ocherki.* (M. Gosstatizdat, 1956), Table 56, p. 98.

1867. Russia. Tsentral'nyi Statisticheskii Komitet. *Statisticheskii Vremennik Rossiiskoi Imperii,* seriia 2, vypusk 1. (Sanktpeterburg, 1871), pp. 34–35, 98–99.

1885. Russia. Tsentral'nyi Statisticheskii Komitet. *Sbornik Svedenii po Rossii za 1884–1885 gg.* "Statistika Rossiiskoi Imperii Tom 1" (S.-Peterburg, 1887), p. 15 and 11. Total for the Russian Empire less figures for the Grand Duchy of Finland.

1897. Russia. Tsentral'nyi Statisticheskii Komitet. *Pervaia Vseobshchaia Perepis' Naseleniia Rossiiskoi Imperii 1897 g. Obshchii Svod po Imperii.* Rezul'tatov Razrabotki dannykh ... N. A. Troinitskii, ed. Tom I. (S.-Peterburg, 1905), p. 7.
In boundaries of the USSR of 1967: SSSR. Tsentral'noe Statisticheskoe Upravlenie. *Narodnoe Khoziaistvo SSSR v 1965 g.,* Statisticheskii Ezhegodnik. (M. 1966), p. 7.

1913. Russia. Tsentral'nyi Statisticheskii Komitet. *Statisticheskii Ezhegodnik Rossii 1913 g.* (S.-Peterburg, 1914), p. 57.
In boundaries of the USSR of 1938 and 1967: SSSR. Tsentral'noe Statisticheskoe Upravlenie. *Itogi Vsesoiuznoi Perepisi Naseleniia 1959 goda. SSSR (Svodnyi Tom).* (M. 1962), p. 13.

1917 and 1920. SSSR. Tsentral'noe Statisticheskoe Upravlenie. *Itogi Vsesoiuznoi Perepisi Naseleniia 1959 goda. SSSR (Svodnyi Tom).* (M. 1962), p. 13.

1926. SSSR. Tsentral'noe Statisticheskoe Upravlenie. Otdel Perepisi. *Vsesoiuznaia Perepis' Naseleniia 1926 goda. Tom 17. Soiuz Sovetskikh Sotsialisticheskikh Respublik.* Otdel 1. (M. 1929), Table 1, pp. 2–3.

1939 and 1959. SSSR. Tsentral'noe Statisticheskoe Upravlenie. *Itogi Vsesoiuznoi Perepisi Naseleniia 1959 goda. SSSR (Svodnyi Tom).* (M. 1962), p. 13.

1950. SSSR. Tsentral'noe Statisticheskoe Upravlenie. *Narodnoe Khoziaistvo SSSR v 1965 g. Statisticheskii ezhegodnik.* (M. 1966), p. 7.

1967 and 1969. SSSR. Tsentral'noe Statisticheskoe Upravlenie. *Narodnoe Khoziaistvo SSSR v 1968 g. Statisticheskii ezhegodnik.* (M. 1969), p. 7.

TABLE 25

PERCENTAGE INCREASE IN URBAN POPULATION
RUSSIA AND THE SOVIET UNION BY PERIODS, 1811–1967

Area Covered by Data and Years	Years in Period	Percentage Increase in Urban Population For the Stated Period	Per Decade	Per Year
European Russia				
1811–1825	14	20.4	14.2	1.3
1825–1840	15	40.2	25.2	2.3
1840–1856	16	21.8	13.1	1.3
1856–1867	11	15.1	13.6	1.3
1811–1867	56	136.6	16.6	1.5
Russian Empire				
1867–1885	18	57.3	28.6	2.5
1885–1897	12	26.1	21.4	2.0
1897–1913	16	44.8	26.1	2.3
1867–1913	46	187.3	25.7	2.3
USSR (Boundaries of 1938)				
1913–1917	4	3.9	10.2	1.0
1917–1920	3.6	− 19.1	− 44.4	− 5.7
1920–1926	6.3	26.0	44.3	3.7
1926–1939	12.1	113.3	87.0	6.5
1913–1939	26.0	126.1	36.9	3.2
USSR (Boundaries of 1967)				
1897–1913	16	54.6	31.3	2.8
1913–1939	26	112.3	33.6	2.9
1939–1950	11	14.9	13.3	1.3
1950–1959	9	44.1	50.0	4.1
1959–1967	8	28.0	36.2	3.1
1897–1967	70	595.6	31.9	2.8
1939–1959	20	64.7	28.3	2.5
1939–1967	28	111.9	30.8	2.7
1967–1969	2	4.8	26.7	2.4

Calculated on the basis of data in Tables 23 and 24

These long-range averages can be broken down into shorter periods, which show successive peaks of higher rates of annual increase in urban population: 2.3 per cent per annum for the period 1825–1840, 2.5 per cent per annum for 1867–1885, 3.7 per cent per annum for 1920–1926, and 6.5 per cent per annum for 1926–1939 (Table 25 and Figure 53). For a 70-year period 1860–1930 the Soviet statistician E. Z. Volkov made year-by-year estimates of the total urban population on a comparable territorial base (the

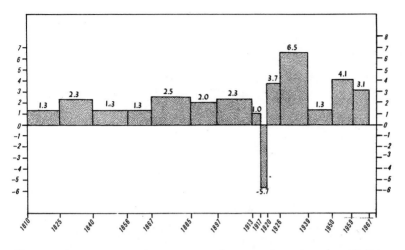

Fig. 53 Average annual percentage increase in urban population, 1810–1967, by periods.

Soviet Union within boundaries as of 1930, with only minor irregularities in 1879 and 1924).[5] The total urban population shows a fairly regular growth each year (Figure 54 top line) and a generally increasing rate of increase per year either on a year-by-year basis (Figure 54 middle line) or with 5-year averages (Figure 54 lower line). Annual data are not available for the years of peak rates of urban growth, 1926–1939, when the average annual rate of increase of urban population was 6.5 per cent per annum (Figure 53). However, it is clear that this peak period started with slower rates of growth, 4.2 per cent per annum for 1927 and 1928 (Figure 54), that the rate increased during the 8-year period from January 1, 1929, to January 1, 1937, with an average rate of increase of urban population of 6.2 per cent per annum, rose further to 6.8 per cent in the year 1937 and reached a peak of 10.9 per cent in the year 1938.[6]

Annual data are again available for the years since 1950 and show a steady increase in total urban population for the years be-

[5] E. Z. Volkov, *Dinamika narodonaseleniia SSSR za vosem'desiat let* (M. Gosudarstvennoe izd., 1930), pp. 239–271. His data cover the years 1850–1930 but his urban data for the period 1850–1860 do not seem consistent with other sources and are thus omitted here.
[6] Calculated from data in *Narodnoe khoziaistvo 1962 g.*, pp. 7–8.

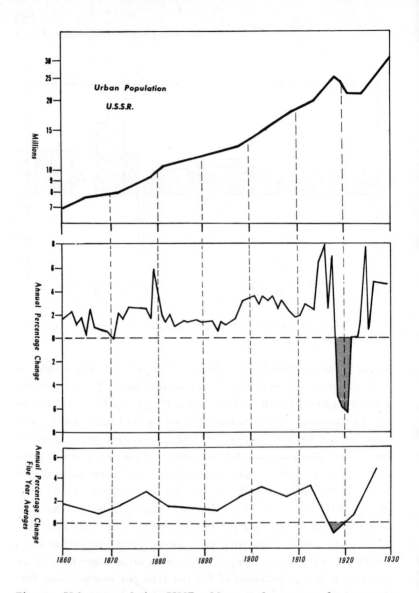

Millions

Annual Percentage Change

Annual Percentage Change
Five Year Averages

Urban Population

U.S.S.R.

Fig. 54 Urban population USSR 1860–1930 by years and percentage change each year in boundaries as of 1930. Based on data in E. Z. Volkov, *Dinamika narodonaseleniia SSSR za vosem'desiat let* (M. Gos. izd., 1930), "Svodnaia tablitsa," pp. 264–271.

In 1879 data include territories then in the Russian Empire of the Transcaspian Kray (Turkestan) and also territories that formed parts of Kars and Batumi guberniyas, taken from Turkey in a war.

The jump in urban population in 1924 results in part from the inclusion in the USSR from the date of data on the people's republics of Khorezm and Bukhara.

tween 1950 and 1967 (Figure 55 top line) but with a decreasing
rate of annual increase, from 5.2 per cent in 1950 and 1951 to 2.4
per cent during 1968 (Figure 55 lower line). The general downward trend is broken by one valley of much lower rates of increase,
the years 1954–1956, when the virgin and idle lands agricultural
program inspired by Khrushchëv sent many young people from
the cities to help establish farms on the arid frontier of dry farming in Kazakhstan.[7]

The clear downward trend in the rate of urban increase per
annum since 1950 reflects in part the much higher proportion
which urban population forms of the total population and the
consequent lesser potential contribution which rural-urban migra-

[7] In the 17 year period January 1, 1950, to January 1, 1967, the rural population decreased in 12 years and increased in 5 years; the calandar years with
largest increases were 1954 with 0.7 million increase in rural population, 1955
with an increase of 1.6 million, and 1956 with an increase of 0.3 million (the
other two years with increases were 1961 and 1962 with 0.1 million each). The
12 years with decreases in rural population had an average decrease of 0.5 million per annum. In this 17-year period the total rural population decreased
from 109.1 million to 106.4 million. Data from *Narodnoe khoziaistvo SSSR v
1965 g., statisticheskii ezhegodnik,* p. 7, and *Strana sovetov za 50 let; sbornik
statisticheskikh materialov,* p. 15.

Fig. 55 Urban population
USSR 1950–1967 by years and
percentage change each year in
boundaries as of 1967. Based on
data in SSSR. Tsentral'noe statisticheskoe upravlenie, *Narodnoe
khoziaistvo SSSR v 1965 g.,* p. 7,
and *Strana sovetov za 50 let:
sbornik statisticheskikh materialov,* p. 15.

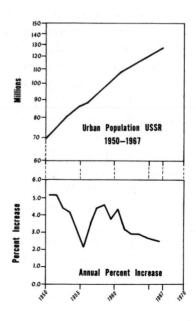

tion can make to urban growth. As the American sociologist Kingsley Davis has observed, the urban revolution is a transformation of society from rural to urban with high rates of growth during the process of transferring much of the rural population to cities but with much lower rates as the cities must depend more and more on their own natural increase for population growth.[8]

The principal interruption to long-range continued urban growth occurred just after 1917. The urban population of the Soviet Union (boundaries of 1938) dropped from 25.8 million to 20.9 million during the period 1917–1920, or at an average rate of −5.7 per cent per annum (Tables 24 and 25 and Figure 52). The sharp drop in urban population was particularly marked in some of the larger cities. Petrograd (Leningrad) fell from 2,165,000 in 1915 to 706,000 in 1920; it thus lost 67 per cent of its population (Table 27 below). Moscow dropped from 1,806,000 to 1,028,000 in this period; a decline of 43 per cent. The population of Kiev was reduced from 610 to 366 thousand, or a drop of 40 per cent. The year-by-year data (Figure 54) make more precise the timing of this loss in urban population and make clear that the period of greatest decline was not during World War I but rather in the aftermath of the Revolution and the ensuing civil war and disorganization of economic life, but possibly also some return to rural areas as a result of land reform. A peak of urban population for the country as a whole was reached on January 1, 1918. In each of the 3 following years the urban population decreased sharply (5.0 per cent during 1918, 6.1 per cent during 1919, and 6.5 per cent during 1920). The 2 following years, 1921 and 1922, were characterized by urban stagnation. Only during 1923 did the urban population begin to rise again (Figure 54). The level of urban population at the time of the October Revolution of 1917 was not again attained until 1926.

During World War II there was also a reduction in the rate of urban growth. Data are not available on the war period alone, when there was doubtless a sharp decline for many cities. But the period 1939–1950 shows up on Table 25 and Figures 53 and 54 as having the second lowest rate of increase in the century 1867–

[8] Kingsley Davis, "The urbanization of the human population," *Scientific American*, vol. 213, no. 3 (September, 1965), pp. 41–53.

1967. The destruction of World War II was very intense in all the Western portions of the Soviet Union and seriously depressed urban growth in this area.

The outstanding period of rate of growth far above the long-run average was 1926–1939 (Table 25 and Figures 52 and 54) with the record-breaking rate of increase of 6.5 per cent per annum, the highest in any period in Russian or Soviet history. This was the period of great industrialization drive of the first 3 Five-Year Plans. Two other periods had rates of increase above the long-range averages, 1920–1926 with 3.7 per cent per annum, and 1950–1959 with 4.1 per cent per annum, but both represent recovery from preceding periods of slow growth or losses during wartime.

The rural population in 1967 was almost exactly the same as 70 years earlier in 1897, i.e., 106 million in the present boundaries of the Soviet Union (Table 24). It had grown between 1897 and 1926 from about 106 to about 137 million,[9] then declined slightly in the 1930s to about 130 million in 1939, dropped sharply in World War II to 109 million in 1950, and then declined gently again in the 1960s to stand at a level of 104.7 million on January 1, 1969 (Table 24).

The urban population, which was only one-fourteenth as large as the rural population in 1811 and one-sixth as large in 1867, equalled it by the end of 1960, and surpassed it by 28 per cent on January 1, 1969 (estimated 134.2 million urban as compared with 104.7 million rural). Thus Soviet society has been transformed from a predominantly rural one to a dominantly urban one, mainly in the Soviet period since 1926. In the 115 years between 1811 and 1926 the percentage of the urban population rose by only 11 percentage points (from 7 per cent to 18 per cent), whereas in the 41 years between 1926 and 1967 it rose by 37 percentage points (from 18 per cent to 55 per cent) (Table 24). Thus Russia was essentially a land of peasants, but in the Soviet period it has been metamorphosed into a land of the industrial proletariat.

[9] There are no official estimates of the 1926 population in present boundaries but the estimates for both 1913 and 1939 indicate a rural population of about 16 million in the areas added to the Soviet Union during the period 1939–1945: these 16 million added to the rural population of 120.7 million in the 1926 boundaries would indicate an estimated rural population in the present boundaries of about 137 million.

A dramatic watershed in the growth of the urban population of and in the urbanization of the Soviet Union was reached in the late 1920s with the collectivization of agriculture and the industrialization of the country in the five-year plans. Up until this time rural as well as urban population had been increasing, although at a slower rate. After this date rural population declined. Hence the entire population increase was concentrated in the cities, which grew not only from their own natural increase but also with a massive migration from rural areas.

The period of rapid urban growth 1926–1939, is unmatched in the earlier or later history of the Soviet Union or in the period of rapid urbanization or industrialization in any other major country before World War II.[10] During the intercensal period 1926–1939, the urban population increased 113.3 per cent, or at the rate of 87 per cent per decade, or 6.5 per cent per annum; this was at a rate of growth more than twice as high as for the previous period of most rapid growth, 1897–1913, with 2.8 per cent per annum (present boundaries and urban definition) or for the later periods 1939–1959 and 1959–1967, for which the growth was 2.5 per cent and 3.1 per cent, respectively. (Table 25).

Comparisons with other countries are difficult because of differing definitions and structures of settlement. But it may be worth noting that in the United States only one decade has seen such a high percentage of increase in urban population, 1840–1850, with a 92 per cent increase for the decade (see Figure 2 in Chapter 1), but at that time both the total urban population and the proportion of urban population in the United States were very much lower. The remarkable growth of urban population in the Soviet Union in the 12-year intercensal period (December 1926 to January 1939) saw an increase in proportion of urban population from 18 to 33 per cent that had required 3 decades in the United States (from about 1856 to 1887) and probably about a century in most European countries. The growth in total urban population in the Soviet Union from 1926 to 1939 was from 26.3 to 56.1 million; similar growth in the total urban population in the United States had taken about 3 decades (from the mid-1890s to the mid-1920s).

[10] Chauncy D. Harris, "The Cities of the Soviet Union," *Geographical Review*, Vol. 35, No. 1 (January, 1945), pp. 107–121.

With an increasing percentage of the total population in cities, the rate of growth of the urban population would be expected to slow down. If the entire population growth is concentrated in cities and the total population is increasing at a rate of one per cent per annum, the rate of growth of cities is an inverse function of the proportion of the population that is urban, since under such conditions the percentage increase in urban population equals the percentage increase in total population times 100 divided by the per cent of the population that is urban. Thus if only 10 per cent of the population is urban, at an over-all rate of increase of population of one per cent (and no increase in rural population), the urban population would increase 10 per cent per annum, whereas when the population is 50 per cent urban, the rate of urban growth, under these conditions, would be only 2 per cent; and if the population were entirely urban, only one per cent (Figure 56).

The significance of this inverse relationship between percentage of population that is urban and expected rate of urban growth (when the rural population remains constant) is both temporal and areal.

It is temporal in that over time with the increasing proportion of the Soviet population urban, the high rate of growth of urban

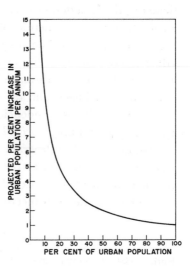

Fig. 56 Relationship of rate of increase of urban population to proportion of population urban (under conditions in which the total population increase of one per cent per annum is entirely concentrated on cities and the rural population remains constant, i.e., rural natural increase is balanced by rural-urban migration).

population will be more and more difficult to maintain. The relatively high rates of urban growth in the Soviet Union were maintained during the period 1939–1959 only by massive shifts of population from rural to urban areas and a marked reduction in the rural population, particularly in the western areas, which were densely populated, long settled, and subjected to terrible war damage. During the period 1959–1967 the high rate of urban growth depended both on a moderate decline in rural population and a relatively high rate of over-all population increase.

The expected inverse relationship between rate of urban growth and the percentage of the population that is urban has an areal expression in the Soviet Union in that older long-settled regions with high percentages of urban population can be expected to have lower rates of urban growth than either (1) new areas with low proportions of urban population, or (2) certain long-settled areas that have had a low degree of urbanization but are now in the process of an urban and industrial transformation.

V. G. Davidovich forecasts the following trends for the period up to 1980:[11] (1) continued rapid growth of the urban population, (2) continued rapid increase in the percentage which urban population forms of the total population, (3) continued increase in the average size of urban settlements, (4) increase in the number of urban settlements and consequently a higher density of such settlements, that is a denser network of cities over the territory of the Soviet Union, (5) reduction of rural population with continued high rates of rural-urban migration, (6) reduction in number of villages and hence in their density over the territory of the country and a greater average distance between villages, (7) increase in average size of villages, and (8) decrease in average number of villages per city. These tendencies were characteristic of the period 1926 to 1959 and are expected to accelerate.

According to the Program of the Communist Party of the Soviet Union announced at the 22nd Party Congress in 1961, the urban population is expected to continue to increase at a high rate. The long-range projection envisages a growth in the urban

[11] V. G. Davidovich, "O zakonomernostiakh i tendentsiiakh gorodskogo rasseleniia v SSSR, *Voprosy geografii,* sbornik 66 (M. Izd. "Mysl'," 1965), p. 13.

population to 190 million in 1980.[12] This would be a net increase of 62 million or 48.5 per cent for the period 1967–1980, since the urban population in 1967 was 128 million. It is interesting that this rate of projected increase averages out at 3.1 per cent per annum, which is at exactly the same rate as for the period 1959–1967.

THE 20 LARGEST CITIES IN 1811, 1867, 1915, AND 1967

In 1811 only 2 cities had more than 100 thousand population: St. Petersburg with 336 thousand and Moscow with 181 thousand. Only a score of cities in the entire country had as many as 15 thousand inhabitants.

The 20 largest cities of Russia in 1811 (Table 26 and Figure 57) stand in sharp contrast to the largest cities of the Soviet Union

TABLE 26
THE TWENTY LARGEST CITIES OF RUSSIA AND THE SOVIET UNION, 1811, 1867, 1915, AND 1967
Population in thousands; rank as of each date and also in parentheses for 1967; names as of the dates indicated

	1811				*1867*		
Rank	*Name*		*Population*	*Rank*	*Name*		*Population*
1	St. Petersburg	(2)	336	1	St. Petersburg		539
2	Moscow	(1)	181	2	Moscow		399
3	Vil'no	(59)	56	3	Odessa	(17)	121
4	Kazan'	(14)	54	4	Kishinëv	(63)	104
5	Tula	(45)	52	5	Riga		98
6	Astrakhan'	(47)	38	6	Saratov		93
7	Riga	(24)	32	7	Tashkent	(4)	80
8	Saratov	(22)	27	8	Vil'no		79
9	Orël	(93)	25	9	Kazan'		79
10	Yaroslavl'	(33)	24	10	Kiev		71
11	Kursk	(71)	23	11	Nikolayev	(64)	68
12	Kiev	(3)	23	12	Tiflis	(11)	61
13	Kaluga	(104)	23	13	Khar'kov	(6)	60
14	Voronezh	(27)	22	14	Tula		58
15	Revel'	(52)	18	15	Berdichev	(320)	53
16	Tver'	(58)	18	16	Astrakhan'		48
17	Tobol'sk	(x)	17	17	Kherson	(78)	46
18	Vitebsk	(97)	17	18	Orël		44
19	Tambov	(88)	17	19	Voronezh		42
20	Penza	(53)	15	20	Nizhniy Novgorod	(7)	41

[12] SSSR. Tsentral'noe statisticheskoe upravlenie, *SSSR v tsifrakh v 1963 g.* (M. Izd. Statistika, 1964), p. 11.

TABLE 26 — Continued
THE LARGEST CITIES OF RUSSIA AND
THE SOVIET UNION, 1811, 1867, 1915, AND 1967

	1915				1967	
Rank	*Name*		*Popu- lation*	*Rank*	*Name*	*Popu- lation*
1	Petrograd		2165	1	Moscow	6507
2	Moscow		1806	2	Leningrad	3706
3	Kiev		610	3	Kiev	1413
4	Riga		569	4	Tashkent	1239
5	Odessa		500[a]	5	Baku	1196
6	Tiflis		328	6	Khar'kov	1125
7	Tashkent		272	7	Gor'kiy	1120
8	Khar'kov		258	8	Novosibirsk	1064
9	Baku	(5)	237	9	Kuybyshev	992
10	Saratov		236	10	Sverdlovsk	961
11	Yekaterinoslav	(15)	220	11	Tbilisi	842
12	Vil'na		204	12	Donetsk	840
13	Kazan'		195	13	Chelyabinsk	836
14	Rostov-na-Donu	(20)	172[a]	14	Kazan'	821
15	Astrakhan'		164	15	Dnepropetrovsk	816
16	Ivanovo-Voznesensk	(38)	147[a]	16	Perm'	796
17	Orenburg	(56)	147	17	Odessa	776
18	Samara	(9)	144	18	Omsk	774
19	Tula		141	19	Minsk	772
20	Omsk	(18)	136	20	Rostov-na-Donu	755

Sources:
1811: Karl German, *Statisticheskiia Issledovaniia Otnositel'no Rossiiskoi Imperii.* Chast' 1. O Narodonaselenii. (S.-Peterburg, 1819), pp. 231–233 and 246.
1867: Russia. Tsentral'nyi Statisticheskii Komitet. *Statisticheskii Vremennik Rossiiskoi Imperii,* seriia 2, vypusk 1. (Sanktpeterburg, 1871), pp. 157–198.
1915: Tabulated from Russia. Tsentral'nyi Statisticheskii Komitet. *Statisticheskii Ezhegodnik Rossii 1915 g.* (Petrograd, 1916), pp. 153–154, except for cities marked by letter "a", which are from other sources and for other years: Odessa and Rostov-na-Donu for 1914 and Ivanovo-Voznesensk for 1917.
1967: Tabulated from *Administrativno-Territorial'noe Delenie Soiuznykh Respublik na 1 iiuliia 1967 goda.* (Moskva, 1967), pp. 592–604.
(x) Not among the 201 largest cities in 1967 (i.e., those with more than 100,000 population), and therefore the rank in size for 1967 is not given.

in 1967. Indeed of the 20 largest cities of 1811 only 4 were still among the 20 largest a century and a half later: St. Petersburg (now Leningrad), Moscow, Kazan', and Kiev. One of the 20 largest of 1811, Tobol'sk in Western Siberia, has shown little growth and was largely by-passed by modern developments.

The changes in the composition of the largest cities has both economic and geographic aspects that result from the profound changes in Russian and Soviet economy, society, and distribution of population. The former commercial and regional centers for the early developed and densely populated western agricultural

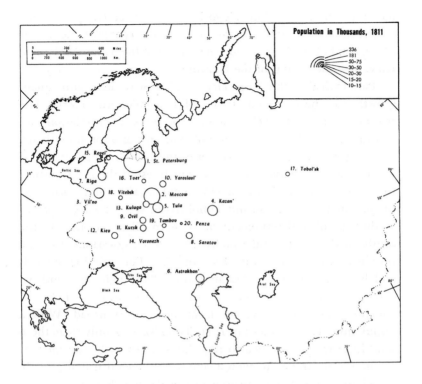

Fig. 57 The 20 largest cities of 1811. See Table 26.

zone of the Russian Empire west and south of Moscow have declined relatively (Figure 57) and have been replaced among the largest cities by new manufacturing cities that lie in more recently developed mining and industrial areas to the east, particularly in districts that combine mining and manufacturing, or as regional centers for developing lands east of the Volga River (Figure 60 below).

The 4 large cities of 1811 that were still among the very largest cities a century later have been continuing major regional centers, usually with substantial political-administrative functions, diversified industries, varied economic activities, and excellent locations with a high degree of accessibility and good transportation facilities (Figure 57). In order of size in 1811 these were St. Petersburg, then the capital of the Russian Empire, a major port, a leading industrial and cultural center; Moscow, now the capital, center of the transportation network of the Soviet Union and the largest industrial center; Kazan', the ancient center of the Tatars at the bend of the Volga, and now capital of the Tatar ASSR; and Kiev, now the capital of the Ukraine.

Paradoxically, the large city of 1811 with least subsequent growth was the easternmost: Tobol'sk in Western Siberia. The reason is not far to seek: changing patterns of population and transportation. Tobol'sk was founded in 1587 and for more than a century (1708–1824) was the center of the Guberniya of Siberia. It was located in the northern coniferous forest at the key transport junction in the early days of movement by river and portage at the junction of the Irtysh and Tobol rivers. With the development of the agricultural settlement of Western Siberia farther to the south on the steppe and wooded steppe, the government of the province was transferred to Omsk in 1824. The building of roads and later of the Trans-Siberian Railroad through this southern agricultural zone confirmed the peripheral location of Tobol'sk, which was until 1967, 254 km. from the closest railroad. With a population of 17 thousand in 1811, Tobol'sk grew only to 20 thousand in 1897 and declined to 18.5 thousand in 1926—conspicuous stagnation during more than a century of general urban growth, especially in the eastern regions of the Russian Empire.

The other 15 large cities of 1811 are similar in that they were all commercial and regional centers in the early and densely settled western European part of the Soviet Union between the western boundary and the Volga River, and that all have had substantial growth through the following century and a half to 1967. None of these 15 lies as far east as the Urals or in the Asiatic part of the country. Their 1811 populations varied from 56 thousand for Vil'no (now Vil'nyus), the largest, to 15 thousand for Penza, the smallest (Table 26). In 1967 the populations of these same 15 western centers varied from 720 thousand for Saratov, the largest, to 179 thousand for Kaluga, then the smallest of this group. Their ranks in size of population among Soviet cities in 1967 ranged from number 22 for Saratov to number 104 for Kaluga. All were centers of guberniyas in the Russian Empire and are still centers of political units, i.e., Vil'no (Vil'nyus), Riga, and Revel' (Tallin) are now the capitals of the Baltic republics of Lithuania, Latvia, and Estonia, while Vitebsk, Tver' (Kalinin), Yaroslavl', Kaluga, Tula, Orël, Kursk, Voronezh, Tambov, Penza, Saratov, and Astrakhan' are now centers of oblasts.

Among the 20 largest cities of 1867 are 9 newcomers not among such cities a half century earlier in 1811 (Figure 58 and Table 26). Three of these were ports, 3 inland commercial centers, and 3 were in territories added to the Russian Empire only comparatively late.

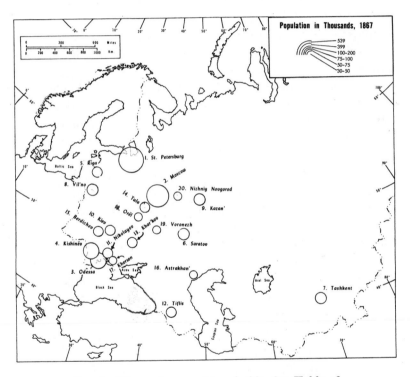

Fig. 58   The 20 largest cities of 1867. See Table 26.

The 3 ports on the Black Sea reflected the 19th century rise of international trade, particularly the export of wheat from the great grain belt of the semiarid steppe country of the southwestern part of the Russian Empire: Odessa, which was already the third largest city in Russia in 1867; Nikolayev (grain export, shipbuilding, and naval base); and Kherson.

Three were inland commercial centers: Berdichev, Nizhniy Novgorod, and Khar'kov. Berdichev, which ranked 15th in size among Russian cities in 1867 with a population of 53 thousand was a major regional commercial center in the 19th century with a largely Jewish population but in the following century in contrast to these other 2 cities, it failed to grow. Its population actually decreased 1885–1897, 1913–1920, and 1939–1959, as competitive commercial centers developed at its expense and it failed to acquire major industries; in 1967, it ranked only about 320 in size among Soviet cities. In spite of its size in 1867, it was not granted administrative functions; in 1867 it was a subordinate city in Kiev Guberniya; in 1967, it was still a subordinate city but in Zhitomir Oblast.

Nizhniy Novgorod (now Gor'kiy) on the Volga, was a commercial city famous for its fairs. Nizhniy Novgorod developed rapidly in the latter 19th century as a commercial city but experienced its most dramatic growth later as an industrial city (automobiles) and by 1967 was the seventh city in size in the country.

Khar'kov in the developing grain-export lands of the eastern Ukraine grew rapidly in the 19th century as a commercial center and transport node with the building of railroads; with 8 rail lines it became the third largest transport center in the country. From the 1870s with the rise of the Donets coal-mining and steel district to the south, Khar'kov's manufacturing industries, particularly machinery, also flourished and its rank in size among cities of the country rose rapidly, from 34 in 1811 to 13 in 1867 to 8 in 1915, and to 6 in 1967.

Three large cities of 1867 reflected territorial expansion of the Russian Empire; Kishinëv, Tiflis, and Tashkent. In 1867 Kishinëv was the fourth largest city of Russia with a population of 104 thousand. It had been annexed to Russia in 1812 as a relatively small settlement (7 thousand) but grew rapidly in the early 19th century as the capital of Bessarabia. Thereafter, possibly because of its peripheral positions, Kishinëv was relatively stagnant both in the Russian Empire and in the interwar period in Romania. Since World War II with incorporation into the Soviet Union, it has again grown rapidly. Tiflis (now Tbilisi) has been among the larger cities in 1867, 1915, and 1967. One of the oldest cities on the present territory of the Soviet Union, it is the center of Georgia in the Transcaucasus and came into the Russian Empire at the beginning of the 19th century. Tashkent in Middle Asia fell to Russia in 1865 and has been one of the largest cities in the country ever since.

In 1867 two cities now part of the Soviet Union but then in other countries were of a size comparable with the largest Russian cities. Königsberg in East Prussia (now Kaliningrad) had a population of 106 thousand in 1870 and was then of a size exceeded by only 3 Russian cities, but it suffered heavily in World War II and in 1967 ranked only 70th in size among Soviet cities. Lemberg in Galicia in Austria-Hungary (now L'vov) had an 1869 population of 87 thousand and was then exceeded in size by only 6 Russian cities. These 2 cities are not included in Table 26 as they were not then part of the Russian Empire and did not become part of the Soviet Union until World War II.

Seven of the 20 largest cities near the end of the Tsarist period of the Russian Empire had not been among the largest a half century before (Figure 59 and Table 26). They were generally located farther to the east than the earlier large cities, extending from Yekaterinoslav (now Dnepropetrovsk) on the Dnepr River in the Ukraine eastward to Omsk in Western Siberia.

Three were new industrial cities, forerunners of the industrial giants that were to arise in the following half century of Soviet power. Yekaterinoslav on the Dnepr (now Dnepropetrovsk) dates from the 1870s with the arrival of a railroad; it developed with the opening of the nearby Donets coal basin to the east, the iron-ore mines of Krivoy Rog to the west, the manganese mines of Nikopol' to the south-southwest, and its own steel industries. Ivanovo-Voznesensk was the center of the great cotton-textile industry of Russia but lacked an administrative role until the later Soviet period. Baku in the Caucasus on the west shore of the Caspian Sea arose in the 1870s and grew rapidly as the seat of the oilfield, which produced about half the entire world supply of petroleum at the end of the 19th century.

The other four cities were all commercial and regional centers associated with the developing grain lands from the Volga River to Western Siberia. Rostov-na-Donu on the west was a port on the

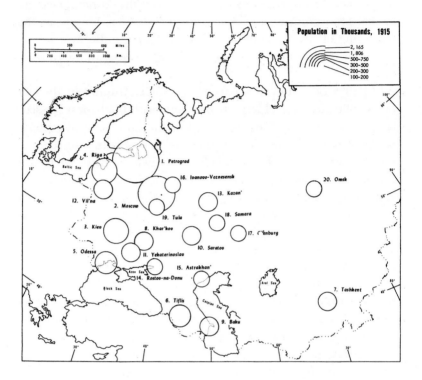

Fig. 59 The largest cities of 1915. See Table 26.

lower Don near the northeasternmost penetration of sea transportation toward the eastern interior wheat lands of the Russian Empire; it was a major grain-exporting port throughout the 19th century. To the northeast Samara (now Kuybyshev) at the easternmost point on the Volga River became a flour-milling center in the wheat belt and much later in the Soviet period grew rapidly with the production of metals and machinery but also as a regional center for the Volga-Urals oilfield. Orenburg on the small Ural River developed rapidly with the building in 1905 of the Trans-Caspian Railroad that connected Middle Asia with European Russia. Omsk on the Irtysh River and at a junction point of the Trans-Siberian Railroad lines arose as the commercial and transport center and remained for some time the largest city of Siberia.

The 1967 list of the 20 largest cities contained 6 not among the largest cities in any of the three previous lists (Figure 60 and Table 26). These are giants largely created during the Soviet period of rapid and extensive industrialization: Donetsk on the Donets coal basin and steel district; Novosibirsk, the regional center of Western Siberia and also of the nearby Kuznetsk coal basin and industrial district; Sverdlovsk, Chelyabinsk, and Perm' in the industrial district of the Urals, and finally Minsk, in the west, the capital of Belorussia, and a city of very rapid recent growth and industrialization.

Donetsk had not existed in either 1811 or 1867. It was founded in 1870 and grew with the exploitation of the Donbas coalfield, with the use of coke in blast furnaces, with the consequent rise of an iron and steel industry on the coalfield, and with the development of the related machinery and chemical industries. Originally

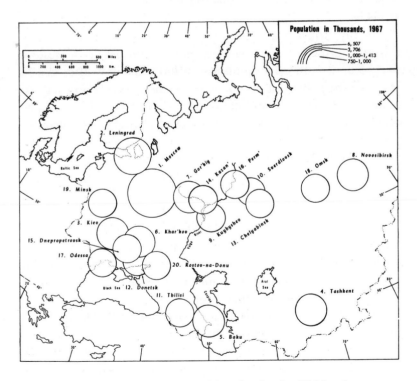

Fig. 60 The 20 largest cities of 1967. See Table 26.

called Yuzovka after a Scottish industrialist, Hughes, it was later renamed Stalin or Stalino (1924–1961). It is not only an important industrial city but also the center for the great Donbas industrial area.

Novosibirsk (formerly Novonikolayevsk) developed only after 1893 with the construction of the Trans-Siberian Railroad at its bridging of the Ob River; thereafter it rose rapidly as a regional center for Siberia surpassing Omsk in the early 1930s with the development of the nearby Kuznetsk coalfield and industrial area.

Sverdlovsk (formerly Yekaterinburg), Chelyabinsk, and Perm' (called Molotov 1940–1957) all date back to the 18th century but were small settlements until the Soviet period. All began industrial development with the rise of the metals industry of the Urals; they have accelerated growth in recent years with the expansion of metal, machinery, and chemical production, and with their regional roles within the industrial districts of the mineral-rich Urals.

Finally, Minsk stands in contrast to the other cities of unusually rapid growth in the Soviet period in that it lies in the western part of the country. Its rapid growth has come only after World War II, when the western boundary of the Soviet Union was extended to the west by adding considerable territory to Belorussia, of which Minsk is the capital. Diversified industry has expanded very rapidly in recent years doubtless in part because of good location, skilled labor, and an abundant labor supply migrating to the city from the densely settled surrounding rural regions.

GROWTH PATTERNS OF CITIES
OVER THE CENTURY 1867–1967

Variations in rate and patterns of growth over the last century suggested by the simple comparisons of the very largest cities in 1867 and 1967 can now be examined in more detail for individual cities and for groups of similar cities.

Data for these comparisons are contained in Table 27 which records, insofar as information has been located for the 201 cities of more than 100 thousand population in 1967, the population in thousands in the years 1867, 1885, 1897, 1915, 1920, 1926, 1939, 1959, and 1967. The estimates for 1915 are less accurate and the census figures for 1920 are less complete than for other years but these data are particularly useful in making more precise the period of stagnation, decline, and destruction of World War I and the Civil War following the October Revolution.

Figures 61, 62, 63, 65, and 67 depict in graphic form the growth patterns of selected cities and Figures 58, 59, 60, 64, 66, and 68 show their location. The growth data are plotted on semilog paper in order to show a constant rate of growth by a uniform slope. The years for which data are available are spaced at irregular intervals, but graphic representation adjusts these intervals automatically and facilitates visual comparisons. Also, for some cities data are available only for years other than the standard ones, but again the graphs easily rectify these variations.[13] Of course, some inconsistencies in the data remain but nevertheless the general comparisons both over time for any individual city and for different cities as of the same data remain generally valid.

The typical growth pattern is one of fairly rapid growth during the period 1867–1915; a very sharp drop between 1915 and 1920 as a result of World War I and, in many cases even more, as a result of the fighting and the disorganization of production and economic life during the Civil War; recovery 1920–1926; the most rapid growth of all during the amazing period of 1926–1939; a somewhat slower rate of increase during the longer period 1939–1959, primarily as a result of destruction and loss of life during World War II; and, finally, for 1959–1967 more rapid growth once again, except for the very largest cities and for the cities that grew at very high rates in the preceding period. The individual patterns thus reflect the same general trends as the urban population as a whole (Table 25 and Figure 52), but the individual city data reveal more details and many variations.

The Largest Cities of 1967

The growth patterns over the past century for the 16 largest cities of 1967 are shown on Figure 61 (see also Tables 26 and 27 and Figure 60).

---

[13] The year of the supplementary data from the great geographical and statistical dictionary of the Russian Empire, *Geografichesko-Statisticheskii Slovar' Rossiiskoi Imperii*, ed. by P. Semenov, Sanktpeterburg, 5 vols. 1863–1885, varies widely reflecting the 22 years over the course of which these volumes were published.

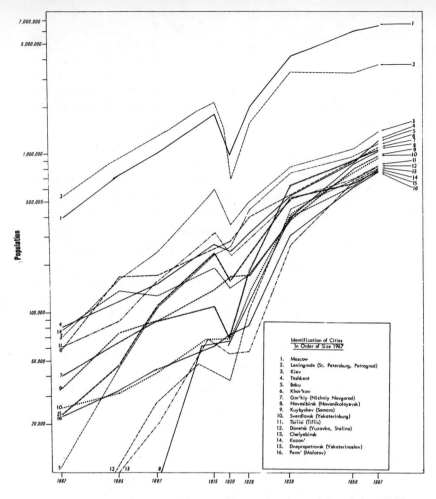

Fig. 61 Growth patterns 1867–1967 of the 16 largest cities of the USSR in 1967. For location of cities, see Figure 60. For population data, see Table 27.

Moscow (1),[14] traditional and historical center of the Russian state, grew rapidly in the period 1867–1915 and had a smaller loss than Petrograd during the period 1915–1920 when it passed Petrograd to become the largest city in the country. The lesser loss of Moscow can be attributed to the transfer of the capital to Moscow and to the greater abundance of food from the nearby countryside. Moscow grew very rapidly 1920–1939, more slowly 1939–1959, and since 1959 even more slowly as governmental policy has called for limiting the size of the largest cities. Over

[14] Figures in parentheses indicate rank in population in 1967, identification numbers used on the graphs of population growth, and order of data on Table 27.

the century 1867–1967 the population increased from 399 to 6,507 thousand.

Leningrad or St. Petersburg until 1914 and then Petrograd from 1914 to 1924 (2), the Baltic port, capital of the Russian Empire (1713–1918), industrial center, and largest Russian city up to World War I, had a rapid growth at fairly uniform rate from 1867 to 1915, increasing in this period from 539 to 2,165 thousand. It then suffered a precipitous loss of two-thirds of its population to decline to 706 thousand in 1920 (most of this loss was in the period 1918–1920). Rapid growth 1920–1939 was again interrupted by loss during World War II when Leningrad suffered a cruel and prolonged siege, a loss not fully recovered by 1959.

Kiev (3), mother of Russian cities and center of the Ukraine, had a very rapid growth in population 1867–1915 increasing from 71 to 610 thousand or more than eightfold in less than 50 years. It also lost population in the period 1915–1920 and thereafter grew at a somewhat slower rate, particularly as the capital of the Ukraine was shifted to Khar'kov during the period 1917–1934.

The only other large city on Figure 61 with such a rapid rate of growth in the half-century 1867–1915 was Baku (5) which increased from 12 thousand in 1867 to 237 thousand population in 1915 with the development of the oil industry. Unlike most Soviet cities, it continued growth in the crisis period 1915–1920, but slackened its pace somewhat after 1939 with the relative decline of its oilfields during and after World War II.

Tashkent (4) in Soviet Middle Asia was incorporated into the Russian Empire only in 1865 but has had a rapid and steady growth ever since with very little variation in rate, reflecting in part its remoteness from the military operations along the western border in 2 world wars and the continuous development of Middle Asia over the last century.

Khar'kov (6) in the eastern Ukraine grew very rapidly in the period 1867–1885 with the railroad construction boom and the opening of the Donbas coalfield, then slowed its pace during the period 1885–1897 before resuming rapid growth again that continued without interruption at a steady and high rate to 1967.

Gor'kiy (7), the former Nizhniy Novgorod on the Volga, as a commercial city grew at a modest rate from 1867 to 1915 and dropped sharply in population during the period 1915–1920, but

TABLE 27
Population of Larger Cities of the Soviet Union
1867, 1885, 1897, 1915, 1920, 1926, 1939, 1959, and 1967
(In order of size in 1967. Population in thousands.)
For location of cities, see Figures 5 and 6.

No.	Name of City	Location[b]	1867	1885	1897	1915	1920	1926	1939	1959	1967	Notes and Former Names
1	Moscow (Moskva)	Moscow R2	399	753	1039	1806	1028	2026	4183	6009	6507	
2	Leningrad	Leningrad R1	539	861	1265	2165	706	1614	3385	3321	3706	Sankt-Peterburg 1703–1914; Petrograd 1914–1924.
3	Kiev (Kiyev)	Kiev U2	71	166	248	610	366	514	847	1104	1413	
4	Tashkent	Tashkent Uz	80	121	156	272	245	324	550	912	1239	
5	Baku	Azerbaydzhan	12	46	112	237	263	453	775	971	1196	
6	Khar'kov	Khar'kov U1	60	171	174	258	284	417	833	934	1125	
7	Gor'kiy	Gor'kiy R3	41	67	90	112	70	185	644	942	1120	Nizhniy Novgorod to 1932.
8	Novosibirsk	Novosibirsk R8			8	63[a]	68	120	404	886	1064	Gusevka 1894–1903; Novonikolayevsk 1903–1926.
9	Kuybyshev	Kuybyshev R5	34	75	90	144	176	176	390	806	992	Samara to 1935.
10	Sverdlovsk	Sverdlovsk R7	25	32	43	70[a]	70	136	423	779	961	Yekaterinburg to 1924.
11	Tbilisi	Georgia	61	90	160	328	234[a]	294	519	695	842	Tiflis to 1936.
12	Donetsk	Donetsk U1			28	49[a]	38	106	466	699	840	Yuzovka 1869–1924; Stalin 1924–ca. 1935; Stalino ca. 1935–1961.
13	Chelyabinsk	Chelyabinsk R7	5	10	20	70[a]	57	59	273	689	836	
14	Kazan'	Tatar A R5	79	140	130	195	146	179	398	647	821	
15	Dnepropetrovsk	Dnepropetrovsk U1	23	47	113	220	164	233	527	660	816	Yekaterinoslav (1786); Novorossiysk; Yekaterinoslav 1802–1926.
16	Perm'	Perm' R7	23	33	45	63	74	85	306	629	796	Yegozhikhinskiy Zavod 1723–1780; Perm' 1780–1940; Molotov 1940–1957.

TABLE 27—continued

No.	Name of City	Location[b]	1867	1885	1897	1915	1920	1926	1939	1959	1967	Notes and Former Names
17	Odessa	Odessa U3	121	240	404	500[a]	435	421	602	667	776	
18	Omsk	Omsk R8	27	34	37	136	145	162	289	581	774	
19	Minsk	Minsk B	36	58	91	118	104	132	237	509	772	
20	Rostov-na-Donu	Rostov R6	39	61	119	172[a]	177	308	510	600	757	
21	Volgograd	Volgograd R5	12	36	55	101[a]	81	148	445	592	743	Tsaritsyn to 1925; Stalingrad 1925–1961.
22	Saratov	Saratov R5	93	123	187	236	188	215	372	581	720	
23	Ufa	Bashkir A R5	20	26	49	106	93	99	258	547	704	
24	Riga	Latvia	98	175	282	569	x	338[a]	348	580	680	1918–1940 in independent Latvia.
25	Yerevan	Armenia	14	15	29	34	48[a]	65	204	509	665	Erivan' to 1936.
26	Alma-Ata	Alma-Ata K1	10	22	23	42	47	45	222	456	652	Vernyy to 1921.
27	Voronezh	Voronezh R4	42	56	81	95	93	120	344	448	611	
28	Zaporozh'ye	Zaporozh'ye U1	5	7	19	52[a]	50	56	282	435	595	Aleksandrovsk to 1917 (1921?).
29	Krasnoyarsk	Krasnoyarsk R9	11	20	27	88	68	72	190	412	576	
30	L'vov	L'vov U2	87[a]	110[a]	160[a]	206[a]	x	312[a]	340	411	512	Lemberg in Austria 1772–1918; Lwów in Poland 1919–1939.
31	Krivoy Rog	Dnepropetrovsk U1	3[a]	x	15	x	22	31	189	388	510	Village of Grigor'yevka in mid-19th century.
32	Karaganda	Karaganda K1							156	387	498	
33	Yaroslavl'	Yaroslavl' R2	37	35	72	120	73	114	309	407	498	
34	Novokuznetsk	Kemerovo R8	3	6	3	x	5	4	166	377	493	Kuznetsk (Kuznetsk-Sibirskiy) and Novokuznetsk to 1932; Stalinsk 1932–1961.
35	Khabarovsk	Khabarovsk R10	1[a]	3	15	51	34[a]	50	207	323	435	Khabarovka to 1883.
36	Irkutsk	Irkutsk R9	27	39	51	130	104	99	250	366	420	
37	Makeyevka	Donetsk U1						51	242	358	414	Dmitriyevsk to after 1926 census.
38	Ivanovo	Ivanovo R2	7[a]	33	54	168[a]	58	111	285	335	407	Ivanovo-Voznesensk 1871–1932.
39	Krasnodar	Krasnodar R6	9	40	66	103	143	163	193	313	407	Yekaterinodar to 1920.

TABLE 27—continued

No.	Name of City	Location[b]	1867	1885	1897	1915	1920	1926	1939	1959	1967	Notes and Former Names
40	Barnaul	Altay R8	13	17	21	61[a]	68	74	148	305	407	
41	Vladivostok	Primorskiy R10		13	29	91[a]	107[a]	108	206	291	397	
42	Frunze	Kirgizia		2	7	x	13	37	93	220	396	Pishpek to 1926.
43	Zhdanov	Donetsk U1	8	17	31	55[a]	55	41	222	284	385	Mariupol' to 1948.
44	Nizhniy Tagil	Sverdlovsk R7		26[a]	31	45[a]	38	39	160	339	377	Nizhne-Tagil'skiy Zavod; Tagil.
45	Tula	Tula R2	58	64	115	141	129	153	272	316	377	
46	Izhevsk	Udmurt A R7	21[a]	x	41	39[a]	44	63	176	285	376	Izhevskiy Zavod.
47	Astrakhan'	Astrakhan' R5	48	71	113	164	125	177	254	296	368	
48	Kemerovo	Kemerovo R8					6	22	133	278	364	Shcheglovsk to 1932.
49	Magnitogorsk	Chelyabinsk R7							146	311	357	
50	Lugansk	Lugansk U1	10	16	20	56[a]	57	72	215	275	352	Voroshilovgrad 1935–1958, 1970–
51	Gorlovka	Donetsk U1						23	181	293	343	
52	Tallin	Estonia	27	51	65	98	x	122[a]	160	282	340	Revel' to 1917; in independent Estonia 1918–1940.
53	Penza	Penza R5	27	45	60	83	85	92	160	255	333	
54	Dushanbe	Tadzhikistan						6	83	224	333	Dyushambe 1925–1929; Stalina-bad 1929–1961.
55	Groznyy	Chechen-Ingush A R6	3	6	16	34[a]	45	71	172	242	331	
56	Orenburg	Orenburg R7	33	56	72	147	109	123	172	267	326	Chkalov 1938–1957.
57	Tomsk	Tomsk R8	24	37	52	117	90	92	145	249	324	
58	Kalinin	Kalinin R2	30	39	54	64	65	108	216	261	318	Tver' to 1931.
59	Vil'nyus	Lithuania	79	103	155	204	x	195[a]	215	236	316	Wilno (in Poland 1920–39); Vil'no or Vil'na (Russian); Vilnius (Lithuanian).
60	Ryazan'	Ryazan' R2	18	30	46	50	41	51	95	214	311	
61	Arkhangel'sk	Arkhangel'sk R1	20	18	21	44	45	73	251	256	310	
62	Kirov	Kirov R3	20	24	25	60	41	62	144	252	309	Khlynov 1174–1781; Vyatka 1781–1934.

TABLE 27—continued

No.	Name of City	Location[b]	1867	1885	1897	1915	1920	1926	1939	1959	1967	Notes and Former Names
63	Kishinëv	Moldavia	104	120	108	129	x	115[a]	112	216	302	Chişinău (in Romania 1918–1940).
64	Nikolayev	Nikolayev U3	68	67	92	104[a]	109	105	169	226	300	
65	Ul'yanovsk	Ul'yanovsk R5	25	39	42	70	77	72	98	206	294	Simbirsk to 1924.
66	Prokop'yevsk	Kemerovo R8						11	107	282	290	Prokop'yevskiy Rudnik; Prokop'yevskiy to 1931.
67	Bryansk	Bryansk R2	14	16	25	30[a]	35	27	174	207	288	
68	Murmansk	Murmansk R1					2	9	119	222	287	
69	Kaunas	Lithuania	35	50	71	93	x	92[a]	152	214	284	Capital of independent Lithuania 1918–1940; Kovno (Russian).
70	Kaliningrad	Kaliningrad R1	106[a]	151[a]	189[a]	246[a]	261[a]	280[a]	372[a]	204	270	Königsberg (in East Prussia, Germany, to 1945).
71	Kursk	Kursk R4	29	50	76	90	79	99	120	205	255	
72	Lipetsk	Lipetsk R4	14	16	21	x	13	21	67	157	253	
73	Samarkand	Samarkand Uz	x	33	55	98	84	105	136	196	248	In independent khanate of Bukhara to 1868.
74	Taganrog	Rostov R6	25	56	51	68[a]	81	86	189	202	245	
75	Tyumen'	Tyumen' R8	13	14	30	34[a]	44	50	79	150	240	
76	Ashkhabad	Turkmenia		11	19	54	26	52	127	170	238	Askhabad 1881–1919; Poltoratsk 1919–1927.
77	Gomel'	Gomel' B	15	26	37	105[a]	61	86	139	168	237	
78	Kherson	Kherson U3	46	67	59	99	75	59	97	158	235	
79	Ulan-Ude	Buryat A R9	3	5	8	x	22[a]	29	126	175	227	Udinskoye (Udinsk) 1666–1783; Verkhneudinsk 1783–1934.
80	Dneprodzerzhinsk	Dneprodzerzhinsk U1	3[a]	x	17	35[a]	17	34	148	194	224	Kamenskoye to 1936.
81	Simferopol'	Crimea U3	18	37	49	84	78	88	143	186	223	

TABLE 27—continued

No.	Name of City	Location[b]	1867	1885	1897	1915	1920	1926	1939	1959	1967	Notes and Former Names
82	Ordzhonikidze	N. Oset A R6	9	39	44	80	61	78	131	164	219	Vladikavkaz to 1931; Ordzhonikidze 1931–1944; Dzaudzhikau 1944–1954.
83	Chimkent	Chimkent K4	4	9	11	x	18[a]	21	74	153	219	Formerly also Chemkent or Chimkend.
84	Orsk	Orenburg R7	3	20	14	x	16	14	66	176	215	
85	Kurgan	Kurgan R7	4	9	10	x	27	28	53	146	215	
86	Rybinsk	Yaroslavl' R2	15	20	25	32[a]	39	55	144	182	212	
87	Ust'-Kamenogorsk	E. Kazakh K1		7	9	x	16	14	20	150	212	
88	Tambov	Tambov R4	29	36	48	71	67	76	106	172	211	
89	Vladimir	Vladimir R2	15	18	28	44	23	40	67	154	211	
90	Shakhty	Rostov R6		13	16	43[a]	18	33	134	196	209	Aleksandrovsk-Grushevskiy to 1920.
91	Komsomol'sk-na-Amure	Khabarovsk R10							71	177	209	
92	Kostroma	Kostroma R2	23	28	41	74	48	74	121	172	209	
93	Orël	Orël R2	44	78	70	97	64	78	111	150	209	
94	Sevastopol'	Crimea U3	11	34	54	62[a]	73	75	114	148	209	
95	Semipalatinsk	Semipalatinsk K1	14	17	26	35	44	57	110	156	204	
96	Chita	Chita R9	4	6	12	79	50[a]	62	121	172	203	
97	Vitebsk	Vitebsk B	29	55	66	109	80	99	167	148	203	
98	Dzerzhinsk	Gor'kiy R3					1	9	103	164	201	Formed in 1930 by union of Rastyapino, Imeni Sverdlova, and Chernorechenskiy Zavod.
99	Smolensk	Smolensk R2	23	34	47	76	57	79	157	147	196	
100	Sochi	Krasnodar R6			1	x	8	10	71	127	188	
101	Poltava	Poltava U1	32	42	54	82	72	92	128	143	184	

TABLE 27—continued

No.	Name of City	Location[b]	1867	1885	1897	1915	1920	1926	1939	1959	1967	Notes and Former Names
102	Angarsk	Irkutsk R9								135	183	
103	Biysk	Altay R8	6	18	17	x	42	46	80	146	181	
104	Kaluga	Kaluga R2	36	40	50	57	41	52	89	134	179	
105	Zlatoust	Chelyabinsk R7	15[a]	19	21	34[a]	42	48	99	161	178	
106	Chernovtsy	Chernovtsy U2	34[a]	46[a]	68[a]	87[a]	x	112[a]	106	146	178	Czernowitz (in Austria 1775–1918); Cernăuţi (in Romania 1918–1940); Chernovitsy (Russian name to 1944).
107	Cheboksary	Chuvash A R3	4	5	5	x	7	9	31	104	178	
108	Stavropol'	Stavropol' R6	21	37	42	65	64	59	85	141	177	Voroshilovsk 1935–1943.
109	Tselinograd	Tselinograd K2	3	5	10	x	10	13	32	102	176	Akmolinsk to 1961; in early records also Akmoly.
110	Mogilëv	Mogilëv B	39	42	43	72	40	50	99	122	176	Also Mogilëv-na-Dnepre.
111	Kirovabad	Azerbaydzhan	15	20	34	63	41	57	99	116	174	Gandzha to 1804 and 1918–1935; Yelisavetpol' 1804–1918.
112	Petrozavodsk	Karelian A R1	11	12	13	19	19	27	70	136	171	
113	Vologda	Vologda R1	18	17	28	42	47	58	95	139	170	
114	Syzran'	Kuybyshev R5	19	29	32	48[a]	52	50	83	149	169	
115	Andizhan	Andizhan Uz	x	31	48	82[a]	80	73	85	130	169	In independent khanate of Kokand to 1876.
116	Kirovograd	Kirovograd U2	32[a]	58	61	76[a]	77	66	100	128	168	Yelisavetgrad to 1924; Zinov'yevsk 1924–1934; Kirovo 1934–1939.
117	Kopeysk	Chelyabinsk R7						9	60	161	166	Ugol'nyye Kopi, Goskopi to 1928; Kopi 1928–1933.
118	Petropavlovsk	N. Kazakh K2	8	14	20	42[a]	36	47	92	131	166	
119	Cherepovets	Vologda R1	3	6	7	x	14	22	32	92	165	

TABLE 27—continued

No.	Name of City	Location[b]	1867	1885	1897	1915	1920	1926	1939	1959	1967	Notes and Former Names
120	Makhachkala	Dagestan A R6	4	4	10	x	27	32	87	119	165	Petrovskoye 1844–1857; Petrovsk (-Port) 1857–1922.
121	Podol'sk	Moscow R2	8	11	4	x	12	20	72	124	163	
122	Vinnitsa	Vinnitsa U2	11	19	31	48[a]	42	58	93	122	163	
123	Sterlitamak	Bashkir A R5	6	9	16	x	27	25	39	112	162	
124	Kamensk-Ural'skiy	Sverdlovsk R7	5[a]	x	6	x	6	5	51	141	161	Kamenskiy Zavod; Kamensk.
125	Novocherkassk	Rostov R6	28	33	52	70	61	62	76	95	161	
126	Kutaisi	Georgia	8	20	32	54	45[a]	48	78	128	159	Kutais to 1936.
127	Namangan	Andizhan Uz	x	31	62	79[a]	71	74	80	123	158	
128	Dzhambul	Dzhambul K4	1	6	12	x	17	25	64	113	158	Auliye-Ata to 1938; also called Mirzoyan ca. 1933–1937; Taraz (7th Century), Yany (Yangi).
129	Saransk	Mordov A R3	14	14	15	x	14	15	41	91	154	
130	Pavlodar	Pavlodar K2	1	3	8	x	14	18	29	90	154	Koryakovskiy Forpost or Koryakovskaya Stanitsa to 1861.
131	Temirtau	Karaganda K1							5	77	150	
132	Tol'yatti	Kuybyshev R5	4	5	6	x	11	6	x	61	143	Stavropol' (Kuybyshev Oblast) to 1964.
133	Rubtsovsk	Altay R8						16	38	111	142	Rubtsov
134	Kramatorsk	Donetsk U1						12	94	115	141	
135	Zhitomir	Zhitomir U2	38	56	66	97	68[a]	77	95	106	141	
136	Sumy	Sumy U1		16	28	50[a]	37	44	64	98	140	
137	Kadiyevka	Lugansk U1	14					17	135	180	139	Sergo 1937–1943; major reduction in area in city, between 1959 and 1967.
138	Armavir	Krasnodar R6			18	47[a]	64	75	84	111	129	
139	Chernigov	Chernigov U2	17	27	28	38	30	35	69	90	139	

TABLE 27—continued

No.	Name of City	Location[b]	1867	1885	1897	1915	1920	1926	1939	1959	1967	Notes and Former Names
140	Leninsk-Kuznetskiy	Kemerovo R8						20	83	132	138	Kol'chugino or Lenino to 1925.
141	Kiselëvsk	Kemerovo R8							44	130	138	
142	Yoshkar-Ola	Mari A R3	1	2	2	x	2	4	27	89	137	Tsarevokokshaysk to 1919; Krasnokokshaysk 1919–1927.
143	Kremenchug	Poltava U1	20	42	63	99[a]	72	59	90	87	136	
144	Aktyubinsk	Aktyubinsk K3			3	x	12	21	49	97	135	
145	Berezniki	Perm' R7							51	106	134	
146	Leninakan	Armenia	17	23	31	49[a]	44[a]	42	68	108	133	Aleksandropol' to 1924.
147	Kolomna	Moscow R2	20	28	20	31[a]	21	31	75	100	131	
148	Kokand	Fergana Uz	x	54	81	119[a]	121	69	85	105	131	Center of independent khanate of Kokand to 1876.
149	Klaypeda	Lithuania	20[a]	19[a]	20[a]	21[a]	x	x	43[a]	90	131	Memel in Germany to 1919, then in independent Lithuania (autonomous region 1924–1939), in Lithuanian SSR from 1945. Klaipéda (Lithuanian).
150	Noril'sk	Krasnoyarsk R9							13	109	129	
151	Belgorod	Belgorod R4	15	23	27	x	20	31	34	72	129	
152	Cherkassy	Cherkassy U2	14[a]	21	30	42[a]	45	40	52	85	128	Cherkasy.
153	Novomoskovsk	Tula R2					2	1	76	107	126	Bobriki to 1934; Stalinogorsk 1934–1961.
154	Ussuriysk	Primorskiy R10			11	47[a]	31[a]	35	72	104	124	Nikol'skoye, Nikol'sk-Ussuriyskiy to 1935; Voroshilov 1935–1957.
155	Kommunarsk	Lugansk U1						16	55	98	124	Alchevsk to 1931; Voroshilovsk 1931–1959.
156	Novorossiysk	Krasnodar R6		8	17	67	51	68	95	93	123	
157	Ural'sk	Ural'sk K3	15	26	36	48	33	36	67	104	123	

TABLE 27—continued

No.	Name of City	Location[b]	1867	1885	1897	1915	1920	1926	1939	1959	1967	Notes and Former Names
158	Petropavlovsk-Kamchatskiy	Kamchatka R10						2	35	86	123	
159	Engel's	Saratov R5	13[a]	x	22	x	30	34	69	91	122	Pokrovskaya Sloboda 1747–1914; Pokrovsk 1914–1931.
160	Miass	Chelyabinsk R7	9[a]	x	17	x	25	19	38	99	122	Miyasskiy Zavod, Miyasskoye Selo.
161	Bratsk	Irkutsk R9								51	122	
162	Serpukhov	Moscow R2	14	21	31	42[a]	28	56	91	106	121	
163	Blagoveshchensk	Amur R10	3	9	33	62	58[a]	61	59	95	121	
164	Severodvinsk	Arkhangel'sk R1							21	79	121	Sudostroy to 1938; Molotovsk 1938–1957.
165	Lisichansk	Lugansk U1						7	26	38	120	
166	Bobruysk	Mogilëv B	25	57	34	42[a]	32[a]	51	84	98	120	
167	Lyubertsy	Moscow R2					3	6	46	91	120	
168	Melitopol'	Zaporozh'ye U1	6	13	15	x	22	25	76	95	119	
169	Nal'chik	Kabardino-Balkar A R6	1[a]	x	5	x	7	13	48	88	119	
170	Osh	Kirgizia		14	34	48[a]	48	31	33	65	119	
171	Kerch	Crimea U3	20	29	33	56[a]	36	35	104	98	118	
172	Kustanay	Kustanay K2		7	14	29	23	25	34	86	118	
173	Orekhovo-Zuyevo	Moscow R2			10	x	32	63	99	108	117	
174	Elektrostal'	Moscow R2							43	97	117	Zatish'ye to 1938.
175	Anzhero-Sudzhensk	Kemerovo R8						30	69	116	116	
176	Belovo	Kemerovo R8							43	107	116	
177	Kovrov	Vladimir R2	5	8	15	x	17	27	67	99	116	
178	Volzhskiy	Volgograd R5								67	114	
179	Slavyansk	Donetsk U1	11	16	16	x	31	29	78	83	113	
180	Mytishchi	Moscow R2					3	11	60	99	112	

TABLE 27—continued

No.	Name of City	Location[b]	1867	1885	1897	1915	1920	1926	1939	1959	1967	Notes and Former Names
181	Pskov	Pskov R1	13	22	30	38	31	44	60	81	112	In Poland 1921–1939.
182	Grodno	Grodno B	25	40	47	64	x	50[a]	49	73	111	
183	Pervoural'sk	Sverdlovsk R7	5[a]	x	7	x	8	9	44	90	110	Shaytanskiy Zavod; Pervoural'skiy Zavod, Pervoural'skiy.
184	Nikopol'	Dnepropetrovsk U1	9	8	17	x	13	14	58	83	110	
185	Cheremkhovo	Irkutsk R9			2	x	7	9	56	123	109	
186	Novoshakhtinsk	Rostov R6						7	48	104	107	Imena III Internatsionala Shakhta to 1929; Komintern 1929–1939.
187	Novokuyb-yshevsk	Kuybyshev R5								63	107	
188	Novgorod	Novgorod R1	17	24	26	28	26	33	40	61	107	
189	Maykop	Krasnodar R6		28	34	53[a]	50	53	56	82	106	
190	Serov	Sverdlovsk R7			6	x	19	33	65	98	104	Nadezhdinskiy Zavod, Nadezhdinsk; Kabakovsk.
191	Sumgait	Azerbaydzhan							6	52	104	
192	Konstantinovka	Donetsk U1						25	96	89	103	
193	Krasnyy Luch	Lugansk U1			11			7	59	94	102	Krindachevka to 1929.
194	Noginsk	Moscow R2	2	2		x	16	38	81	93	102	Bogorodsk to 1930.
195	Bukhara	Bukhara Uz	x	x	70[a]	x	x	47	50	69	102	Capital of independent Bukhara khanate to 1868, and of Russian protectorate 1868–1920; Staraya Bukhara to 1935.
196	Syktyvkar	Komi A R1	4	4	4	x	5	5	24	64	102	Ust'-Sysol'sk to 1930.
197	Gur'yev	Gur'yev K3	16	6	9	x	11	12	41	78	101	
198	Batumi	Georgia	x	12	29	46	61[a]	48	70	82	100	Batum to 1936.
199	Leninabad	Tadzhikistan	20	35	30	40[a]	36	37	46	77	100	Khodzhent to 1936.

TABLE 27—continued

No.	Name of City	Location[b]	1867	1885	1897	1915	1920	1926	1939	1959	1967	Notes and Former Names
200	Rovno	Rovno U2	7	7	25	35[a]	x	41[a]	43	56	100	In Poland 1921–1939: Równe.
201	Chirchik	Tashkent Uz							15	66	100	

NOTES:

x Indicates data not available in the sources cited.

[a] Data not uniform with other data in this table because of difference in year or difference in source or both (as in census of another country).

[b] The locations for the 201 cities of more than 100,000 population in 1967 are shown by oblasts or krays or autonomous soviet socialist republics (A) and by economic regions for the Russian, Ukrainian, and Kazakh republics, by oblasts for the Belorussian and Uzbek republics, and by republic only for the ten smaller republics, with the following abbreviations. Numbers record the number of cities of more than 100,000 population in 1967 in each unit.

Location shown by oblast, economic region, and republic

Russian Soviet Federated Socialist Republic (R)
- R1 Northwest — 11
- R2 Central — 23
- R3 Volga-Vyatka — 6
- R4 Central-Black-Earth — 5
- R5 Volga — 14
- R6 North Caucasus — 15
- R7 Urals — 16
- R8 Western Siberia — 14
- R9 Eastern Siberia — 8
- R10 Far East — 6

Ukraine, or Ukrainian SSR
- U1 Donets-Dnepr — 22
- U2 Southwest — 9
- U3 South — 6

Kazakhstan, or Kazakh SSR
- K1 Central and East Kazakhstan — 5
- K2 Tselinnyy Kray (Virgin Lands) — 4
- K3 West Kazakhstan Kray — 3
- K4 South Kazakhstan Kray — 2

Russian Soviet Federated Socialist Republic (R) — 118

Ukraine, or Ukrainian SSR — 37

Kazakhstan, or Kazakh SSR — 14

Principal sources:

1867. Russia. Tsentral'nyi statisticheskii komitet. *Statisticheskii vremennik Rossiiskoi Imperii*, seriia 2, vypusk 1. Sanktpeterburg, 1871. Tablitsa 14, "Ekonomicheskoe sostoianie gorodov," pp. 157–198.

Major supplementary source: *Geografichesko-Statisticheskii Slovar' Rossiiskoi Imperii*. P. Semenov, ed. Sanktpeterburg: Imperatorskoe Russkoe Geograficheskoe Obshchestvo, 1863–1885. 5 vols.

1885. Russia. Tsentral'nyi statisticheskii komitet. *Sbornik svedenii po Rossii za 1884–1885 gg*. "Statistika Rossiiskoi Imperii, tom 1," S.-Peterburg, 1887. Tablitsa 2, "Gorodskiia poseleniia Imperii," pp. 16–27.

1897. Russia. Tsentral'nyi statisticheskii komitet. *Pervaia vseobshchaia perepis' naseleniia Rossiiskoi Imperii 1897 goda*. S.-Peterburg, 1899–1905. 89 vols., p. 1 in each volume.

——. ——. Vypusk 5. *Okonchatel'no ustanovlennoe pri razrabotke perepisi. Nalichnoe naselenie gorodov*. 1905. Tablitsa 1, pp. 5–39.

——. ——. ——. *Goroda i poseleniia v uezdakh imeiushchie 2,000 i bolee zhitelei*, 1905, pp. 9–108.

1915. Russia. Tsentral'nyi statisticheskii komitet. *Statisticheskii ezhegodnik Rossii 1915 g*., Petrograd, 1916. "Naselenie gubernskikh i oblastnykh gorodov Rossiiskoi Imperii k 1 ianvaria 1915 g.," pp. 153–154.

Major supplementary sources: A. G. Rashin. *Naselenie Rossii za 100 Let (1811–1913 gg.)*, *Statisticheskie Ocherki*, Moskva, Gosstatizdat, 1956, Tablitsa 68, p. 110, "Goroda Rossii s naseleniem svyshe 100 tys. chel. na 1 ianvaria 1914 g."; and *Statesman's Yearbook 1916*, London, pp. 1286–1287. Data mainly for 1913 but vary from 1908 to 1915. Source of data for cities and towns not centers of guberniyas or oblasts.

1920. RSFSR. Tsentral'noe statisticheskoe upravlenie. *Statisticheskii ezhegodnik 1918–1920 gg*. Vypusk 1. "Trudy tsentral'nogo statistichesk-

266

TABLE 27—continued

Notes (continued):
Locations shown by oblast and republic
  Belorussia, or Belorussian SSR (B)
  Uzbekistan, or Uzbek SSR (Uz)
Locations shown by republic only
  Estonia, or Estonian SSR
  Latvia, or Latvian SSR
  Lithuania, or Lithuanian SSR
  Moldavia, or Moldavian SSR
  Georgia, or Georgian SSR
  Armenia, or Armenian SSR
  Azerbaydzhan, or Azerbaydzhan SSR
  Kirgizia, or Kirgiz SSR
  Tadzhikistan, or Tadzhik SSR
  Turkmenia, or Turkmenistan, or Turkmen SSR

PRINCIPAL SOURCES (continued):

ogo upravleniia, tom VIII, vypusk 1." Moskva, 1921. Tablitsa 3, "Nalichnoe naselenie gorodskikh poselenii 28 avgusta 1920 g."

6
7 pp. 23–37. Lacks data on Soviet Far East, Middle Asia, Caucasus, and southern and western parts of the Ukraine, then politically unsettled.

1 ———. *Statisticheskii ezhegodnik 1921 g. vypusk 1.* "Trudy tsentral'nogo statisticheskogo upravleniia, tom. 8, vypusk 3." Moskva,
3 1922. Tablitsa 3. "Gorodskie poseleniia Kryma, Turkestana, Azerbaidzhana i 7 gubernii Ukrainy," p. 23. Data on cities in the
1 Crimea, Middle Asia, Azerbaydzhan, and parts of the Ukraine
3 missing from the previous yearbook.

3 SSSR. Tsentral'noe Statisticheskoe Upravlenie. *Statisticheskii ezhegodnik 1922 i 1923.* Vypusk 1. "Trudy tsentral'nogo statisticheskogo upravleniia. Tom 8, vypusk 5," Moskva, Tablitsa 3, "Goroda i
2 poseleniia gorodskogo tipa s naseleniem 10,000 Zhitelei i bolee po perepisiam," 1923/1920 gg., pp. 21–23. Data for 1921, 1922, or
2 1923 for some cities for which 1920 data are lacking.

1 ———. *Sbornik statisticheskikh svedenii po soiuzu S.S.R. 1918–1923,* "Trudy tsentral'nogo statisticheskogo upravleniia, tom 18," Moskva, 1924, Tablitsa 4. "Naselenie krupneishikh gorodov Rosii po perepisiam 1920 i 1923 gg. (svyshe 50,000 zhitelei)," p. 38.

1926. SSSR. Tsentralnoe statisticheskoe upravlenie. *Vsesoiuznaia perepis' naseleniia 1926 g.* Moskva, 1928–1933. 56 volumes. Otdel 1, vols. 1–16, Tablitsa 5, "Nalichnoe i postoiannoe naselenie gorodskikh poselenii," page numbers vary from volume to volume.

1939 and 1959. SSSR. Tsentral'noe statisticheskoe upravlenie. *Itogi vsesoiuznoi perepisi naseleniia 1959 goda.* Moskva, 1962–1963. 16 vols. Tablitsa 6 "Chislennost' naseleniia gorodov i poselkov gorodskogo tipa v 1939 i 1959 gg." Page numbers vary from volume to volume.

1967. SSSR. *Administrativno-territorial'noe delenie soiuznykh respublik na 1, iiulia 1967 goda.* Moskva, 1967, "Perechen' gorodov s ukazaniem chislennosti naseleniia," pp. 592–604. Estimates for January 1, 1967.

then grew more rapidly than any other large Soviet city from 70 to 644 thousand 1920–1939 with the development of the automobile industry. It then slackened its pace somewhat.

Novosibirsk (8), the youngest of the large cities of Figure 61, was founded as the settlement of Gusevka only in 1894 and renamed Novonikolayevsk from 1903 to 1926. It grew with particular rapidity in the period 1897–1911 (from 8 to 63 thousand) with the building of the Trans-Siberian Railway and from 1920 to 1939 (68 to 404 thousand) with industrialization and the development of the nearby Kuzbas coalfield and industrial district.

Kuybyshev (9), formerly Samara, has had continued rapid growth in population, notable for substantial increases in both World War I and the Civil War (1915–1920) and during World War II, when, safe from immediate military threat by virtue of its inland location but still fairly centrally located, it was the temporary war time capital of the Soviet Union. A Volga port and flour-milling city in the 19th century, it has become a major industrial center in the 20th century (machinery and chemicals).

Sverdlovsk, formerly Yekaterinburg (10), center of the Ural mining and industrial district, had relatively modest growth 1867–1920 (25 to 70 thousand) but very rapid growth 1920–1967 (70 to 961 thousand).

Tbilisi (11), capital of Georgia in the Caucasus, had rapid growth 1885–1915, then stagnation to 1926, followed by renewed rapid growth.

Donetsk, formerly Yuzovka and Stalino, (12), the center of the Donbas coal mining and industrial district, has had very rapid growth. The settlement of Yuzovka arose only in 1870 and was not recognized as a city until 1917. Its growth from 28 thousand in 1897 to 840 thousand in 1967 was especially rapid in the period of the early Five-Year Plans with emphasis on coal and steel, when the city increased from 106 to 466 thousand in a little over 12 years (1926–1939).

Chelyabinsk (13), the Ural industrial center, although founded as a fortress in 1736 and made a city in 1787, reached a population of 10 thousand only in 1885, but thereafter grew at a very high rate to 1915, then stagnated to 1926 before resuming very rapid increases, especially in the period 1926–1939.

Kazan' (14) will be discussed in the next section as it has lost in relative position.

Dnepropetrovsk, (15) formerly Yekaterinoslav, the industrial city on the Dnepr River in the Ukraine, had very rapid growth in the late 19th century, increasing from 23 thousand in 1867 to 220 thousand in 1912. The opening of the Donbas coalfield and industrial district in the 1870s, the building of railroads, and the exploitation of the Krivoy Rog iron ore deposits to the west from 1881, all stimulated its growth. It lost population during World War I and the Civil War but again grew very rapidly to 1939. Since 1939, however, its pace of growth has been slower.

Perm', formerly Molotov 1940–1957 (16), the industrial city in the northwest Urals, grew at a modest but steady pace from 1867 to 1926, then it grew very rapidly in the period 1926–1939 and has continued a high rate of increase up to the present with the development of the resources of the Kama River and the Urals (coal, chemicals, metals, water power) and the production of machinery.

The Largest Cities of 1867

Growth patterns during the century 1867–1967 of the 17 cities on the present territory of the USSR that had been the largest in 1867 are shown in Figure 62. During the past century they generally have had much lower rates of increase in population than the cities that are now the largest in the Soviet Union, for even if still among the largest the growth rate was lower than for cities that have become the largest only later; in fact, many of them are no longer among the very largest. The growth patterns of the 6 that are still among the very largest have already been discussed: Moscow, Leningrad, Kiev, Tashkent, Tbilisi, and Khar'kov. The others will now be treated in order of size in 1867 (cf. Table 26).

Odessa (17), the port on the Black Sea, was the third largest city of the Russian Empire for the last half century of Tsarist Russia. It grew from 121 thousand in 1867 to 631 thousand, 550 thousand, or 500 thousand on the eve of World War I, according to various estimates.[15] Indeed of all the large cities in European

[15] 631 thousand in 1912 according to *Statesman's Yearbook 1916*, p. 1286; 550 thousand in 1911 according to Sovet S"ezdov Predstavitelei Promyshlennosti i

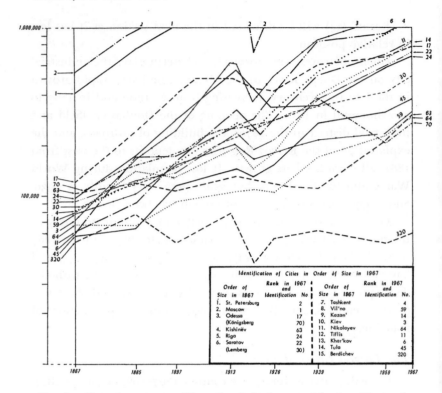

Fig. 62 Growth patterns 1867–1967 of the largest cities in 1867 on the present territory of the Soviet Union. For location of cities, see Figure 58.

Russia, it had according to Rashin the highest rate of increase during the period 1811–1914, when it increased its population 45-fold (from 11 to 500 thousand).[16] It grew with the booming export trade in wheat from the hinterland in the Ukraine based on expanding grain production in the Russian black-earth steppes, the construction of railroads capable of cheaply transporting the grain to export ports, the development of ocean shipping for bulk

---

Torgovli, *Statisticheskii Ezhegodnik na 1912 god.*, V. I. Sharyi, ed. (S.-Peterburg, 1913), p. 3; and 500 thousand in 1914 according to A. G. Rashin, *Naselenie Rossii za 100 Let (1811–1913 gg.)*, *Statisticheskie ocherki*, (M. Gosstatizdat, 1956), p. 110. The problem is that in these years Odessa was not the center of a guberniya and thus its population was not officially recorded in the statistical yearbooks then issued annually.
[16] Rashin, *op. cit.*, p. 89.

commodities, and the rise of markets in Western Europe. With new social, political, and economic conditions that grew out of the October Revolution of 1917, with emphasis of national rather than international economic ties, with shifting interest to industrialization rather than trade, and with focus on interior rather than peripheral centers of production, the city declined in population from 1915 to 1920 and again from 1920 to 1926. Thereafter, it grew at the slowest rate of any of the large Soviet cities.

Kishinëv (63), the capital of the Moldavian SSR, was the fourth largest city in the entire Russian Empire in 1867 but had a peripheral position for the country as a whole. It was the center of a densely settled and productive agricultural region. Already large in relation to its immediate tributary area by 1867, it grew modestly in the period 1867–1885 with the building of railroads in the 1870s, but then declined in the period 1885–1897. Without much of an increase in 1897–1913, it moved into a long period of declining population for the two following periods 1913–1920 and 1920–1939 when between the 2 world wars, it was part of Romania. Since World War II it has grown rapidly with the development of a modern machinery industry that has provided a more dynamic employment base than the traditional food and clothing industries.

Riga (24), Baltic port and capital of Latvia, like its fellow port city Odessa, grew very rapidly in the period 1867–1915 as the export trade of the old Russian Empire prospered with the building of the railroads and the rise of international trade. It was the fourth city in size in the Russian Empire in the late 19th century after it passed Kishinëv about 1870. It lost population in the period 1913–1925 and had a relatively stable population 1925–1939 as new political boundaries cut off a large part of its natural hinterland, but then has grown rapidly since 1939 with industrial expansion.

Saratov (22) on the Volga River has had continuous fairly rapid growth except for the period 1915–1920. Its relative decline from position 6 in 1867 to 22 in 1967 was not due to slowness of growth but rather to the even faster growth of a number of other major Soviet cities. In the 19th century it was a center of the grain trade and a transfer point for Volga-shipped oil and timber and in the Soviet period has witnessed the rise of a large machinery industry. Recently oil and gas have been developed in its vicinity.

Vil'no, Vil'na, or Vil'nyus (59), the capital of the Lithuanian SSR, an inland city, grew somewhat less rapidly than the port cities of Odessa or Riga but more rapidly than inland Kishinëv in the period 1867–1915. It decreased in population during World War I and its aftermath and by 1931 had not yet recovered its 1915 population. Its subsequent growth was slow until the period 1959–1967. Vil'no was annexed to Poland in 1922 and passed to Lithuania in 1939. It suffered heavily in World War I and the Civil War. A leading center of Jewish culture, it again suffered a heavy loss of life in World War II.

Kazan' (14), the Tatar center at the bend of the Volga, was the fourth largest city in the Russian Empire in 1811. It grew slowly and somewhat irregularly from 1811 to 1920 with decreases both in 1885–1897 and 1915–1920 but high rates of increase in 1867–1885 and 1926–1939, and a quickening of growth in recent years (1959–1967) with the rise of the Volga-Ural oilfield, which lies partly in the Tatar ASSR, of which Kazan' is the capital. It is not uncommon for a period of very rapid growth (and construction) in a city to be followed by a slackening of pace or even decrease as occurred in Kazan' in the contrasting successive periods 1867–1885 and 1885–1897.

Nikolayev (64), a port on the Black Sea at the mouth of the Yuzhnyy Bug, grew rapidly in the early part of the 19th century from 4 thousand in 1811 to 65 thousand in 1863,[17] a consequence of its role as a center of shipbuilding and a naval base, but then had very slow growth from 1867 to 1926. It participated in the export of grain and ores from the Ukraine.

Tula (45), like Saratov, has grown substantially in the last century from 57 to 371 thousand but other Soviet cities have grown even more rapidly. One of the oldest Russian industrial centers, it has been a major producer of arms from the 17th cen-

---

[17] Rashin, *op. cit.*, p. 90.

tury. It grew at highest rates 1885–1897 and 1925–1939 with further industrial development.

Berdichev (320), in Zhitomir Oblast in the Ukraine, west of Kiev, is one of the few sizeable cities in the Soviet Union that have had no substantial growth in the last century, having had a fluctuating but generally declining population since 1885 with sharp drops 1885–1897 and 1913–1920 and a modest decline 1939–1959. Center of great fairs and an important entrepôt for southwest Russia in the 19th century, it declined in competition with other commercial centers in the late 19th century; its commerce and handicraft industries stagnated or declined in the Soviet period; and its Jewish component (55 per cent of the population of the city in the 1926 census) suffered grievously during World War II.

Two cities not within the Russian Empire in 1867 but of a size that would have ranked them among the largest 8 cities of that date within the present boundaries of the Soviet Union are Kaliningrad and L'vov (Figure 62).

Kaliningrad (70) as the city of Königsberg, the commercial and administrative center of East Prussia, grew steadily, though at a somewhat slower rate than most large cities now within the Soviet Union, throughout the 19th century and the 20th century up to World War II. On its occupation and annexation by the Soviet Union at the end of the war and on the expulsion of its German inhabitants, the city suffered a sharp drop in population not yet fully replaced (1939 population, 372 thousand; 1959 population, 204 thousand; 1967 population, 270 thousand) (Table 27).

L'vov, formerly Lemberg or Lwów (30), an important regional center successively under Austria-Hungary (as capital of Galicia), Poland, and the Soviet Union, had an amazingly steady growth in population throughout the century without lasting drops in population at the times of the 2 world wars or the transfers of its political subordination.

Other Cities Among the Largest Throughout the Last Century

In Figure 63 are plotted the growth patterns over the last century of 11 other cities, which had already attained a population of

274

Cities of the Soviet Union

about 30 thousand by the year 1867, 50 thousand by 1885, and 100 thousand by 1967. They thus have been sizeable cities for more than a century and have also shown substantial growth over the century.

Six of these 11 cities are located in the non-Russian western part of the Soviet Union, 2 in the Belorussian SSR and 4 in the Ukrainian SSR (Figure 64).

Minsk (19), the capital of the Belorussian SSR near the western border of the Soviet Union, has shown rapid growth throughout the period but particularly since 1920. It has had concentrated in it much of the economic development of its tributary region. It accounts for 31 per cent of the industrial production of the whole Belorussian SSR.[18] It has become an administrative and industrial

[18] *Kratkaia Geograficheskaia Entsiklopediia*, tom 3, 1962, p. 8.

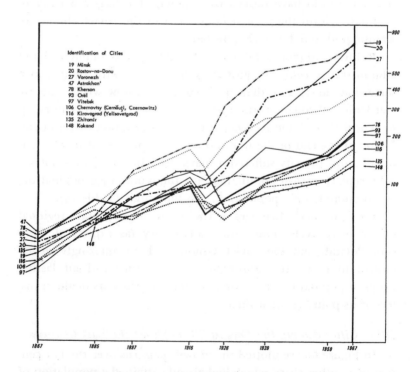

Fig. 63 Growth patterns 1867–1967 of eleven other cities large throughout the century. For location of cities, see Figure 64.

center: machinery, especially automobiles and tractors, and metal working, especially machine tools. It is one of the few cities near the western borders of the Soviet Union to have had continuous rapid growth throughout the entire century, except only in the crisis period of 1915–1920.

Vitebsk (97) similarly had rapid growth until 1915 and from 1920 to 1939 but suffered during both world wars decreasing in population 1915–1920 and also 1939–1959. It is characterized by light industry, especially textiles, clothing, knit goods, and shoes.

The largest of the cities in the Ukraine in Figures 63 and 64 is Kherson (78), river port on the lower Dnepr River, 25 kilometers from its mouth in the Black Sea. Periods of rapid growth 1867–1885, 1897–1915, and since 1926 have alternated with periods of population shrinkage, 1885–1897, 1915–1920, and 1920–1926. A shipbuilding and grain-shipment port, it declined under the com-

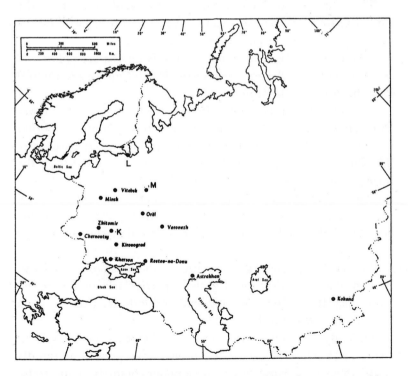

Fig. 64 Location of eleven cities large throughout the century, 1867–1967.

petition of the other Black Sea ports, Odessa and Nikolayev, in the late 19th century until the deepening of the river channel (1901) revived its growth; its second period of decline, which occurred during the Soviet period and extended into the 1920s was arrested by the development of the Dnepr River navigation after 1932 with the construction of the Dnepr dams.

Chernovtsy or Chernăuţi (106), the regional center of Bukovina, in the western part of the Ukraine has had fairly steady growth at a moderate pace throughout the century (in its Austrian period to 1918, its Romanian period 1918–1940, and its Soviet period since 1940) except for a dip at the onset of World War II.

Kirovograd, formerly Yelisavetgrad (116), in the agricultural Ukraine, has had slow growth, with stagnation 1885–1897 and 1915–1920 and a decline in the period 1920–1926. It processes agricultural products and produces agricultural machinery.

Zhitomir (135), regional center of Volhynia, of which it was the capital until 1925, has had steady but rather slow growth, except for the decline of the period 1915–1920.

Three other cities shown on Figures 63 and 64 are oblast and regional centers of the grain-producing North Caucasus or Central Russian Black-Earth Region.

Rostov-na-Donu (20), center for the North Caucasus and lower Don country, has had fairly rapid growth throughout the century except for the relatively slow growth 1914–1920 and 1939–1959. The apparently very rapid increase 1920–1926 resulted from the incorporation of the Armenian suburb of Nakhichevan'. Rostov grew as a commercial (including grain export) and industrial center in the 19th century and maintained its rapid growth in the Soviet period with development of agricultural machinery production.

Voronezh (27), the regional center of the Russian Black-Earth Region, has had fairly rapid growth, particularly in the period 1926–1939. It is a diversified regional and industrial center, lying between Moscow and the Donbas.

Orël (93), another oblast center in the Russian Black-Earth Center, was actually larger than Voronezh and grew more rapidly in the 1860s and 1870s when it was a major commercial and transshipment center (on the Oka River), but with the building of the railroad from Moscow south, the transshipment function of Orël declined and the population fell from 78 thousand in 1885 to 70 thousand in 1897. The population fell again during war periods, 1915–1920 and 1939–1959.

Kokand (148) in the Fergana basin in Middle Asia was the center of the independent Khanate of Kokand that flourished particularly in the 18th and 19th centuries until its conquest by Russia in 1876. It increased rapidly in population before the Revolution (from 54 thousand in 1885 to 119 thousand in 1911) but lost population heavily during the Civil War, when it was the seat of a counter-revolutionary government. Its population dropped from 121 thousand in 1920 to 69 thousand in 1926 (Table 27). Since 1926 it has grown at a modest rate even though it is not even the administrative center of an oblast (it is in Fergana Oblast in the Uzbek SSR).

Astrakhan' (47) was a comparatively large city (16th in size in the Russian Empire in 1867) during the late 19th century and grew quite rapidly up to 1915. It lies near the mouth of the Volga River in the Caspian Sea and thus profited from the expanding oil production of the Baku district on the western shore of the Caspian and the shipment of this oil via the Caspian and the Volga, from fishing on the Caspian, and from traffic on the Volga. Its growth in the Soviet period has been relatively modest, for it lacks a large productive tributary area (since it is located in semidesert country) and has not had industrial development as rapid as many other Soviet cities.

Some Smaller Cities That Reached Pre-Soviet Population Peaks

Figure 65 shows the growth patterns of 10 cities that reached peaks of population on the eve of World War I, followed by declining populations during the early Soviet period and usually slow growth thereafter (Table 28). They are all in early and densely settled agricultural lands, for which they typically have been historical centers (Figure 66). Some have suffered heavily in wartime both in World War I and World War II. The former functions of some have been reduced by new economic modes with state ownership and organization of trade and with the decline of old handicraft industries. New technology or new transport facilities have by-passed some of them. Five were involved in changes in international boundaries and 5 were not (Table 28).

Daugavpils (formerly Dvinsk, Dinaburg) in Latvia is a testimony to the terrible destructive power of war. Between 1867 and 1910 it grew from 30 to 110 thousand. But largely destroyed during World War I and the Civil War, it had a population of only 41 thousand in 1925. Its growth thereafter was relatively slow until after 1959.

Yelgava (formerly Mitava), also in Latvia, historical center of Kurland, similarly suffered in both world wars with successive evacuations of population, destruction, and conquests and reconquests. Its 1913 population of 46 thousand was not reached again until 1965.

Liyepaya (formerly Libava), also in Latvia, bears witness to the importance of the tributary area to a port. It grew rapidly from 1867 to 1911, increasing in this period in population from 9 to 91 thousand. The railroad which reached it in 1871 opened up a vastly larger tributary area and port construction was completed in 1890. It soon became one of Russia's chief ice-free Baltic ports. This tributary area was truncated by political boundaries that arose after World War I and the population fell to 61 thousand in 1925 and even further to 53 thousand in 1939. Subsequent growth has been relatively slow until after 1959.

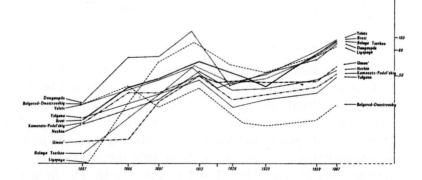

Fig. 65 Growth patterns 1867–1967 of some old cities that reached pre-Soviet peaks in population and stagnated in the early Soviet years. See Table 28 and Figure 66.

Brest (formerly Brest-Litovsk) in Belorussia on the boundary with Poland is a transportation center, a railroad junction and river port on the Western Bug River. A large segment of the population is employed in transportation. It grew before World War I from 22 to 64 thousand, 1867–1913, but with the political separation of Poland and Russia and the decline of trade across this border the city went into a long depression with its population falling to 48 thousand in 1931 and 41 thousand in 1939, but it has revived with new political arrangements after World War II. By virtue of its border position it was selected as the site for the sign-

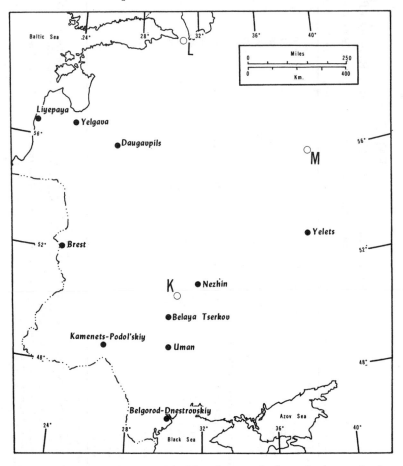

Fig. 66 Location of some old cities that reached pre-Soviet peaks in population.

TABLE 28
POPULATION OF SOME OLD CITIES THAT REACHED PRE-SOVIET
POPULATION PEAKS AND STAGNATED IN EARLY SOVIET YEARS

Name of City	Location	1867	1885	1897	1913	1920	1926	1939	1959	1967
A. Involved in Boundary Changes:										
Daugavpils	Latvia	30	69	70	110[a]	x	41[c]	52	66	89
Liyepaya	Latvia	9	30	64	91[b]	x	61[c]	53	72	86
Yelgava	Latvia	23	30	35	46	x	28[c]	32	36	49
Brest	Belorussia	22	40	47	64	x	48[e]	41	74	96
Belgorod-Dnestrovskiy	Odessa O.	30	41	28	40	x	21[d]	20	22	29
B. Not Involved in Boundary Changes:										
Kamenets-Podol'skiy	Khmel'nitskiy O.	21	36	36	50	x	32	35	40	52
Uman'	Cherkassy O.	15	16	31	50	44	45	44	45	59
Belaya Tserkov	Kiev O.	12	x	35	60[b]	x	43	47	71	92
Nezhin	Chernigov O.	21	x	32	53	29	38	39	46	55
Yelets	Lipetsk O.	30	39	47	58[f]	40	43	51	78	96

[a] 1910
[b] 1911
[c] 1925
[d] 1930
[e] 1931
x—not available

Alternative Names:
Daugavpils: formerly Dvinsk, Dinaburg. (German: Dünaburg.)
Liyepaya: formerly Libava. Lettish: Liepāja. Alternative transliteration: Liepaya, Liepaia, or Liepaja. (German: Libau.)
Yelgava: formerly Mitava. Lettish: Jelgava. Alternative transliteration: Elgava. (German: Mitau.)
Brest: formerly Brest-Litovsk, Brześć nad Bugiem. (Polish), Berest'ye.
Belgorod-Dnestrovskiy: formerly Akkerman (Turkish), Cetatea-Albă (Rumanian). Anciently: Tyras.
Yelets. Alternative transliteration: Elets.
Sources: Same as Table 27.

ing of the treaty of Brest-Litovsk between the Soviet Union and Germany in 1918.

Farther to the south the city of Belgorod-Dnestrovskiy (literally, white city on the Dnestr River) is an exceedingly ancient settlement with a checkered history, formerly known by its Turkish name, Akkerman ("white fortress"), and later by its Romanian name, Cetatea-Albă ("white city"). Located on the Dnestr Bay near the Black Sea near the border of the Ukraine, Moldavia, and Romania and peripheral to all 3, it was in Romania between the world wars. Although a commercial center it has not developed a large tributary area and although possessing food industries (such as fish canning) it has been by-passed by modern growth industires. Thus its population of 30 thousand in 1867 exceeded its population of 29 thousand, a century later, in 1967.

Also near the western borderlands of the country but not actually engaged in boundary shifts is Kamenets-Podol'skiy, historically the political, commercial, and industrial center of Podolia but now merely the terminal of a branch-line railroad from Khmel'nitskiy, the center of the oblast to which it is now administratively subordinate. Kemenets-Podol'skiy reached a population of 50 thousand in 1913, dropped to 32 thousand in 1926 and reached its 1913 size only in 1966.

Uman' in Cherkassy Oblast in the Ukraine similarly near the former boundary of the USSR reached 50 thousand in 1913, decreased to 44 thousand in 1920, and remained at that level through 1959.

Belaya Tserkov, south of Kiev in the Ukraine, developed as a large commercial marketing point in the 19th century, especially for the sale of agricultural produce, such as sugar. It thus grew in population from 12 to 60 thousand between 1867 and 1911. But after the Revolution this form of marketing was replaced by state procurements and the city declined in population to 43 thousand in 1926; it stagnated during the great period of urban growth of other cities in 1926–1939 but after World War II it experienced industrial expansion.

Nezhin, in Chernigov Oblast in the Ukraine, was similarly an important commercial center of the 19th century that declined sharply from 53 to 29 thousand between 1913 and 1920 and grew only slowly thereafter. In 1967 it had just again attained the population of more than half a century earlier.

Yelets, in Lipetsk Oblast, in the Russian Black-Earth Center, is similar to Belaya Tserkov in being an important 19th century agricultural center for grain. The first Russian grain elevator was built here in 1887. But as a commercial city it declined in the early years of Soviet power.

All of these older but smaller western cities with slow growth patterns in the early Soviet period have shown a higher rate of increase since 1959. Possible factors in this recent revival of growth may be the policy of locating industries so as to utilize labor reserves, the wave of migration to the cities of the young people from the densely settled adjacent rural areas, and the policy of developing the smaller centers and of limiting the growth of the very large cities. Perhaps with the development of the Council for Mutual Economic Assistance (Comecon) and the rise of important markets to the west of the Soviet Union, these western cities are not so marginal to economic life of the country as formerly.

Some New Soviet Industrial Giants

In sharp contrast to the relatively stagnant agricultural and commercial centers of the west, 18 new industrial settlements of more than 100 thousand population in the east are boom towns, mighty symbols of the Soviet devotion to heavy industry (Figures 67 and 68). They are new creations of the Soviet period and are located near sources of raw material or energy or are centers of heavy industries.[19]

Of these 18 raw-material oriented new industrial giants, 8 are on coalfields, 2 are at hydroelectric sites, 2 lie at ore deposits, 2 are steel centers, and 4 developed on the basis of oil and chemical industries. The 8 on coalfields are Karaganda in Kazakhstan; Novokuznetsk, Kemerovo, Prokop'yevsk, Kiselëvsk, and Belovo in the Kuzbas in Western Siberia; Novoshakhtinsk in an eastern extension of the Donbas; and Novomoskovsk in the Moscow basin

[19] For discussions of the industrial bases that gave rise to these cities see Theodore Shabad, *Basic Industrial Resources of the U.S.S.R.* (New York: Columbia University Press, 1969), the index of which lists each of these 18 cities, and the pages on which they are treated.

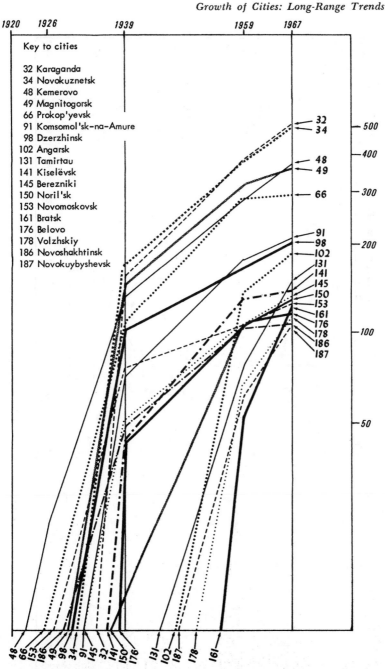

Fig. 67 Growth patterns of some large new Soviet cities. For location of cities, see Figure 68.

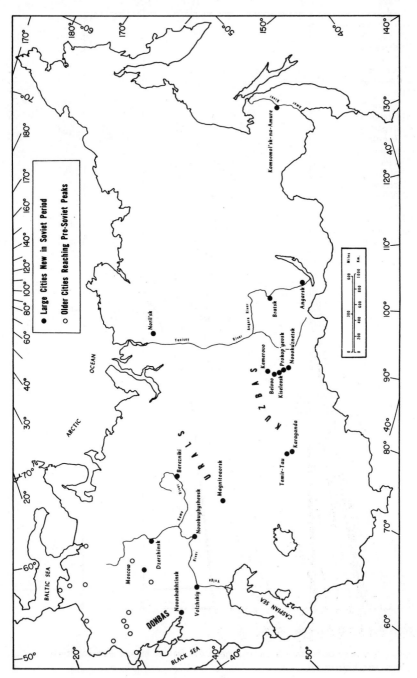

Fig. 68 Location of some large new Soviet cities.

south of Moscow. The 2 at sites of hydroelectric development are Volzhskiy on the Volga near Volgograd and Bratsk on the Angara in Eastern Siberia. The 2 at ore deposits are Magnitogorsk in the southern Urals and Noril'sk in Eastern Siberia near the lower Yenisey River. The 2 engaged primarily in iron and steel production are Komsomol'sk on the Amur River in the Soviet Far East and Temirtau near Karaganda in Kazakhstan; in addition several other iron and steel centers are on coalfields or at iron-ore deposits. The 4 based on the chemical industry or oil refining or both are Dzerzhinsk on the Volga River near Gor'kiy, Novokuybyshevsk on the Volga near Kuybyshev, Berezniki on the Kama River in the northwest Urals, and Angarsk on the Angara River in Eastern Siberia.

Especially noteworthy are the 8 new large cities on coalfields, typically combining coal mining with industries located on the coalfield for cheap fuel, since cities devoted exclusively to coal mining rarely achieve a size of 100 thousand.

The largest of the new coalfield cities is Karaganda (32) in the arid country of Kazakhstan that only 40 years ago was without cities as the home of wandering Kazakh herdsmen. Substantial coal production began in Karaganda in 1930, the railroad arrived in 1931; yet the city reached a population of nearly half a million by 1967 (Table 27).

The greatest cluster of new large coalfield cities is in the Kuzbas in Western Siberia, one of the greatest coalfields in the world in terms of quantity of reserves, thickness of seams, quality of coal, and ease of mining. Novokuznetsk, called Stalinsk 1932–1961 (34), by its name, its size, and its diversified coal-mining, steel, aluminum, chemical, and machinery industries epitomizes this group of cities. The city developed in the 1930s with the bold, expensive, and massive construction of the Ural-Kuznetsk Combine under the First Five-Year Plan. By 1967 it had reached nearly half a million population.

Other large cities of the Kuzbas, similar in type, are Kemerovo (48), the oblast center, an old settlement that grew rapidly, however, only with the development of the coalfield (coal, chemicals, and machinery), Prokop'yevsk (66) (coking coal, mining equipment), Kiselëvsk (141) (coal and coal machinery), and Belovo (176) (also nonferrous metallurgy).

The Donbas coal-mining and industrial district of the eastern Ukraine received its start somewhat earlier though it has grown very rapidly in the Soviet period. For example Donetsk, formerly Stalino (12), its major center, began its development about 1870 as we have already noted above and grew from 106 thousand in 1926 to 840 thousand in 1967. But the eastern extension of the coalfield into the RSFSR in Rostov Oblast has been developed more recently and here Novoshakhtinsk ("new mine") (186) is a new Soviet city based on anthracite mining and coal-derived chemicals.

In the lignite (brown coal) field south of Moscow in connection with the campaign to use focal fuels (even if of low quality), Novo-moskovsk, formerly Bobriki and then Stalinogorsk, 1934–1961 (153), was founded in 1930 (during the First Five-Year Plan) as a mining and lignite-based chemical and machinery center.

A notable feature of these large cities based primarily on coal mining has been a marked reduction in rate of growth in the most recent period, 1959–1967. This can be seen on Figure 67 especially in the cases of Prokop'yevsk (66), Kiselevsk (141), and Novoshakh-tinsk (186). In part this may be the result of shifting emphasis to oil and gas as a source of fuel and energy; in part an expression of an appropriate scale for the exploitation of a segment of a coal-field.

Many new Soviet cities are located at the sites of development of waterpower resources. Two particularly striking cases are Vol-zhskiy (178), which arose only in 1951 with the construction of the Volga dam and hydroelectric station just above Volgograd, and Bratsk (161) on the Angara River, north of Irkutsk in Eastern Siberia, which arose in 1955 in connection with the construction of the Bratsk hydroelectric station.

Two new cities are located at mineral deposits for mining of ores and smelting of metals. The most famous of these is Magnito-gorsk (49) located at the great reserve of high-grade iron ore, Mag-nitnaya Gora, unused in the days of charcoal furnaces, since it is located on the treeless southern steppe portion of the Urals; but with changing technology — the rise of smelting with coke and the building of a railroad — and with new economic policies (low rail-road rates for coal from the Kuzbas 2,000 kilometers away) and new sources of investment funds with the government financing of the Ural-Kuznets Combine in the First Five-Year Plan, the city was created from scratch at a hectic pace beginning in 1929. The iron and steel works were then named after Stalin, the driving force behind the concentration of national effort on heavy industry. In 1967 it was a city of 357 thousand, twice the size of Gary, Indiana, the American steel city at the south end of Lake Michigan.

In contrast to Magnitogorsk, which lies on the southern steppe margin of the great forests, Noril'sk (150) lies on the other, northern, tundra edge of the forest in the Far North of Western Siberia in an isolated bleak environment. The magnet for a settlement here is rich mineral deposits of nickel, copper, and cobalt. Construction of Noril'sk, one of the most northern cities in the world, began in 1935. By 1937 it was connected by a short railroad with Dudinka, a port on the Yenisey River, but, except for the river connection, separated from the closest station on the railroad network of Siberia by about 1,500 km. of trackless forest. With only 13 thousand inhabitants in 1939, it grew to 129 thousand in 1967 as a nonferrous mining and smelting center.

Two new cities have steel industries. The largest and most famous of these is Komsomol'sk-na-Amure ("city of communist youth on the Amur River") (91), in the Soviet Far East, an entirely new city for an iron and steel industry remote from main centers of population; construction began in 1932. The other steel city, Temirtau (131) in Kazakhstan near Karaganda, has been built only during and after World War II with iron and steel and synthetic rubber factories.

Four new cities have developed on the basis of the oil and chemical industries. Dzerzhinsk (98) near Gor'kiy was formed in 1930 and boomed during the 1930s with the building up of a chemical industry (phosphate fertilizers, insecticides, chemicals for synthetic fibers). Berezniki (145) in the Urals north of Perm', was formed in 1932 and as the seat of a giant chemical works constructed in the 1930s became the then leading center of the Soviet chemical industry with the production of chemical fertilizers (including all 3 of the major types of fertilizers, potash, nitrate, and phosphate); these were based in part on local deposits of salt and potash, nearby phosphorites, and nearby coal. This large new enterprise was not built in an empty space but was on the site of earlier though small industries; the salt works date back to the 16th century and the first Russian soda plant was established here in 1883. But the scale of development was new to the Soviet period.

The other two chemical centers, Novokuybyshevsk (187) near Kuybyshev and Angarsk (102) near Irkutsk are both much newer and are associated with the explosion in petroleum production after World War II. Novokuybyshevsk arose in 1948 with the oil industry and has a large oil refinery. The construction of Angarsk also began in 1948 with various industries culminating in an oil refinery and chemical works.

REGIONAL CONTRASTS IN GROWTH OF URBAN POPULATION AND DEGREE OF URBANIZATION 1897–1959

Marked regional contrasts both in rate of urban growth and in increase in degree of urbanization have characterized all recent periods in the Soviet Union. Long-range regional comparisons based on areal units rather than on individual cities have been difficult to make, however, because of the changing boundaries of oblasts (and thus of statistical units), the varying external boundaries of the country (particularly during the 2 world wars), the changing definitions of urban (particularly the contrast between Tsarist and Soviet practices on definition of cities), and finally differing current criteria for the recognition of cities in the different republics that constitute the Soviet Union.[20] Lorimer in his study of regional patterns of population increase for the period 1926–1939 had to take into account numerous changes in the internal administrative boundaries of the Soviet Union during those years.[21] Fortunately Lewis and colleagues have made elaborate

[20] O. A. Konstantinov, "Sovremennoe Sostoianie Deleniia Naselennykh Punktov SSSR na Gorodskie i Sel'skie," *Izvestiia Akademiia Nauk SSSR, Seriia Geograficheskaia*, 1958, No. 6, pp. 69–78.

[21] Frank Lorimer, *The Population of the Soviet Union: History and Prospects*, (Geneva: League of Nations, 1946). "Series of League of Nations Publications. II. Economic and Financial. 1946. II. A. 3." See especially Chapter 5, "Population Redistribution within the Soviet Union, 1926–1939," pp. 145–174.

statistical adjustments in order to provide data for comparable statistical units over long periods of time.[22] They adopted as areal units the major economic regions as of 1961, since data for them were generally provided in the 1959 census publications covering both 1959 and 1939 and other data on socio-economic characteristics for these areal units were sometimes available (Figure 69).

Fig. 69   Regions for comparison of 1897 and 1959 urban population.

Calculations were then made for the 1926 and 1897 censuses adjusted to these boundaries. Because of varying definitions of cities and urban population, both over space and over time, a new but uniform criterion was chosen for calculations: centers with more than 15,000 population, the smallest units for which published individual city data were available in the RSFSR for 1939 and 1959. Comparable regional data for urban population and for per cent of population urban for 1897 and for 1959, and for their increase between those years, are presented in Table 29.

[22] J. William Leasure and Robert A. Lewis, *Population Changes in Russia and the USSR: a set of Comparable Territorial Units.* (San Diego, California: San Diego State College Press, 1966), "Social Science Monograph Series, Vol. 1, No. 2"; Robert A. Lewis and J. William Leasure, "Regional Population Changes in Russia and the USSR since 1851," *Slavic Review,* Vol. 25, No. 4 (December, 1966), pp. 663–668; and Robert A. Lewis and Richard H. Rowland, "Urbanization in Russia and the USSR: 1897–1966." *Annals of the Association of American Geographers,* vol. 59, no. 4 (December, 1969), pp. 776–796.

TABLE 29

INCREASE IN URBAN POPULATION AND IN PERCENTAGE URBAN, 1897–1959, BY MAJOR ECONOMIC REGIONS

(In cities of more than 15,000 population)

Region	Urban Population (thousands)			Average Annual Percent Increase	Per Cent Urban			Ratio of Per Cent Urban
	1897	1959	Increase 1897–1959	1897–1959	1897	1959	Increase 1897–1959	1959–1897
Interior Core:								
Center	1,846	13,132	11,285	3.16	12.1	53.0	40.9	4.4
Volga-Vyatka	115	2,410	2,295	4.91	1.9	29.2	27.3	15.4
Volga	836	5,184	4,348	2.94	8.6	41.6	33.0	4.8
Urals	508	8,821	8,313	4.60	5.6	47.4	41.8	8.5
Western Siberia	128	4,776	4,648	5.84	6.5	47.0	40.5	7.2
Kazakhstan	121	3,189	3,068	5.27	2.5	34.3	31.8	13.7
Eastern Siberia	78	2,600	2,522	5.65	3.7	37.4	33.7	10.1
Donets-Dnepr	829	8,231	7,402	3.70	10.6	49.7	39.1	4.7
Southern and Eastern Margins:								
North Caucasus	629	4,469	3,840	3.16	10.1	37.9	27.8	3.8
Transcaucasus	527	3,481	2,954	3.04	11.5	36.6	25.1	3.2
Middle Asia	618	3,678	3,060	2.88	11.4	26.9	15.5	2.4
Far East	62	2,061	1,999	5.66	14.6	47.4	32.8	3.2

TABLE 29 – Continued
INCREASE IN URBAN POPULATION AND IN PERCENTAGE URBAN, 1897–1959, BY MAJOR ECONOMIC REGIONS

Region	Urban Population (thousands)			Average Annual Percent Increase	Per Cent Urban			Ratio of Per Cent Urban
	1897	1959	Increase 1897– 1959	1897–1959	1897	1959	Increase 1897– 1959	1959– 1897
Western Zone:								
Northwest	1,736	6,013	4,277	2.00	21.7	52.4	30.7	2.4
West	837	1,930	1,093	1.35	14.6	32.2	17.6	2.2
Belorussia	444	1,698	1,254	2.16	6.9	21.1	14.2	3.1
Black-Earth Center	609	1,863	1,254	1.80	7.4	21.4	14.0	2.9
Southwest	1,337	3,825	2,488	1.69	7.6	18.9	11.3	2.5
South	854	1,959	1,104	1.34	22.7	38.7	16.0	1.7
Moldavia	206	439	233	1.22	13.4	15.2	1.8	1.1
TOTAL	12,321	79,761	67,440	3.01	9.9	38.2	28.3	3.9

Source: Robert A. Lewis and Richard H. Rowland, "Urbanization in Russia and the USSR: 1897–1966," *Annals of the Association of American Geographers*, vol. 59, no. 4, (December, 1969), pp. 776–796, tables 3 and 4 (rearranged). Regions as in the 1959 census volumes.

For a broad picture of regional differences in rate of growth of urban population and of proportion of population urban over the period between the first Russian census (1897) and the latest Soviet census (1959), the country may be divided into 3 very large areas: (1) an Interior Core of rapid increase in urban population and urbanization (including the Donets-Dnepr Region of the Eastern Ukraine), (2) the Southern and Eastern Margins of intermediate increase, and (3) a Western Zone of low rates of increase, including the Black-Earth Center (Table 29).

In terms of average annual percentage increase in urban population 1897–1959 by region, the country falls into a three-fold west-to-east division (Figure 70): a western zone with low rates (less than 2.5 per cent per annum); a zone farther to the east including the eastern parts of the European USSR, the Urals, the Caucasus, and Soviet Middle Asia, with intermediate rates of increase (2.5 to 5.0 per cent per annum); and an eastern zone of Kazakhstan, Siberia, and the Far East with high rates of increase (more than 5.0 per cent per annum). The highest rates thus occur in the eastern part of the Interior Core and the Soviet Far East;

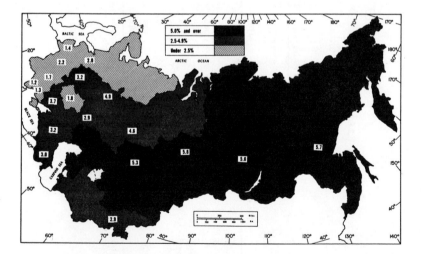

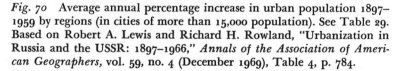

Fig. 70 Average annual percentage increase in urban population 1897–1959 by regions (in cities of more than 15,000 population). See Table 29. Based on Robert A. Lewis and Richard H. Rowland, "Urbanization in Russia and the USSR: 1897–1966," *Annals of the Association of American Geographers,* vol. 59, no. 4 (December 1969), Table 4, p. 784.

intermediate rates in the western part of the Interior Core and in the Southern Margins, and the lowest rates in the Western Zone.

If one looks at the total numerical increase in urban population by regions for 1897–1959, however, one observes that the largest figures occur in the western part of the Interior Core in the regions that include the three greatest industrial concentrations of the country: the Center, with an increase of 11.3 millions in urban population 1897–1959; the Urals, with 8.3 million increase; and the Donets-Dnepr Region, with 7.4 million (Table 29 and Figure 71). The 2 next largest increases also took place in the Interior Core in Western Siberia (which includes the industrial Kuzbas), 4.6 million, and the Volga, 4.3 million. In comparison with other regions, Eastern Siberia and the Soviet Far East with small total urban populations had relatively small total numerical increases, 2.5 and 2.0 millions respectively, but still larger than nearly all regions of the Western Zone. The Volga-Vyatka Region of the Interior Core, small in size and in total urban population, also had a relatively small numerical increase (but a very high percentage increase). Except for the Northwest Region (which includes Leningrad) the regions of the Western Zone had smaller in-

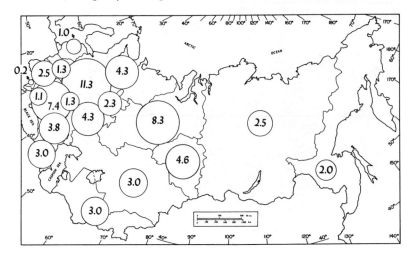

Fig. 71 Increase in urban population 1897–1959 by regions (in cities of more than 15,000 population). See Table 29. Based on Robert A. Lewis and Richard H. Rowland, "Urbanization in Russia and the USSR: 1897–1966," *op. cit.*, Table 4, p. 784.

creases than the regions in the Southern Margin (North Caucasus, Transcaucasus, and Soviet Middle Asia).

A measure of increase in degree of urbanization between 1897 and 1959 is provided by subtracting the percentage urban in 1897 from the percentage urban in 1959. The resulting figure of increase in percentage of the population urban is considered by Lewis and Rowland, on the basis of rank correlations with other measures of increasing urbanization or urban population, to be the best single index of changes in the level of urbanization.[23] The Interior Core contains the 4 regions of very high increase in level of urbanization, i.e., with increases of 39–42 percentage points: the Urals, Western Siberia, the Center, and the Donets-Dnepr Region (Table 29 and Figure 72). They are also the 4 regions of the country with the highest increase 1897–1959 in the percentage of the total population in cities of more than 100 thousand population.[24] These are also the 4 regions with the largest numerical increase in urban population 1897–1959 (Table 29

[23] Lewis and Rowland, *op. cit.*, p. 779.
[24] *Ibid.*, Table 6, last column, p. 785.

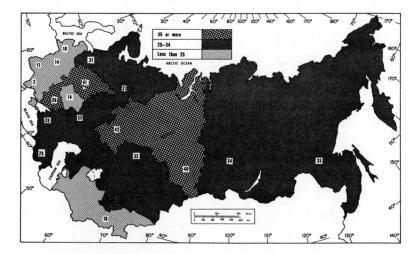

Fig. 72 Increase between percentage of population urban in 1897 and percentage urban in 1959 by Regions (in cities of more than 15,000 population). See Table 29. Based on Robert A. Lewis and Richard H. Rowland, "Urbanization in Russia and the USSR: 1897–1966," *op. cit.*, Table 4, p. 784.

and Figure 71). They are also 4 of the 6 regions of the country with the highest percentage of total population in cities of more than 15 thousand in 1959 (Table 29).[25] They contain the 4 leading industrial districts of the country: the Central Industrial District, the Donbas, the Urals, and the Kuzbas. Regions in the Western Zone had low increases in level of urbanization: 2 to 18 percentage points except for the Northwest, which had marked growth in its northern portions. Soviet Middle Asia also had low rates of increase. Other parts of the Interior Core and the Southern and Eastern Margins had intermediate levels of change (25–34 percentage points).

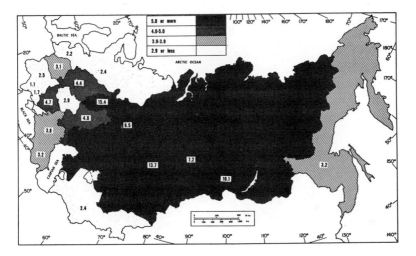

Fig. 73 Ratio of percentage of population urban in 1959 to percentage urban in 1897 by regions (in cities of more than 15,000 population). See Table 29. Based on Robert A. Lewis and Richard H. Rowland, "Urbanization in Russia and the USSR: 1897–1966," *op. cit.*, Table 4, p. 784.

Another measure of increase in degree of urbanization between 1897 and 1959 is the ratio of percentage of population urban in 1959 to the percentage urban in 1897 (Table 29 and Figure 73). The Interior Core is very prominent. Regions in the Interior Core with low levels of urbanization in 1897 show the very highest ratios: the Volga-Vyatka Region (ratio of 15.4), Kazakhstan (13.7),

[25] The other 2 are the Northwest and the Soviet Far East, both of which had a relatively small rural population.

and Eastern Siberia (10.1), followed by the Urals (8.5) and Western Siberia (7.2). Western parts of the Interior Core with a high level of urbanization already in 1897 have lower ratios, but still higher than in any other parts of the country: the Volga (4.8), the Donets-Dnepr Region (4.7), and the Center (4.4). Intermediate ratios (3.0–3.9) characterize the Southern and Eastern Margins (except for Soviet Middle Asia) and also Belorussia. All other regions of the Western Zone have low ratios.

VIII.

Growth of Cities: The Soviet Period

It is not the lure of market stalls, nor the
might of kremlins, nor the holiness of monas-
teries which rally people to [Soviet cities].
It is the industrialization of the country.

> — N. N. MIKHAILOV,
> *Soviet geography: the new indus-
> trial and economic distributions
> of the U.S.S.R.*, 1935, p. 208.

Commerce . . . has ceased, since 1926–1928,
to be a factor in urbanization and urban
growth in the Soviet Union. It is industry
which has seized the torch, which is generator
of cities, which attracts the peasantry to the
cities, where factories are created or enlarged.

> — PIERRE GEORGE,
> *L'U.R.S.S.* 2nd ed., 1962, p. 410.

WE NOW TURN FROM AN ANALYSIS of the long-range trends in
growth patterns of Russian and Soviet cities and of the degree of
urbanization to a more detailed consideration of the spectacular
growth during the Soviet era. The most rapid rate of growth was
in the early period of 1926–1939. More attention is devoted in this
monograph, however, to 2 later periods, the intercensal years of
1939–1959, during which World War II occurred, and the most
recent time, 1959–1967.

The urban population rose four-fold from 26.3 million in 1926
to nearly 100 million in 1959. The sources of this increased urban
population are of great interest, whether from natural increase

within the urban areas, from rural-urban migration, from changes in definition of urban, or from changes in the external boundaries of the country. Calculations of the Soviet statistician P. I. Popov cover the period 1926–1939 and data in B. S. Khorev include the whole period 1926–1959.[1] These data permit estimates that of the 29.8 million increase in urban population in the Soviet Union 1926–1939, only 5.5 million came from the natural increase within the urban areas themselves, 18.5 million came from migration from rural areas to urban areas, and 5.8 million came from juridical changes in status of villages that became settlements of urban type or cities. In the later period 1939–1959 the corresponding rounded estimates for the increase in urban population of 44 millions are 8 million from natural increase within the urban areas themselves, over 24 million from rural-urban migration, 8 million from change in status of settlements from rural to urban, and 4 million from the enlargement of the external boundaries of the Soviet Union. For this 32-year period 1926–1959 the net rural-urban migration within the Soviet Union was thus about 43 million persons.

One of the stated aims of Soviet policy with respect to distribution of population has been to work toward a more even distribution throughout the country. Thus the eastern regions, which were settled later and thus are not yet as fully developed as the western regions, have experienced much more rapid population growth. According to calculations of V. G. Davidovich during the period 1926–1962 the eastern regions, that is the areas from the Urals eastward in Asia, increased 92 per cent in total population compared with 18 per cent for the western, European, part of the Soviet Union.[2] He also estimates that 15 million persons migrated from western to eastern regions within the Soviet Union during this period. The urban population increased 265 per cent during this period in the western regions but more than twice as much, 565 per cent, in the eastern regions.

[1] I. Iu. Pisarev, *Narodonaselenie SSSR* (*sotsial'no-ekonomicheskii ocherk*) (M. Sotsekgiz, 1962), p. 97; and B. S. Khorev, *Gorodskie poseleniia SSSR* (*problemy rosta i ikh izuchenie*); *ocherki geografii rasseleniia* (M. Izd. "Mysl'," 1968), p. 10.
[2] V. G. Davidovich, "O zakonomernostiakh i tendentsiiakh gorodskogo rasseleniia v SSSR," *Voprosy geografii*, sbornik 66 (M. Izd. "Mysl'," 1965), pp. 13–20.

GROWTH OF CITIES, 1926–1939

As already noted, the growth of urban population in the Soviet Union in the period of 12 years and one month between the censuses of December 17, 1926, and January 17, 1939, was unequalled in either the earlier history of Russia or the later periods in the Soviet Union or in the history of other countries before World War II (Figure 1 in Chapter I, and Figure 52 in Chapter VII). During this short period the urban population increased from 26.3 to 56.1 million, or 113 per cent (within the boundaries of those years).[3]

High percentages of increase in population characterized all sizes of cities. Of the 82 cities of more than 100,000 population in 1939, 36 had grown at the rate of doubling their population in a decade. Of the cities that had already reached 100,000 in 1926, 8 subsequently grew at the rate of doubling their population in a decade. By way of comparison it may be noted that in the entire history of the United States only 7 cities that had reached the 100,000 mark have subsequently grown so rapidly and no more than 3 in any one intercensal period.[4]

The 8 Soviet cities of more than 100,000 population in 1926 that grew at the rate of 100 per cent per decade in the period 1926–1939 were: Stalino (now Donetsk), center of the Donbas coal-mining and heavy industrial district; Stalingrad (now Volgograd), industrial city on the Volga River; Sverdlovsk, center for the Ural industrial area; Novosibirsk, regional center for Western Siberia and for the Kuzbas coal-mining and industrial district; Voronezh, railroad and industrial center in the Black-Earth Region between Moscow and the Donbas; and Gor'kiy, Yaroslavl', and Ivanovo, industrial cities in the Central Industrial District north and east of Moscow (Figure 74). Of these cities Gor'kiy (formerly Nizhniy Novgorod), the Detroit of the Soviet Union with automobile factories, had the most remarkable growth, increasing in 12 years from 222 to 644 thousand.

---

[3] Within the boundaries of the Soviet Union at the times of both the 1926 and 1939 censuses. During and after World War II significant additions were made to the territory of the Soviet Union. All comparisons in this section are based on the boundaries of 1926–1939.

[4] Chicago, Detroit, Los Angeles, Houston, Phoenix, Tampa, and El Paso.

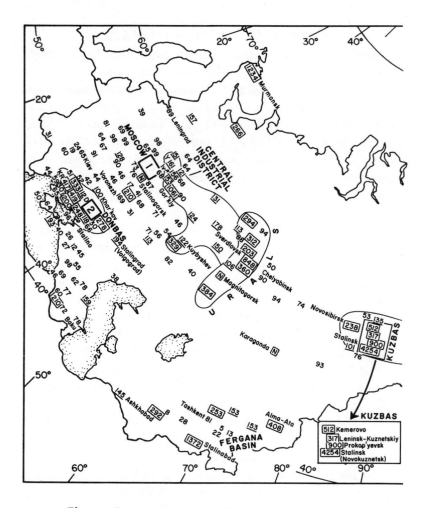

Fig. 74 Percentage increase in population 1926–1939
of 174 cities of more than 50,000 population in 1939.

In absolute as well as in percentage increases the growth of
Soviet cities in this period was unparalleled. In this period 38 cities increased in population at the rate of 100,000 per decade. The
increase in Moscow was 2.1 million, equivalent to approximately
1.74 million per decade. This is considerably greater than the
American record held by New York City, which increased 1.33

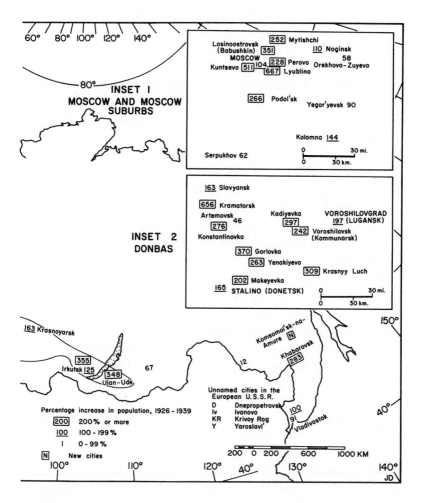

million in the period 1900–1910.[5] The numerical increase for Leningrad in this period was at about the same rate as for New York City at its peak of rapid growth, yet in percentage figures Leningrad was below the average of Soviet cities.

In this period the long-delayed impact of the Industrial Revolution struck the Soviet Union with a suddenness unknown in

[5] Cf. Mark Jefferson, "How American Cities Grow," *Bulletin of the American Geographical Society*, vol. 47 (1915), pp. 19–37. Soviet data are for populations within city limits and thus American data have been taken for political areas also.

Western Europe or the United States. Instead of a gradual evolution, there was a sudden transformation from small handicraft units to huge factories; for example, in the Urals from scattered tiny charcoal iron-smelting furnaces to the mammoth coke-based blast furnaces of the new city of Magnitogorsk. Of course, long before the Revolution large factories, partly foreign owned, had characterized the textile and some other industries. But the penetration of all phases of the economy by industrialization was characteristic of the period of the Five Year Plans that began in 1928. The government planned and executed collectivization and mechanization of agriculture, insured deliveries of food to the cities, and in effect also transferred part of the labor of farming to cities, where agricultural machinery and tractors were made. At the same time industrialization proceeded at a breathless pace in the cities.

The relation of industrialization and urbanization is evidenced by the growth of cities of various functional types. The median rate of increase in this period was 184 per cent for industrial cities but only 69 per cent for trade or diversified cities.[6]

The emphasis on coal mining under the leadership of Stalin is revealed in the names of fast-growing principal towns in the coal-mining districts: Stalino in the Donbas, Stalinsk in the Kuzbas, and Stalingorsk in the Moscow coal basin.

The rates of growth of Soviet cities in this period showed marked regional variation. The 174 cities of more than 50 thousand population in 1939 shown in Figure 74 accounted for an increase of 20 million, virtually the entire increase in urban population in this period. Data for increases in urban population by oblasts are not available because of boundary changes and failure to publish the 1939 census. In the absence of regional data, this map can be used as a rough approximation of the regional variation in growth of total population and in growth of urban population, since the rural population remained approximately constant in this period.

On the basis of rate of growth 4 different categories of districts

[6] Chauncy D. Harris, "The Cities of the Soviet Union," *Geographical Review*, vol. 35, no. 1 (January, 1945), pp. 107-121.

can be recognized, according to whether the majority of cities increased in population more than 200 per cent, by 100–199 per cent, by 50–99 per cent, or by less than 50 per cent in the 12-year period.

In 3 major and 2 minor districts most of the cities trebled in population during this 12-year period. The 3 major districts were the Dnepr-Donbas industrial district in the Ukraine, the Ural industrial district, and the Kuzbas industrial district in Western Siberia.

In the Dnepr-Donbas industrial district the most striking percentage of growth occurred in the cities along the Dnepr River and near the iron-ore mining center of Krivoy Rog to the west, where 4 cities more than quadrupled their population. The 2 largest cities, Dnepropetrovsk and Stalino (now Donetsk), grew much more slowly on a percentage basis, 112 and 165 per cent respectively, but nevertheless in this rather short period increased from 237 to 500 thousand and from 174 to 462 thousand. Zaporozh'ye at the new Dnepr dam and hydroelectric plant grew from 56 to 289 thousand.

Of the 8 cities of this size at this time in the Ural district, one was a new creation (Magnitogorsk) and 6 others more than trebled their populations. Sverdlovsk, the largest city, grew from 140 to 425 thousand and Chelyabinsk from 59 to 273 thousand.

In Western Siberia the four principal industrial cities of the Kuzbas, Stalinsk (now Novokuznetsk), Prokop'yevsk, Kemerovo, and Leninsk-Kuznetskiy, increased 4254, 900, 512, and 317 per cent respectively, and Novosibirsk, regional center for Western Siberia, grew from 120 to 405 thousand, an increase of 238 per cent. Among American cities of this size only Phoenix, Arizona, has ever grown this rapidly (in the decade 1950–1960).

Two minor districts of smaller cities also were characterized by cities trebling in population: Moscow suburbs (Figure 74 inset 1) and a string of cities along the Turk-Sib (Turkestan-Siberia) Railroad, constructed during this period to join Soviet Middle Asia and Siberia, and to open up many areas for economic development, particularly west of Alma-Ata.

A few cities outside these districts increased their populations more than tenfold: Murmansk, the ice-free port on the Barents Sea, had just been joined by a railroad to the developed parts of the European Soviet Union. Stalinabad (now Dushanbe), capital of the new political unit of the Tadzhik SSR in Soviet Middle Asia, was essentially a new city. Komsomol'sk-na-Amure arose as a new industrial center (iron and steel) created in the Soviet Far East on the Amur River. Karaganda developed on the coal field in the sparsely populated Kazakh steppes and reached a population of 166 thousand by 1959.

In the Central Industrial District and adjoining area eastward to the Urals, the larger cities generally more than doubled their populations. This was the earliest developed and largest industrial district of Tsarist Russia. Yaroslavl', Ivanovo, and Gor'kiy lie in this district.

The areas with cities characterized by a 50–99 per cent increase in population in this period had a broad base in the western parts of the Soviet Union and extended eastward to include much of the eastern part of the Black-Earth Center. The eastern part of the Caucasus and North Caucasus also fell in this district.

Finally, in three districts the larger cities generally increased by less than 50 per cent in this 12-year period, which was slow by Soviet standards, but in the corresponding period in the United States, 1930–1940, only 5 of the 140 metropolitan districts grew more rapidly. The cities that grew at this relatively slower rate were mainly trade centers for rural regions of stagnating or declining population. In the western Ukrainian part of the Black-Earth Belt and in the western part of the North Caucasus the great drought and famine and the dislocations associated with collectivization of agriculture made serious inroads on population growth. In Soviet Middle Asia population growth in this period was sharply limited by the amount of water available for irrigation in long-settled basins and oases. The 3 cities in the Fergana basin, for example, grew but little since the agricultural populations that they served as trade centers had already utilized the bulk of water resources then developed. Furthermore, the role of trade was declining as the state turned its back on trade to support expansion of mining and heavy industry.

REGIONAL CONTRASTS IN GROWTH OF TOTAL
URBAN POPULATION 1939–1959 BY MAJOR
ECONOMIC REGIONS AND BY OBLASTS

Two contrasts stand out between the growth of cities in the intercensal periods of 1926–1939 and 1939–1959. The first is concerned
with rate of increase. It was much higher in the first period, one
of forced and rapid industrialization. The second period included
World War II with terrible destruction of cities in the West and
gigantic losses of life (more than 20 million) that affected all parts
of the country. The second contrast is in the regional distribution
of areas of rapid increase. In 1926–1939 rapid growth was highly
localized on coalfields and other centers of heavy industry, wher-
ever located. In 1939–1959 the most rapid growth was in interior
regions of the country, regardless of type.

Urban growth 1939–1959 will now be examined in 3 sections:
(1) regional contrasts in growth of total urban population, (2) regional contrasts in the growth of individual large cities (those
with more than 100,000 population), and (3) a detailed region-by-
region description of cities and towns of rapid growth of all sizes.
These comparisons are based on the 1959 census volumes, which
contain population data on cities of the Soviet Union for 1959 and
for 1939.

The sharp contrast between slow growth in the western old-
settled portions and rapid growth in the newer eastern sections of
the Soviet Union is very clear in Figure 75, which depicts the rate
of growth of urban population 1939–1959 by major economic regions. Increases of urban population of 38, 34, 33, 38, and 46 per
cent occur in some of the major economic regions of the west,
going from north to south in the following regions: Northwest,
Belorussia, Southwest, Southern, and Donets-Dnepr. Increases of
113,124, and 141 per cent characterize the Urals, Western Siberia,
and Kazakhstan. The line between major economic regions with
increases below or above the national average (66 per cent) runs
north-south through the European part of the Soviet Union with
the easternmost major economic regions within Europe and all
major economic regions of Siberia, the Soviet Far East, Kazakh-

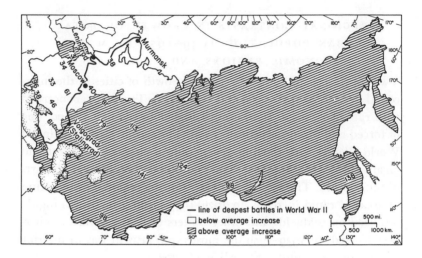

Fig. 75 Percentage increase in urban population 1939–1959 by major economic regions.

stan, Soviet Middle Asia, and the Caucasus having increases above the Soviet average. In addition, the Baltic region and Moldavia in the northwest and southwest, added to the Soviet Union during World War II, had urban increases above average. That the damage of World War II may have been one of the factors in the slower growth of the west is suggested by the rough coincidence (except in the Far North of the European USSR) of the eastward limit of ground fighting and the boundary line between growth at less than or more than the average for the entire country. Since major economic regions cover large areas and show broad averages, Figure 75 is useful in revealing the over-all picture, but it has the limitation of obliterating local detail.

The increase in urban population 1939–1959 by oblasts or comparable smaller areal units reveals the same general distribution but in much finer and more precise areal detail (Figure 76). Again the main contrast is between relatively slow urban growth in the west and more rapid urban growth in the east. In very broad terms in areas west of the Volga River urban population grew more slowly than the average, whereas in the areas east of the Volga, the urban population increased more rapidly than the national average.

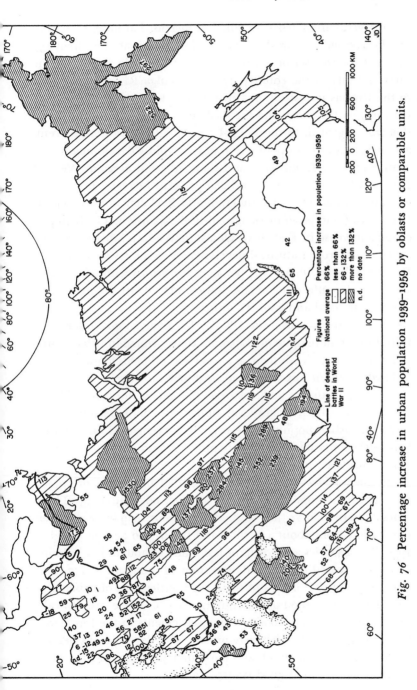

Fig. 76 Percentage increase in urban population 1939–1959 by oblasts or comparable units.

In several areas urban population increased at more than double the average rate for the Soviet Union, that is at more than 133 per cent for the period 1939–1959; these areas lie mainly in the interior heart of the country, from the Volga River on the west to the Kuzbas industrial area in the east. Kuybyshev Oblast (142 per cent) on the Volga and the Bashkir ASSR (137 per cent) owed their rapid growth to the Volga-Ural oil field. Very high percentage increase of urban population in the rapidly developing north-central parts of Kazakhstan and some adjacent areas in Western Siberia (237, 284, 145, 552, and 289 per cent increases in Kurgan, Kustanay, Kokchetav, Tselinograd, and Pavlodar oblasts) reflects the Virgin Land program of agricultural expansion. The high percentage increase in Kemerovo Oblast in Western Siberia (136 per cent) results from industrial development of the Kuzbas coalfield. East Kazakhstan Oblast (194 per cent) has grown with mining and smelting of nonferrous metals. Karaganda Oblast (239 per cent) has mining (coal and copper) and smelting (iron and copper). In the northeastern European USSR, the Komi ASSR underwent initial urban development (1,530 per cent increase in urban population 1939–1959) with the rise of coal and oil fields amid formerly isolated northern forests opened by a new rail line.

On the northwest and northeast margins of the Soviet Union are three northern oblast-level units with high percentage increases in urban population, especially concentrated on small urban settlements under 15,000 population and thus not individually considered in this study.

In the northwest the Karelian ASSR had an increase of 173 per cent in urban population during the period 1939–1959. The 6 cities of more than 15 thousand population in 1959 increased their population from about 122 thousand in 1939 to 224 thousand in 1959. The 43 cities and towns of less than 15 thousand population in 1959 increased their population from 28 thousand to 177 thousand or about six-fold; 33 of these were settlements of urban type with less than 5 thousand population each. These are typically small lumbering and wood-working settlements in the forest zone north of Leningrad which were under active development because of the quality of the stands and particularly because of their proximity to markets and good transportation.

In the northeast are 2 oblasts with high percentage increases in urban population 1939–1959, Kamchatka Oblast with 297 per cent and Magadan Oblast with 522 per cent. Each has only one city of more than 15 thousand population (Petropavlovsk-Kamchatskiy and Magadan respectively). The urban population in the 14 smaller urban settlements in Kamchatka increased from no reported population in 1939 (perhaps because not then considered urban settlements) to 55 thousand in 1959. The urban population in the 32 smaller urban settlements in Magadan Oblast increased from 3 thousand in 1939 to 128 thousand in 1959. In both areas the handling of fish from the sea increased greatly after World War II; in Magadan Oblast mining also expanded (gold, tin, coal). But in both oblasts the high percentage increases are associated with very small numbers and very sparse population over tremendous areas.

Other areas of rapid urbanization, Armenia in the Trans-Caucasus on the southern border of the Soviet Union and the Kara-Kalpak ASSR and Tashauz Oblast (Turkmen SSR) both on the lower Amu-Dar'ya (river) just south of the Aral Sea, are lands of ancient agricultural settlement. In Armenia the rapid urbanization (141 per cent increase 1939–1959) focused on the capital, Yerevan, with 60 per cent of the urban population of the republic, but also infused cities and towns of all sizes. In the areas south of the Aral Sea rapid urban growth was associated with the very low percentages of urban population in agrarian societies. The Kara-Kalpak ASSR was only 12 per cent urban in 1939 (27 per cent in 1959) and in Tashauz Oblast only 10 per cent urban in 1939 (24 per cent in 1959). These are among the lowest percentages in the entire Soviet Union. Large percentage increases here (201 and 140 per cent) thus reflect the very early stages of urbanization and industrialization.

The western areas of relatively low rates of increase in urban population show diversity in detail.

Three oblasts in the western borderlands added to the Soviet Union during World War II had actual decreases in urban population: Kaliningrad (formerly part of East Prussia), −18 per cent; Ivano-Frankovsk (formerly Stanisławów), −15 per cent; and Ternopol' (Tarnopol), −12 per cent. In other oblasts well within the war zone increases were modest, from 1 to 59 per cent but mostly in the range of 10–35 per cent.

In several oblasts (or comparable units) in the western part of the country urban population grew more rapidly: 90 per cent in Estonia, 77 per cent in Latvia, 96 per cent in Moldavia, and 79 per cent in Minsk oblast, a result of the extraordinary growth of Minsk, the capital of the Belorussian SSR. The growth of 70 per cent in the urban population of Kirovograd and 100 per cent in Kherson oblasts in the Ukraine was partly associated with new power developments on the lower Dnepr River. Also, an arm of the eastern area of more rapid urban growth extended westward just south of Moscow to encompass Tula oblast (67 per cent) with its coalfield and industry and Kursk and Belgorod oblasts (67 and 152 per cent respectively), previously lightly urbanized but now booming with the development of deep iron ore deposits. In the North Caucasus, Krasnodar Kray and Stavropol' Kray showed urban growth modestly above the average (87 and 67 per cent), but this is partly merely statistical and administrative redefinition. Many sizeable cities and towns had no 1939 population reported because they were not then considered cities or towns, but rather giant villages.

The rate of growth of the urban population was below average for the Soviet Union in a number of areas outside the western part of the country. The lower Volga, northeast Caucasus, Georgia, and Azerbaydzhan areas form a southeastward extension of the European core of slower relative growth. A number of the oblasts of Soviet Middle Asia were also characterized by relatively slow urban growth; they are mostly based on oases in which available water supplies were developed early and thus later rates of expansion could not be as rapid as in newly developed irrigated lands. These older oases include Kzyl-Orda Oblast (61 per cent) in southern Kazakhstan on the Syr-Dar'ya, Ashkhabad and areas directly under administration of the Turkmen SSR (61 per cent), Chardzhou oblast (52 per cent) on the Amu-Dar'ya in Turkmenistan, and Bukhara and Samarkand oblasts (57 and 64 per cent) on the Zeravshan River in Uzbekistan. And finally, east of Lake Baykal, in Eastern Siberia and beyond, the settlements along the Trans-Siberian Railroad and the upper Amur River grew at moderate

rates, 65 per cent for the Buryat ASSR, 42 per cent for Chita, and
49 per cent for Amur oblast.

The pattern of urban growth can be revealed in more detail in
the discussion of individual urban settlements, first of cities of
more than 100,000 population in 1959 and then of all cities and
towns of more than 10 or 15 thousand in 1959 that had doubled
population during the period 1939–1959.

REGIONAL CONTRASTS IN GROWTH 1939–1959
OF INDIVIDUAL CITIES OF MORE THAN 100,000
POPULATION IN 1959

Of the 146 cities of more than 100,000 population in the Soviet
Union in 1959, 42 increased in population by more than 100 per
cent in the period 1939–1959. These are named in Figure 77.

TABLE 30

Number of Cities of More Than 100,000
Population in 1959 with Increase in Population
1939–1959 of More Than or Less Than
100 Per Cent in the Interior Core Area
and the Rest of the Soviet Union

| | Population Increase 1939–1959 | | |
	More Than 100 Per Cent	Less Than 100 Per Cent	Number of Total
Interior Core Area	36	16	52
Rest of USSR	6	88	94
Total USSR	42	104	146

Compiled from: SSSR. Tsentral'noe statisticheskoe upravlenie. *Itogi vsesoiuznoi perepisi
naseleniia 1959 goda, SSSR (Svodnyi tom)*, table 6, pp. 30–32.

Of these 42 rapidly growing large cities, 36 are located in an interior core area (Table 30), which has been aptly described by
Hooson[7] as stretching from the Volga River in the eastern part of
Europe to Lake Baykal in Eastern Siberia. An outlier of this core
area of rapid growth of large cities lies at the base of the moun-

[7] David J. M. Hooson, *A New Soviet Heartland?* (Princeton, N. J.: Van Nostrand, 1964).

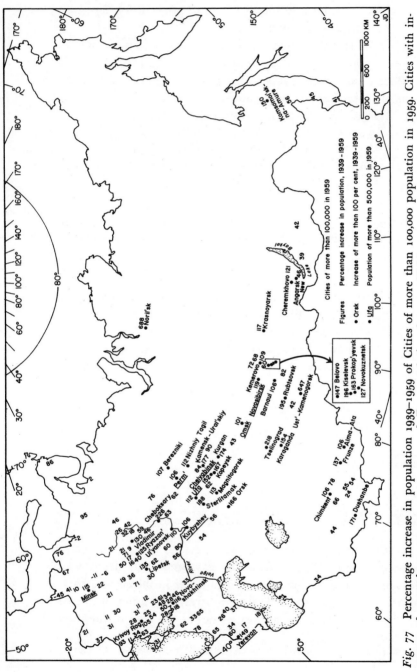

Fig. 77 Percentage increase in population 1939–1959 of Cities of more than 100,000 population in 1959. Cities with increases of more than 100 per cent are named. For population data, see Table 27.

tains in Soviet Middle Asia. In the interior core area 36 of 52 large cities more than doubled their population in this period. In contrast, only 6 of 94 cities in the rest of the Soviet Union grew this rapidly.

The main interior core area of rapid growth of large cities is far from the western, southern, northern, or eastern boundaries of the Soviet Union. The west contains half the large cities of the Soviet Union but very few of them are growing at so rapid a rate. The southern desert and semiarid border of the Soviet Union (except in Soviet Middle Asia) has few large cities of such rapid growth. The vast northlands, sparsely settled and cold, cover more than half the physical area of the country, but have few large cities (only three of 100,000 population). The large eastern segment of the Soviet Union east of Lake Baykal has few large cities and with one exception these are growing more slowly than the average for the country as a whole.

Thus, as Figure 77 reveals, the core of rapid growth of large cities 1939–1959 was not *eastern* as earlier suggested but rather *interior,* since both to the east and west of it large cities grew at slower rates. The map thus refines and makes more areally precise the statistical correlation of rate of urban growth with longitude noted in Chapter IV.

The interior core of rapidly growing large cities which reaches its most intense expression between the Volga and Lake Baykal may be divided into 7 segments (Figure 77). (1) The westernmost extension, west of the Volga, includes Vladimir and Ryazan', 2 very old cities, oblast centers and industrial cities (machinery) just east of Moscow, and Lipetsk, also an old city and oblast center, with an iron and steel industry based on local iron ores. (2) The Volga-Ural industrial area is based on the great oil field developed mainly during and after World War II, which now produces most of the petroleum in the Soviet Union, and to a lesser extent on hydroelectric power from new projects on the Volga River. This area focuses on Kuybyshev on the Volga (site of a hydroelectric project and wartime seat of the government) and on Ufa but includes also Cheboksary and Ul'yanovsk on the Volga and Sterlitamak on the oilfield. (3) The Ural industrial district includes 8 large rapidly growing cities. It focuses on Perm', Chelyabinsk,

Sverdlovsk,[8] Berezniki, Nizhniy Tagil, Kamensk-Ural'skiy, Kopeysk, Magnitogorsk, and Orsk, industrial cities mining or processing iron ore, nonferrous metals (aluminum, nickel, and magnesium), lignite, and salt. They are also centers for many smaller mining and industrial cities in the Urals, the greatest storehouse of metalliferous ores in the Soviet Union and one of the greatest concentrations of such ores in the entire world. (4) The 10 large rapidly growing cities of Western Siberia are of 2 very different types. On the one hand are central places, Novosibirsk, Omsk, Kurgan, and Barnaul, great regional administrative and manufacturing centers and transport foci located at the crossing of large rivers by railroad lines. Rubtsovsk is similar in being a center for an agricultural district (with manufacture of agricultural machinery) though not an oblast center. In contrast are 5 specialized and clustered coal-mining and heavy-industry cities in the Kuzbas, which from north to south are Kemerovo (the oblast center), Belovo, Kiselevsk, Prokop'yevsk, and finally Novokuznetsk, the largest city of this coal field. (5) The 3 cities of Eastern Siberia repeat the pattern of Western Siberia with Krasnoyarsk, a regional and administrative center at the crossing of the major river and railroad in the western part of the region and 2 industrial cities in the eastern part: Cheremkhovo on a coalfield and Angarsk, a new chemical city. (6) The 3 rapidly growing large cities of Central and East Kazakhstan differ from one another. Tselinograd in the steppe is the center for a large semi-arid wheat-growing agricultural district (the virgin lands). Karaganda in the semi-desert is based on coal mining and heavy industry. Ust'-Kamenogorsk in the mountain rim to the east is the center of a nonferrous mining and smelting district. (7) A band of 4 capital and industrial cities is located at the base of the mountains or in the oases of Soviet Middle Asia, from Alma-Ata (capital of the Kazakh SSR) on the northeast, through Frunze (capital of the Kirgiz SSR), and Chimkent (industrial city in South Kazakhstan), to Dushanbe (capital of the Tadzhik SSR).[9]

[8] Sverdlovsk, the major center of the Urals, is not named on the map since its increase was only 84 per cent from 423 thousand to 779 thousand in 1939–1959.
[9] Tashkent, the regional center and largest city of Soviet Middle Asia is not named on the map as it grew only 66 per cent 1939–1959 from 550 to 912 thousand.

Outside the core area there are only 6 large cities of such rapid growth (Table 30 and Figure 77). Northward a vast area of sparse population contains only a single city of more than 100,000 population which grew very rapidly in this period, Noril'sk (688 per cent), the northernmost large city in the Soviet Union, a center of nonferrous mining and smelting (nickel and copper). Eastward a half dozen large cities are strung along the Trans-Siberian Railway or located in the Soviet Far East, but of these only Komsomol'sk-na-Amure, the iron and steel city, more than doubled in population 1939–1959. The older mountain-basin or desert oasis towns of the southern part of Soviet Middle Asia grew relatively slowly. In the western and southwestern parts of the country, only 4 large cities increased so rapidly. Two are political capitals. Minsk, capital of the Belorussian SSR on the western border of the country, exhibited astonishing growth, far exceeding the rates of other cities in its own republic or in adjacent regions. Yerevan, capital of the Armenian SSR on the southern border of the country in the Transcaucasus, also had very rapid growth as part of an urbanization spurt in Armenia. The other 2 are mining cities, Krivoy Rog, the iron-ore mining town and industrial city in the Ukraine, and Novoshakhtinsk, the coal-mining and chemical center in the eastern extension of the Donets Coal Basin.

CITIES AND TOWNS OF ALL SIZES WITH
RAPID GROWTH 1939–1959 BY REGION

Of the 1,247 Soviet cities and towns considered in this study, 381 or 31 per cent increased in population at a rate of more than 100 per cent for the period 1939–1959 (Table 31). These fall into 2 categories, those for which 1939 census data are provided and in which the 1939 population was less than half the 1959 population, and those for which no 1939 census data were provided and which were presumed to be new cities or towns in the absence of data from earlier censuses or other sources indicating substantial size in 1939. A fair number of cities for which the 1959 census did not publish figures for 1939 are not considered new cities or towns since other evidence indicates that they were of substantial size and had 1939 populations of the same order of magnitude as the reported 1959 populations. These cities and towns include some

TABLE 31

Number and Percentage of Cities and Towns More Than Doubling Population 1939–1959 by Regions or Smaller Areas, if Distinctive

(See Figure 78)

	Cities and Towns[a]		
	Total Number in 1959	Number Doubling Population 1939–1959	Per Cent Doubling Population 1939–1959
Areas with Low Percentages of Growth Cities:			
West (Baltic republics, Belorussia, Kaliningrad O.)	70	8	11
Northwest (excluding European North)	33	6	18
Central (excluding Moscow O., and Tula O.)	70	6	9
Ukraine (excluding Donbas, Dnepropetrovsk O.)	181	16	9
Lower Volga	24	4	17
North Caucasus (excluding Rostov O.)	48	4	8
Western Kazakhstan and Western Middle Asia	40	8	20
Eastern Siberia, east of Lake Baykal	9	1	11
Far East	35	8	23
Areas with Medium Percentages of Growth Cities:			
Moscow Oblast	55	17	31
Donbas and Dnepropetrovsk Oblast	120	38	32
Moldavia	13	4	31
Central Black-Earth	27	8	30
Rostov Oblast	22	7	32
Caucasus (excluding Armenia and Baku suburbs)	50	13	26
Volga-Vyatka	37	10	27

316

TABLE 31 – Continued

NUMBER AND PERCENTAGE OF CITIES AND TOWNS MORE THAN DOUBLING POPULATION 1939–1959 BY REGIONS OR SMALLER AREAS, IF DISTINCTIVE

	Cities and Towns[a]		
	Total Number in 1959	Number Doubling Population 1939–1959	Per Cent Doubling Population 1939–1959
Areas with High Percentages of Growth Cities:			
European North	24	17	71
Tula Oblast	17	11	65
Armenia	10	7	70
Baku suburbs	15	7	47
Middle Volga	44	24	55
Urals	92	40	44
Western Siberia	60	26	43
Kazakhstan (except western part)	67	44	66
Middle Asia (except western part)	52	30	58
Eastern Siberia, west of Lake Baykal	32	17	53
Soviet Union as a Whole, Total	1247	381	31

[a] Cities and towns of more than 10 thousand population in 1959 in all parts of the Soviet Union except the RSFSR. In the RSFSR data are available only for cities of more than 15 thousand in 1959.
   Compiled from SSSR. Tsentral'noe statisticheskoe upravlenie. *Itogi vsesoiuznoi perepisi naseleniia 1959 goda*, table 7 in each of the 15 volumes devoted to the constituent union republics.

that were not part of the Soviet Union in 1939.[10] They also include some cities or towns in the Ukraine or the North Caucasus, for which there were 1926 census data but for which 1939 census data are lacking for reasons unknown; these towns may have been considered large villages in 1939 and thus population data on them was excluded from the unpublished 1939 census and are available only in the published volumes of the 1959 census (see also later in this chapter Table 34 and Figure 96).

In the interior core of the Soviet Union more than 40 per cent of all cities and towns either doubled their population 1939–1959 or were new cities and towns (Figure 78 and Table 31). This core area includes the European North (where 71 per cent of the cities and towns grew this rapidly), the Volga-Urals (55 per cent), Urals (44 per cent), Western Siberia (43 per cent), Eastern Siberia west of Lake Baykal (53 per cent), Kazakhstan excluding western Kazakhstan (66 per cent), and eastern Middle Asia (Kirgiz and Tadzhik republics and eastern Uzbekistan) (58 per cent). These are areas of rapid industrialization and urbanization. Only three small areas of high proportion of cities with rapid growth lie outside this vast core region: Tula Oblast (lignite mining) just south of Moscow Oblast (65 per cent), Armenia in the Caucasus (70 per cent), and oil-mining and industrial satellites of the city of Baku, also in the Caucasus (47 per cent).

At a level of greater areal detail, one can recognize 9 areas within the core in which a very high proportion of cities and towns grew rapidly (Figure 79). These areas experienced great economic and urban growth during the period 1939–1959 especially in connection with the development of coalfields and oilfields but also in individual cases with agricultural expansion, industrial advancement, or economic modernization. In four of the nine areas urban growth was based primarily on coal mining and associated heavy industries: in Tula Oblast just south of Moscow

---

[10] As for example in southern Sakhalin (then part of Japan), Moldavia (then part of Romania), the Trans-Carpathian Oblast (then part of Czechoslovakia), Kaliningrad Oblast (then part of East Prussia in Germany), and parts of the Karelian ASSR or Leningrad Oblast (then part of Finland). On the other hand 1939 census data or estimates are provided in the 1959 census volumes for the Baltic republics (Estonia, Latvia, and Lithuania) and for the parts of Poland joined to the Soviet Union after the taking of the census of January 17, 1939.

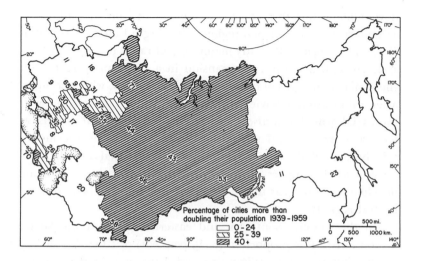

Fig. 78 Percentage of cities and towns more than doubling population 1939–1959.

(the so-called Moscow Basin); in the Komi coalfields in the north-east corner of the European part of the Soviet Union; in the Kuzbas coalfields at the eastern edge of Western Siberia, and the Karaganda coalfields in central Kazakhstan. The major oilfield of rapid

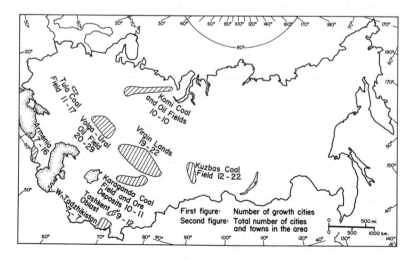

Fig. 79 Areas with high proportion of growth cities, 1939–1959.

development was the Volga-Ural field,[11] but oil also played a secondary role in the Komi region. The Virgin Lands of Northern Kazakhstan formed the only major area of rapid urban growth associated with agricultural expansion in a dry-farming region on the semiarid margins of farming. Tashkent Oblast, which occupies a central position in Soviet Middle Asia, included many cities with industrial growth but also some centers of agricultural expansion with new irrigation. Tadzhikistan[12] and Armenia on the mountain borders of the Soviet Union both experienced an urban explosion as the impact of Soviet industrialization and economic development hit areas that had lagged economically behind more central regions.

In the western, southern, and eastern regions of the Soviet Union only a low proportion (8–23 per cent) of cities doubled in population 1939–1959 (Figure 78 and Table 31). In the 3 major regions of the long-developed and densely populated western part of the Soviet Union, only 9 to 11 per cent of cities and towns grew this rapidly. In the Northwest, in several southern regions, and in Eastern Siberia east of Lake Baykal or in the Soviet Far East the proportion of rapidly growing cities and towns was also relatively low.

A transition area with intermediate proportions of cities and towns of rapid growth (26–32 per cent) lies between the western area of slow growth and the interior core of rapid growth (Figure 78); it includes the Volga-Vyatka Region, Moscow Oblast, the Central Black-Earth Region in the central part of the European RSFSR, the eastern industrial part of the Ukraine from Krivoy Rog eastward through the Donbas to Rostov, and most of the Transcaucasus to the south.

In terms of numbers of rapidly growing cities and towns (in contrast to proportions), the Urals with 40 such cities and Kazakhstan with 44 are leading regions (Table 31). Many also occur in other parts of the interior core area in the Middle Volga (24), in southern Siberia (both Western Siberia and Eastern Siberia west

---

[11] Kuybyshev Oblast and Bashkir ASSR and immediately adjacent segments of the Tatar ASSR and Orenburg Oblast.
[12] Excluding the northern part of the Tadzhik SSR in the earlier developed Fergana basin.

of Lake Baykal) (43), and in eastern Middle Asia (30). Outside the core area there are large numbers of such cities in the great urban concentrations of the Donbas and adjacent industrial areas (38), Moscow Oblast (17), Tula Oblast (11), and the Caucasus (27).

These 281 rapidly growing or new cities and towns of the Soviet Union shown on Figure 80 will now be discussed region by region, proceeding in general from west to east. Each of the 381 cities shown on Figure 80 is located and named on Figures 81–91, and is discussed individually on the following pages. Many of these cities and towns are relatively small, since it is much easier for a town of 10 thousand population to double in population

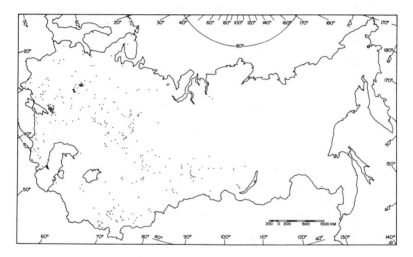

Fig. 80 Cities and towns more than doubling population 1939–1959.

than for a city of a million. In order to save repetition of long phrases the term "growth cities" will be used here to cover not only cities but also towns (which elsewhere in this study refers specifically to settlements of urban type not juridically cities) and to include both urban settlements that more than doubled population in the period 1939–1959 and urban settlements that are essentially new, i.e., did not have reported populations in 1939 or earlier years. Regional maps show the locations and names of these growth cities in the areas of major concentration (Figures 81–91). Figure 81 serves as an index map for the areas covered by the detailed regional maps and carries the names and locations of growth cities outside the areas covered by regional maps.

The analysis of the growth of cities and towns of all sizes with high rates of increase during the intercensal period 1939–1959 will now be made by 11 regions beginning with the European West and North and ending with the Soviet Far East.

(1) *European West and North*

Regional contrasts in proportion and distribution of growth cities for the entire Soviet Union are epitomized in the West and North of the European part of the country. In the older settled sections of the West, only 8 of 70 cities and towns grew so rapidly as to double their population in the period 1939–1959 (Figures 80 and 81 and Table 31). In the long-settled inner Northwest only 6 of 33 cities grew at this rate. But in the more recently developed pioneer European North, 17 of 24 cities and towns increased their population this rapidly. Stated most sharply the contrast is between the cities and towns of Novgorod and Pskov oblasts in the inner Northwest, where none of the cities grew at this rate, and the Komi ASSR in the Northeast where all cities and towns grew at much more than this rate and where most of them were entirely new settlements.

All 8 growth cities in the West were affected by boundary changes of World War II. Indeed, 7 of them were incorporated into the Soviet Union during this war.

In this area the only large city to increase its population at this rate was Minsk, capital of the Belorussian SSR, which grew from 237 thousand in 1939 to 509 thousand in 1959 and to 772 thousand in 1967; the most remarkable growth of any large city in the entire western part of the Soviet Union and one of the most notable in the entire Soviet Union. This growth of Minsk was especially impressive because of heavy physical damage to the city during World War II and its great population losses, especially among its Jewish inhabitants, who made up 41 per cent of its population in 1926 but only 8 per cent in 1959. The development of Minsk in the early Soviet period may have been retarded somewhat by its peripheral location very near a hostile and trade-barren western boundary of the country. With the transfer in 1939 to the Soviet

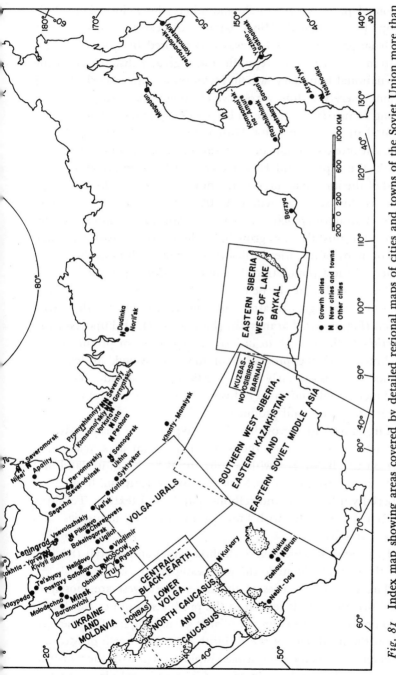

Fig. 81 Index map showing areas covered by detailed regional maps of cities and towns of the Soviet Union more than doubling in population 1939–1959.

Union of parts of eastern Poland where the Belorussian ethnic groups predominated, Minsk became the capital not only of a much larger Belorussia but was also favored by a more central position within its own republic and a greater distance from the international boundary, which, furthermore, after World War II became merely a line across which there was extensive trade among countries that came to be politically and economically associated in the Council for Mutual Economic Assistance (Comecon). An intense rural-urban migration in this region focused on Minsk, the capital and largest city, which alone accounts for a third of the industrial production of the whole of Belorussia. The city has diversified growth industries, but machinery predominates. The development of Minsk is also all the more striking when set against the slow growth, stable size, or decreasing population of many other cities in Belorussia; 7 of 32 cities in the republic actually lost population during the period 1939–1959.

Three small cities in Belorussia, all in Poland in the interwar years had rapid growth after their incorporation into the Soviet Union (Figure 81). Baranovichi (Baranowicze), an important rail junction (6 lines), had an industrial expansion in production of machinery and the processing of food and wood. Molodechno (Molodeczno) is similarly a rail junction (4 lines) and a center for machinery, food, and wood industries. Postavy (Postawy) is a small center processing food products.

Lithuania had 2 growth cities. Klaypeda (the former Memel) increased from 43 to 90 thousand (1940–1959) as a year-round port on the Baltic Sea with a substantial Soviet hinterland and with diverse industries such as machinery (shipbuilding), food (especially fish), wood and cellulose-paper, and textiles. Tel'shyay (Telšiai) a small city with knitting and canning industries, also grew markedly.

In Estonia Kokhtla-Yarve (Kohtla-Järve) and Kiviyli (Kiviõli) owe their development to the processing of oil shales.

The six growth cities of the inner Northwest are mostly of small size and are all related to the products of mines and forests or to position near Leningrad (Table 31 and Figure 81). Cherepovets at the north end of the Rybinsk Reservoir north of Moscow, although an old city, experienced rapid growth with the construction since 1949 of a large integrated iron and steel plant based on distant raw materials: coal from the Vorkuta Basin to the far northeast, and iron ore from the Kola Peninsula to the far northwest. It grew from a population of 32 thousand in 1939 to 92 thousand in 1959, and 165 thousand in 1967. It is easily the largest of the growth cities of the Northwest. Slantsy, as the name suggests, is engaged in the mining and processing of oil shale; Boksitogorsk, again as the name indicates, in the mining of bauxite and the production of alumina; Pikalevo, in the production of alumina based on Kola nephelite — all in Leningrad Oblast; and Segezha in the Karelian SSR, in the utilization of forest resources in wood-working and cellulose-paper combines. A dormitory suburb of Leningrad, Vsevolozhskiy, has received part of the suburban and peripheral growth of that great metropolis, within the city limits of which further residential construction is limited.

The 17 growth cities and towns of the European North are also related to mines, forests, and transportation (Table 31 and Figures 80 and 81).

Seven of these are in Murmansk and Arkhangel'sk oblasts. On the Kola Peninsula (Murmansk Oblast) are Apatity and Nikel', whose names indicate clearly enough their products, apatite and nickel. Apatity is specifically the center of concentration of apatite prior to long-distance transport; it is thus a classical example of the processing near the source of raw material in order to reduce bulk and thus save transport costs. Severomorsk (northern sea) and Severodvinsk (north Dvina) are ports, the first on the ice-free Kola Bay northeast of Murmansk and the second on the White Sea at the estuary of the Northern Dvina River northwest of Arkhangel'sk. Severodvinsk as port and industrial city (metal goods and food products) is the largest of the rapidly growing cities of the region, increasing from 21 to 79 thousand during 1939–1959 and to 121 thousand in 1967. Nearby Pervomayskiy is a suburb of Arkhangel'sk, to which it is administratively subordinate. Kotlas and Vel'sk to the south are river ports, railroad centers, and transshipment points with important wood industries; Kotlas also has ship building and ship repair yards.

In the European Northeast the Komi ASSR experienced an explosion of urban development with 10 growth cities. The urban population of the Komi ASSR increased from 29 thousand to 475 thousand during 1939–1959 with the construction of a railroad to

Vorkuta from Kotlas completed in 1941 and with the opening of oilfields and coalfields. This autonomous republic takes its name from the Komi, who continue to form the predominant rural population (180 out of 290 thousand in 1959), but the urban expansion brought a powerful migration of Russians and Ukrainians; of the 475 thousand urban dwellers in 1959, 282 thousand were Russian and 63 thousand Ukrainians, presumably almost all of whom moved into the area from outside during this period, compared with 65 thousand Komi, many of whom doubtless came from nearby rural settlements.[13] All 10 cities and towns of the Komi ASSR of more than 15 thousand population showed rapid growth; indeed 8 of them were new cities or towns. Only Syktyvkar, the capital, was a city in 1939; it grew from 24 to 64 thousand during 1939–1959, and to 102 thousand in 1967. It is a river station in a forested area with political-administrative functions and wood-working industries. Pechora, a new city located on the river of the same name at the railroad crossing, is similarly a river port with shipyards and wood industries. All the other 8 cities and towns of the Komi ASSR are associated with the production, processing, and transportation of mineral fuels: petroleum, natural gas, or coal. Ukhta and Sosnogorsk are in an oilfield in the Izhma River Basin. Inta is part of the Pechora coal basin on the Inta River. Vorkuta is the center of the main producing part of the Pechora coal basin. Although a new city, it reached a population of 56 thousand by 1959 but then grew slowly to 65 thousand in 1967. Four settlements of urban type cluster around it and are administratively subordinate to its city council: Gornyatskiy, Promyshlennyy, Komsomol'skiy, and Severnyy, whose names mean respectively "mining," "industrial," "communist youth league," and "northern," and which together had a population of 83 thousand in 1959.

(2) Central Region

The 34 growth cities of the Central Region are very unevenly spaced since 17 are in Moscow Oblast, 11 in Tula Oblast, and only 6 in the 9 other oblasts of the region (Table 31 and Figures 81–84).

[13] Figures from *Itogi Vsesoiuznoi Perepisi Naseleniia 1959 goda. RSFSR*, pp. 24–25, 314, 340, and 366.

The range is between Tula Oblast in which 11 of 17 cities and towns grew rapidly to Bryansk and Ivanovo oblasts in which none of the cities even approached a rate of increase of "growth" cities.

Seventeen cities and towns in Moscow Oblast with more than 15,000 population in 1959 more than doubled population in the period 1939–1959 (Figures 82 and 83). Fourteen of these are clustered near Moscow as suburbs or satellites, within easy daily commuting distance. Eleven close-in growth suburbs are shown on Figure 83. These are aligned along the suburban commuting railroad lines that radiate from the great center. To the northwest lie 3 of these rapidly growing suburbs, the largest of which is Khimki, the northern port for the city of Moscow, located on the Moscow Canal that joins the city and Moscow River with the Volga River to the north. The others are Dolgoprudnyy and Skhodnya. Dolgoprudnyy also grew rapidly from 1959 to 1967 increasing from 25 to 50 thousand in this short period. Only one such city lies on the northeastern line: Fryazino. Along the railroad line to the east, and branches from it, are four such rapidly growing suburbs, the 2 largest of which both lie on branch lines, Elektrostal' (which, as the name indicates, also produces high-quality electric steel and machinery) and Balashikha (with textile industries but also a center for summer cottages for Moscow dwellers); these are also the 2 largest suburbs in the entire Moscow area that doubled their population in the period 1939–1959 with populations of 97 and 58 thousand respectively in 1959 or 117 and 74 thousand in 1967. Kuchino and Zheleznodorozhnyy lie on the main line to the east. Zheleznodorozhnyy jumped in population from 19 to 48 thousand in the period 1959–1967. To the southeast lie three suburbs between the Moscow River and the railroad line. The more distant of these, Zhukovskiy, was called Otdykh ("rest") before it became a city. Thus the spread of the residential suburbs of the Moscow metropolitan area, as of those of other countries, has been partly at the expense of recreational areas. Dzerzhinskiy and Lytkarino are on the river. To the south also lie 3 such suburbs. The largest and farthest out of these is Klimovsk, which also manufactures machinery for the textile industry. The others are Domodedovo and Shcherbinka. Beyond the regular daily commuting range of Moscow lie 3 cities (Figure 82): on the south, Stupino, an indus-

Fig. 82 Growth cities of Moscow Oblast 1939–1959.

trial city; on the northeast, Krasnoarmeysk, textile city, not so far from Moscow but 18 kilometers (about 11 miles) from the railroad and thus effectively beyond the daily commuting range; and on the north, Dubna, the atomic research center on the Volga River.

In Tula Oblast to the south 11 of 17 urban settlements were growth cities (Figure 84). Nine of these lie just south and southeast of Tula in the Moscow lignite (brown coal) basin and are coal-mining and industrial towns: Skuratovskiy (new), Shchekino (also chemicals), Lipki, Kireyevsk, Uzlovaya (a railroad junction as indicated by the name, with a population in 1959 of 54 thousand, the largest of the growth cities on the lignite basin), Donskoy (name from the River Don which has its headwaters nearby),

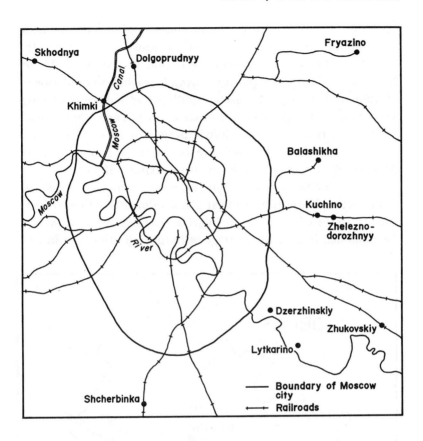

Fig. 83 Growth suburbs of Moscow 1939–1959.

Severo-Zadonsk, Kimovsk (largest of the new cities with a population of 39 thousand in 1959), and Sokol'niki. These all look to Novomoskovsk and Tula for many central urban services. Novotul'skiy, near Tula, is one of the largest settlements of urban type in the Soviet Union with 36 thousand population (it is administratively subordinate to a city council in Tula); it is an iron and steel center. Aleksin to the northwest is a river station on the Oka with sanitaria and rest homes and the manufacture of agricultural equipment.

Outside of Moscow and Tula, of 70 cities and towns in the rest of the Central Region, only 6 grew fast enough to be considered here (Table 31 and Figure 81). All 6 are industrial centers. Four are directly connected with the production of energy. Nelidovo and Safonovo in the west mine lignite. Obninsk, a new town, is the site of the first electric generating station in the Soviet Union based on nuclear power (built in 1955); it reached a population of 16 thousand in 1959 and grew rapidly to 38 thousand in 1967. Uglich on the Volga River is an ancient city but grew rapidly with the construction of a hydroelectric project in 1941. The other 2 cities, Vladimir and Ryazan', are oblast centers to the east of Moscow. Ryazan' has a large new petrochemical industry.

The cities and towns of the Industrial Center of the Soviet Union were obviously growing at a much slower rate than cities to the east in the core area of the interior. The relative slowness is to be explained in part by the stage of industrialization and in part

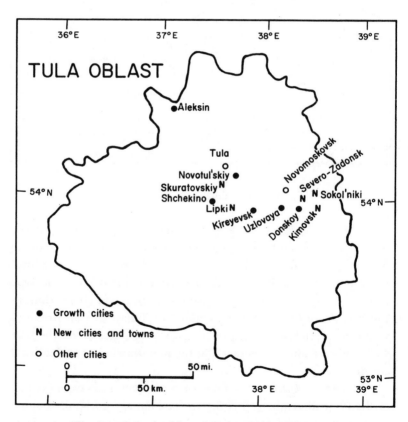

Fig. 84 Growth cities of Tula Oblast 1939–1959.

by the structure of industry. These are old industrial districts compared with the more eastern districts, which are still in an earlier stage of development with the rapid growth of youth. Industry here is historically based on textiles which have had sluggish growth in the Soviet Union in comparison with the metal and machinery industries of the Urals, Siberia, and Kazakhstan.

(3) *Ukraine and Moldavia*

The Ukraine had 41 cities or towns that more than doubled population 1939–1959 and 13 that were essentially new cities or towns, or a total of 54 growth cities. Because of special problems in recognizing the category of "new cities and towns" in the

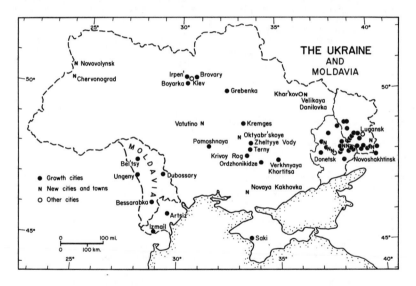

Fig. 85 Growth cities of the Ukraine and Moldavia 1939–1959.

Ukraine, this group will be considered separately after the discussion of those urban settlements which had populations for 1939 recorded in the 1959 census.

Cities and towns with rapid growth 1939–1959 in the Ukraine show sharp regional contrasts (Figure 85).

Of the 41 cities and towns in the Ukraine with populations of more than 10,000 in 1959 that had doubled their population 1939–1959, 27 were in the Donbas coalfield and industrial district, 4 in the Krivoy Rog iron-ore district, 3 in the Kiev metropolitan area, and only 7 were dispersed through the rest of the Ukraine.

The 27 rapidly growing cities and towns in the Donbas, shown in Figure 86, were rather small, mostly under 20 thousand popula-

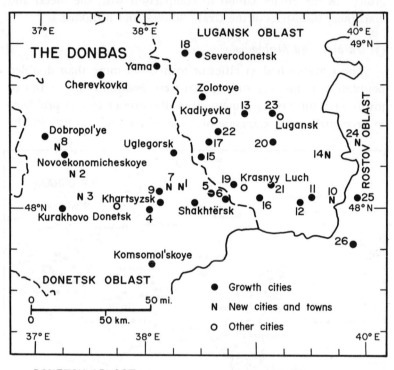

DONETSK OBLAST
 I Kirovskoye
 2 Novogrodovka
 3 Gornyak
 4 Kholodnaya Balka
 5 Pelageyevka
 6 Severnoye
 7 Zhdanovka
 8 Rodinskoye
 9 Nizhnyaya Krynka

LUGANSK OBLAST
 10 Chervonopartizansk
 11 Leninskiy
 12 Dzerzhinskiy
 13 Cherkasskoye

14 Verkhneduvannyy
15 Chernukhino
16 Krepenskiy
17 Yelenovka
18 Novodruzheskoye
19 Vakhrushevo
20 Lutugino
21 Yasenovskiy
22 Krasnopol'ye
23 Aleksandrovsk

ROSTOV OBLAST R. S. F. S. R
24 Donetsk
25 Gukovo
26 Novoshakhtinsk

Fig. 86 Growth cities of the Donbas 1939–1959.

tion. The 2 largest such cities in Donetsk Oblast, Shakhtërsk and Novoekonomicheskoye, had populations in 1959 of only 37 and 36 thousand, respectively. The largest settlement of rapid growth in Lugansk Oblast, Severodonetsk had only 33 thousand. The names often reflect the activity of the settlement: Shakhtërsk ("miners' settlement"), Novoekonomicheskoye ("new economic settlement"), Uglegorsk ("coal mountain"), Gornyak ("miner"). The relatively small size, newness, and specialized function of many of these towns in revealed by their lesser status; of the 27 only 9 had juridical recognition as cities; the other 18 were settlements of urban type at the time of the 1959 census. The greatest concentration of these settlements occurs in a rather narrow band in the southern part of the coalfield eastward from Donetsk through Shakhtërsk and Krasnyy Luch beyond the boundary of Lugansk Oblast into Rostov Oblast in the RSFSR, in which 2 such cities are located. Indeed the largest city of such rapid growth in the Donbas, Novoshakhtinsk ("new mine shaft"), with a 1959 population of 103,000, lies in this eastward extension of the coalfield outside the Ukraine (No. 26 in Figure 86). There are 2 northerly extensions of this east-west band of closely spaced coal-mining settlements. At the western end a line of towns extends northward from Donetsk to Dobropol'ye. In the eastern part of the coal field in Lugansk Oblast a somewhat wider zone of cities and towns spreads northward toward Severodonetsk. Most of the rapidly growing urban settlements in this great cluster are devoted to coal mining but some have related functions in heavy industry and transportation although the larger industrial enterprises such as iron and steel mills and machinery combines tend to be in the larger cities which are not now growing so rapidly in this region. Yama to the north and Komsomol'skoye to the south produce the limestone flux used in the blast furnaces. Severodonetsk to the north has a chemical combine. Khartsyzsk and Lutugino have foundries and metal-working industries. Some of the small settlements of urban type have ceased to exist as separate administrative units since the 1959 census; they have apparently been joined with other nearby urban units.[14]

---

[14] Thus apparently Cherevkovka was incorporated into Slavyansk and Verkhneduvanyy into Krasnodon sometime between January 1, 1962, and April 1, 1963; they had previously been administratively subordinate to these nearby

Krivoy Rog, with a 1959 population of 387,000, was the largest city in the Ukraine with such rapid growth (Figure 85). It was also the center of a major iron-ore mining district with 3 other iron-ore or manganese mining towns, extending from Zhëltyye Vody and Terny on the north (both booming also with uranium mining) to Ordzhonikidze on the south.

Three small cities (populations under 20,000 in 1959) 15–25 miles from Kiev showed rapid suburban and Satellite development: Irpen', Boyarka, and Brovary.

The other 7 of the 41 cities or towns of rapid growth in the Ukraine are scattered, of diverse types, and mostly small (under 20 thousand population). Four are associated with transportation. The largest of these is Izmail on the Danube River, which was transferred to the Soviet Union from Romania during World War II and thereafter became the base of the new Soviet fleet and commerce on this river; in 1959 it had a population of 48 thousand. Three are railroad junctions with shops: Grebenka, Pomoshnaya, and Artsiz. One developed with the construction of a reservoir and hydroelectric station, Kremges on the Kremenchug reservoir on the Dnepr River. One produces salt, Saki in the Crimea. Verkhnyaya Khortitsa is a suburb of Zaporozh'ye, to which it is administratively subordinate.

The appearance of 29 "new" cities and towns in the 1959 census parallels the rapid growth of cities and towns that already existed at the time of the 1939 census. The 1959 census volume for the Ukraine gives no population figures for 1939 for these 29 cities and towns of more than 10,000 population in 1959. The presumption might well be that these are new cities and towns which did not exist in 1939.

That this assumption does not apply to all 29 settlements, however, is quickly revealed by the absence of 1939 population data for 5 of the cities and towns of the Trans-Carpathian Oblast, which was not part of the Soviet Union at the time of the 1939

---

larger cities (*SSSR Administrativno-territorial'noe Delenie Soiuznykh Respublik na 1 ianvariia 1962 goda,* pp. 283 and 307, and *SSSR Administrativno-territorial'noe Delenie Soiuznykh Respublik na 1 aprelia 1963 goda,* pp. 259 and 286). The larger cities also showed an appropriate jump in population at this time (*SSSR Administrativno-Territorial'noe Delenie Soiuznykh Respublik ianvar' 1965 goda,* pp. 596 and 600).

census.[15] The examination of other sources reveals that each of these cities and towns was in existence in 1939 and with a population approximately that of the 1959 census.

Careful analysis of the 1926 Soviet census volumes reveals that of the remaining cities and towns of the Ukraine for which the 1959 census records a 1959 population of more than 10 thousand but no 1939 population, 11 others had substantial populations reported at that earlier time, though often not yet juridically recognized as cities. For example, Novaya Praga in Kirovograd Oblast was considered a village in 1926 with a population of 13,096, whereas, though recognized as a settlement of urban type in the 1959 census, it then had a population of only 10,696, or a loss of 18 per cent in the period 1926–1959. Or Borispol', in Kiev Oblast, also without a reported population in 1939, yet first mentioned in 1590 and with a 1926 census figure of 11,578; the 1959 population of 17,180 was an increase over 1926 but a very modest one compared with other cities.[16] Thus 16 cities or towns that might appear as "new" from the omission of 1939 census data are in reality older urban settlements.

The remaining 13 cities and towns in the Ukraine with populations of more than 10,000 in 1959 but without previously reported population data are considered new cities and towns and are depicted as such in Figures 85 and 86.

Seven of these new urban settlements are in the Donbas in newly exploited margins of the coalfield just northwest of Donetsk, or near the eastern edge of the coalfield in the eastern part of Lugansk Oblast (Figure 86).

Of the 6 new cities and towns in other parts of the Ukraine, 4 are also associated with coal or lignite mining. The largest of the new cities, Novovolynsk (with a 1959 population of 24 thousand that grew to 37 thousand in 1967) is in Volyn' Oblast on the Polish border. Nearby Chervonograd in L'vov Oblast reached 12 thou-

---

[15] This area was in Austria-Hungary to 1920, then in Czechoslovakia from 1920 to 1938, and in Hungary 1938–1945.

[16] Other such cities and settlements of urban type in the Ukraine without 1939 reported populations but not depicted as new cities and towns on Figures 85 and 86 are: Vasil'kovka in Dnepropetrovsk Oblast, Selidovo in Donetsk Oblast, Globino in Poltava Oblast, Uzin in Kiev Oblast, Gorodishche, Kamenka, and Zhashkov in Cherkassy Oblast, and Novyy Bug and Snigirëvka in Nikolayevsk Oblast.

sand in 1959 and grew to 35 thousand in 1967. Both are in the
L'vov-Volynian Coal Basin. Vatutino in Cherkassy Oblast (between Krivoy Rog and Kiev) is in a lignite basin. Oktyabr'skoye,
a settlement of urban type also in a lignite basin in Kirovograd
Oblast, was later incorporated into the city of Aleksandriya.
Novaya Kakhovka was founded in 1951 in connection with the
construction of the Kakhovka Reservoir and hydroelectric project
on the lower Dnepr River. Velikaya Danilovka was a suburb of
Khar'kov.[17]

Combining both the cities and towns that were essentially new
(13) and others that more than doubled population 1939–1959
(41), one arrives at a figure of 54 growth cities in the Ukraine, of
which 34 were highly concentrated in the coal-mining district of
the Donbas, 4 were in a closely associated cluster in iron-ore mining settlements of the Krivoy Rog district in Dnepropetrovsk
Oblast, and 16 were scattered through the other parts of the
Ukraine. In the Donbas-Krivoy Rog industrial cluster 32 per cent
of the cities and towns grew rapidly, whereas in the rest of the
Ukraine only 9 per cent (Table 31 and Figure 78). As in the European West and North and the Central Industrial District, clusters of growth cities were closely associated with the production
of fuel (coal or oil in the Komi ASSR, lignite in Tula Oblast, and
coal in the Donbas).

In Moldavia 4 cities or towns showed rapid growth (Figure
85). Bel'tsy, the largest, increased in population from 30 to 67
thousand during 1939–1959. Actually Bel'tsy had great fluctuations in population from 35 thousand (1930 Romanian census)
through sharp declines during the war and the successive transfers of territory to 30 thousand (1939) and 18 thousand (1941), to
rise rapidly to 67 thousand in 1959. The rapid growth is thus
partly recovery from the war but partly Soviet industrialization of
this agricultural processing center of the Bel'tsy steppe, which continued to grow, reaching 87 thousand in 1967. The other 3 towns
are small: Dubossary, an agricultural processing center with wood
working and a hydroelectric station on the Dnestr (built 1954),
(5 thousand in 1939, 12 thousand in 1959, 23 thousand in 1967);

[17] Later by a decree of August 29, 1963, incorporated into the city of Khar'kov,
to which it previously had been administratively subordinate.

Ungeny, a railroad center on the main line Kiev-Bucureşti at the Romanian frontier; and Bessarabka, also a railroad center.

(4) *Black-Earth Center, Lower Volga, and North Caucasus*

The Central Black-Earth, Lower Volga, and North Caucasus regions are here grouped as they‚have many similar characteristics. The Central Black-Earth Region and Rostov Oblast have medium percentages of growth cities, with 30 and 32 per cent respectively (Table 31 and Figure 78). The Lower Volga and the North Caucasus (excluding Rostov Oblast) have relatively low proportions of growth cities, 17 and 8 per cent respectively.

The Central Black-Earth (Chernozëm) Region is primarily a rich agricultural area with modest urbanization and urban growth (northern part of Figure 87). Eight of its 27 cities and towns grew rapidly 1939–1959. Lipetsk, an oblast center, grew from 67 to 157 thousand during 1939–1959 on the basis of local iron ores, an iron and steel mill, and a tractor factory. In the southern part of the region, Belgorod, also an oblast center, after stagnation from 1897 to 1939, grew from 34 to 72 thousand in the period 1939–1959, also on the basis of local iron-ore deposits and metal working (boiler works). Between these 2 are Staryy Oskol and Gubkin similarly centers of iron-ore mining based on the ores of the Kursk Magnetic Anomaly (a broad name covering widespread but deep iron ores, occurring at various places between Belgorod and Lipetsk and now in active development). Gubkin is almost exclusively a mining town, whereas Staryy Oskol also has machinery and food factories reflecting both its mineral and agricultural hinterland. L'gov, Ostrogozhsk, and Zherdevka have food and machinery industries. Gribanovskiy recognized as a settlement of urban type just before the 1959 census is presumably an agricultural center. Thus of the 8 rapidly growing or new cities or towns of the Central Black-Earth Region, 4 are associated with iron-ore mining and the rest with processing of agricultural products and with metals or machinery.

The Lower Volga was not an area of rapid urban growth in the period 1939–1959. Of 24 cities and towns in our study group only 4 grew more than 100 per cent in this period or were new (northeast part of Figure 87). Volzhskiy ("of the Volga") is the

Fig. 87 Growth cities of Black-Earth Center, Lower Volga, North Caucasus, and Caucasus regions 1939–1959.

largest. Made a city only in 1954, it had a population of 67 thousand by 1959 and 114 thousand by 1967. It arose in connection with the construction of the gigantic Volgograd dam and hydroelectric project on the Volga River just above Volgograd. Privolzhskiy ("on the Volga") is similarly located on the low east bank of the Volga as an industrial suburb of an oblast center, Saratov. Kamyshin on the west bank of the Volga is a transshipment point between railroad and river with diversified food, machinery, and wood industries and also a large cotton textile factory. Kalach-na-Donu is also a river port, but as its name indicates on the Don River at the outlet of the Volga-Don Canal (built in 1952), which joins the Volga River with the Don and thus with the Black Sea.

The North Caucasus as a whole is not a region of rapid urban growth. Of 70 cities and towns in our study group only 11 were growth cities.

The only concentration of rapid urban growth in the North Caucasus was in Rostov oblast which had 7 growth cities (Figure 87). Four of these are coal-mining centers in an eastward extension of the Donbas coalfield: Novoshakhtinsk, the largest, grew from 48 to 104 thousand (it has a large coke-oven by-product chemical industry also); Gukovo grew from 9 to 53 thousand; Donetsk, a new city, reached 42 thousand by 1959; and Belaya Kalitva, also a new city, with 23 thousand in 1959, is the easternmost point of important coal mining in this basin (though not the limit of the coal deposits). As the name suggests the new city of Volgodonsk owes its rise to the Volga-Don Canal and the Tsimlyansk Reservoir which makes the canal possible; Volgodonsk is at the dam on the Don River, which backs up the river to produce the reservoir and to provide a head of water for the hydroelectric station; it also has a chemical industry. Oktyabr'skiy, an unusually large settlement of urban type (28 thousand), is a suburb of the city of Novocherkassk (to which it is administratively subordinate); its railroad station is Lokomotivstroy ("locomotive factory"), suggesting its industrial tie to Novocherkassk, the machinery and locomotive-building center. Sal'sk to the southeast is the center of an agricultural district and has food and machinery industries.

In the other parts of the North Caucasus only 4 of 48 cities or towns grew rapidly; these are widely spaced. Akhtyrskiy and Khadyzhensk owe their growth to new oil and gas wells. Yessentuki, located at mineral springs at the base of the Caucasus mountains, is a major spa, growing from 16 to 48 thousand population in the period 1939–1959. Beslan in the North Oset ASSR in a maize-producing agricultural region has Europe's largest corn-products factory. The North Caucasus has 11 cities or towns for which the 1959 census shows no 1939 population data but which are not really new cities or towns (except juridically) as they had quite large populations in the 1926 census, often as giant agricultural villages.

(5) *Caucasus*

The 27 growth cities or towns of the Caucasus are about equally distributed among the three republics of the Transcaucasus: 7 in Armenia, 7 in Georgia, and 6 in Azerbaydzhan, plus 7 suburbs of Baku (Table 31 and Figure 87). Armenia stands preëminent in the proportion of its urban settlements in this category, 7 out of 10, in comparison with Georgia with 7 out of 29 or Azerbaydzhan with 6 out of 21. A special category are the suburbs of the city of Baku, 7 of 15 of which grew rapidly 1939–1959.

Yerevan, the capital of Armenia, is the fastest growing large city in the Caucasus and indeed one of the 2 fastest growing cities of more than half a million in the entire Soviet Union (the other is Chelyabinsk). It grew from 204 to 509 thousand in 1939–1959 and to 665 thousand in 1967. It is a capital city, the focus of the cultural, political-administrative, and economic life of Armenia, the Soviet home of the Armenians, a people with a long history of culture and national identity. The very rapid urban growth of Armenia in the period 1939–1959 probably reflects the sudden impact of modernization and industrialization, an impact that arrived here somewhat later than in the Russian or European parts of the Soviet Union and one which was accelerated by the Second World War when other parts of the USSR suffered heavy war damage. As in other areas in which national minorities live, this impact has struck with particular force the national center, which mediates between external (to the republic) innovation and internal economic development and reorganization of life. In addition after World War II there was a considerable influx of Armenians from abroad who, in search of a national home, migrated to Soviet Armenia and settled especially in Tbilisi. Also, because of a high birth rate, the natural increase in population has been very high, about double the average for the Soviet Union (27.4 per thousand for Armenia compared with 17.0 for the entire

Soviet Union in 1940; or 33.5 compared with 17.8 in 1960; or 23.3 compared with 11.1 in 1965).[18] As the rural population of Armenia declined in the period 1939–1959 this high natural increase was entirely channeled into cities, especially Yerevan. Besides its political administrative and cultural roles, Yerevan is a major center of industry, especially for machinery (specialization in electrical machinery). It also has a chemical industry (synthetic rubber and automobile tires) and nonferrous metallurgy (aluminum). There is water power (now heavily supplemented by natural gas) from Sevan-Razdan Cascade on the Razdan River which has a steep mountainous gradient as it leaves the high Lake Sevan.

Other cities of Armenia also grew rapidly. Kirovakan (at an elevation of 1,350 meters or more than 4,000 feet) is a nitrate-fertilizer and machinery center with growth from 18 to 49 thousand (1939–1959) and to 82 thousand (1967). Dilizhan, also at an elevation of about 1,300 meters, is a mountain health resort with mineral springs. Echmiadzin, just west of Yerevan, a very old but small city going back to the second century, has had rapid recent growth with the rise of a chemical industry (plastics). Oktember-yan, also west of Yerevan, is a food-processing and regional center for an irrigated wine and cotton-producing area. Kafan, to the southeast, has grown on the basis of mining of copper ore and its concentration through the flotation process before shipment of the concentrate to the copper smelter at Alaverdi, also in Armenia. The new city of Kadzharan (elevation 2,300 meters or about 7,500 feet) is similarly a copper and molybdenum mining and concentrating center.

In Georgia, the outstanding new city is Rustavi, just southeast of Tbilisi; founded in 1948 with the construction of the Trans-caucasian iron and steel works, it attained a population of 62 thousand by 1959 and 95 thousand by 1967. Nearby Marneuli, in sharp contrast, though also newly a city, is a small food-processing center in an agricultural district. In the northwest part of Georgia are Tkibuli and Tkvarcheli, mountain-edge coal-mining settlements; Tskhaltubo, a health resort with hot radioactive mineral springs; and Zugdidi in the northern part of the Colchis lowland,

[18] *Narodnoe Khoziaistvo SSSR v 1965 g.,* pp. 46–47.

former capital of Mingrelia, with recent growth as center of a developing agricultural area (food industries such as canning, tea processing, and wine making) and forest products (cellulose and paper). Kobuleti on the Black Sea coast is a year-round resort with a good beach and warm winters and also processing plants for subtropical agricultural products, such as tea and citrus fruits.

The largest city of very rapid growth in the Azerbaydzhan SSR is Sumgait on the Caspian Sea coast north of Baku; it grew from 6 thousand in 1939 to 52 thousand in 1959 and 104 thousand in 1967 with the development of a large chemical industry (synthetic rubber and superphosphates) and a metallurgical industry (smelting of aluminum, production of steel and rolled pipes). Also, on the Caspian Sea is the very different small city of Khachmas, center of an agricultural district with a canning industry (vegetables, fruits, and fish). Ali-Bayramly to the south is a river station on the Kura River and a center of an agricultural district and a newly developing oil field. In the western part of the Azerbaydzhan SSR are the new cities of Mingechaur with a new hydroelectric station on the Kura River and an agricultural-machinery factory and Barda, an ancient settlement that declined but has revived recently as a center of the cotton-producing Karabakh steppe irrigated by the Upper Karabakh canal, and the growing city of Khanlar (originally a German settlement named Yelenendorf) in a wine-producing district.

The suburbs of Baku are a special case, since the 1959 census reported their population separately and also reported the population of Baku within its city limits proper (643 thousand) or including settlements of urban type administratively subordinate to the city councils of Baku (971 thousand). Of these 15 industrial settlements with 1959 populations of more than 10 thousand, 7 either doubled the reported 1939 population or had no population reported for that year (inset in Figure 87). They range in population from 10 to 32 thousand (1959). They are located to the north and east of Baku on the oil-rich Apsheron Peninsula which juts into the Caspian Sea. Although each is a settlement of urban type, none is juridically a city. Each is subordinate to one of the 9 district councils within Baku. Stepan Razin, Zabrat, Surakhany, Kirovskiy, Artëm-Ostrovskiy, and Binagadi are based on oil drilling, whereas Shuvelyan is a health resort.

(6) *Volga-Urals*

The Volga-Urals area consists of 3 regions: the Volga-Vyatka Region centered on Gor'kiy, with a moderate percentage of the cities that are counted as growth cities (27 per cent) and 2 regions with high percentages of growth cities, the Middle Volga, centered on Kuybyshev (55 per cent) and the Urals, centered on Sverdlovsk (44 per cent) (Figure 78 and Table 31). Thus the Volga-Vyatka Region falls in the transition zone between the western area with few cities of rapid growth and the interior region with many cities of rapid growth. The Middle Volga region marks the beginning of the interior core which lies between the Volga River on the west and Lake Baykal on the east and which had a high proportion of cities with rapid growth during the period 1939–1959.

The Volga-Urals contain 74 growth cities or a fifth of such cities in the entire Soviet Union, 10 in the Volga-Vyatka Region, 24 in the Middle Volga Region, and 40 in the Urals (Figures 80 and 88 and Table 31).[19]

The 10 growth cities of the Volga-Vyatka Region (named after the 2 main rivers of the region) are divided into 3 types based on central-place administrative functions, fuel and energy supply, and forest products (northwest part of Figure 88).

First, the 3 largest cities of the Volga-Vyatka Region are all administrative centers, as capitals of autonomous republics (ASSR), which give recognition to ethnic minorities within the Russian Soviet Federated Socialist Republic. They are points through which the mainstream of Soviet economic and cultural development is channeled, points of contact at which the country-wide modernization process is mediated for the non-Russian peoples of these republics. As the initial impact of industrialization and urbanization has been felt first in the capitals, they have grown rapidly: Yoshkar Ola (Mari ASSR) increased from 27 to 89 to 137 thousand (1939–1959–1967); Cheboksary (Chuvash ASSR), from 31 to 104 to 178 thousand); and Saransk (Mordov ASSR), from 41 to 91 to 154 thousand.

[19] The cities of Kurgan Oblast and Tyumen' Oblast, which lie in the West Siberian plain, are here considered in the West Siberian Region, though these two oblasts were grouped with the Urals in the 1959 census.

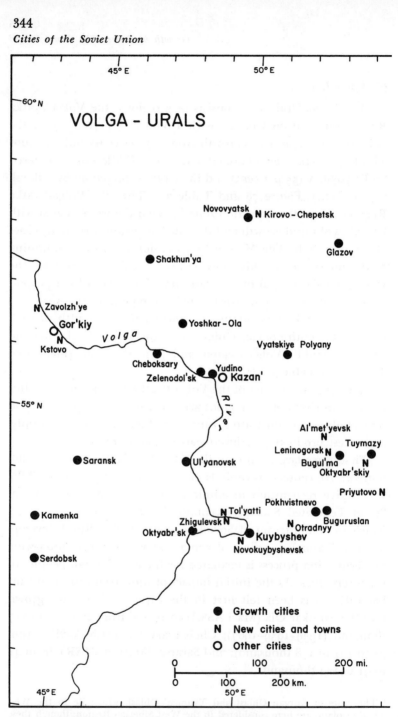

Fig. 88   Growth cities in the Volga-Urals area 1939–1959.

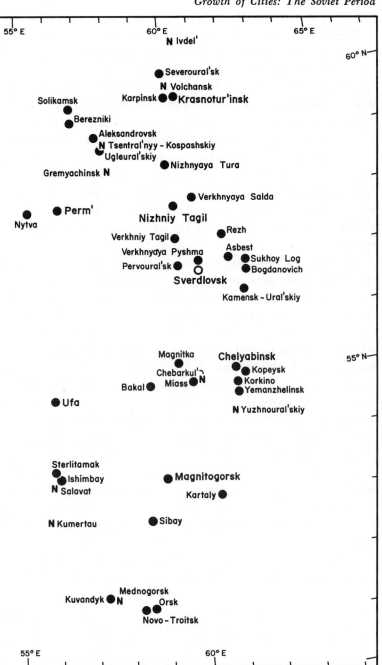

The second group of three urban settlements in the Volga-Vyatka Region are concerned with the handling of fuel and energy: Kstovo, on the Volga just below Gor'kiy, has an oil refinery; Zavolzh'ye ("at the Volga") arose on the basis of the construction of the dam, reservoir, and hydroelectric station on the Volga above Gor'kiy; Kirovo-Chepetsk near Kirovo, developed with the construction of a peat-burning thermal-electric station.

The third group of 4 urban settlements in the Volga-Vyatka Region are all associated with lumber mills and woodworking that reflect the forests along the northern boundary of cleared land and of continuous agriculture: Shakhun'ya (also railroad shops), Novovyatsk, Glazov (also machinery), and Vyatskiye Polyany.[20]

The Middle Volga Region with 24 growth cities is dominated by the dramatic new development of the Volga-Urals oilfield, which since World War II has expanded its production to surpass the output not only of the old Baku field in the Soviet Union but also the output of the great oil state of Texas or indeed of any other state in the United States and also of such major petroleum countries as Venezuela, Kuwait, Saudi Arabia, or Iran. Based primarily on the Volga-Urals field, the Soviet Union has become the second-largest petroleum producing country in the world (second only to the United States). As would be expected this expansion of the petroleum industry has led to a great upsurge in population in the Middle Volga Region and in the rapid growth of many of its cities and towns. Bashkir ASSR, which includes part of this petroleum region, is grouped with the Middle Volga Region.[21]

Seventeen of the 24 growth cities of this Middle Volga Region are closely associated with the production or processing of petroleum or natural gas, and often with the chemical industry.

In first place stand the regional and administrative centers of Kuybyshev and Ufa. Kuybyshev has oil refineries, chemical plants,

[20] Glazov is in the Udmurt ASSR, usually attached to the Urals Region, but is here grouped with the Volga-Vyatka Region to which it seems more akin.
[21] The Bashkir ASSR has traditionally been grouped with the Urals and was so treated in the 1959 census reports. However, in the definition of the major economic regions used for planning purposes and in the regional statistics in recent issues of the statistical yearbook, *Narodnoe Khoziaistvo SSSR*, it has been grouped with the Volga Region.

and many machinery factories. Located on the Volga River near one of the large Volga River dams, reservoirs, and hydroelectric power stations, it also serves as the general center for Kuybyshev Oblast, the Volga Region, and especially the Volga-Ural oilfield. During the attack on Moscow in World War II, it served as the seat of the Soviet government. It was the second largest city in the Soviet Union in 1959 that had more than doubled population in the period 1939–1959 (the largest was Novosibirsk). Kuybyshev increased in population from 390 thousand in 1939 to 886 thousand in 1959 and 992 thousand in 1967. Ufa, the capital of the Bashkir ASSR, lies outside the oil-producing area but serves the oilfields with oil- and gas-producing equipment and geophysical instruments as well as many other types of supplies and services; it receives from the oilfields supplies for its oil refinery and chemical plants. It increased population from 258 thousand in 1939 to 547 thousand in 1959 and 704 thousand in 1967.

Of the 15 other oil towns, 10 are new settlements and 5 are other rapidly growing centers. Four of the 10 new cities and towns in the expanded Middle Volga Region had reached a population of more than 60 thousand by 1959: Novokuybyshevsk and Tol'yatti in Kuybyshev Oblast and Oktyabr'skiy and Salavat in the Bashkir ASSR. Novokuybyshevsk and Tol'yatti[22] on the Volga River in the great industrial concentration with oil and hydroelectric power near Kuybyshev, both with major chemical industries, continued to grow rapidly; Tol'yatti (synthetic rubber, nitrogen fertilizer) had reached 143 thousand by 1967 and Novokuybyshevsk (oil refining and synthetic alcohol), 107 thousand. Salavat similarly combines oil refining and a chemical industry (petrochemicals). Otradnyy (in Kuybyshev Oblast), Al'met'yevsk (in the Tatar ASSR), and Tuymazy, Priyutovo, and Ishimbay (in the Bashkir ASSR) also have oil refineries. Ishimbay was the first major center of the oil industry in the entire Volga-Ural oilfield, dating back to 1932. Nearby Sterlitamak utilizes petroleum in the production of synthetic rubber, and Pokhvistnevo, in the production of carbon black. Other centers of oilfields and oil production

[22] Formerly called Stavropol' (not to be confused with the city of the same name in the North Caucasus), renamed in 1964 in honor of Palmiro Togliatti, long-time leader of the Italian communist party who died in that year.

are Zhigulëvsk in Kuybyshev Oblast, at the site of the Volga dam and hydroelectric station, Bugul'ma, Leninogorsk (Tatar ASSR). Kumertau to the south produces natural gas and also lignite. Buguruslan just east of Kuybyshev lies in Orenburg Oblast but is functionally one of this group of cities although Orenburg Oblast is grouped with the Urals.

The seven growth cities of the Middle Volga Region not associated with the oil industry reflect other resources and conditions. Kamenka and Serdobsk in Penza Oblast in the agricultural regions to the west of the Volga are machinery centers, agricultural machinery and auto trailers, respectively. Of the 4 other centers on the Volga River, two are identified with machinery industries, Ul'yanovsk (automobiles), also an oblast center, and Yudino near Kazan'; and 2, with the milling of grain from these agricultural areas and the working of wood brought down the Volga from the forests to the north, Zelenodol'sk and Oktyabr'sk. The other city, Sibay, although within the Bashkir ASSR, lies far to the southeast to the south of Magnitogorsk and deep in the southern Urals and is a copper-mining and smelting center; functionally it is part of the Urals system of cities, to which we now turn.

The Urals Region contains 40 growth cities and is thus second only to Kazakhstan in number of such cities (Table 31). They fall naturally into 6 clusters: the northwest Urals centered on Perm' (8 growth cities), then a series of cities extending for more than a thousand kilometers (650 miles) in a north-south direction along the eastern flanks of the Urals clustered around Krasnotur'insk (5), Sverdlovsk (11), Chelyabinsk (9), Magnitogorsk (2), and Orsk (5) (Figure 88).

(a) The Perm' cluster of 8 growth cities is focused on Perm', the regional center on the Kama River, which grew from 306 thousand in 1939 to 629 thousand in 1959, and to 796 thousand in 1967. Railroad junction, river port, and administrative center, it has become a major industrial center producing varied machinery that serves the needs of its hinterland: machinery for coal mining, the oil industry, lumbering, chemical production, ship building, and the food industry. Six other growth cities are aligned north-south along a railroad northeast of Perm' from Solikamsk (88 thousand) and Berezniki (134 thousand), chemical cities producing fertilizers (potash and nitrogen), salt, and magnesium on the north, southward through the Kizel coalfield with Aleksandrovsk (machinery), the new town of Tsentral'nyy Kospashkiy, the town of Ugleural'skiy ("coal of the Ural"), and the new city of Gremyachinsk. Southwest of Perm' lies the city of Nytva, with its steel mills.

(b) The northernmost cluster of 5 rapidly expanding mining and ore-processing cities clustered around Krasnotur'insk includes Severoural'sk (the name, appropriately, means "Northern Urals"), the bauxite-mining center which supplies the alumina works at Krasnotur'insk nearby; the new city of Volchansk, with open-pit lignite mining; Karpinsk, also a lignite-mining city, which makes mining equipment; Ivdel', a new city with iron and manganese mines; and Krasnotur'insk itself, the largest city of the area, which grew from a village of 9,582 in 1939 to a city of 61,990 in 1959, primarily on the basis of the aluminum industry, although it is also in the coalfield.

(c) The biggest of these sub-clusters is that in southern Sverdlovsk Oblast with 11 cities and towns of very rapid growth. This cluster of industrial settlements goes back to the 18th century to the establishment of iron foundries based on local ore and charcoal. Thus the first state iron foundry in the Urals at Kamensk-Ural'skiy was established in 1701 to produce cannons and cannon balls for Peter the Great; similar metallurgical plants were established at Nizhniy Tagil in 1725 and at Pervoural'sk in 1732. The metallurgical tradition, extending over two-and-a-half centuries, finds expression today in large modern iron and steel combines, still based on Ural iron ores but now on coking coal brought from other regions. The iron and steel industry remains an important factor today in rapid urban growth: iron and steel mills in Nizhniy Tagil and steel mills and steel products in Verkhnyaya Salda, Nizhnyaya Tura, Pervoural'sk, and Kamensk-Ural'skiy. The larger cities have diversified the metallurgical base with manufacture of metal products and machinery, notably railroad cars at Nizhniy Tagil. Nonferrous metals also play a role in the rapid expansion of cities, nickel at Rezh, copper at Verkhnyaya Pyshma, and aluminum at Kamensk-Ural'skiy, and other minerals at Asbest, whose name clearly reveals its product. Sukhoy Log has nonferrous metallurgy and a cement industry. Bogdanovich produces firebrick used in metallurgy.

Sverdlovsk, the largest city of the Urals, lies within this cluster. It increased its population from 423 thousand in 1939 to 779 thousand in 1959, a remarkable growth (84 per cent) but still below the lower limit of 100 per cent increase for cities shown on the map. Its estimated population reached 961 thousand in 1967. The second and third largest cities of Sverdlovsk Oblast, Nizhniy Tagil with an increase from 160 to 339 thousand during 1939–1959, and Kamensk-Ural'skiy, with an increase from 51 to 141 thousand both more than doubled their population in the period 1939–1959.

(d) The sub-cluster near Chelyabinsk includes 9 rapidly growing cities and towns. Chelyabinsk, the oblast center and largest city, increased 152 per cent during 1939–1959 from 273,116 to 689,049, the highest rate of growth of any city of this size in the entire Soviet Union. It grew further to 836 thousand in 1967. A major center of metallurgy and machinery (especially tractors and heavy forges and presses), it received during World War II 60 large factories (mainly machinery) transported from the war zones in the West. Southeast and south of Chelyabinsk in the Chelyabinsk lignite basin are 4 urban settlements with rapid growth, all associated with lignite mining and power. Kopeysk (also a maker of mining machinery) grew from 60 to 161 thousand during 1939–1959; Korkino, the main center of the Chelyabinsk coal basin, grew from 12 to 85 thousand in this period; Yemanzhelinsk; and the new city, Yuzhnoural'sk ("South Urals"), with a gigantic one million kilowatt thermoelectric generating station based on local lignite and supplying electricity to the Urals grid. To the west of Chelyabinsk, along the important east-west rail line Moscow-Kuybyshev-Chelyabinsk that joins the Trans-Siberian lie 4 cities based on metals, metal working, and machinery. Miass, the largest of these cities, was founded as a copper-smelting and gold-mining center but its modern growth has been based on machinery production (especially the Urals auto works). The other towns are iron-ore mining towns (as Bakal and Magnitka) or producers of high-quality steel (as Chebarkul', a new city which reached 30 thousand population in 1959).

(e) The sub-cluster of Magnitogorsk consists of 2 cities of rapid growth. Magnitogorsk ("magnetite mountain") built since 1929 in the empty steppe at the site of large and very rich iron-ore deposits, now has one of the largest iron and steel plants in the world; its population grew from 146 to 311 thousand (1939–1959) and reached 357 thousand in 1967. Kartaly is a rail junction, from which the branch line extends west to Magnitogorsk.

(f) The Orsk sub-cluster of 5 growth cities at the southern end of the Ural mountains, in Orenburg Oblast, where the Ural River turns westward, is a metallurgical complex of iron, nickel, and copper. Orsk with a population increase from 66 to 176 thousand during 1939–1959 (215 thousand in 1967), is an industrial complex with nonferrous metallurgy (nickel) based on several nearby nickel deposits, oil refining and chemicals based on oil by pipeline from Gur'yev on the northeast coast of the Caspian Sea, and machinery based on metals from the Urals. The nearby city of Novo-Troitsk is essentially new, having increased from a population of only 3 thousand in 1939 to 54 thousand in 1959 and 82 thousand in 1967, in response to the construction of a large integrated iron and steel plant based on the nearby Khalilovo iron-ore deposits. The new city of Mednogorsk ("copper mountain") is a new copper-smelting center, founded only in 1939, to work local copper ore, and attaining a population of 36 thousand by 1959. Kuvandyk, a small city, has railroad shops and cryolite production. As already noted, Orenburg Oblast has one other growth city, Buguruslan, far to the northwest in the Volga-Urals oilfield, whereas Sibay, just to the north of Orsk and with a similar nonferrous metallurgy (copper), lies in the Bashkir ASSR.

(7) *Western Siberia*

In Western Siberia there were 26 growth cities (Figures 89 and 90 and Table 31).

Of these 17 are concentrated in a relatively small, southeastern part of the region in the Novosibirsk-Kuzbas-Barnaul area; 3 near Novosibirsk, 12 in the Kuzbas, and two near Barnaul (Figure 90).

The largest of these is the great regional center, Novosibirsk, which increased in population from 404 to 886 thousand during 1939–1959 and was thus the largest city in the Soviet Union to

more than double its population during this period. It reached a
population of 1,064,000 in 1967. It is the largest city in Siberia, the
regional capital of Western Siberia, and a major transport center
for railroads (on the Trans-Siberian trunk line with other lines
to the Kuzbas and southward to Barnaul and to Soviet Middle
Asia), for river traffic (on the Ob' River), and for air lines. It is
also the largest industrial center of Siberia with specialization on

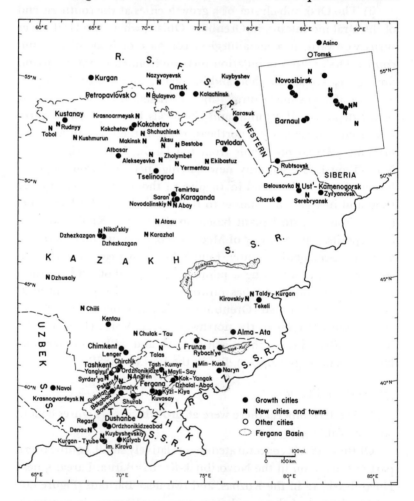

Fig. 89 Growth cities of Southern West Siberia (RSFSR), Eastern
Kazakhstan, and Eastern Soviet Middle Asia 1939–1959.

metal working and machinery (utilizing the metals of the Ural-Kuznetsk Combine, especially from the Kuzbas). Its name means "New Siberia" and it was founded as late as 1893 at the time of the construction of the Trans-Siberian and at the point of bridging the Ob' River.

Just south of Novosibirsk on the Novosibirsk Reservoir are 2 industrial growth cities, Berdsk (hydroelectric station, flour mills, and radios) and Iskitim (cement).

Twelve cities and towns of the Kuzbas (Kemerovo Oblast) showed rapid growth (Figure 90); all are associated with mining and heavy industry. The district is a major producer of coal, iron and steel, chemicals, and machinery. The 3 largest cities (1967), Novokuznetsk (493 thousand) (called Stalinsk from 1932 to 1961), Kemerovo (364), and Prokop'yevsk (290) are all important coal-mining centers with Novokuznetsk distinguished by its large iron

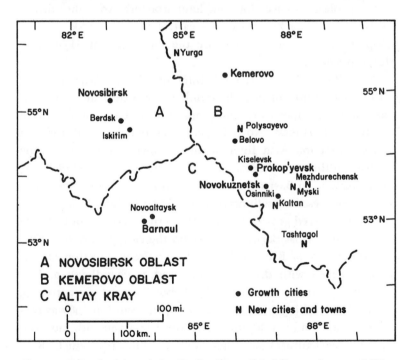

Fig. 90 Growth cities of the Kuzbas-Novosibirsk-Barnaul area of West Siberia 1939–1959.

and steel works (one of the largest in the Soviet Union), Pro-kop'yevsk by its production of coking coal, and Kemerovo by being the oblast center; all also have substantial production of machinery, and Novokuznetsk and Kemerovo of chemicals as well. The other 9 settlements from north to south are: Yurga, a railroad junction and railroad servicing center on the Trans-Siberian at a point where a branch line runs south to the Kuzbas; Polysayevo, a new coal-mining town; Belovo (116 thousand population), a center of coal mining and of nonferrous metallurgy (zinc smelter) based originally on ores of nearby Salair; Kiselevsk (138 thousand), coal-mining city which also produces coal-mining machinery; Osinniki, also a coal-mining city; Kaltan, a new coal-mining city but primarily for use in a large regional electricity-generating station opened here in 1951; Tashtagol, a new iron-ore mining town, which has helped to reduce the need of the Novokuznetsk blast furnaces for long-haul iron ore from the distant Urals (Magnitogorsk); and to the east of Novokuznetsk in a developing part of the coalfield are the new cities of Myski and Mezhdurechensk.

Near Barnaul two cities fall into this cluster: Barnaul itself with a population of 407 thousand, the political and commercial center of Altay Kray and a machinery center, and, only 8 km. to the northeast, Novoaltaysk (Chesnokovka until 1962), a railroad junction with lines north to Novosibirsk, east to the Kuzbas, southeast to the nonferrous mining district around Biysk, and southwest to Barnaul and thence either south to Soviet Middle Asia or west to Tselinograd and northern Kazakhstan.

Nine scattered growth cities of Western Siberia lie outside the Novosibirsk-Kuzbas-Barnaul cluster on the east (Figure 89). Kurgan, the center of Kurgan Oblast, is a railroad junction on the Trans-Siberian with diverging lines west to Sverdlovsk and to Chelyabinsk, at the crossing of the Tobol River; it grew from 53 to 146 thousand (1939–1959) and to 215 thousand in 1967 as center for a large and developing agricultural area and with industry, especially agricultural machinery and agricultural products. Kurgan Oblast is usually grouped with the Urals, but in the spacing of its cities and their relation to railroads, rivers, and agricultural hinterlands, it more nearly resembles Western Siberia and is thus included here. Omsk similarly is a transport center on the Trans-Siberian Railway, with two diverging lines to the west to Sverdlovsk and Chelyabinsk, on a major river crossing (the Irtysh), an oblast center, and with production of machinery and food products (but also with a petroleum refinery and chemicals); it is larger, however, growing from 289 to 581 thousand in 1939–1959 and to 774 thousand in 1967; formerly a main gateway to Western Siberia, it has been somewhat eclipsed by Novosibirsk, farther east. The other 2 cities in Omsk oblast are both small railroad towns and centers of agricultural districts: Nazyvayevsk and Kalachinsk. In Novosibirsk Oblast 2 cities of rapid growth lie well to the west of Novosibirsk and thus apart from the main cluster of large and expanding cities of the oblast: Kuybyshev, a small industrial center in the Baraba Steppe (food products) and Karasuk, a food-processing center in the Kulunda Steppe. Rubtsovsk in the southwest part of Altay Kray, relatively distant from Barnaul, the kray center, grew rapidly from 38 to 111 thousand during 1939–1959 and to 142 thousand in 1967, particularly as a result of the construction of a large agricultural machinery factory during World War II. The rapid growth of these cities thus reflects industrial development, especially during the Second World War or in connection with agriculture, and later the great expansion of the area under cultivation in Western Siberia and Northern Kazakhstan in the Virgin and Idle Lands campaign. Asino, the terminus of a branch rail line northward from Tomsk and the Trans-Siberian Railway, is a major transshipment point for timber from the Chulym River onto the railroad and, as would be expected, a saw milling and wood-working center (northeast corner of Figure 89). Khanty-Mansiysk near the confluence of the Irtysh and Ob rivers, administrative center of the Khanty-Mansi National Okrug, large in area but small in population, in the poorly drained, cold, and remarkably flat West Siberian plain, has industries reflecting both the forest and rivers, wood-working and fish canning. It is relatively remote from the cities and towns of the southern part of West Siberia or from those of the Urals and thus is shown on Figure 81 rather than on one of the detailed regional maps. Although it had a high percentage increase in population 1939–1959, it is still relatively small attaining a population of only 24 thousand in 1967.

(8) *Kazakhstan*

Kazakhstan or the Kazakh SSR is an enormous territory of 2.7 million square kilometers (about a million square miles). Its cities and towns are part of the central interior core of very rapid urban growth. Of its 75 cities and towns of more than 10 thousand population in 1959, 45 had more than doubled their population during the years 1939–1959 or were new urban settlements. The only rapidly growing town in the western part of Kazakhstan (Figure 81) is Kul'sary, founded in 1939, as an oil-drilling center in the Emba oil field northeast of the Caspian Sea. The other 44 growth cities are located in the central or eastern part of the republic (Figure 89 and Table 31).

These 44 growth cities of Kazakhstan fall into 5 main clusters: (a) a northern group of 19 associated with the agricultural expansion of the New Lands or the Virgin Lands, north of Tselinograd; (b) a central group of 10 mining and industrial centers in Karaganda Oblast tied to coal or metalliferous ores or their processing; (c) an eastern group of 5 mining or industrial centers on the edges of the Altay mountains near Ust'-Kamenogorsk; (d) a southeastern group of 4 centers in the mountain-base oases dominated by Alma-Ata, the capital of the republic; and (e) a southern group of 6 cities and towns divided between mining or smelting centers near Chimkent or agricultural towns in the elongated oases along the Syr-Dar'ya (river) to Dzhusaly.

(a) The northern group of 19 rapidly growing or new cities or towns north of Tselinograd are associated with the enormous, bold, but risky campaign substantially to expand the frontier of farming into semiarid country with conditions similar to those of the American dust bowl of the western Great Plains. Between 1950 and 1958 the sown area in Kazakhstan was increased from 7.76 million hectares to 28.54 million hectares,[23] or an increase of 20.78 million hectares (51 million acres); this expansion in these years in

[23] *Narodnoe Khoziaistvo SSSR v 1965 g. Statisticheskii ezhegodnik.* M. 1966, p. 294.

this one republic is equal to the total harvested acreage of North Dakota, South Dakota, and Nebraska taken together. Tselinograd (formerly Akmolinsk) was renamed in 1961. Its present name, which means "virgin-land city," gives recognition to this great campaign. Tselinograd increased in population from 32 thousand in 1939 to 102 thousand in 1959 (and to 176 thousand in 1967). It was made the center of Tselinnyy Kray (Virgin Land District) which included the whole northern part of the Kazakh SSR and which, for a period, joined together 5 oblasts.

Of 22 cities and towns in this northern part of Kazakhstan, 19 grew so rapidly as to be depicted on Figure 89. This is the largest cluster of rapidly growing cities in the Soviet Union associated with agricultural development, as in most parts of the country rapid growth has been dependent on manufacturing, mining, or regional administrative functions. The old regional capital, Petropavlovsk, located where the Trans-Siberian runs through a corner of northern Kazakhstan and crosses the Ishim River, the largest city of the region at the time of the 1959 census and the largest until Tselinograd passed it in size at the end of 1964, was the only city in the region to have merely a moderate growth (43 per cent between 1939 and 1959), although 2 small cities in the region (Stepnyak and Dzhetygara), associated with gold mining, lost population.

The five rapidly growing oblast centers or their suburbs are typified and symbolized by Tselinograd, which serves as a transportation center (crossing of north-south and east-west railroad lines) and manufacturing center (agricultural machinery, pumps supplied to farms, and meat and flour based on agricultural products). Other oblast centers are similarly transport and industrial centers serving the expanding farmlands with machinery or processing meat and flour from farm products: Kustanay on the Tobol River; Kokchetav and its growth suburb, a settlement of urban type, also called Kokchetav; and Pavlodar on the Irtysh (which also has ship repair and the processing of fish).

Five rapidly growing mining or ore-processing centers include Rudnyy (iron ore), Aksu, Zholymbet, and Bestobe (gold), and Ekibastuz (coal). Of these Rudnyy, "ore," is the most striking. A very rich and large iron-ore deposit was discovered here accidentally in 1949 through the erratic behavior of a compass needle in an airplane. Rudnyy arose in 1957 as the center of mining operations and reached a population of 37 thousand by 1959 and 89 thousand by 1967.

Ekibastuz is the center of a large newly developed bituminous coal basin with deposits near the surface that can be mined by strip mining. The first open-cut mine began operations as recently as in 1954; Ekibastuz became a city in 1957 and reached populations of 26 thousand in 1959 and 40 thousand in 1967. Plans call for the construction of gigantic pit-head power stations to transmit electric power over long distances.

Nine smaller growth cities and towns (8 of which are new) are located on railroad lines and serve as transshipment points and centers for local agricultural regions, providing and repairing agricultural machinery (and automobiles), storing and shipping grain, and processing agricultural products especially flour, meat, and butter; some also have railroad shops. Tobol (railroad junction), Kushmurun (railroad shops), Atbasar (flour mills), and Yermentau are located on the new railroad which extends from Magnitogorsk and Kartaly on the west eastward through Tselinograd to Pavlodar and Barnaul. Alekseyevka, Makinsk, Shchuchinsk (railroad shops), and Krasnoarmeysk are on the north-south line Tselinograd-Petropavlovsk. Bulayevo is on the Trans-Siberian east of Petropavlovsk.

(b) A central cluster of 10 mining and industrial cities and towns are located in Karaganda Oblast and focus on the city of Karaganda, the oblast center. They are clearly part of the central core of rapidly growing cities of the Soviet Union, but they are very different from the group of cities in the agricultural steppes of Northern Kazakhstan, since they are mining or industrial points set in a virtually empty desert or semi-desert, tied to highly localized sources of mineral raw materials and are separated from one another by long distances virtually devoid of urban or rural population but linked by railroads. Ten of 11 cities and towns of this oblast more than doubled population during the period 1939–1959 or were new settlements. Karaganda grew from 156 thousand in 1939 to 387 thousand in 1959 and 498 thousand in 1967 with the expansion of coal mining in the Karaganda Coal Basin, third largest producer in the USSR (after the Donbas and the Kuzbas), and also with the development of other mining and industrial centers in the oblast. Nearby Temirtau, which grew from 5 thousand in 1939 to 77 thousand in 1959 and 150 thousand in 1967, is the site of a large integrated iron-and-steel plant built to utilize coking coal of Karaganda Basin and various iron ores; the city also has a chemical works (synthetic rubber). Other nearby settlements in the Karaganda Basin are the coal-mining cities of Saran' and Abay, and the town of Novodolinskiy. To the southwest of Karaganda are other mining towns but for metalliferous ores not coal. Atasu mines iron ore for the blast furnaces of Temirtau. Karazhal was developed to mine iron and manganese ores. The city of Dzhezkazgan, a subordinate town of exactly the same name, and the town of Nikol'skiy, also subordinate to the city council of Dzhezkazgan, are in a complex of copper mining, concentration of ores, and smelting.

(c) Eastern Kazakhstan extends into the lofty Altay mountains; its five rapidly growing and new cities are related to the products of the mountains, ores and water power, or to transportation. Ust'-Kamenogorsk, the center of the East Kazakhstan Oblast, has mushroomed from a population of 20 thousand in 1939 to 150 in 1959 and 212 in 1967. It is a center of nonferrous metals with smelting of lead and zinc and the production of titanium and magnesium, light metals used in aircraft and spacecraft. At a convergence of valleys in an important mining area, it is a railroad junction and a river station on the Irtysh River. Upstream on the Irtysh are 2 large hydroelectric stations. Zyryanovsk, deep in the mountains and at the end of the railroad, is a mining center for polymetals — a favorite Russian term for various combinations of nonferrous metals, such as lead, zinc, and often silver or other metals or their ores — and also has a lead combine. Belousovka is a new mining town, also for polymetals. Serebryansk, also a new city, is near the large Bukhtarma hydroelectric station, dam, and reservoir on the Irtysh River. Charsk is a small city on the Turk-Sib (Turkestan to Siberia) railroad with railroad shops, it serves a grain-growing region at the base of the mountains.

(d) Four growth cities lie near Alma-Ata in the southeastern part of the Kazakh SSR. Alma-Ata, the capital of the Kazakh SSR, at the foothills of the mountains, had rapid growth particularly as a political-administrative center; it also has diversified light industries and serves as center of an agricultural area. Its population jumped from 222 thousand in 1939 to 456 thousand in 1959 and 652 thousand in 1967. Somewhat to the north are 2 other centers for agricultural areas at the junction of mountain and plain: Taldy-Kurgan and Kirovskiy. To the east in the mountains lies Tekeli, which owes its growth to polymetals: lead and zinc mining.

(e) The southern part of Kazakhstan has 6 varied growth cities. Chimkent, the center of Chimkent Oblast and the former South Kazakhstan Kray, which included three oblasts, is primarily an industrial center based on nonferrous metals (lead smelter), machinery, chemicals, and textiles. To the north lies Kentau, "ore mountain" in Kazakh, which mines and concentrates polymetallic ores for the Chimkent smelter and to the south, Lenger, which mines the coal (lignite) that provides the fuel. To the northeast is Karatau, formerly Chulak-Tau, the phosphate-rock-mining center. To the northwest lie two entirely different sorts of towns, Chiili and Dzhusaly, centers of agricultural oases along the Syr-Dar'ya (river) on its long course through the desert to the Aral Sea and also railroad towns on the railroad from Soviet Middle Asia to Europe.

(9) *Soviet Middle Asia*

Soviet Middle Asia may be divided into 2 contrasting parts in terms of proportion of cities and towns that increased rapidly in population 1939–1959. In the eastern part of Middle Asia of 52 cities and towns, 30 grew rapidly, or 58 per cent (Table 31 and Figure 78). In the western part of 32 cities and towns only 7 grew rapidly; these combined with the 8 cities and towns in West Kazakhstan of which only one was a growth city form an area in western Kazakhstan and western Middle Asia in which the 8 growth cities constitute only 20 per cent of the 40 cities and towns.

The 30 growth cities of eastern Middle Asia are located in the irrigated oases at the base of the high mountains, in mountain valleys, or along streams issuing from them, or at mining or industrial settlements based on them (Figure 89).[24] Thus eastern Soviet Middle Asia has many cities of rapid growth; but it also has urban settlements that are relatively stable in population or even declining somewhat; most of the latter are small centers of oases long since fully occupied and therefore with limited possibilities for further growth. In the part of the Fergana Basin in the Uzbek SSR (Andizhan and Fergana oblasts), for example, of 8 cities and towns only 2 are counted as growth cities. The rapidly growing centers are in newly opened irrigated lands (and projects), at new mining settlements, at new transportation facilities, or at nodes of new industrial or administrative functions.

The boundaries of the three union republics of the eastern part of Soviet Middle Asia (the Kirgiz SSR, the Uzbek SSR, and the Tadzhik SSR) are quite irregular, following the distribution of the 3 main ethnic groups, recognized in the formation of these republics. For example, all 3 republics have segments in the beautiful, high, mountain-girt Fergana basin separated from other parts of each republic by high mountains. Nevertheless, the description of rapidly growing cities and towns in this area will follow the political divisions from northeast to southwest.

The Kirgiz SSR has 10 growth cities. Frunze, the capital of the republic, with a 1959 population of 220 thousand, about half the industrial production of the entire republic, and a diversified industrial structure, is the leading city. It is located at the northern base of the Kirgiz mountain range, a part of the mighty Tyan'-Shan', where a series of small short parallel streams flowing northward from the mountains provide irrigation water for the oasis between the mountain edge and the desert in the basin of the Chu River, which drains Issyk-Kul' (lake) and disappears westward into the desert. Frunze is an example of an oasis center and regional capital. Rybach'ye, at the western end of Issyk-Kul' in an agricultural valley within the mountains, is a transport node, i.e., the terminus of a rail line, the station for lake transportation, and a center for highways to Frunze, along the lake, and over the moun-

[24] Tashkent, the great regional center for Soviet Middle Asia, is not counted a "growth city" since its population increase 1939–1959 was *only* 66 per cent. Nevertheless its growth has been remarkable, from 550 thousand in 1939 to 912 thousand in 1959 and 1,239,000 in 1967. It is now the largest Soviet city in Asia and the fourth largest city in the Soviet Union.

tains to Naryn, center of the former Tyan'-Shan' (mountain) oblast. Rybach'ye and Naryn were both relatively small (only 18 and
15 thousand respectively in 1959 and only 5 thousand each in
1939) but rapidly growing centers of large but sparsely populated
mountain regions in the process of development of commercial
grazing (sheep), lumbering, and mining. Talas and Min-Kush are
similar high mountain towns.

A group of rapidly growing urban settlements in the Kirgiz
SSR are associated with the eastern part of the Fergana Basin in
the southern part of the republic along the boundary with the
Uzbek SSR. Four are centers of mineral production, Tash-Kumyr
(coal), Mayli-Say (oil and gas), and Kok-Yangak (coal) in the foothills of the mountains that enclose the basin on the north and
Kyzyl-Kiya (lignite) in the foothills of mountains to the south of
the basin. Dzhalal-Abad lies within the agricultural cotton-producing valley near its northeast edge.

Within the Fergana Basin are also 2 growth cities of the Uzbek
SSR and 2 of the Tadzhik SSR. Fergana, center of Fergana Oblast,
is an administrative and industrial center, and Kuvasay, an industrial city (cement) in the Uzbek SSR. Shurab (coal) in the Tadzhik
SSR is in the foothills in the southwest edge of the basin. In addition Sovetabad in the Tadzhik SSR is located in the valley of the
Syr-Dar'ya, which drains the Fergana Basin, in the section where
the river cuts through the mountains that separate the Fergana
Basin from the great desert plains of Soviet Middle Asia to the
west.

Tashkent Oblast of the Uzbek SSR has nine growth cities. Four
are near the great regional center of Tashkent, aligned along river
and irrigation canals, roads, and railroads of the Chirchik valley in
which Tashkent is located; from northeast to southwest these are
Chirchik (the largest, with an electrochemical industry based on
electricity generated from the water of the Chirchik as it descends
from the mountains), Ordzhonikidze[25] and Yangiyul', both virtually industrial surburbs of Tashkent, and the new town of Syr-
Dar'ya, which as the name suggests is located on the Syr-Dar'ya
(river) near the mouth of the Chirchik. The other 5 are aligned

[25] Incorporated into Tashkent in late 1966.

along the eastern boundary of the Uzbek SSR and thus in general at the base of the high mountains of Soviet Middle Asia or near the junction of high mountain and lowland desert. From north to south these are: Angren, a new coal-mining city which had reached a population of 56 thousand as early as by 1959; Almalyk, also a new city, center of nonferrous smelters (copper, molybdenum, lead, and zinc); the small new town of Pskent; Gulistan (formerly Mirzachul'), a center for the Hunger Steppe (Golodnaya Step'), a major new cotton-growing area of Uzbekistan developed with new irrigation canals; and Bekabad (formerly Begovat), the rapidly growing industrial city on the Syr-Dar'ya at the gateway to the Fergana Basin, with its iron and steel plant, cement works, and hydroelectric station.

In the mountainous and somewhat isolated Tadzhik SSR at the extreme southeast of the Soviet Union, urbanization is now proceeding very rapidly as evidenced by the fact that 9 of the 14 cities and towns of more than 10,000 population in 1959 had more than doubled their population since 1939 or were new. Dushanbe (formerly Stalinabad), the capital and largest city, is a product of the Soviet period and had populations of 6, 83, 224 and 333 thousand in 1926, 1939, 1959, and 1967. As typical of newly developing regions in early stages, one third of the entire industrial production of the republic is concentrated in this capital city. Two cities in the northern part of the republic associated with the Fergana Valley have already been mentioned. The other 6, like Dushanbe, are located in a series of valleys that lead from high mountains southward to the border of Afghanistan and the Amu-Dar'ya (river): Regar, Ordzhonikidzeabad, Kuybyshevskiy, Kurgan-Tyube, Sovkhoz imeni Kirova, and Kulyab are all small but growing towns, processing agricultural products, and serving nearby farming areas.

Of the 8 growth cities of western Kazakhstan and western Soviet Middle Asia, one is in the Kazakh SSR (already discussed), 5 in the Uzbek SSR, and 2 in the Turkmen SSR. Three Uzbek oblasts have one such growth city each (western part of Figure 89). In Samarkand Oblast is Krasnogvardeysk, a new town and center of irrigated lands on the high-line Bulungur Canal, which takes its water from the famous Zeravshan River at the crossing of the canal by railroad and highway from Tashkent to Samarkand. In Bukhara Oblast farther to the west Navoi, also in the irrigated valley of the Zeravshan, has a large chemical fertilizer plant and a large regional electric-power station burning natural gas. In the southeast corner of the Uzbek SSR in the Surkhandar'ya Oblast, Denau lies in a mountain-bordered agricultural valley that slopes southward to the boundary of Afghanistan and produces cotton and wine. Two cities of the Uzbek SSR and one of the Turkmen SSR are in the oasis of the lower Amu-Dar'ya just before it empties into the Aral Sea (Figure 81). Nukus, the capital of the Kara-Kalpak ASSR grew from 10 to 39 thousand, 1939–1959, based on its political-administrative functions and varied local industries. Tashauz and Biruni are centers for other parts of the oasis with cotton-ginning and cottonseed oil plants. Nebit-Dag in extreme southwestern Turkmenistan near the eastern shore of the Caspian Sea is the center of the Nebit-Dag oil field.

(10) *Eastern Siberia*

Eastern Siberia divides into 2 very different parts (Table 31 and Figure 78). West of Lake Baykal 17 of 32 cities and towns grew rapidly; east of Lake Baykal only one of 9. Lake Baykal is the eastern boundary of the interior core in which a high proportion of cities grew rapidly.

Of the 17 growth cities of Eastern Siberia west of Lake Baykal 15 are located in the southern part of the region between the Yenisey River and Lake Baykal. They lie on the axis of the Trans-Siberian Railway or its branches, on the great river system of the Yenisey and its tributary, the Angara, or near the 2 oblast centers Krasnoyarsk and Irkutsk (Figure 91). In the vast expanses east or northeast of Lake Baykal there are few cities that are either large or growing rapidly.

Along the Trans-Siberian Railway are 7 growth cities. From west to east we come first to Krasnoyarsk, the largest growth city in Eastern Siberia; it grew from 190 to 412 thousand 1939–1959 and reached 576 thousand in 1967. Located at the crossing by the Trans-Siberian Railway of the Yenisey River, it is a major transshipment point and commercial and political-administrative center. It is also one of the principal industrial cities of Siberia, spe-

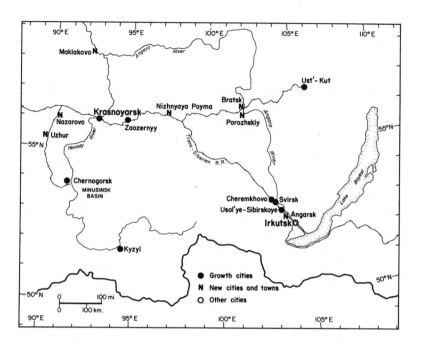

Fig. 91 Growth cities of the southern part of East Siberia west of Lake Baykal 1939–1959.

cializing in machinery, chemicals (synthetic rubber and tires), wood working and a cellulose-paper combine, food, and cement. It lies in an area of abundant energy resources with high water-power potential and many coalfields. The next city is Zaozernyy, a lignite-mining and mica-processing center in the Kansk-Achinsk basin, which grew from 9 to 35 thousand in 1939–1959 and then to 55 thousand in 1964 but apparently dropped to 31 thousand in 1967. Nizhnyaya Poyma, formed in 1951, as a settlement of urban type or a workers' settlement, achieved a population of 32 thousand by 1959 and thus became one of the largest urban settlements in the Soviet Union not juridically a city; it is built on a large saw-mill and wood-chemical works making use of the great forests of Siberia. Four cities lie just northwest of Irkutsk along the railroad and Angara River. Cheremkhovo, the center of Cheremkhovo bituminous coal basin, grew from 56 to 123 thousand (1939–1959); it also has machinery (mining equipment) and food factories. Next is the smaller machinery center of Svirsk, followed by the salt-mining city of Usol'ye Sibirskoye, with machinery and chemical factories. Finally the new city of Angarsk, which was constructed in 1948, became a city in 1951 but attained a population of 134 thousand by 1959 and 183 thousand by 1967. It is a rapidly expanding industrial satellite of Irkutsk with a chemical industry, oil refining, and cement production.

South of the Trans-Siberian are 4 cities or towns of recent foundation or rapid growth, all on the rail line to the Minusinsk Basin or on the Yenisey River. Nazarovo is a new lignite-mining center with a regional electric power station based on the local lignite and with food industries based on local agricultural products. Uzhur, a new city, is a local agricultural center with food industries. Chernogorsk in the Minusinsk Basin on the upper Yenisey River is a center for the mining of bituminous coal. Kyzyl, in a basin surrounded by mountains at the junction of 2 rivers that together form the Yenisey, is the center of the Tuva ASSR. High mountains lying between the area and Russia on the north and China on the south made the boundary unclear with the result that the basin was at various times part of the Chinese Empire, a Russian protectorate, independent (1921–1944 as Tannu-Tuva or Tuva), and since 1944 part of the Soviet Union. Kyzyl as center of this relatively isolated region is both administrative center and processor of local materials (food, leather, and wood).

Four new or rapidly growing cities or towns lie to the north of the Trans-Siberian. Maklakovo on the Yenisey River just below the mouth of the Angara, is a new wood-working town. Bratsk on the railroad line to Ust'-Kut, at its crossing of the Angara River and site of the gigantic Bratsk hydroelectric power project and dam on the river, although an old fortress, is essentially a new city that reached a population of 50 thousand by 1959 and 122 thousand by 1967. It has wood-working industries. Many power-intensive industries are projected to utilize the electric power generated here. Nearby the new town of Porozhskiy ("town on the rapids") is administratively subordinate to Bratsk. Ust'-Kut ("mouth of the Kuta rivers"), as the name indicates, is at the confluence of the Kuta and the Lena and is the terminus of the rail line from Tay-shet on the Trans-Siberian. It thus is an important transshipment point and a center for the wood industry and ship building for the Lena fleet.

In Eastern Siberia west of Lake Baykal only 2 growth cities lie outside the southern segment shown in Figure 91. These are shown on the general map of the Soviet Union (Figure 81). Noril'sk in the Far North is a mining and smelting center for nonferrous ores (nickel, copper, cobalt) utilizing also local bituminous coal. It is an excellent example of a city located at a site of raw materials in spite of a harsh environment. Construction on the city began in 1935 and it increased in population from 14 thousand in 1939 to 109 thousand in 1959. Dudinka, the port on the lower Yenisey River, can be reached by ocean-going ships using the Northern Sea Route through the Arctic Ocean; it was founded as long ago as 1616 but its recent growth dates from its establishment as the port for Noril'sk, with which it was linked by a short rail line in 1937.

That the core of rapidly growing cities in the USSR extends eastward as far as Lake Baykal only is evidenced by the paucity of such cities farther east. Borzya is the only rapidly growing city in Eastern Siberia east of Lake Baykal (Figure 81). It is a rail junction for lines from the Trans-Siberian in the Soviet Union southwest into the eastern part of the Mongolian People's Republic and southeast into Manchuria and the Chinese People's Republic, where the old Chinese Eastern Railway was the subject of international dispute and was controlled in turn by Russia, Japan, and China, or by various combinations of them. Borzya is thus a railroad center with associated rail shops; it is also a meat-packing center in a livestock-raising area.

(11) *Soviet Far East*

The Soviet Far East had eight widely spaced cities that grew rapidly in the period 1939–1959 (Figure 81). As befits a far-flung maritime territory tied together mainly by water transportation, 6 of these growing cities were seaports or river ports. The largest and most publicized of these is Komsomol'sk-na-Amure, which, as the name indicates, was built by the Communist Youth League on the lower Amur River. It is the site of a large steel works (Amurstal'), of machinery production, oil refining, and lumber, cellulose and paper combines, all based on raw materials from the region. It grew from 71 thousand in 1939 to 177 thousand in 1959 and 209 thousand in 1967. Its seaport, Sovetskaya Gavan' ("Soviet harbor") on the Tatar Strait leading to the Sea of Japan, at the eastern terminus of a railroad built during World War II, is a center of wood and fish processing as well as port and naval base; it grew from 12 to 50 thousand in the wartime period 1939–1959 but decreased to 26 thousand in 1967. Nakhodka, just east of Vladivostok, on the Sea of Japan, is similarly a railroad terminal, port, and fish-processing center. Recognized as a city only in 1950 it grew to 64 thousand population in 1959 and 96 thousand in 1967. Two regional centers grew rapidly. Yuzhno-Sakhalinsk (earlier Russian Vladimirovka, later Japanese Toyohara), as the present name indicates, is in Southern Sakhalin; it grew from 39 to 85 thousand (1940–1959), whereas most of the other cities acquired from Japan after World War II in this area lost population. It is a regional center with diverse political-administrative functions and industries. Petropavlovsk-Kamchatskiy, the regional center and port for remote Kamchatka grew from 35 to 86 thousand during 1939–1959 and to 123 thousand in 1967. Its special industry is fish processing, but it also has ship repair yards. Another port and regional center with repair facilities and fish processing is Magadan, which grew from 27 to 62 thousand in 1939–1959 and 82 thousand in 1967. It is the center of a vast sparsely inhabited territory which includes the Kolyma gold fields. Two relatively small interior cities not on the coast or a major river or on main through rail lines also grew rapidly: Arsen'yev, a wood-working settlement, and Raychikhinsk, a lignite-mining center.

GROWTH IN URBAN POPULATION 1959–1966
BY REGION

The urban population increased from 100 million on January 17, 1959, to 128 million on January 1, 1967, or 28.0 per cent. In this period the urban population of the Soviet Union grew by an average of 3.5 million each year at an average rate of 3.1 per cent per year or 36.2 per cent per decade. This represented some slowing down of the earlier rates of growth of Soviet cities, which had been 6.5 per cent per year for the period 1926–1939 and 4.1 per cent per year for the period 1950–1959 (Tables 24 and 25). Indeed, the rate dropped to 2.6 per cent for the year 1966, 2.3 per cent for 1967, and 2.4 per cent for 1968.

Estimates of urban population on January 1, 1966, by oblasts permit regional comparisons of rates of growth 1959–1966.[26] Data on urban population by oblasts for 1967 were not available at the time this monograph was written and thus the regional comparisons are for the period 1959–1966. The over-all average for the Soviet Union was an increase of 24.8 per cent in urban population for the years 1959–1966. As in previous periods this growth was not uniformly spread over the Soviet Union but rather exhibited marked areal variations.

These areal variations in rate of urban growth 1959–1966 are both more complex and more narrow in range than in earlier periods (Figure 92). The core of most rapid growth, more than 50 per cent or twice the average rate for the Soviet Union, lies in the interior of the country in Kazakhstan and Soviet Middle Asia. Oblasts increasing 25–49 per cent (more than the average rate for the country as a whole but at less than double the rate), are widespread and occupy much of the territory from the western boundary of the Soviet Union east to Lake Baykal, excluding principally the more densely settled and urbanized areas of the Donbas in the Eastern Ukraine, of the Central Industrial District, of the Urals, and of the Kuzbas in Western Siberia, the very areas that had had the most rapid growth in the period 1926–1939. Other pockets of slower than average rate of urban growth also lie within the western regions, in Eastern Siberia, and in parts of the Soviet Far East. The recovery of the west as an area of rapid urban development 1959–1966 was remarkable.

The core of very high rates of urban growth 1959–1966 (more than 50 per cent) in Kazakhstan and Soviet Middle Asia consisted of 3 different types of areas. First, northern Kazakhstan had the highest rates of urban growth in the entire country, 107 per cent in Pavlodar Oblast, 82 per cent in Kustanay Oblast, and 55 per cent in Tselinograd Oblast (Figure 92). Urban development fol-

---

[26] *Narodnoe Khoziaistvo SSSR v 1965 g.*, pp. 14–29. Later estimates for January 1, 1969, are contained in *Narodnoe Khoziaistvo SSSR v 1968g.*, pp. 13–18, published in the autumn of 1969.

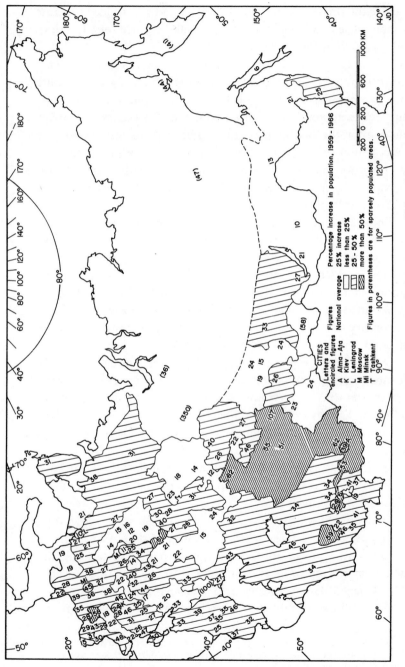

Fig. 92 Percentage increase in urban population 1959–1966 by oblasts.

lowed the Virgin Lands campaign of expanding the arid frontier of agriculture. New and enlarged cities serve the farmlands newly settled during this campaign. Second, Karaganda Oblast, with 51 per cent increase, represents urban growth based on coal, iron, and copper mining and related industries. Third, the remaining oblasts of this core located at the bases of the mountains of Soviet Middle Asia are founded on agricultural, industrial and mining development with new irrigation projects in Bukhara Oblast (59 per cent increase), industrialization in Tashkent Oblast (76 per cent increase) and varied development in Alma-Ata Oblast in Kazakhstan (62 per cent), and in the Kirgiz SSR (53 per cent). The cities of Tashkent and Alma-Ata, separately shown on the map as circles, grew more slowly than the urban population as a whole for thes? areas.

The nearly continuous belt of oblasts with growth somewhat above the average for the Soviet Union (25–50 per cent), stretching from the western boundary eastward to Lake Baykal may be broken into various segments, proceeding in general from west to east (Figure 92):

(1) The western areas stretching from Leningrad Oblast (outside the city of Leningrad) on the north to the Moldavian SSR on the south, that is from the Gulf of Finland on the Baltic Sea to the Black Sea and including most of the political units that touch the western boundary of the country. With the sole exception of Moldavia, all these oblasts that grew more rapidly than the country-wide average 1959–1966 had grown more slowly than the national average in the preceding period, 1939–1959, presumably because of great war damage during World War II. They include all the areas added to Belorussia and the Ukraine from Poland in 1939.[27] The oblasts at or near the pre-1939 western boundary of the Soviet Union in the Ukraine form a band of slower urban growth 1959–1966 (18, 22, and 22 per cent). All oblasts in Belorussia had above-average urban growth in this period, culminating in the capital, the city of Minsk, with 45 per cent. The natural increase in the population here is only about the national average; thus the rapid urban growth is clearly the result of migration,

---

[27] Rovno Oblast had an increase in urban population of 58 per cent 1959–1966, or more than double the average Soviet rate.

probably mostly rural-urban. Adjacent oblasts of previous slow growth in the RSFSR, Smolensk, Pskov, and Novgorod, also fall in this area with increases above the national average. This rapid growth reflects partly recovery from wartime damage, but I hypothesize that two other important factors in very rapid industrial and urban expansion are (1) large migration from labor-surplus densely populated surrounding rural regions and (2) good location to serve markets or utilize materials from the countries that are members of the Council for Mutual Economic Assistance and that developed close economic relations with the Soviet Union during this period (see Chapter IV).

(2) A Central band in the Ukraine including all the oblasts that touch the Dnepr River on east or west and extending from Belorussia on the north to Crimea and the Black Sea on the south. Here rapid growth is associated with the hydroelectric power of the Dnepr, coal from the Donbas, iron ore from Krivoy Rog, and iron and steel produced within the area or from the Donbas to the east.

(3) The North Caucasus and the Transcaucasus had fairly uniform rates of urban growth somewhat above the national average (clustering around 32–39 per cent).

(4) Suburbs and satellites of Moscow had rates just barely above the average for the country as a whole (25–34 per cent), although the large city of Moscow grew at only 11 per cent, far below the average for the country.

(5) Oblasts of the Central Black-Earth Region that had formerly lagged in urban development experienced an upsurge of urban growth with the exploitation of the iron-ore reserves of the so-called Kursk Magnetic Anomaly, reaching a high point in Belgorod Oblast (44 per cent).

(6) The Northern European areas continued rapid urban growth associated with active development of the resources of mines and forests.

(7) The autonomous republics of the ethnic minorities at the bend of the Volga felt the impact of rapid urbanization, culminating in the Mordov ASSR (61 per cent).

(8) The Middle Volga area of oilfields, industry, and hydroelectric power that had grown very rapidly 1939–1959 continued a growth rate just above the national average.

(9) The western oblast of Western Siberia (Omsk) and the adjacent oblasts just east of the Urals (Tyumen' and Kurgan) represented a ridge of growth just above the national average between the 2 highly urbanized and industrialized axes of the Urals and of the Kuzbas-Novosibirsk area that grew at a slower rate during 1959–1966 (though still with large numerical increases).

(10) Eastern Siberia west of Lake Baykal with hydroelectric power and industrial developments had rates of increase of urban population slightly above the national average.

(11) The other parts of Soviet Middle Asia and of Kazakhstan mostly had rates of urban increase substantially above average.

(12) Finally some of the sparsely settled regions with few, small, and widely scattered cities had high percentage increases, based, however, on small numbers. For example, the Khanty-Mansi National Okrug, which occupies a large area in the northern part of Western Siberia increased its urban population from 33 to 148 thousand or 350 per cent, in small settlements of urban type formed in the period 1963–1964, with the discovery of oil and gas.

We now turn to a review of individual cities of rapid growth in this period.

CITIES OF MORE THAN 50,000 POPULATION IN 1967 WITH RAPID GROWTH 1959–1967

Some 55 cities of more than 50,000 population in 1967 grew during the preceding 8 year period, 1959–1967, by more than 50 per cent, or nearly twice the average rate of urban growth for the entire Soviet Union for this period (28 per cent) (Table 32).

Of the 55 cities 18 fall into a broad band along the Volga and nearby land extending south to the Caucasus, 8 lie in western areas, 3 are suburbs of Moscow, 4 are located along the northern margins of settlement in Europe, 15 lie in the Asiatic part of the Soviet Union, and in 7 (mostly in the Donbas) the growth was due to boundary changes rather than any organic growth (Figure 93).

Before discussing each of these groups in turn we may highlight the types of cities of very rapid growth by mentioning the seven that more than doubled in population in the years 1959–1967. In their connection with hydroelectric power, chemicals, and minerals, they reveal in dramatic form the main thrust of Soviet economic development during this period. Three are industrial

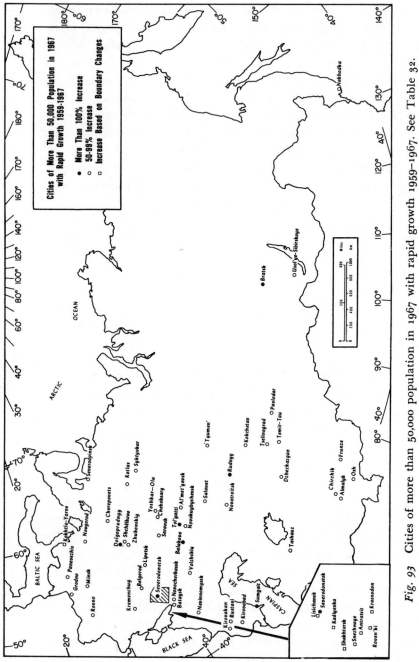

Fig. 93 Cities of more than 50,000 population in 1967 with rapid growth 1959-1967. See Table 32.

cities located at or near giant new hydroelectric construction projects, 4 are homes of new chemical industries at or near sources of cheap power (2 at hydroelectric sites already counted), one is an iron-ore mining center, and one is a residential suburb of Moscow.[28]

Bratsk on the Angara River in Eastern Siberia northwest of Irkutsk and Lake Baykal has a hydroelectric station with a capacity of 3.8 million kilowatts, the largest in the Soviet Union or in the world at the time of its construction, begun in 1955 and first unit put into operation in 1961. This tremendous upsurge of power deep in vast sparsely settled forest expanses posed the problem of how such large amounts of electrical energy were to be utilized. Initially the power station operated at only a fraction of its capacity. Four ultra-high-voltage long-distance power lines were built to carry energy to existing urban centers and industrial markets: two 500-kilovolt lines 580 kilometers (360 miles) southeast to the Irkutsk area, and two other lines 630 kilometers (390 miles) southwest to the Krasnoyarsk area with an extension to the Kuznetsk Basin. Also large industrial plants with high energy requirements were constructed in the area: an aluminum works and Siberia's largest wood-pulp plant producing viscose for rayon for tire cord and paperboard. Thus industrial workers are replacing construction gangs. The city grew from 51 thousand in 1959 to 122 thousand in 1967.

Balakovo on the Volga River between Kuybyshev and Saratov, which grew from 36 to 85 thousand (1959–1967), is the site both of the Saratov hydroelectric station with a planned capacity of 1.35 million kilowatts, construction of which was begun in 1956, and of a new chemical industry (synthetic fiber combine).

Tol'yatti, which grew from 61 thousand to 143 thousand in this 8-year period also lies on the Volga River, just above Kuybyshev near the Lenin Volga hydroelectric station, with a capacity of 2.3 million kilowatts, the first unit of which was put in opera-

[28] The industrial bases of these cities are treated in Theodore Shabad, *Basic industrial resources of the U.S.S.R.* (New York: Columbia University Press, 1969), 393 pp. and the chemical industries in Leslie Dienes, *Locational factors and locational developments in the Soviet chemical industry,* "University of Chicago, Department of geography, Research paper no. 119" (Chicago, 1969), 262 pp.

TABLE 32
CITIES OF MORE THAN 50,000 POPULATION
IN 1967 THAT GREW RAPIDLY 1959–1967
(In order of discussion in text)

City	Oblast or Republic	Region	Population in thousands 1959	1967
A. The Volga-Caucasus Band:				
*Balakovo	Saratov	Volga	36	85
*Tol'yatti	Kuybyshev	Volga	63	107
*Sumgait	Azerbaydzhan	Caucasus	52	104
*Severodonetsk	Lugansk	Donets-Dnepr	33	74
Al'mat'yevsk	Tatar	Volga	49	74
Salavat	Bashkir	Volga	61	98
Novokuybyshevsk	Kuybyshev	Volga	63	107
Nevinnomyssk	Stavropol'	N. Caucasus	40	63
Kirovakan	Armenia	Caucasus	49	82
Rustavi	Georgia	Caucasus	62	95
Novotroitsk	Orenburg	Urals	54	82
Novocherkassk	Rostov	N. Caucasus	95	161
Volzhskiy	Volgograd	Volga	67	114
Yoshkar-Ola	Mari	Volga-Vyatka	89	137
Cheboksary	Chuvash	Volga-Vyatka	104	178
Saransk	Mordov	Volga-Vyatka	91	154
Kirovabad	Azerbaydzhan	Caucasus	116	174
Bataysk	Rostov	N. Caucasus	52	85
B. In Western Regions:				
Novgorod	Novgorod	Northwest	61	107
Minsk	Minsk	Belorussia	509	772
Grodno	Grodno	Belorussia	73	111
Panevezhis	Lithuania	Baltic	41	65
Rovno	Rovno	Southwest	56	100
Kremenchug	Poltava	Donets-Dnepr	86	136
Belgorod	Belgorod	Black-Earth Center	72	129
Lipetsk	Lipetsk	Black-Earth Center	157	253
C. Suburbs of Moscow:				
*Dolgoprudnyy	Moscow	Central	25	50
Shchëlkovo	Moscow	Central	45	72
Zhukovskiy	Moscow	Central	42	63
D. On Northern Margins of Settlement:				
Cherepovets	Vologda	Northwest	92	165
Kotlas	Arkhangel'sk	Northwest	39	61
Syktyvkar	Komi	Northwest	64	102
Severodvinsk	Arkhangel'sk	Northwest	79	121
E. In Asiatic USSR:				
Tselinograd	Tselinograd	Kazakhstan	102	176
Pavlodar	Pavlodar	Kazakhstan	90	154
Kokchetav	Kokchetav	Kazakhstan	40	76
Frunze	Kirgiz	Middle Asia	220	396
Osh	Kirgiz	Middle Asia	65	119
Tashauz	Turkmen	Middle Asia	38	60

TABLE 32 — Continued
CITIES OF MORE THAN 50,000 POPULATION
IN 1967 THAT GREW RAPIDLY 1959-1967

City	Oblast or Republic	Region	Population in thousands	
			1959	1967
*Rudnyy	Kustanay	Kazakhstan	37	89
Temir-Tau	Karaganda	Kazakhstan	77	150
Dzhezkazgan	Karaganda	Kazakhstan	32	58
Almalyk	Tashkent	Middle Asia	40	73
Chirchik	Tashkent	Middle Asia	66	100
*Bratsk	Irkutsk	E. Siberia	51	122
Usol'ye-Sibirskoye	Irkutsk	E. Siberia	48	75
Tyumen'	Tyumen'	W. Siberia	150	240
Nakhodka	Maritime	Far East	64	96
F. Cities with Increases Based Largely on Boundary Changes:				
Lisichansk	Lugansk	Donets-Dnepr	38	120
(Kadiyevka	Lugansk	Donets-Dnepr	180(46)	139)
Antratsit	Lugansk	Donets-Dnepr	24	55
Snezhnoye	Donetsk	Donets-Dnepr	26	72
Krasnodon	Lugansk	Donets-Dnepr	38	68
Roven'ki	Lugansk	Donets-Dnepr	32	60
Shakhtërsk	Donetsk	Donets-Dnepr	38	72
Kokhtla-Yarve	Estonia	Baltic	29	66

° Cities with more than 100 per cent increase 1959–1967.
Regional boundaries as in 1967.
Sources: SSSR. Tsentral'noe statisticheskoe upravlenie, *Itogi vsesoiuznoi perepisi naseleniia 1959 goda* (M. Gosstatizdat, 1962–1963), table 6 in each volume. SSSR. *Administrativno-territorial'noe delenie soiuznykh respublik na 1 iiulia 1967 goda* (M. 1967), pp. 592–604.

tion in 1955 (also at the time of completion the largest hydroelectric station in the Soviet Union or in the world). It has large new plants for synthetic rubber (using raw materials from nearby oil fields) and nitrogen fertilizers.

Severodonetsk, which grew in this period from 33 to 74 thousand, lies on the northern edge of the Donbas coalfield; it has a large chemical industry (plastics).

Sumgait on the western shore of the Caspian Sea close to the Baku oil fields has a large chemical industry with synthetic rubber and superphosphate fertilizers.

Rudnyy (which means ore) has grown from 37 to 89 thousand (1959–1967) with the development of iron-ore mines; it is in Kazakhstan just south of Kustanay and about 300 kilometers east of Magnitogorsk, the great iron-ore center of the South Urals. It is

increasingly supplying the iron ore for the three large Ural iron
and steel plants at Magnitogorsk, Chelyabinsk, and Novotroitsk.
Before shipment, the crude ore with an iron content of 45 per
cent is beneficiated through magnetic concentration into a concentrate with 59 per cent iron content. Some is dressed in the
form of self-fluxing pellets.

Dolgoprudnyy is a suburb of Moscow on the growing northern
fringe of the city.

These 7 cities have all shown rapid sustained real growth in
population during this period but all are of modest size; the largest, Tol'yatti, had a population of only 143 thousand in 1967.

We now turn to a discussion, region by region, of the 55 cities
of more than 50 thousand population in 1967 that increased in
population by more than 50 per cent in the period 1959–1967.

Eighteen of these rapidly growing cities lie in a broad band
along the Middle or Lower Volga or nearby lands and extending
south to the Caucasus; many of them are associated with the production of energy and chemicals (Table 32 and Figure 93). Four
centers of the chemical industry have already been mentioned
among the cities that more than doubled in population, 1959–
1967: Balakovo and Tol'yatti with hydroelectric power, Sumgait
with nearby oil, and Severodonetsk with nearby coal. Near the
bend of the Volga in the Volga-Ural oilfield, Al'met'yevsk in the
Tatar ASSR, Salavat in the Bashkir ASSR, and Novokuybyshevsk
in Kuybyshev Oblast are all centers of oil production and petrochemical industries and each has specialized chemical products:
tires at Al'met'yevsk, nitrogen fertilizers at Salavat, and synthetic
alcohol and plastics at Novokuybyshevsk. Al'met'yevsk is also a
major pipeline center with lines extending west to Moscow and to
Yaroslavl' (to be extended west to Leningrad), northeast to Perm',
and eastward through Chelyabinsk, Novosibirsk, and Krasnoyarsk
to Angarsk near Irkutsk. In the North Caucasus Nevinnomyssk is
also a chemical center for nitrogen fertilizers and plastics based
on natural gas. Farther south in Armenia Kirovakan is also a
chemical center for mineral fertilizers. Rustavi in Georgia and
Novotroitsk in the South Urals, although mainly iron and steel
centers, do have related chemical production. Novocherkassk in
the North Caucasus also has chemicals in addition to its more

famous machinery production (locomotives and machinery for the oil industry and mining). Volzhskiy, like Balakovo, combines location at a major hydroelectric site with the production of synthetic fibers. Very different from these burgeoning industrial centers are 3 capitals of autonomous republics giving recognition to ethnic minorities near the bend of the Volga. They have grown rapidly as these republics have been brought into the mainstream of Soviet economic life, especially through their capitals, Yoshkar-Ola of the Mari ASSR, Cheboksary of the Chuvash ASSR, and Saransk of the Mordov ASSR. Kirovabad is a major regional center for the western part of the Azerbaydzhan SSR and has diversified industries. Finally Bataysk is a railroad junction and a suburb of Rostov.

Eight cities in the western part of the Soviet Union in regions of relative stagnation of urban growth in the early Soviet period give evidence of the greater areal range of urbanization in recent times in the country. For example Novgorod, an oblast center, in the Northwest, is one of the most ancient and famous of Russian cities. It had grown only modestly, barely doubling in the 62-year period 1897–1959. Since 1959 it has grown rapidly increasing in the 8-year period 1959–1967 from 61 to 107 thousand with the industrial expansion stimulated by a new chemical complex. Minsk, the capital of the Belorussian SSR, is the largest city in the entire Soviet Union to grow rapidly in the period 1959–1967, from 509 to 772 thousand. As mentioned previously, it has had concentrated on it much of the urban and industrial growth, especially machinery production, of the Belorussian SSR. A major industrial and administrative center, it has grown rapidly with the increase in size of the Belorussian SSR, with the closer economic ties between the Soviet Union and the people's democracies to the west, and with heavy migration from the densely populated surrounding rural areas. Grodno, also in Belorussia and also an oblast center, lies near the Polish boundary and was in Poland 1920–1939. It had stagnated for many years. Its population in 1939 was only about the same as in 1897. Its recent rapid growth reflects its role as a railroad junction (lines to Poland and Lithuania) and center of growing diversified industries (especially automobile parts, petrochemicals, and nitrogen fertilizers). Panevezhis in Lithuania and Rovno, an oblast center in the western Ukraine, were similarly outside the Soviet Union between the world wars (the latter in Poland); both have experienced diversified industrial expansion. The next 3 cities lie somewhat to the east. Kremenchug in the Ukraine on the Dnepr River is the site of a hydroelectric station with associated production of transport machinery and chemicals (oil refining). Belgorod and Lipetsk, 2 cities in the Central Black-Earth Region of the RSFSR, both oblast centers, were stimulated by the development of iron-ore mining of the Kursk Magnetic Anomaly and thus continued to grow rapidly in the period 1959–1967 as they had in the longer preceding period 1939–1959.

Three suburbs of Moscow have grown rapidly with the expansion of the metropolitan area: Dolgoprudnyy to the north (already mentioned), Shchëlkovo to the northeast, and Zhukovskiy to the southeast.

Four cities along the northern margins of settlement in the European part of the RSFSR also grew rapidly: Cherepovets, Kotlas, Syktyvkar, and Severodvinsk. Cherepovets owes its rapid growth to a large new iron and steel industry (operating from 1955). Kotlas, has developed rapidly as a transportation center (junction of 3 river routes and 3 rail lines with shipbuilding and the main repair yards for the northern river fleet) and the sawing and working of wood from the northern forests. Sktyyvkar is the capital of the Komi ASSR with its coal and oil fields and forests; it also has lumber industries. Severodvinsk ("North Dvina") at one of the mouths of the Severnaya Dvina River, is an industrial and transportation suburb of Arkhangel'sk.

The 15 cities of Soviet Asia that grew by more than 50 per cent in the 8-year period 1959–1967 had all also grown very rapidly in the preceding intercensal period 1939–1959.[29] Eleven are in the core of rapid urban growth that extends from Kazakhstan south to Soviet Middle Asia, 3 in Siberia, and one in the Soviet Far East. Three are oblast centers in the Virgin Lands semiarid region of recent pioneer settlement: Tselinograd, Pavlodar, and Kokchetav. Three others are similarly political-administrative or

---

[29] i.e., by more than 100 per cent in that period and thus have been discussed already in an earlier section, except for Osh, which had increased only 96 per cent in that period.

regional centers: Frunze, of the Kirgiz SSR, the second largest city in the entire USSR of such rapid recent growth; Osh of Osh Oblast in the Kirgiz SSR and part of the Fergana basin; and Tashauz of the Turkmen part of the irrigated lands along the lower Amu-Dar'ya south of the Aral Sea. Four are associated with minerals: Rudnyy, the iron-ore mining city already mentioned; Temir-Tau, the iron and steel center; and Dzhezkazgan and Almalyk, copper centers. One, Chirchik, near Tashkent, has a hydroelectric station and a related chemical industry (nitrate fertilizers and ammonium compounds). In all of Siberia only 3 such cities grew rapidly: Bratsk already discussed; Usol'ye Sibirskoye, the chemical center (based on salt), near Irkutsk; and Tyumen', an oblast center just east of the Urals (formerly considered in the Urals region), an old city at crossing of railroad and river, which has had rapid recent growth with the discovery of oil farther north in Western Siberia in the Khanty-Mansi National Okrug. Nakhodka, the port east of Vladivostok, was the only city in Soviet Far East to grow this rapidly.

Among the largest 15 cities in the Soviet Union none grew during 1959–1967 at a rate exceeding the national rate of urban increase (28 per cent). This slowdown in rate of population increase among the largest cities may reflect in part the Soviet policy of limiting the growth of these cities. Their growth rate differs sharply from the period 1939–1959 when 5 of the largest 15 cities also grew at above average rates: Tashkent, Novosibirsk, Kuybyshev, Sverdlovsk, and Chelyabinsk, the great regional centers for Soviet Middle Asia, Western Siberia, the Volga, and the Urals. But for the next 35 largest cities, about half increased at more than average rates for the whole country in both 1939–1959 and 1959–1967.

The 4 large cities of the Soviet Union with the highest rates of growth 1959–1967 were all capitals of union republics with important political-administrative and cultural functions as well as diversified industries. Frunze, capital of the Kirgiz SSR, had by far the highest rate of growth, 80 per cent, or 3 times the national average rate. Minsk with an increase of 52 per cent 1959–1967, capital of the Belorussian SSR, was the largest city in the Soviet Union to grow significantly faster than the country-wide average.

Other large cities with rates of growth 1959–1967 above average were Dushanbe, capital of the Tadzhik SSR (49 per cent), and Alma-Ata, capital of the Kazakh SSR (43 per cent). These cities are all in regions and republics of high rates of urban growth but in all of them (except Alma-Ata) the capital city grew at a faster rate than the other cities of the republic, as is typically the case in the early stages of rapid economic growth, when economic and cultural impulses, technology, and capital are being channeled into an area from other more developed regions.

One city showed a spectacular drop in population in this period, Sovetskaya Gavan' ("Soviet harbor") in the Far East at a railroad terminus on the Tatar Strait joining the Sea of Japan and the Okhotsk Sea and separating Sakhalin from the mainland. Its population grew in World War II but fell from 50 thousand in 1959 to only 26 thousand in 1967.

CITIES WITH GROWTH BASED MAINLY ON BOUNDARY CHANGES

Six cities where growth apparently was due to boundary changes are based on coal mining in the Donbas (Figure 93, inset) and one on oil-shale production in Estonia (Table 32). Close comparison of successive population data and of administrative handbooks reveals that in these cases shifts in city boundaries, rather than actual demographic growth, accounted for most of the reported increase in population. These will be discussed separately to illustrate some of the difficulties and pitfalls in the study of the population increase of individual cities.

Lisichansk, the coal-mining city in Lugansk Oblast in the Donbas, for example, had a population of 38 thousand in 1959 which increased to 120 thousand in 1967. But analysis of the intermediate years shows a gradual increase to 41 thousand in 1964,[30] then a sudden jump to 117 thousand in 1965,[31] or an increase of 76 thousand in one year. Analysis of the administrative handbook for 1965 reveals that on January 4, 1965, the boundaries

---

[30] *Kratkaia geograficheskaia entsiklopediia*, tom 5, p. 359.
[31] *Narodnoe khoziaistvo SSSR v 1964 g.*, p. 26. The data are reported to be as of January 1, 1965, but obviously are for the boundaries approved on January 4, 1965.

of Lisichansk were expanded to include 2 nearby cities, Verkhneye with a 1959 census population of 40 thousand, and Proletarsk, with a 1959 census population of 26 thousand, or a total of 66 thousand, which nearly matches the increase in the population of Lisichansk that took place in that year.[32] This growth was not the urban expansion of Lisichansk into previously rural areas but rather the mere political assemblage of existing cities without any real increase in population. The actual increase in total population within these 3 cities (as of 1959) or one city (as of 1967) was only 6 thousand from 114 to 120 thousand during the period 1959–1967.

In a basic source Kadiyevka, also a coal-mining city in Lugansk Oblast in the Donbas, had a reported population increase from 46 thousand in 1959 to 139 thousand in 1966.[33] The 1959 census, however, reported a population of 180 thousand which would indicate an actual loss of population 1959–1966. The city therefore is enclosed in parentheses in Table 32 and is not counted as one of the 7 cities with increases based on boundary changes. On December 30, 1962, out of northern and southern parts of the city of Kadiyevka, the new cities of Bryanka and Kirovsk were created[34] with 1959 populations of 78 and 56 thousand[35] respectively, or a total of 134 thousand, exactly matching the 1959 difference in population in Kadiyevka of 180 thousand in the 1959 boundaries and 46 thousand ostensibly in the 1966 boundaries. But the reported total populations for Kadiyevka (or the 3 cities after December 30, 1962) grew very slowly from 1959 to 1962, increasing from 180 to 192 thousand,[36] then jumped suddenly to 271 thousand in 1964,[37] and subsequently decreased slightly to 270 thousand in 1966.[38] This sudden jump of 79 thousand 1962–1964 in the face of modest growth in the 3 preceding years and the slight decline in the 2 following years seems unlikely to repre-

[32] *SSSR. Administrativno-territorial'noe Delenie Soiuznykh Respublik ianvar' 1965 goda*, p. 679, and *Itogi Vsesoiuznoi Perepisi Naseleniia 1959 goda, Ukrainskaia SSR*, p. 18.
[33] *Narodnoe khoziaistvo v 1965 g.*, p. 32.
[34] *Narodnoe khoziaistvo v 1964 g.*, p. 31, footnote 2.
[35] *Narodnoe khoziaistvo v 1965 g.*, pp. 31 and 33.
[36] *Narodnoe khoziaistvo v 1961 godu*, p. 21.
[37] *Kratkaia geograficheskaia entsiklopdiia*, tom 5, pp. 356 and 358.
[38] *Narodnoe khoziaistvo v 1965 g.*, pp. 31, 32, and 33.

sent an actual increase in population. Comparison of the administrative handbooks for 1962 and 1963 reveals that one city and 6 settlements of urban type that were subordinate to the city council of Kadiyevka on January 1, 1962, but not within the city limits of Kadiyevka at that time, had disappeared as separate units by April 1, 1963.[39] Four of these were large enough to be separately reported in the 1959 census: the city of Irmino with 22 thousand, and the settlements of urban type, Krivorozh'ye with 14 thousand, Almaznaya with 11 thousand, and Krasnopol'ye with 10 thousand, or a total of 57 thousand of the jump in population of 79 thousand that occurred at that time.[40] The other 3 settlements of urban type with populations of less than 10 thousand each may account for most of the other 22 thousand.[41] But the basic source for 1966 population data does not correct the 1959 population figures for Kadiyevka for these territorial additions to the city as it does for the territorial losses from the city.

Antratsit, as the name indicates an anthracite mining center, in the Donbas coal basin and also in Lugansk Oblast, apparently had similar incorporation of nearby settlements of urban type that largely accounted for its growth.[42]

Snezhnoye also a coal-mining city in the Donbas, but in Donetsk Oblast, apparently had similar annexations.[43]

Three other cities in the Donbas apparently incorporated nearby settlements of urban type[44] and these incorporations pre-

---

[39] *SSSR. Administrativno-territorial'noe delenie soiuznykh respublik na 1 ianvaria 1962 goda*, Luganskaia oblast', pp. 304-310, and *USSR. Administrativno-territorial'noe delenie soiuznykh respublik na 1 aprelia 1963 goda*, Luganskaia oblast', pp. 284-289.

[40] *Itogi vsesoiuznoi perepisi naseleniia 1959 goda, Ukrainskaia SSR*, p. 18.

[41] Petrogrado-Donetskoye, Sabovka, and Zamkovko. The *Slovar' geograficheskikh nazvanii SSSR* (M. Izd. "Nedra," 1968), passim, published after this section was written, confirms the accuracy of these conclusions by noting that the city of Irmino and the town of Almaznaya were incorporated into Kadiyevka; that the towns of Krivorozh'ye, Krasnopol'ye, Sabovka, and the workers' settlement of Zambovka are now incorporated into Bryanka; and that the towns of Petrogrado-Donetskoye and Krasnogvardeyskiy and the village of Golubovka are now incorporated into Kirovsk.

[42] Tsentral'no-Bokovskiy with a 1959 population of 14 thousand and Shakhtërskiy, 11 thousand, both of which were separate settlements of urban type on January 1, 1962, but not on April 1, 1963.

[43] Novyy Donbas, a city with a 1959 population of 16 thousand, a separate city on January 1, 1962, but not on April 1, 1963.

[44] Based on comparisons of successive administrative handbooks and maps.

sumably accounted for about half of their reported population increases. Krasnodon in Lugansk Oblast apparently incorporated Verkhneduvannyy with a 1959 population of 13,052. Roven'ki, also in Lugansk Oblast, apparently incorporated Dzerzhinskiy with a 1959 population of 17,257. Shakhtërsk in Donetsk Oblast apparently incorporated Alekseyevo-Orlovka with a 1959 population of 18,693.

The oil-shale processing city of Kokhtla-Yarve (Kohtla-Järve) in northeast Estonia on the Gulf of Finland incorporated 2 adjacent cities in October 1960[45] that accounted for somewhat over half of its growth 1959–1967 (22 thousand of the 37 thousand growth in this period from 29 to 66 thousand). Its growth was still moderately rapid in this period, continuing at a reduced pace the very rapid growth of 1939–1959.

SOME SMALL GROWTH CITIES 1959–1967

Forty-one of the smaller cities that more than doubled in population in the period 1959–1967 are listed in Table 33 and located in Figure 94.[46] Nearly three-fourths of these cities (29 out of 41) are based on production of energy or minerals (Table 33): 11 with generation of electricity, 7 with mining of fuels, and 11 with production of mineral products. The other 12 are diverse but the chemical industry and suburban development played major roles.

The 11 cities associated with production of electricity include 3 with thermoelectric stations, 7 at or near hydroelectric projects, and one with an atomic power plant.

The 3 sites of large regional thermoelectric stations are Pridneprovsk near Dnepropetrovsk in the Ukraine, Takhiatash on the lower Amu-Dar'ya in Soviet Middle Asia, and Yermak, south of Pavlodar in Kazakhstan (which also has ferro-alloy industries and is the beginning of a canal to take water from the Irtysh River to water-deficient Karaganda). Pridneprovsk with a capacity of 2.4 million kilowatts is the largest steam-power elec-

---

[45] Akhtme with a 1959 population of 11.2 thousand and Yykhvi with a 1959 population of 10.5 thousand (*Itogi vsesoiuznoi perepisi naseleniia 1959 goda. Estonskaia SSR*, p. 12, footnote).
[46] Of these 41, 31 were so small in 1959 as not to have population data reported in the published census volumes for cities of more than 10,000 population.

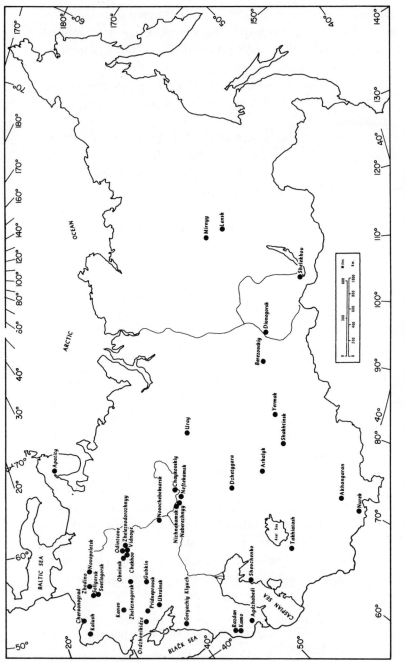

Fig. 94 Some small cities with rapid growth 1959–1967. See Table 33.

TABLE 33
Some Small Cities That Grew Rapidly 1959–1967

City	Oblast or Republic	Region	Population in thousands	
			1959	*1967*
Generation of Electricity:				
Thermoelectric				
Pridneprovsk	Dnepropetrovsk	Donets-Dnepr		16
Takhiatash	Kara-Kalpak ASSR	Middle Asia	6	16
Yermak	Pavlodar	Kazakhstan		17
Hydroelectric and associated activities				
Divnogorsk	Krasnoyarsk	E. Siberia		21
Chaykovskiy	Perm'	Urals		33
Naberezhnyy-Chelny	Tatar	Volga	16	33
Kanev	Cherkassy	Southwest	7	17
Nurek	Tadzhik	Middle Asia		22
Razdan	Armenia	Caucasus	8	20
Kamo	Armenia	Caucasus	9	18
Atomic				
Obninsk	Kaluga	Center	16	38
Fuels:				
Coal				
Ukrainsk	Donetsk	Donets-Dnepr		18
Shakhtinsk	Karaganda	Kazakhstan		32
Berezovskiy	Kemerovo	W. Siberia		31
Chervonograd	L'vov	Southwest	12	35
Petroleum				
Neftekamsk	Bashkir	Volga		30
Shevchenko	Gur'yev	Kazakhstan		28
Uray	Khanty-Mansi	W. Siberia		22
Mineral products:				
Zheleznogorsk	Kursk	Black-Earth Center	2	19
Gubkin	Belgorod	Black-Earth Center	21	42
Ordzhonikidze	Dnepropetrovsk	Donets-Dnepr	18	37
Arkalyk	Kustanay	Kazakhstan	1	16
Shelekhov	Irkutsk	E. Siberia		27
Akhangaran	Tashkent	Middle Asia		22
Apatity	Murmansk	Northwest	20	38
Kalush	Ivano-Frankovsk	Southwest	13	34
Dzhetygara	Kustanay	Kazakhstan	15	31
Mirnyy	Yakut	Far East	6	22
Lensk	Yakut	Far East		19
Chemical Industry:				
Novopolotsk	Vitebsk	Belorussia		26
Svetlogorsk	Gomel'	Belorussia		27
Soligorsk	Minsk	Belorussia		28
Nizhnekamsk	Tatar	Volga		38
Novocheboksarsk	Chuvash	Volga-Vyatka		24
Machinery:				
Zhodino	Minsk	Belorussia		18
Suburbs and Satellites:				
Vidnoye	Moscow	Center		32

TABLE 33 — Continued

SOME SMALL CITIES THAT GREW RAPIDLY 1959–1967

City	Oblast or Republic	Region	Population in thousands	
			1959	1967
Chekhov	Moscow	Center	14	28
Odintsovo	Moscow	Center	20	43
Zheleznodorozhnyy	Moscow	Center	19	48
Resorts:				
Goryachiy Klyuch	Krasnodar	N. Caucasus	10	21
Agricultural Centers:				
Agdzhabedi	Azerbaydzhan	Caucasus		17

Sources: 1959. SSSR. Tsentral'noe statisticheskoe upravlenie. *Itogi vseoiuzoni perepisi naseleniia 1959 goda* (M. Gosstatizdat, 1962–1963), table 6 in each volume. 1967. *Administrativno-territorial'noe delenie Soiuznykh respublik na 1 iiulia 1967 goda* (M. 1967), pp. 592–603.

tricity-generating station in the Soviet Union; although near the Donbas coalfield and Dnepr River hydroelectric power, it is fueled by natural gas from Shebelinka brought by pipeline.

Seven small growth cities have arisen in connection with the construction of dams, reservoirs, hydroelectric projects, and associated industries: Divnogorsk with the Krasnoyarsk hydroelectric station on the Yenisey south of Krasnoyarsk in Eastern Siberia; Chaykovskiy (33 thousand) with the Votkinsk hydroelectric station on the Kama River southwest of the city of Perm'; Naberezhnyye Chelny in the Tatar ASSR with the construction of a hydroelectric station a little lower on the Kama River; Kanev, an old but small city, which grew on the Dnepr River southeast of Kiev in the Ukraine; Nurek, southeast of Dushanbe in the Tadzhik SSR on the Vakhsh River with a 1000-foot-high dam; Razdan in Armenia near the famous hydroelectric works of the Sevan-Razdan group aligned between Lake Sevan and Yerevan in the valley of the Razdan River (it also has a thermoelectric station based on natural gas with a capacity several times that of the original hydroelectric project and with a planned huge thermoelectric station and a chemical industry), and Kamo, in the coastal zone southwest of Lake Sevan (with traditional textile industries and a modern cable factory under construction).

The first atomic power plant in the Soviet Union has generated the growth of Obninsk in Kaluga Oblast southwest of Moscow.

Seven cities have grown rapidly with the production of fuels: coal and oil. Four new coal-mining cities are Ukrainsk in the Donbas (Donetsk Oblast), Shakhtinsk near Karaganda, Berezovskiy (31 thousand) in the Kuzbas, and Chervonograd north of L'vov in the western Ukraine in the L'vov-Volyn' coalfield. Three centers of petroleum and/or natural gas are Neftekamsk in the Bashkir ASSR (30 thousand) on the Kama River in the great Volga-Ural oilfield; Shevchenko (28 thousand) (formerly Aktau) on the eastern shore of the Caspian Sea in the Kazakh SSR in a desert region in which, because of a shortage of water, settlement is concentrated in a few larger towns rather than being scattered and in which fresh water is supplied by a desalting plant based on the Caspian Sea and now fueled by natural gas but expected to be powered by an atomic reactor under construction (not to be confused with Fort-Shevchenko farther north); and Uray (22 thousand) in the sparsely settled Khanty-Mansi National Okrug in the promising and rapidly developing field east of the Urals in the marshy West Siberian Plain.

Eleven cities have grown with new mining or the processing of mineral products: Zheleznogorsk in Kursk Oblast and Gubkin in Belgorod Oblast in the Black-Earth Center with the development of iron-ore mining in the Kursk Magnetic Anomaly; Ordzhonikidze in Dnepropetrovsk Oblast with the mining of manganese ore; Arkalyk in Kustanay Oblast in Kazakhstan with the mining of bauxite; Shelekhov (27 thousand) near Irkutsk in Eastern Siberia with an aluminum factory (put into operation in 1962 using energy from the Irkutsk hydroelectric station); Akhangaran in Tashkent Oblast in Soviet Middle Asia with the production of cement; Apatity in Murmansk Oblast with the production of apatite (for phosphate fertilizer); Kalush in Ivano-Frankovsk Oblast in the western Ukraine with the production of potash and salt and associated chemical industries (aided by local natural gas); Dzhetygara in Kustanay Oblast in Kazakhstan with the production of asbestos; and diamonds in the Yakut ASSR in northeast Siberia have stimulated the growth of Mirnyy in the producing area in the basin of the Vilyuy River and of Lensk (formerly Mukhtuya), the shipping point on the Lena River to the south.

In recent years the chemical industry has received particular attention in Soviet planning. Five cities owe their growth to it. Three small cities, all in Belorussia, have recently grown rapidly with new chemical works: Novopolotsk (26 thousand) in Vitebsk Oblast with an oil refinery and petrochemicals; Svetlogorsk (27 thousand) in Gomel' Oblast with synthetic fibers; and Soligorsk (28 thousand) in Minsk Oblast with chemical fertilizers (potash). Nizhnekamsk, (38 thousand) "lower Kama," is a new chemical center on the lower part of the Kama River in the Tatar ASSR with a large petrochemical complex producing synthetic rubber and plastics. Novocheboksarsk, on the Volga River about 20 kilometers below Cheboksary in the Chuvash ASSR, is the site of a chemical complex producing aniline dyes, chlorine compounds, and ammonium sulfate developed in the 1960s and a hydroelectric station planned for construction in the 1970s.

Remarkably few of these small growth cities are dominated by machinery industries (which seem to be characteristic of larger cities) but Zhodino in Minsk Oblast in Belorussia owes its recent growth to the Belorussian automobile works there.

Four suburbs and satellites of large cities, either residential or industrial, have experienced rapid growth. The prime example is Moscow with several such cities, including Vidnoye (which grew from 18 to 32 thousand in the three-year period 1964-1967); Chekhov, and the larger cities of Odintsovo and Zheleznodorozhnyy.

Goryachiy Klyuch in Krasnodar Kray in the North Caucasus Region, as the name indicates, is at a hot spring and is a resort in the foothills of the Caucasus.

Centers of expanding agricultural lands are relatively rare. Agdzhabedi in the Azerbaydzhan SSR in the Trans-Caucasus is in an area of new irrigation development on the Upper Karabakh Canal, which takes water from the new Mingechaur Reservoir on the Kura River and irrigates a cotton-producing region between it and the Araks River to the south.

Many of the cities which appear to be new cities in the 1967 population estimates, or at least rapidly growing cities, turn out on closer study to be cities that have been near their present size for some time or to be the result of boundary changes or juridical change. These types will be illustrated by 5 cities that had populations of more than 10,000 in censuses earlier than the 1959 one, although absent from the published volumes of the 1959 census and thus from our study group of 1,247 cities; by 2 cities in Latvia that result from the combination of 2 or more pre-existing urban units; by 3 cities, all in the Donbas, that were carved out of sections of large cities; and by 9 large agricultural villages recently given the juridical status of city and thus with reported populations, though not necessarily an increase in population.

Five cities absent from the 1959 published census volumes had had populations of more than 10 thousand each in earlier censuses. Mtsensk in Orël Oblast had a population of 10 thousand in 1926 that grew to 14 in 1959 and to 22 in 1967; its regular growth is concealed by the omission of published data in the 1959 census for cities of less than 15 thousand in the RSFSR.[47] Ryazhsk in Ryazan' Oblast grew from 15 thousand in 1897 to 16 in 1926 but dropped sharply to 7 thousand in 1959 and recovered to 24 thousand in 1967. Usman' in Lipetsk Oblast dropped from 13 to 10 thousand in the period 1926–1959 but rose again to 16 thousand in 1967. Krasnoarmeysk (formerly Bal'tser) in Saratov Oblast had steady but slow growth from 12 thousand in 1926 to 14 in 1959 and 16 in 1967, concealed again by the absence of the 1959 published census data for the RSFSR for cities under 15 thousand. Finally Buturlinovka in Voronezh Oblast grew from 13 thousand in 1959 to 23 thousand in 1967. These cities typically have small manufactures and also serve as centers in the rich farmlands of the Central Black-Earth Region and adjacent lands to north and east.

Two cities in Latvia illustrate another type of creation of a larger city, by the combination of several existing settlements. Yurmala with a 1967 population of 48 thousand was formed in November 1959 from the existing cities of Kemeri and Sloka and from Yurmal'skiy rayon of the city of Riga and included an uninterrupted chain of resort towns on the Gulf of Riga (Liyelupe,

---

[47] 1959 population data in the following pages are from city articles in *Kratkaia geograficheskaia entsiklopediia.*

Bulduri, Dzintari, Mayori, Dubulty, Pumpuri, and Melluzhi).[48] Yekabpils or Jēkabpils, formerly called Jakobstadt, was chartered in 1670, and had a 1967 population of 21 thousand; it apparently includes the 2 former cities of Yekabpils and Krustpils with populations of 7.4 and 9.3 thousand respectively in 1959, but which formed an economic unit with much cross-commuting.

Three large new cities in the Ukraine, all in the coal-mining Donbas, in Lugansk Oblast, illustrate a rare type of new city in the Soviet Union, one resulting not from new construction or population growth but rather from the creation of a new city by the juridical separation of a section of an existing city. Bryanka, Kirovsk, and Pereval'sk with 1967 populations of 79, 50, and 34 thousand respectively did not exist at the time of the 1959 census. Bryanka and Kirovsk were carved out of northern and southern sections of the existing city of Kadiyevka on December 30, 1962,[49] and Pereval'sk was created out of the southeast part of Kommunarsk on December 30, 1964.[50]

Large agricultural villages that have been given the status of city only recently are illustrated by 6 settlements in the North Caucasus in the RSFSR, one in the Ukraine, and 2 near Alma-Ata in Kazakhstan. Four are in Krasnodar Kray: Kurganinsk (31 thousand in 1967), Timashevsk (26 thousand), Korenovsk (24 thousand), and Abinsk (22 thousand). Each was a *stanitsa* (large Cossack village) at the time of the 1959 census and was thus considered rural. They were juridically recognized as cities at various dates between 1961 and 1966. Two are in Stavropol' Kray: Zelenokumsk (formerly the village of Sovetskoye) (29 thousand) and Svetlograd (formerly the village of Petrovskoye) (22 thousand); both became cities in 1965. Nosovka (20 thousand) in Chernigov Oblast in the Ukraine is similar. Talgar (31 thousand) and Kaskelen (24 thousand) near Alma-Ata in Kazakhstan also fall into this category. In the absence of 1959 population data, it is difficult to ascertain whether the present populations represent recent substantial growth or merely the availability of data for

[48] *Kratkaia geograficheskaia entsiklopediia*, tom 5, p. 30.
[49] *Narodnoe khoziaistvo v 1964 g.*, p. 31, footnote 2.
[50] *SSSR. Administrativno-territorial'noe delenie soiuznykh respublik, ianvar' 1965 goda*, p. 679.

already existing giant villages previously considered rural and thus not separately reported.

URBAN SETTLEMENTS THAT HAVE STAGNATED, DECLINED OR DISAPPEARED BY ANNEXATION TO LARGER CITIES

The growth of Soviet cities and towns has been widespread and rapid, but some cities and towns have failed to grow. Though few in number, small in size, and modest in economic importance, they are instructive in emphasizing some of the factors important in urban growth, particularly accessibility. The 1897 census tables on cities by guberniyas, oblasts, and uyezds provide data on 32 urban centers of more than 10 thousand population in that year that are missing from the 1959 census volumes. The 1926 census includes figures on 56 urban places with more than 10,000 population not in the 1959 census publications. Of these urban settlements 19 had populations of 10,000 or more in both the 1897 and 1926 censuses, 13 in the 1897 census only, and 37 in the 1926 census only.

The vast majority of these stagnating urban settlements are located in the European part of the Soviet Union, particularly west of the Volga River in the rich black-earth farming belt (Figure 95). Centers of agricultural areas, they typically have been by-passed by the industrial development of the Soviet period. The 1926 census also reported 173 villages as having populations of more than 10 thousand but these are considered rural not urban.

The 32 urban settlements of more than 10 thousand population in the 1897 census that are not included in our study group of 1,247 cities and towns of more than 10 thousand population in 1959 (15 thousand in the RSFSR) fall into two main categories: isolated or suburban. As judged by the criterion of not being on a railroad line or not having a railroad station, 21 of these are relatively isolated, even though located, for the most part, in the densely settled and long-developed European section with a dense rail net. Four of the settlements are at the other extreme, near large cities that have expanded to encompass them and thus to remove them from separate census enumeration as independent

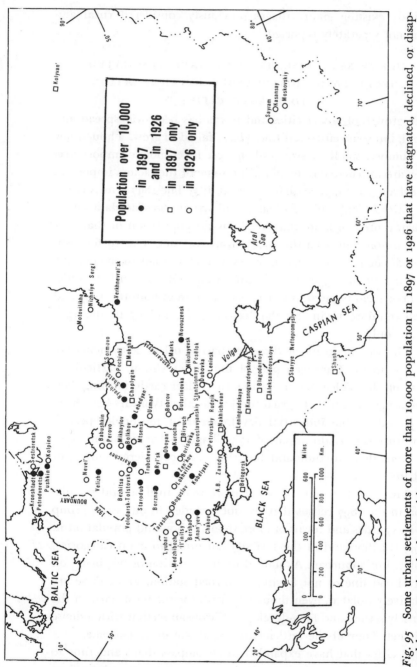

Fig. 95 Some urban settlements of more than 10,000 population in 1897 or 1926 that have stagnated, declined, or disappeared by annexation by larger cities.

urban entities, even though some of them have grown substantially; three have been incorporated into Leningrad and one into Rostov-na-Donu. Of the remaining 7 settlements, 5 located in the RSFSR did have 1959 populations of more than 10 thousand (though not reported in the published census volume for the RSFSR which records cities and towns of more than 15 thousand only); these did not actually decline but were relatively stagnant. The remaining 2 settlements were large rural villages in the North Caucasus not juridically recognized as urban centers in 1959 but reported in the 1897 census tables of urban settlements since, though villages, they served as administrative centers of rayons.

From the above data it can be seen that poor transportation emerges as the crucial factor in the actual decline in population of cities and towns with more than 10 thousand population in the 1897 census.

A good example of an old but isolated city by-passed by modern transportation and industry is Velizh in the western part of the RSFSR on the Western Dvina River, founded in 1536 as a fortified point and river landing when rivers were the transport arteries. Its peripheral isolated modern position is revealed in 2 ways: (1) Its marginal location at the outer edge of the political unit to which attached; in 1897 it was near the northeast boundary of Vitebsk Guberniya, in 1926 it was near the southeast boundary of Pskov Guberniya, and in 1959 it was near the northwest boundary of Smolensk Oblast. In each case Velizh was remote from the center of political administration. (2) Its distance from modern railroad transportation; it is 93 kilometers (nearly 60 miles) by a secondary road from the railroad station of Rudnya (on the Smolensk-Vitebsk line). Its census population in 1897 was 12,193; in 1926, 10,510; and in 1959 about 8,000.[51] It has woodworking industries.

Anan'yev, made a city in 1834, later reduced to a settlement of urban type, but made a city for a second time in 1941, now in Odessa Oblast in the Ukraine (but in 1897 in Kherson Guberniya and in 1926 in the Moldavian ASSR), is similar to Velizh in its

[51] In the following few pages 1959 population data not contained in the 1959 published census are from articles for each city in *Kratkaia geograficheskaia entsiklopediia.*

peripheral isolated position. It is 15 kilometers from the small railroad station Zherebkovo. Its population was 16,684 in 1897, rose to 18,230 in 1926, but dropped to 7,800 in 1959.

Another example is Bolkhov in Orël Oblast in the Black-Earth Center of the RSFSR, first mentioned as a city in 1556. It had a census population of 21,446 in 1897, which dropped to 17,535 in 1926, and to 11,100 in 1959; it is 50 kilometers from the railroad station Mtsensk in Orël Oblast in an agricultural area.

Shatsk, southeast of Moscow in Ryazan' Oblast (Tambov Guberniya in 1897), established in 1553 as a fortified point in the defense of Moscow against the Tatars, is 31 kilometers from the closest railroad station and has a marginal position in the oblast in which located. It increased slightly in population from 1897 to 1926 (from 13,840 to 15,120) but then declined sharply to 5,700 in 1959.

Shusha, now in the Nagorno-Karabakh Autonomous Oblast of the Azerbaydzhan SSR in the Caucasus, once had an estimated population of more than 40,000 and in the 1897 census had a population of 25,881 (then in Yelisavetpol' Guberniya). It had a tragic fall to a population of 5,424 in 1939 and 6,117 in 1959. It had flourished as a political center of the Karabakh Khanate before its conquest by the Russians in 1805 and continued as a large city with a weaving industry within Russia until 1920 when its predominantly Armenian population was largely massacred by Muslim mountaineers and nearly the entire city was destroyed. It was replaced as the economic and political center by the new city of Stepanakert, only 11 kilometers away. The closest railroad station at Barda is 84 kilometers away.

Kolyvan', a river port, founded in 1713, was the former commercial center on the old Siberian road at the Ob River crossing. Its 1897 population was 11,711 but declined with the building of the Trans-Siberian Railroad, which crossed the Ob River 30 kilometers to the south where a new city, Novosibirsk, arose and grew very rapidly to become the great metropolis of Western Siberia.

Of the 56 urban places with more than 10,000 population in the 1926 census that are not included in our study group of 1,247 cities and towns because the published census volumes for 1959 do not record populations for them (or their populations were under 10,000), 19 also had reported populations of more than 10 thousand in the 1897 census, 13 occupied relatively isolated positions not on railroads, 11 with rail transportation were also stagnant, 2 were counted as villages in 1959 and thus had no population reported in the census,[52] and 11 were suburbs or satellites that have since been incorporated into other cities.

The 13 stagnant or declining urban settlements of 1926 that are characterized by relative isolation include many old cities and towns that have been missed in the development of modern industry and transportation. Two examples will illustrate the type. Kassan, now Kasansay, in Andizhan Oblast at the northern edge of the Fergana Basin in Soviet Middle Asia lies 28 kilometers from the railroad station Namangan; it declined in population from 18,705 in 1926 to 8,881 in 1939 but rose slightly to 9,525 in 1959. As in the case of Velizh its peripheral position is also reflected in its transfer between political units from Fergana Oblast to Andizhan Oblast in March 1961. Less isolated is Buturlinovka, a city in Voronezh Oblast in the Black-Earth Region, only 5 kilometers from a railroad station but processing mainly local agricultural products. It declined in population from 23,443 in 1897 (then a village) and 27,537 in 1926 to 13,000 in 1959.[53] Since 1959, however, it has grown to recover in 1967 its 1897 population level.

Of the 11 stagnant or declining urban settlements on or near railroads, 8 are in the Russian Soviet Federated Socialist Republic, 3 in the Ukrainian SSR, and one in the Uzbek SSR. The populations in 1926 ranged between 10 and 14 thousand and thus for

[52] Pochinki (Gor'kiy O.) and Sayram (Chimkent O.).

[53] The other 11 urban settlements in this group, distances from the closest railroad station, and political units in which located in the RSFSR are: Trubchevsk, 35 km. (Bryansk); Borisovka, 7 km. (then Kursk Guberniya, now Belgorod Oblast); Bal'tser, now Krasnoarmeysk, 18 km. (then German Volga ASSR, now Saratov O.); Marksshtadt, now Marks, 50 km. (then German Volga ASSR, now Saratov O.); Dubovka, 52 km. (Stalingrad G., now Volgograd O.); Nikolayevsk, 7 km. (Stalingrad G., now Volgograd O.). In the Right-Bank Subregion of the Ukrainian SSR: Tarashcha, 19 km. (Belotserkovskiy Okrug, now in Kiev O.); Lyubar, 25 km. (then in Berdichev Okrug, now in Zhitomir O.); Il'intsy, 16 km. (Vinnitsa); Medzhibozh, 2 km. (then in Proskurov Okrug, now in Khmel'nitskiy O.). In the Left-Bank Subregion of the Ukrainian SSR: Lokhvitsa, 12 km. (then in Romny Okrug, now in Poltava O.).

those in the RSFSR, in which the 1959 census reported only places of more than 15 thousand, some of the cities or settlements of urban type may well have been stagnant rather than declining, although Mikhaylov in western Ryazan' Oblast declined from 11.6 to 6.5 thousand population in the period 1926–1959.[54]

Eleven urban places of 10,000 population in 1926 incorporated into larger cities before the 1959 census were Kolpino and Sestroretsk made subordinate to the Leningrad city council, Bezhitsa and Volodarsko-Tolstovsk joined to Bryansk, Losinoostrovskaya (now Babushkin) and Perovo incorporated into Moscow, Sormovo joined to Gor'kiy, Staryye Neftepromysly apparently joined to Groznyy; Novoslavyanskiy Stantsionnyy Posëlok apparently joined to Slavyansk, A.B. Zavody apparently now part of Zhdanov (formerly Mariupol'), and Motovilikha joined to Perm'. Some of these exhibited rapid growth before their disappearance by incorporation into larger cities. Thus Losinoostrovskaya grew from 16 thousand in 1926 to 70 thousand in 1939 to 112 thousand in 1959 and Perovo from 14 thousand in 1926 to 78 thousand in 1939 to 143 thousand in 1959; both were incorporated into Moscow on August 18, 1960, before the publication of the 1959 census and thus were not included as cities in the report of that census.[55] Bezhitsa grew from 36 thousand in 1926 to 82 thousand in 1939; it was incorporated into Bryansk in 1956.

The 173 rural settlements with more than 10 thousand inhabitants each in 1926 had a total population of 2.2 millions in that year. These included several different types of villages, the most famous and striking of which is the large Cossack village (*stanitsa*). Except for 3 large rural settlements in Soviet Middle Asia, these giant villages are concentrated in the European part of the steppe, in areas of grain production in a relatively small triangle with a southern base along the Black Sea and the Caucasus mountains,

---

[54] These settlements and the oblasts in which located are: Nevel' (Pskov O.), Mikhaylov (Ryazan'), Bobrov (Voronezh), Usman' (now Lipetsk Oblast but in Voronezh Guberniya in 1926), Mtsensk (Orël), Leninsk (Volgograd), Nizhniye Sergi (Sverdlovsk), Petrovskiy Rudnik (Donetsk), Boguslav (Kiev), Bershad' (Vinnitsa); and Shaarikhan, later Stalino, now Moskovskiy (Andizhan).

[55] But their 1959 populations are reported in a footnote: SSSR. Tsentral'noe Statisticheskoe Upravlenie, *Itogi Vsesoiuznoi Perepisi Naseleneiia 1959 goda. RSFSR*, M. 1963, p. 38, footnote 3.

an eastern edge near the Volga River, and a northwestern edge along the boundary of the steppe (Table 34 and Figure 96). Of the 173 mammoth villages of the Soviet Union, 105 are concentrated in the rich farming country of the North Caucasus. The other major concentration lies in a broad band between Odessa in the southwest and Kuybyshev (formerly Samara) on the Volga River in the northeast and lies mainly in the steppe region of the Ukraine and the Black-Earth Region of the RSFSR.

The existence of these large villages has complicated this study of the growth of smaller cities in that some of the villages have been made into settlements of urban type or cities or *vice*

Fig. 96 Dot map of the distribution of villages with more than 10,000 population in 1926. The dots are plotted by guberniyas, oblasts, okrugs, and uyezds. See Table 34.

TABLE 34

NUMBER OF RURAL SETTLEMENTS OF MORE THAN
10,000 POPULATION IN 1926
(By 1926 political units)

Soviet Union			173
RSFSR			134
North Caucasus Kray		105	
Kuban Okrug	46		
Armavir Okrug	15		
Stavropol' Okrug	13		
Don Okrug	10		
Sal'sk Okrug	8		
Terek Okrug	7		
Other okrugs	6		
Central Black-Earth Region		17	
Voronezh Guberniya	8		
Tambov Guberniya	8		
Kursk Guberniya	1		
Middle Volga Region		3	
Lower Volga Region		7	
Kazakh ASSR		2	
Ukraine			38
Right Bank (west of the Dnepr River)		4	
Left Bank (east of the Dnepr River)		13	
Steppe Region		11	
Dnepropetrovsk Region		9	
Mining Region		1	
Uzbek SSR			1

Tabulated from data in SSSR. Tsentral'noe statisticheskoe upravlenie. *Vsesoiuznaia perepis' naseleniia 1926 goda,* table 4, vols. 3, 5, 8, 9, 11, 12, 13, 15, and 17.

versa, possibly without any substantial change in population. In the 1897 census the population of such villages was reported in the urban tables if the villages were administrative centers. In 1926 the population of such villages often can be determined. In 1959 the population of such villages was not reported. In this respect as in many others the 1959 census is niggardly compared with the rich detail of the earlier 1897 or 1926 censuses.

The genesis, evolution, distribution, present functions, and trends of the giant villages of the Soviet Union would provide an interesting subject for investigation, but since our study is devoted to urban settlements proper, we will not linger on these villages, which are in some ways intermediate between rural and urban settlements.

IX.

Summary and Conclusions

The dominant impression which one recognizes throughout the Soviet Union is one of a
massive, rapid, and still unfinished transformation of the urban network.
— Jacqueline Beaujeu-Garnier
in *Traité de géographie urbaine*
by Jacqueline Beaujeu-Garnier
and Georges Chabot, 1963, p. 70.

THE SOVIET UNION is a land of large cities. In 1969 it had 209
cities of more than 100,000 population, a greater number than
any other country, except possibly the United States (depending
on the definition). In that year its total urban population was
134 million, second only to that of the United States. During the
Soviet period the USSR has been transformed from a predominantly rural society (18 per cent urban in 1926) to a predominantly urban one (56 per cent urban in 1969). The rapid urbanization of the Soviet Union is part of a world-wide process of
urbanization and economic development but this process has had
special features in the USSR associated with Socialist planning
and industrialization in a series of Five-Year Plans. Most of the
cities are located in an ecumene, the main inhabited portion of
the country, often called the Fertile Triangle, which occupies less
than a quarter of the country.

The main literature on Soviet cities has been produced, of
course, by Soviet scholars in Russian. More than 400 Soviet geographers have written on some phase of cities of the USSR. A bib-

liography of their works runs to more than a thousand items. N. N. Baranskiy of Moscow helped both to establish the content of urban geography and to train the first group of graduate students in this field. O. A. Konstantinov of Leningrad in articles extending over 35 years has played a leading role in defining the methodology and philosophy of Soviet urban geography and in reviewing its development and literature. In the classification of cities of the Soviet Union the contributions of O. A. Konstantinov, Iu. G. Saushkin, V. V. Pokshishevskii, A. A. Mints, B. S. Khorev, E. V. Knobel'sdorf, O. R. Nazarevskii, G. M. Lappo, N. I. Blazhko, L. L. Trube, V. Sh. Dzhaoshvili, and V. V. Vorob'ëv have been of widest scope and greatest interest. In the analysis of the network, size, and growth of cities V. G. Davidovich has made ingenious contributions. B. S. Khorev wrote the first general monograph treating the geography of the cities of the entire Soviet Union, with particular attention to their classification, size, and development. Some of the outstanding Soviet publications on the cities of the USSR are reviewed briefly in Chapter II.

In Chapter III the 304 Soviet cities of more than 50,000 population in 1959 have been classified according to predominant function (Tables 12 and 13). The classification is based on occupational structure, administrative functions, and size. About 90 per cent of the cities of this size fall into two very large classes: diversified administrative centers (134) and industrial cities (136). Other types recognized are local centers (15), transport centers (5), resorts (4), educational and research cities (2), naval bases (2), and suburbs (6). The 30 largest cities are all diversified administrative centers. Among administrative centers, there is a close relationship between size and amount of industrialization. Industrial cities heavily predominate among smaller cities. They constitute 310 of the 444 cities with populations of 20,000–49,999. Among cities of less than 10,000 population, however, there are few industrial cities and numerous local centers lacking industrial development. In general the larger the city the more likely it is to have diverse functions. The smaller the city, the more likely it is to be unifunctional. The diversified administrative centers, as central-place type settlements of high rank, form the main network of regional and oblast centers, widely spaced from one another, surrounded by tributary areas, and serving complex economic, cultural, and political-administrative functions. Specialized industrial cities, whether of manufacturing or mining, show sharp localizations at sources of raw material or in historically evolved industrial districts.

On the basis of data assembled from such diverse sources as the census publications, administrative handbooks, encyclopedias, gazetteers, atlases, maps, and scholarly publications on Soviet urban geography, 30 variables (characteristics) were recorded for 1,247 cities. These data were subjected to statistical analysis in Chapter IV. Three principal components were found to be highly significant in that they measured a high proportion of the variation for the thirty characteristics analyzed (Table 15). The first factor to be extracted in the principal components analysis showed highest association with the logarithm of the population in 1959; it is called the *size factor*. The second exhibited the highest association with the logarithm of the urban population potential of each city within its major economic region; it is called the *density factor*. The third revealed highest association with the percentage increase in population 1926–1959; it is called the *growth factor*.

The importance of the size factor confirms the assertion of O. A. Konstantinov[1] that size should be one of the principal criteria for the classification of cities. The size factor showed a high correlation not only with population in 1959 but also, although with decreasing strength, with size in earlier dates—thus a correlation of 0.944 for 1959, 0.787 for 1939, 0.571 for 1926, and 0.319 for 1897 (Table 16). Size was also closely associated with manufacturing output, with range of industrial activities, with number of administrative functions, and with number of transportation lines. Thus the size factor separates out a group of cities that tend to be relatively large, to be the larger cities within their administrative units, to have been the larger cities for some time, to have important manufacturing and administrative functions, to be centers of transportation networks, and to be widely spaced from

---

[1] O. A. Konstantinov, "Tipologiia i klassifikatsiia gorodskikh poselenii v sovetskoi ekonomiko-geograficheskoi nauke," *Materialy po geografii naseleniia,* vypusk 2 (L. Geograficheskoe obshchestvo SSSR, 1963), p. 7.

similar cities. These are the attributes of central places as studied by Walter Christaller,[2] Brian J. L. Berry,[3] and others.

The density factor shows a high correlation with urban population potential within the major economic regions in which each city is located and with other measures of population potential and thus of market potential. The importance of this factor tends to confirm suggestions made by Harris[4] in his study of market potential in the United States. Characteristics associated inversely with the density factor are distance to nearest neighbor, distance to nearest larger neighbor, distance to Moscow, distance from the center of the economic region in which located, and longitude (eastward position) (Table 17). The density factor is a measure of the tendency of cities to cluster. Clustering is a characteristic of specialized-function cities located at sources of localized raw materials such as coalfields or oilfields as described by Harris and Ullman[5] or in industrial districts that have evolved through complex historical processes.

The growth factor is most closely associated with the percentage increase in population for the entire Soviet period; the nearest approximation to this in the data utilized was for the period 1926–1959. Association with the growth from 1926–1939 was higher than for the period 1939–1959, perhaps because of the distorting effect of World War II in the latter period (Table 18). Positive association of growth rates with longitude (eastward position) and with distance from Moscow record some success for the Soviet policy of developing eastern, peripheral, and formerly

[2] Walter Christaller, *Die zentralen Orte in Süddeutschland: eine ökonomisch-geographische Untersuchung über die Gesetzmässigkeit der Verbreitung und Entwicklung der Siedlungen mit städtischen Funktionen* (Jena: Fischer, 1933).
[3] Brian J. L. Berry and Allan Pred, *Central place studies: A bibliography of theory and applications* (Philadelphia: Regional science research institute, 1961), "Bibliography Series No. 1"; *Supplement through 1964*, by H. Gardiner Barnum, Roger Kasperson, and Shinzo Kiuchi, (1965); and Brian J. L. Berry and Chauncy D. Harris, "Central place," *International encyclopedia of the social sciences* (New York: Macmillan and the Free Press, 1968), vol. 2, pp. 365–370.
[4] Chauncy D. Harris, "The market as a factor in the localization of industry in the United States," *Annals of the Association of American Geographers,* vol. 44, no. 4 (December, 1954), pp. 315–348.
[5] Chauncy D. Harris and Edward L. Ullman, "The Nature of cities," *Annals of the American Academy of political and social science,* vol. 242 (November, 1945), pp. 7–17.

backward regions, but perhaps also recognizes the process of cultural diffusion of that greatest human artifact, the city. Curiously, rate of growth shows low positive correlation with distance to railroad and a negative association with number of roads and with number of railroads; rapid growth on a percentage basis has taken place in new eastern areas beyond the core of well-developed transportation networks; older western centers with better-developed transport facilities have grown less rapidly. Statistical manipulation revealed that the growth was associated both with eastward position in the country (0.559 with longitude) and inversely with distance to nearest neighbor (−0.209) even though those two are positively correlated (0.230). Thus, other things being equal, cities grew more rapidly in the east and they grew more rapidly if clustered, even though most clustered cities are in the west.

The central-place system of the Soviet Union is examined in Chapter V. An urban hierarchy is generated by a simple examination of the size relations among the 1,576 cities of more than 10,000 population in 1959 following the rank-size regularity as postulated by Zipf.[6] Twenty-four major urban regions are defined (Table 19 and Figure 21). Although the 6 in the European RSFSR are clearly subordinate to Moscow, the urban regions of distant parts of the country, the Caucasus, Soviet Middle Asia, Kazakhstan, Western and Eastern Siberia, and the Soviet Far East, appear to be relatively independent. It is hypothesized that the enormous size of the Soviet Union, several times as large as the whole of Europe outside the Soviet Union and larger than South America, results in space friction that tends to impede the integration of the urban system for the country as a whole and to encourage some degree of autonomy of the more distant parts of the urban system.

An alternative hierarchy of central places is constructed by utilization of planning, management, or administrative regions and their centers as established by governmental and party organs in 1963. The resulting hierarchy has one center of first-order (Moscow the capital); 18 of second-order, the centers of the major

[6] G. K. Zipf, *National unity and disunity: the nation as a bio-social organism* (Bloomington, Indiana: The Principia Press, 1941).

economic regions; 50 of third-order, the centers of the so-called industrial-management (*Sovnarkhoz*) regions; and 146 of fourth-order, centers of oblasts or similar administrative units (Table 20 and Figure 23). A comparison of the 18 second-order centers determined by political-administrative and planning organs in the Soviet Union with the 24 centers generated solely by statistical analysis of rank-size relationships reveals a remarkable similarity (Figure 25). In 14 centers and regions the 2 systems are essentially identical. The remaining 4 major economic regions, however, are matched with 10 urban systems. Further subdivision of major economic regions into urban system regions results where there are large numbers of cities closely spaced, as in the Donets-Dnepr Region and the Urals, or where the major economic region is usually large in physical area, as in Kazakhstan and the Soviet Far East.

As indicated in Chapter VI, the population potential of the Soviet Union reaches a peak in Moscow, the capital and largest city (Figure 32). From Moscow the population potential declines regularly but steeply toward the relatively empty North, more gradually eastward toward the Urals or westward to long-settled and densely populated lands, and most gradually of all southward through the Moscow Coal Basin near Tula and toward the greatest center of heavy industry, the Donbas, and the areas of densest rural settlement in the Ukraine and the Black-Earth Center of the RSFSR. Secondary peaks of population potential occur in the Donets-Dnepr Region (which includes the Donbas) to the south and in the oases of Soviet Middle Asia, which are separated from the rest of the Soviet Union by deserts.

The area of highest *rural* population potential occurs in the agricultural heartland extending from the western Ukraine eastward to the Black-Earth Center of the RSFSR (Figure 33).

The map of *urban* population potential shows sharper peaks and sharper gradients with high points in Moscow and in the Donbas coalfield and industrial area (Figure 34).

Analysis of urban population potentials within each of the major economic regions reveals two contrasting patterns: central-place type cities stand as clearly separated but regularly spaced peaks of potential separated by plains of much lower but relatively uniform potential as in much of the western Ukraine; specialized-function industrial cities often exist in clusters that together form complex ridges or plateaus of relatively high potential as in the Donbas, the Urals, or the Kuzbas industrial districts (Figures 37, 39, and 43). With few exceptions, urban population potentials reach peaks in the centers of major economic regions and oblasts.

In 10 of the 18 major economic regions the point of theoretical least transport effort to reach the urban population (which is also mathematically the center of urban population) does not occur at the city which serves as the regional center. In these cases the regional center is typically off center. A good example is Alma-Ata, capital of the Kazakh SSR (Figure 45). It has a peripheral location near the southeastern boundary of the republic and region. Goods moving from it to its region nearly all have to go in one direction. Total movement is minimized if there is a rough balance of movement in all directions. Under the rigorous limiting assumption of direct airline movement, the point of calculated minimum theoretical transport effort to reach the urban population of Kazakhstan lies in Karaganda with a more central position.

If the population potential is calculated for the area of the Council for Mutual Economic Assistance (Comecon), including the Soviet Union, Poland, the German Democratic Republic, Czechoslovakia, Hungary, Romania, and Bulgaria, the highest peaks occur not within the Soviet Union but in Silesia in Poland, in Saxony in the German Democratic Republic, and at Budapest in Hungary, a reflection of the large and dense populations of these western areas (Figure 50). A belt of maximum potential extends from Saxony eastward through Silesia to the Ukraine, the Donbas and the Black-Earth Center of the RSFSR with a ridge running north to Moscow, where a secondary peak occurs (Figure 49). The area of theoretical least transport effort to reach the entire population of this trading bloc area occurs in the area between Moscow, Minsk, Kiev, and Khar'kov (Figure 51). Possibly the very rapid growth of small and middle-sized cities in the western part of the Soviet Union in the period 1959–1967 may be related in part to the advantageous transportation location of this area for this larger market.

As indicated in Chapter VII, the urban population of Russia and the Soviet Union has shown remarkably steady growth over the last century and a half. The urban population increased from 2.8 million in 1811 to 128.0 million in 1967. Analysis of the process of this growth is complicated because of the fluctuating boundaries of the country, the irregular periods between dates of censuses and estimates, and variations in the definition of urban. In the first half century, 1811–1867, the average rate of increase of urban population was 1.5 per cent per annum (Table 25 and Figure 52). The rate of growth in the second half century 1867–1917 was higher and fairly uniform at about 2.3 per cent per annum. The growth in the third half century 1917–1967 has been still more rapid, about 2.8 per cent per annum but with violent fluctuations: an average annual loss of 5.7 per cent per annum in the war years 1917–1920; a record rate of growth of 6.5 per cent per annum in the intercensal period of 1926–1939; slow growth of 1.3 per cent per annum in the period 1939–1950 which included World War II; recovery in rate of growth to 4.1 per cent per annum 1950–1959; and then a decrease to 3.1 per cent per annum 1959–1967 as the proportion of the total population that is urban became higher. Indeed recently there has been a drop in each successive year from 4.3 per cent increase during 1960 down to 2.4 per cent increase during 1968. The rate of growth of urban population 1926–1939 was unmatched up to that time for any other major country for a similar period, although Japan during the period 1945–1955 attained an even higher rate of growth.

The 20 largest cities of Russia in 1811 stand in sharp contrast to the 20 largest cities of 1967 (Table 26); only St. Petersburg (Leningrad), Moscow, Kazan', and Kiev were among the 20 largest on both dates. Typical of a large city of 1811 bypassed by modern developments is Tobol'sk, for more than a century (1708–1824) center of the Guberniya of Siberia. At the junction of the Irtysh and Tobol rivers, it had a key position in the days of river transport, but with the building of the Trans-Siberian Railroad (254 km. away) and the development of agricultural lands farther south, it stagnated. Other large cities of 1811 that declined relatively were guberniya centers in the densely populated primarily agricultural western parts of the country, such as Tambov, Orël,

Kaluga, and Vitebsk. Typical of industrial giants among the 20 largest cities of 1967, but not a half century earlier at the beginning of the Soviet period, are Donetsk (center of the Donbas coal-mining and iron and steel district), Novosibirsk (the regional center for Western Siberia and the nearby Kuzbas coal and iron district), and Sverdlovsk, Chelyabinsk, and Perm' (the three major centers of the Ural mining and metal-processing district). They are monuments of the industrial thrust of Soviet power, which has just celebrated its 50th anniversary.

The growth patterns for the century 1867–1967 for the 201 cities of more than 100,000 population in 1967 reveal great variety. (Table 27 and Figures 61–67). Riga and Odessa, port cities on the Baltic and Black seas, represent cities that grew rapidly in the half century 1867–1917 with the building of railroads and the expansion of international trade, but then slackened their pace with the decline of international trade and changing boundaries. Baku grew very rapidly with the rise of the oil industry in the late 19th century and has continued its growth. Gor'kiy grew faster than any other large Soviet city in the period 1920–1939 with the rise of the automobile industry; it represents the industrial rejuvenation of an old commercial city (Nizhniy Novgorod). Novosibirsk, the youngest of the very large cities, arose only in 1894 with the construction of the Trans-Siberian Railroad. Eighteen new industrial giants of the east are creations of the Soviet period (Figures 67 and 68). Eight are on coalfields, 2 are at hydroelectric developments, 2 are at mineral deposits, 2 are other centers of the iron and steel industry and 4 are based on oil refining and the chemical industry. Fuel and energy, and metals and machinery have provided the bases of a high proportion of the growth cities of the Soviet period.

Chapter VIII examines the growth of cities during the Soviet period, briefly for the intercensal period 1926–1939, in considerable detail for the intercensal period 1939–1959, and finally for 1959–1967.

Study of the distribution of cities with high rates of growth during the period 1926–1939 reveals that they were concentrated in industrial districts, the Donbas, the Kuzbas, and the Urals, or were new political centers (Figure 74). The emphasis on coal min-

ing under the leadership of Stalin is revealed in the names of
Stalino (now Donetsk) in the Donbas, Stalinsk (now Novokuznetsk) in the Kuzbas, and Stalinogorsk (now Novomoskovsk) in
the Moscow Coal Basin. Stalinabad (now Dushanbe), capital of
the Tadzhik SSR, was one of the new political centers and Stalingrad (now Volgograd) an industrial city on the Volga River.

During the period 1939–1959, in which World War II took
place, the core area with many cities of rapid growth was located
in the deep interior of the country between the Volga River and
Lake Baykal, far from the eastern or western borders (Figures
75–79). The 381 growth cities (those that doubled in population
in this period) among the 1,247 cities studied are treated region
by region and city by city (Figures 80–91). The highest proportion
of such cities occurred in a series of coalfields and oilfields in the
Komi coalfields and oilfields of the northeastern European part
of the RSFSR (10 such cities out of 10 cities with more than
15,000 population in 1959), in the Moscow coalfield near Tula
(11 growth cities out of a total of 17 cities in the study group), in
the Volga-Ural oilfield (20 of 29), in the Kuzbas coalfield (12 of 22),
and in the Karaganda coalfield and nearby ore deposits (10 of 11)
(Figure 79 and Table 31). The only large agricultural area with
a predominance of growth cities was the Virgin Lands of northern
Kazakhstan (19 growth cities out of 22 cities in the study group);
it was the scene of a major agricultural expansion on the dry
margins of agriculture. Small new agricultural areas with irrigation, together with new hydroelectric projects and mining or
smelting towns, accounted for 2 smaller areas with a high proportion of growth cities in Soviet Middle Asia: Tashkent Oblast and
the southwest part of Tadzhikistan.

The period since 1959 has been characterized by a more widespread distribution of cities of rapid growth extending from the
western boundary of the Soviet Union to Lake Baykal in Eastern
Siberia. The only large area with average rates of urban growth
more than double the national average occurred in Kazakhstan
and some parts of Soviet Middle Asia (Figure 92). Analysis of individual cities of rapid growth 1959–1967, both those with more
than 50,000 population in 1967 (Figure 93) and smaller cities
(Figure 94), reveals a wide dispersion of such cities from Minsk

in Belorussia on the west to Bratsk in Eastern Siberia on the east. Several small and medium-sized cities specializing in chemical industries in Belorussia in the west typify a new attention to a greater range of industries (including consumer goods), to smaller urban settlements (as part of the policy of limiting the growth of the very large cities), and to cities in the western margins of the country, which in earlier Soviet periods had been relatively neglected.

Finally, an analysis of some urban settlements that have stagnated or declined in population since the 1897 or 1926 censuses reveals the crucial role of location and transportation in the prosperity and growth of cities in the Soviet industrialization periods. The vast majority of the cities that have shown little or no growth are located in the European part of the Soviet Union, particularly west of the Volga River in the rich black-earth farming belt of the Ukraine and the RSFSR (Figure 95). Typically, they are centers of agricultural areas, often not on a railroad, and have been bypassed by the industrial development that has stimulated rapid growth in other cities of the country.

This study has been confined to an analysis of certain characteristics of the system of cities in the Soviet Union: their functions, their size, their spacing (density), and their growth. In functional classification, based on economic activity, Soviet cities fall into two major types, diversified administrative centers, which have central-place type hierarchical structure and widely spaced distribution, and industrial cities which show strong tendencies to locate in clusters. Size has a strong relationship with the central-place administrative hierarchy. Density reflects the cluster patterns of special-function cities and finds a generalized expression in the urban population potential. Growth of Soviet cities is related both to location (being generally higher in interior and industrial districts) and to function, the cities based on the production of energy or fuel (coal, oil, or hydroelectric power) or metals (particularly iron and steel) generally having highest growth rates, although machinery is prominent among the larger cities and the chemical industries have been increasingly active in recent years. New administrative centers have also grown rapidly in the Soviet period.

Selected Bibliography

The following categories are generally excluded from this bibliography: works on planning, guidebooks, local histories, studies of individual cities, unpublished dissertations, abstracts of dissertations, book reviews, notes, brief summaries of papers presented orally in conferences, and papers of ephemeral interest.

Standard short names are used for publishers and the following other abbreviations are also utilized:

AN   Akademiia Nauk (Academy of Sciences)
VGO   Vsesoiuznoe Geograficheskoe Obshchestvo (Geographical Society of the USSR)
izd.   izdatel'stvo (publisher)
M.   Moscow
L.   Leningrad

For each author papers are arranged chronologically beginning with the earliest.

The bibliography is arranged in the following organization:

I. BASIC SOURCES OF DATA

1. General Censuses

Russia. Tsentral'nyi statisticheskii komitet. *Pervaia vseobshchaia perepis' naseleniia Rossiiskoi Imperii 1897 goda.* S.-Peterburg, 1899–1905. 89 vols. (1897 census)

———. ———. *Pervaia vseobshchaia perepis' naseleniia Rossiiskoi Imperii 1897 g.* Vypusk 5. *Okonchatel'no ustanovlennoe pri razrabotke perepisi. Nalichnoe naselenie gorodov.* S.-Peterburg, 1905. (1897 census)

———. ———. *Goroda i poseleniia v uezdakh imeiushchie 2,000 i bolee zhitelei.* S.-Peterburg, 1905. (1897 census)

———. ———. *Naselennyia mesta Rossiiskoi Imperii v 500 i bolee zhitelei s ukazaniem vsego nalichnago v nikh naseleniia . . . po dannym Pervoi vseobshchei perepisi naseleniia 1897 g.* S.-Peterburg, 1905. (1897 census)

SSSR. Tsentral'noe statisticheskoe upravlenie. *Vsesoiuznaia perepis' naseleniia 1926 g.* M. 1928–1933. 56 vols. (1926 census)

———. ———. *Itogi vsesoiuznoi perepisi naseleniia 1959 goda.* M. Gosstatizdat, 1962–1963. 16 unnumbered volumes, one covering the USSR as a whole and one for each of the 15 union republics. (1959 census with data for 1939 census)

2. Statistical Yearbooks and Official Statistical Publications

Russia. Tsentral'nyi statisticheskii komitet. *Statisticheskiia tablitsy Rossiikoi Imperii, za 1856–i god.* Vypusk pervyi. S.-Peterburg, 1858. (1856 population data)

———. ———. *Statisticheskiia tablitsy Rossiiskoi Imperii,* vypusk 2. *Nalich-noe naselenie imperii za 1858 god.* A. Bushen. Sanktpeterburg, 1863. (1858 population data)

———. ———. *Statisticheskii vremennik Rossiiskoi Imperii.* Seriia 2, vypusk 1. Sanktpeterburg, 1871. (1867 population data)

———. ———. *Sbornik svedenii po Rossii za 1884–1885 gg.* "Statistika Rossiiskoi Imperii, tom 1," S.-Peterburg, 1887. (1885 population data)

———. ———. *Statisticheskii ezhegodnik Rossii 1913 g.* S.-Peterburg, 1914. (1913 population data)

———. ———. *Statisticheskii ezhegodnik Rossii 1915 g.* Petrograd, 1916. (1915 population data)

RSFSR. Tsentral'noe statisticheskoe upravlenie. *Statisticheskii ezhegod-nik 1918–1920 gg.* vypusk 1. "Trudy Tsentral'nogo statisticheskogo upravleniia, tom 8, vypusk 1," M. 1921. (1920 census)

———. ———. *Statisticheskii ezhegodnik 1921 g.* vypusk 1. "Trudy Tsen-tral'nogo statisticheskogo upravleniia, tom 8, vypusk 3." M. 1922. (1920 census)

———. ———. *Statisticheskii ezhegodnik 1922 i 1923.* vypusk 1. "Trudy Tsentral'nogo statisticheskogo upravleniia, tom 8, vypusk 5." (1920 census)

———. ———. *Sbornik statisticheskikh svedenii po Soiuzu S.S.R. 1918–1923.* "Trudy Tsentral'nogo statisticheskogo upravleniia, tom 18," M. 1924. (1920 census)

"Itogi Vsesoiuznoi gorodskoi perepisi 1923 g." 4 parts. M. 1924–1925. (*Trudy Tsentral'nogo statisticheskogo upravleniia, otdel demografii.* tom 20, chasti 1–4.) (1923 urban census)

SSSR. Tsentral'noe statisticheskoe upravlenie. *Vsesoiuznaia gorodskaia perepis' 1923 goda.* vypuski 1–2. M. 1926. Vypusk 2. "Kratkaia prom-yshlennaia kharakteristika gorodov i poselenii gorodskogo tipa." M. 1926. 598 p. (1923 urban census)

———. ———. *Narodnoe khoziaistvo SSSR: statisticheskii sbornik.* M. Gos-statizdat, 1956. 262 p.

———. ———. *Narodnoe khoziaistvo SSSR v 1956 godu: statisticheskii ezhegodnik.* M. Gosstatizdat, 1957. 295 p.

———. ———. *Narodnoe khoziaistvo SSSR v 1958 godu: statisticheskii ezhegodnik.* M. Gosstatizdat, 1959. 958 p.

———. ———. *Narodnoe khoziaistvo SSSR v 1959 godu: statisticheskii ezhegodnik.* 1960. 895 p.

———. ———. *Narodnoe khoziaistvo SSSR v 1960 godu: statisticheskii ezhegodnik.* 1961. 942 p.

———. ———. *Narodnoe khoziaistvo SSSR v 1961 godu: statisticheskii ezhegodnik.* 1962. 860 p.

———. ———. *Narodnoe khoziaistvo SSSR v 1962 godu: statisticheskii ezhegodnik.* 1963. 735 p.

———. ———. *Narodnoe khoziaistvo SSSR v 1963 godu: statisticheskii ezhegodnik.* 1965. 759 p.

———. ———. *Narodnoe khoziaistvo SSSR v 1964 g.: statisticheskii ezhegodnik.* 1965. 886 p.

———. ———. *Narodnoe khoziaistvo SSSR v 1965 g.: statisticheskii ezhegodnik.* 1966. 909 p.

———. ———. *Narodnoe khoziaistvo SSSR v 1967 g.: statisticheskii ezhegodnik,* 1968. 1007 p.

———. ———. *Narodnoe khoziaistvo SSSR v 1968 g.: statisticheskii ezhegodnik,* 1969. 831 p.

———. ———. *Strana sovetov za 50 let: sbornik statisticheskikh materialov.* 1967. 351 p.

———. ———. *SSSR v tsifrakh v 1963 g.* M. Izd. Statistika, 1964.

"Perechen' gorodov s ukazaniem chislennosti naseleniia," in *SSSR. Administrativno-territorial'noe delenie Soiuznykh respublik na 1 iiulia 1967 goda* (Prezidium Verkhovnogo Soveta SSSR) M. 1967. pp. 592–604 (1967 population estimates for all cities of more than 15,000 population.)

3. Other Statistical Sources

Geografichesko-statisticheskii slovar' Rossiiskoi Imperii. P. Semenov, ed. Sanktpeterburg. Imperatorskoe russkoe geograficheskoe obshchestvo, 1863–1885. 5 vols.

German, Karl Fëdorovich. *Statisticheskiia issledovaniia otnositel'no Rossiiskoi Imperii.* Chast' 1. *O narodnaselenii.* S.-Peterburg, 1819. (1811 population data.)

Kabuzan, Vladimir Maksimovich. *Narodonaselenie Rossii v XVIII-pervoi polovine XIX v. (po materialam revizii).* M. Izd. AN SSSR, 1963. 228 p.

Pisarev, Innokentii Iul'evich. *Narodonaselenie SSSR (sotsial'no-ekonomicheskii ocherk).* M. Sotsekgiz, 1962. 188 p. (Especially Glava 6, "Gorodskoe i sel'skoe naselenie." 93-114). In English: *The population of the U.S.S.R.: a socio-economic survey.* M. Progress Publishers, 1964. 157 p.

Pod"iachikh, Petr Gavrilovich. *Naselenie SSSR.* M. Gospolitizdat, 1961. 192 p.

Rashin, Adol'f Grigor'evich. *Naselenie Rossii za 100 let (1811–1913 gg.): statisticheskie ocherki.* S. G. Strumilin, ed. M. Gosstatizdat, 1956. 350 p.

Sovet s"ezdov predstavitelei promyshlennosti i torgovli. *Statisticheskii ezhegodnik na 1912 god.,* V. I. Sharyi, ed. S.-Peterburg, 1913, 747 p.

Volkov, Evgenii Zakhariivich. *Dinamika narodonaseleniia SSSR za vosem'desiat let.* Foreword by S. G. Strumilin. M. Gosudarstvennoe izd., 1930. 271 p.

Leasure, J. William and Lewis, Robert A. *Population changes in Russia and the USSR: a set of comparable territorial units,* "Social Science Monograph Series, Vol. 1, No. 2." San Diego, California: San Diego State College Press, 1966. 43 p.

Lorimer, Frank. *The population of the Soviet Union: history and prospects.* (II. Economic and financial. 1946. II.A.3) Geneva: League of Nations, 1946. 289 p.

——. "Population," *Encyclopaedia Britannica,* 1965 ed. vol. 18, 230–235.

United Nations, Statistical Office. *Demographic yearbook.* New York: United Nations, 1948–. Annual. Especially 1960, 1962, 1963, 1964, 1966, and 1967.

U. S. Bureau of the census. *Historical statistics of the United States, colonial times to 1957.* Washington, D.C., 1960. 789 p.

——. ——. *Continuation to 1962 and revisions.* 1965. 154 p.

4. Encyclopedias and Gazetteers

Bol'shaia sovetskaia entsiklopediia. S. I. Vavilov, ed. M. Izd. Bol'shaia sovetskaia entsiklopediia, 2nd ed. 1950–1958. 51 vols. plus 2 index vols.

——. *Ezhegodnik.* 1957–. Annual.

Malaia sovetskaia entsiklopediia. B. A. Vvedenskii, ed. M. Izd. Bol'shaia sovetskaia entsiklopediia, 3rd ed. 1958–1961. 10 vols. plus index vol.

Kratkaia geograficheskaia entsiklopediia. A. A. Grigor'ev, ed. M. Gos. izd. "Sovetskaia entsiklopediia," 1960–1966. 5 vols.

SSSR. Glavnoe upravlenie geodezii i kartografii. *Slovar' geograficheskikh nazvanii SSSR.* Utverzhden Glavnym upravleniem geodezii i karto-grafii pri Sovete Ministrov v kachestve obiazatel'nogo posobiia. M. B. Volostnovaia, ed. M. "Nedra," 1968. 272 p.

Ekonomicheskaia zhizn' SSSR: khronika sobytii i faktov 1917–1965. S. G. Strumilin, ed. M. Izd. "Sovetskaia entsiklopediia," 2nd ed. 1967. 2 vols.

Encyclopaedia britannica. Chicago: Encyclopaedia britannica, 1965 edition. 24 vols. (Articles by R. A. French).

Britannica book of the year. Chicago: Encyclopaedia britannica, 1938–. Annual.

Grand Larousse encyclopédique en dix volumes. Paris: Librarie La-rousse, 1960–1964. 10 vols. Supplément, 1968.

Der grosse Brockhaus. Wiesbaden: F. A. Brockhaus, 16th ed., 1952–1963. 12 vols. plus 2 supplementary volumes. 17th ed., 1966–. 20 vols.

Columbia Lippincott gazetteer of the world. Leon E. Seltzer, ed. with the geographical research staff of Columbia University Press and with the cooperation of the American Geographical Society. New York: Columbia university press by arrangement with J. B. Lippincott com-pany, 1952. 2148 p. (Entries on Soviet cities largely by Theodore Shabad, assistant editor).

U. S. Board on geographic names. *Gazetteer no. 42. U.S.S.R. and certain neighboring areas.* Washington, D.C.: Government printing office, 1959. 7 vols. (362,000 entries).

The Times index-gazetteer of the world. London: Times Publishing Co., 1965. 959 p.

Meckelein, Wolfgang. *Ortsumbenennungen und -neugründungen im europäischen Teil der Sowjetunion. Nach dem Stand der Jahre 1910/1938/1951 mit einem Nachtrag für Ostpreussen 1953.* "Osteuropa-Institut an der Freien Universität Berlin. Wirtschaftswissenschaftliche Veröffentlichungen, Band 2." Berlin: Duncker & Humblot, 1955. 134 p.

5. Atlases and Maps

Akademiia Nauk Armianskoi SSR *and* SSSR. Glavnoe upravlenie geodezii i kartografii. *Atlas Armianskoi Sovetskoi Sotsialisticheskoi Respubliki.* Yerevan-Moskva, 1961.

Akademiia Nauk Azerbaidzhanskoi SSR. Institut Geografii. *Atlas Azerbaidzhanskoi Sovetskoi Sotsialisticheskoi Respubliki.* Baku-Moskva: GUGK, 1963.

Akademiia Nauk BSSR *and* SSSR. Glavnoe upravlenie geodezii i kartografii. *Atlas Belorusskoi Sovetskoi Sotsialisticheskoi Respubliki.* Minsk-Moskva, 1958.

Akademiia Nauk Gruzinskoi SSR. Institut Geografii im Vakhushti. *Atlas Gruzinskoi Sovetskoi Sotsialisticheskoi Respubliki.* Tbilisi-Moskva: GUGK, 1964.

Akademiia Nauk SSSR. Sibirskoe Otdelenie. Institut Geografii Sibiri i Dal'nego Vostoka. *Atlas Zabaikal'ia (Buriatskaia ASSR i Chitinskaia Oblast').* Moskva-Irkutsk: GUGK, 1967.

Akademiia Nauk Tadzhikskoi SSR. Sovet po Izucheniiu Proizvoditel'nykh Sil. *Atlas Tadzhikskoi Sovetskoi Sotsialisticheskoi Respubliki.* Dushanbe-Moskva: GUGK, 1968.

Akademiia Nauk Uzbekskoi SSR *and* SSSR. Glavnoe upravlenie geodezii i kartografii. *Atlas Uzbekskoi Sovetskoi Sotsialisticheskoi Respubliki.* Tashkent-Moskva, 1963.

Atlas Volgogradskoi oblasti. M. GUGK, 1967.

Geograficheskoe obshchestvo SSSR, Stavropol'skii otdel, *and* Stavropol'skii gosudarstvennyi pedagogicheskii institut. *Atlas Stavropol'skogo Kraia.* M. GUGK, 1968.

Kiyvskii Derzhavnii Unyversitet im T. G. Shevchenka. Geografychnii Fakul'tet. *Geografiia Kiyvskoy Oblasty Atlas.* Kiyv: Vidavnitsvo Kiyvskogo Derzhavnogo Unyversitetu, 1962.

Leningradskii Gosudarstvennyi Universitet im A. A. Zhdanov. Nauchnoissledovatel'skii Geografo-ekonomicheskii Institut. *Atlas Leningradskoi Oblasti.* M. GUGK, 1967.

Leningradskii Gosudarstvennyi Universitet im A. A. Zhdanov. Nauchno-issledovatel'skii geografo-ekonomicheskii Institut *and* Akademiia Nauk SSSR. Komi Filial. *Atlas Komi Avtonomnoi Sovetskoi Sotsialisticheskoi Respubliki.* M. GUGK, 1964.

Moskovskii Gosudarstvennyi Universitet imeni M. V. Lomonosova. Geograficheskii Fakul'tet. *Atlas Tselinnogo Kraia.* M. GUGK, 1964.

Moskovskii Gosudarstvennyi Universitet im M. V. Lomonosova. Geograficheskii Fakul'tet *and* Akademiia Nauk Kazakhskoi SSR. *Atlas Kustanaiskoi Oblasti.* M. GUGK, 1963.

Moskovskii Gosudarstvennyi Universitet imeni M. V. Lomonosova. Geograficheskii Fakul'tet *and* Akademiia Nauk SSSR. Sibirskoe Otdelenie. Vostochno-Sibirskii Filial. *Atlas Irkutskoi Oblasti.* Moskva-Irkutsk: GUGK, 1962. Especially "Tipy poselenii," 128–129.

Sakhalinskaia Oblast'. Sovet deputov trudiashchikhsia. Ispolnitel'nyi komitet, *and* Akademiia Nauk SSSR. Sibirskoe otdelenie. Sakhalinskii kompleksnyi nauchno-issledovatel'skii institut. *Atlas Sakhalinskoi oblasti.* M. GUGK, 1967.

SSSR. Glavnoe upravlenie geodezii i kartografii SSSR. *Atlas avtomobil'nykh dorog SSSR.* M. GUGK, 1966.

———. ———. *Atlas Astrakhanskoi Oblasti.* M. 1968.

———. ———. *Atlas Iaroslavskoi Oblasti.* M. 1964.

———. ———. *Atlas Kalininskoi Oblasti.* M. 1964.

———. ———. *Atlas Karagandinskoi Oblasti.* M. 1969.

———. ———. *Atlas Kirovskoi Oblasti.* M. 1968.

———. ———. *Atlas Mira.* A. N. Baranov, chief. ed., M. 1954. Separate index volume: *Ukazatel' geograficheskikh nazvanii.* M. 1964. 572 p.

———. ———. *Atlas Moskovskoi Oblasti.* M. 1964.

———. ———. *Atlas Razvitiia Khoziaistva i Kul'tury SSSR.* A. N. Voznesenskii, chief ed., M. 1967.

———. ———. *Atlas Riazanskoi Oblasti.* M. 1965.

———. ———. *Atlas Smolenskoi Oblasti.* M. 1964.

———. ———. *Atlas sel'skogo khoziaistva SSSR.* M. 1960.

———. ———. *Atlas skhem zheleznykh dorog SSSR.* M. 1961.

———. ———. *Atlas SSSR.* A. N. Baranov, chief ed., M. 1962, 2nd ed., 1969.

———. ———. *Atlas SSSR.* 2nd ed. M. 1955.

———. ———. *Atlas Ukrainskoi SSR i Moldavskoi SSR.* M. 1962.

———. ———. *Atlas Vologodskoi Oblasti.* M. 1965.

———. ———. *Atlas Voronezhskoi Oblasti.* M. 1968.

———. ———. *Bol'shoi Sovetskii Atlas Mira.* M. 1937–1939. 2 vols.

———. ———. *Geograficheskii Atlas dlia Uchitelei Srednei Shkoly.* 1st ed. M. 1954; 2nd ed., 1959; 3rd ed., 1967.

———. ———. Oblast maps (administrative). Various scales and dates, not separately listed. (About 150 maps, each typically showing cities and settlements of urban type, and other settlements, railroads, roads, and administrative divisions into rayons.)

———. ———. *Soiuz Sovetskskikh Sotsialisticheskikh Respublik: politiches-kaia-administrativnaia karta*, 1:4,000,000. M. 1962. 4 sheets. Other editions 1966, 1968, etc., revised every few years.

———. ———. *Zheleznye dorogi SSSR; napravleniia i stantsii.* M. 2nd ed., 1966.

Kingsbury, Robert C., and Taaffe, Robert N. *An Atlas of Soviet Affairs.* New York: Praeger, 1965.

Kish, George. *Economic Atlas of the Soviet Union.* With the assistance of Ian M. Matley and Betty Bellaire. Ann Arbor, Michigan: The University of Michigan Press, 1960.

Oxford Regional Economic Atlas: the U.S.S.R. and Eastern Europe. Prepared by the Economic Intelligence Unit and the Cartographic Department of the Clarendon Press. London: Oxford University Press, 1956.

Soviet Union in Maps: its Origin and Development. Fullard, Harold ed. London: George Philip & Son, 1965.

6. Administrative Handbooks

SSSR. *Aministrativno-territorial'noe delenie soiuznykh republik.* M. Izd. Izvestiia sovetov deputatov trudiashchikhsia SSSR, vol. 1– 1924–. Irregular but recently about every two years. Especially the following:
... na 1 ianvariia 1958 goda. 9th ed.
... na 1 aprelia 1960 goda. 10th ed.
... na 1 ianvariia 1962 goda. 11th ed.
... na 1 aprelia 1963 goda. 12th ed.
... ianvar' 1965 goda.
... na 1 iiulia 1967 goda.

7. General Newspapers and Serials
Izvestiia.
Pravda.
Ekonomicheskaia Gazeta.
The New York Times.
Current Digest of the Soviet Press.
Statesman's Yearbook.

II. SOVIET WORKS ON GEOGRAPHY OF CITIES OF
THE U.S.S.R. AS A WHOLE
1. Bibliographies

Khorev, Boris Sergeevich. "Sovetskaia literatura po geografii naseleniia i smezhnym distsiplinam (1955–1961 gg)." *Materialy I Mezhduvedomstvennogo soveshchaniia po geografii naseleniia (ianvar'-fevral' 1962 g.),* vypusk 6, Obzor issledovanii po geografii naseleniia v SSSR. M-L. Geograficheskoe obshchestvo Soiuza SSR. 1962, 28–144, especially pp. 43–58 (213 entries for geography of cities).

Parkhomenko, Iia Ivanovna, and Ternovskaia, G. N. "Sovetskaia literatura po geografii naseleniia (1961–1965 gg.) in *Itogi nauki; seriia geografiia: Geografiia SSSR,* vypusk 3, Geografiia naseleniia v SSSR. M. VINITI, 1966, 34–168, especially "IV. Geografiia gorodov i gorodskogo naseleniia," 83–120 (508 entries for urban geography, planning, and general urban studies).

Konstantinov, Oleg Arkad'evich. "Geograficheskoe izuchenie gorodskikh poselenii v SSSR," in *Geografiia naseleniia v SSSR: osnovnye problemy.* M-L. Izd. "Nauka," 1964, 32–68; bibliography, pp. 52–65 (365 entries).

Varlamov, Viktor Sergeevich, Kudriavtsev, O. K., and Shatsilo, E. S. "Noveishaia literatura po probleme gorodov-sputnikov." *Goroda-sputniki; sbornik statei.* M. Geografgiz. 1961, 179–193. (119 entries for Soviet works).

Geografiia naseleniia Sibiri i Dal'nego Vostoka: bibliograficheskii ukazatel'. V. V. Vorob'ev, ed. (Akademiia Nauk SSSR. Sibirskoe Otdelenie. Institut Geografii Sibiri i Dal'nego Vostoka. Nauchnaia biblioteka Vostochno-Sibirskogo Filiala). Irkutsk, 1968. 223 p. Especially "Gorodskoe naselenie i goroda," 23–60 (410 entries).

Referativnyi Zhurnal: Geografiia. (AN SSSR. Vsesoiuznyi Institut Nauchnoi i Tekhnicheskoi Informatsii). 1954–. "E. Geografiia SSSR: Geografiia naseleniia i naselennykh punktov," in each monthly issue.

2. *Substantive Works*

Ainberg, E. S. "Zony vliianiia goroda srednei velichiny, ikh granitsy i passazhiropotoki," *Voprosy geografii,* sbornik 77. M. Izd. "Mysl'," 1968, 148–158. In English: "Zones of influence of middle-size cities, their boundaries and passenger flows," *Soviet geography: review & translation,* vol. 10, no. 9 (November, 1969), 549–558.

Alaev, Enrid Borisovich, and Khorev, Boris Sergeevich. "Puti razvitiia malykh i srednikh gorodov SSSR" in *Nauchnye problemy geografii naseleniia.* M. Izd. Moskovskogo universiteta, 1967, 138–150.

Alampiev, Petr Martynovich. *Ekonomicheskoe raionirovanie SSSR.* M. Gosplanizdat, 1959. 263 p.

———. ———. *Kniga 2-ia.* M. Ekonomizdat, 1963. 248 p.

Aleksandrova, Tat'iana Aleksandrovna, and Zhurkin, L. P. "Problemy razvitiia gorodov i ispol'zovaniia trudovykh resursov: konferentsiia v Kuibysheve," *Izvestiia AN SSSR, seriia geograficheskaia,* 1968, no. 4, 150–152.

Al'tman, Leonid Pridikovich, Ata-Mirzaev, O., Afonskaia, M., Dmitrevskii, Iu., and Sergeeva, K. "Vtoroe Mezhduvedomstvennoe nauchnoe soveshchanie po geografii naseleniia," *Izvestiia, VGO,* 1967, no. 4, 315–320, followed by "Rezoliutsiia II Mezhduvedomstvennogo nauchnogo soveshchaniia po geografii naseleniia (Moskva, 31 I-4 II 1967)," 320–323.

Bainberg, E. I., and Savranskaia, R. Ia. "Geografiia naseleniia kurort-nogo raiona," *Vestnik Moskovskogo universiteta, seriia 5, geografiia*, 1966, no. 5, 56–62.

Baranskii, Nikolai Nikolaevich. "Ob ekonomiko-geograficheskom izuche-nii gorodov." *Voprosy geografii*, sbornik 2, M. Geografgiz, 1946, 19–62. Also revised in his book *Ekonomicheskaia geografiia; Ekonomicheskaia kartografiia*. M. Geografgiz, 1956, 164–214, 2nd ed., 1960, 172–221. Also in abbreviated form in his *Ocherki po shkol'noi metodike eko-nomicheskoi geografii*. M. Uchpedgiz, 1946, 1954, 1955 and in *Me-todika prepodavaniia ekonomicheskoi geografii*. M. Uchpedgiz, 1960, 250–268.

Blazhko, Nina Ivanovna. "K voprosu o metodakh izucheniia koliche-stvennykh pokazatelei, neobkhodimykh pri klassifikatsii gorodov," *Trudy konferentsii po voprosam razmeshcheniia promyshlennosti i razvitiia gorodov*. Vil'nius: AN Litovskoi SSR, 1963, 57–63.

———. "Ekonomiko-geograficheskoe matematicheskoe modelirovanie gorodov," *Vestnik Moskovskogo universiteta, seriia 5, geografiia*, 1964, no. 4, 18-27. In English: "Economic-geographic mathematical models of cities," *Soviet geography: review and translation*, vol. 6, no. 9 (No-vember, 1965), 66–78.

———. "Kolichestvennye metody izucheniia sistemy gorodskikh poselenii," in *Geografiia naseleniia i naselennykh punktov SSSR*. L. "Nauka," 1967, 175–214. English abstract, "Study of urban places system by quantitative methods," 214.

Blazhko, N. I., Grigor'ev, S. V., Zabotin, Ia. I., and Shafir, G. G. "Mate-maticheskii podkhod k opredeleniiu stupenei razvitiia gorodskikh poselenii Tatarskoi ASSR," *Izvestiia AN SSSR, seriia geograficheskaia*, 1968, no. 3, 115–125.

———. "Matematicheskii metod opredeleniia stupenei razvitiia gorod-skikh poselenii v sisteme," *Voprosy geografii*, sbornik 77. M. "Mysl'," 1968, 99–114. in English: "Mathematical method for determining levels of development of urban places within a system," *Soviet geog-raphy: review & translation*, vol. 10, no. 9 (November, 1969), 523–537.

———. "Matematiko-geograficheskii analiz stupenei razvitiia gorodskikh poselenii v sisteme," *Teoriia i praktika ekonomicheskogo mikro-raionirovaniia*, A. M. Kolotievskii, ed. Riga: Izd. "Zinatne," 1969, 77–84.

Blazhko, N. I., and Gurevich, B. L. "O Strukturno-matematicheskom analize sistem gorodskikh poselenii," *Izvestiia AN SSSR, seriia geo-graficheskaia*, 1967, no. 6, 105–113. In English: "Structural-mathe-matical analysis of systems of urban places," *Soviet geography: review and translation*, vol. 10, no. 7 (September, 1969), 374–383.

Blazhko, N. I., Voskoboinikova, S. M., and Gurevich, B. L. "Sistemy gorodskikh poselenii," in *Nauchnye problemy geografii naseleniia*. M. Izd. Moskovskogo universiteta, 1967, 87–99. In English: "Systems of urban places," *Soviet geography: review & translation*, vol. 10, no. 7 (September, 1969), 364–373.

Bogorad, Daniil Il'ich. *Raionnaia planirovka; voprosy planirovki promyshlennykh kompleksov.* M. Gosstroiizdat, 1960. 243 p.

——. "Geografiia naseleniia i problemy raionnoi planirovki," *Materialy I Mezhduvedomstvennogo soveshchaniia po geografii naseleniia (ianvar'-fevral' 1962 g.*), vypusk 1, Doklady i reziume dokladov na plenume M.-L. Geograficheskoe obshchestvo Soiuza SSR, 1961, 74–84. Rotaprint.

——. "Opyt postroeniia perspektivnoi seti gorodov," in *Voprosy raionnoi planirovki.* Kiev: Gosstroiizdat, 1963, 22–31.

——. "Geografiia naseleniia i problemy raionnoi planirovki," in *Geografiia naseleniia v SSSR: osnovnye problemy.* M.-L. Izd. "Nauka," 1964, 106–112.

——. *Konstruktivnaia geografiia raiona: osnovy raionnoi planirovki.* M. "Mysl'," 1965. 407 p. (bibliography, pp. 382–405, 279 entries).

——. "Zadachi izucheniia i regulirovaniia rosta gorodskikh aglomeratsii," in *Nauchnye problemy geografii naseleniia.* M. Izd. Moskovskogo universiteta, 1967, 100–112.

Bogorad, D. I., and Izrailevich, A. S. "Predposylki razmeshcheniia promyshlennykh novostroek v srednikh i malykh gorodov," in *Voprosy gradostroitel'stva*, vypusk 1. Kiev, 1965, 17–24.

Bukhgol'ts, Ol'ga Eduardovna, Demidov, S. S., and Koval'skaia, N. Ia. "Izuchenie naseleniia gorodov," in *Sovremennaia geografiia v period stroitel'stva kommunizma.* M. Geografgiz, 1963, 225–233.

Bukhgol'ts, O. E., and Maergoiz, I. M. "Krupnomasshtabnoe izuchenie gorodov," in *Metody geograficheskikh issledovanii.* M. Geografgiz, 1960, 333–345.

Davidovich, Vladimir Georgievich. "Formy rasseleniia v ugol'nykh basseinakh SSSR," *Voprosy geografii*, sbornik 14. M. Geografgiz, 1949, 3–28.

——. "O tipologii rasseleniia v gruppakh gorodov i poselkov SSSR," *Voprosy geografii*, sbornik 38. M. Geografgiz, 1956, 27–77.

——. "O razvitii seti gorodov SSSR za 40 let," *Voprosy geografii*, sbornik 45. M. Geografgiz, 1959, 37–71.

——. "Gorodskie poseleniia," *Kratkaia geograficheskaia entsiklopediia*, vol. 1. M. "Sovetskaia entsiklopediia," 1960, 479–480.

——. *Rasselenie v promyshlennykh uzlakh (inzhenerno-ekonomicheskie osnovy).* M. Gosstroiizdat, 1960. 324 p. (bibliography, pp. 314–323, 266 entries).

——. "O zakonomernostiakh i tendentsiiakh gorodskogo rasseleniia v SSSR," in *Materialy I Mezhduvedomstvennogo soveshchaniia po geografii naseleniia, (ianvar'-fevral' 1962 g.*), vypusk 1, Doklady i reziume dokladov na plenume. M-L. Geograficheskoe obshchestvo SSSR, 1961, 49–58. Rotaprint.

———. "Goroda i poselki-sputniki v SSSR," in *Goroda-sputniki; sbornik statei.* M. Geografgiz, 1961, 5–39. In English: "Satellite cities and towns of the USSR," *Soviet geography: review and translation,* vol. 3, no. 3 (March, 1962), 3–35.

———. "Velichina gorodskikh poselenii SSSR. (po itogam Vsesoiuznoi perepisi naseleniia 1959 g.)," *Voprosy geografii,* sbornik 56. M. Geografgiz, 1962, 5–29.

———. "Gorodskie aglomeratsii v SSSR," in *Materialy k IV s"ezdu geograficheskogo obshchestva SSSR, Simpozium B, Osnovnye voprosy ekonomicheskoi geografii. Doklady,* chast' 1. L. Geograficheskoe obshchestvo SSSR, 1964, 34–47. Rotaprint. In English: "Urban agglomerations in the USSR," *Soviet geography: review and translation,* vol. 5, no. 9 (November, 1964), 34–44.

———. *Planirovka gorodov i raionov; inzhenerno-ekonomicheskie osnovy.* M. Stroiizdat, 2nd ed., 1964. 325 p. 1st ed., *Planirovka gorodov,* 1947, 316 p. (Bibliography, pp. 321–324, 104 entries).

———. "Gorodskie aglomeratsii v SSSR," in *Voprosy gorodskogo rasseleniia.* Kiev: "Budivel'nik," 1964, 16–25.

———. "O zakonomernostiakh i tendentsiiakh gorodskogo rasseleniia v SSSR," *Voprosy geografii,* sbornik 66. M. "Mysl'," 1965, 6–33. In English: "On the patterns and tendencies of urban settlement in the USSR," *Soviet geography: review and translation,* vol. 7, no. 1 (January, 1966), 3–31.

———. "Kolichestvennye zakonomernosti rasseleniia otnositel'no mest raboty (v predelakh gorodskikh territorii i lokal'nykh grupp gorodov i poselkov)," in *Problemy rasseleniia, v pomoshch' proektirovshchiku.* Kiev: "Budivel'nik," 1966, 19–34.

———. "Territorial'nye sistemy rasseleniia v SSSR," in *Nauchnye problemy geografii naseleniia.* M. Izd. Moskovskogo universiteta, 1967, 71–86.

———. "Razvitie seti gorodskikh poselenii SSSR za 50 let," *Vestnik Moskovskogo universiteta, seriia 5, geografiia,* 1968, no. 6, 3–11.

———. "Kolichestvennye zakonomernosti rasseleniia otnositel'no mest raboty," in *Rasselenie v gorodakh.* M. "Mysl'," 1968, 5–74.

———. "Zakonomernosti vzaimosviazannogo rasseleniia v lokal'noi gruppe gorodov, poselkov i sel," *Geografiia naseleniia,* vypusk 2. M. Geograficheskoe obshchestvo SSSR, Moskovskii filial, 1968, 11–16.

Davidovich, V. G., Kovalev, S. A., and Pokshishevskii, V. V. "Ob osnovakh klassifikatsii naselennykh punktov SSSR (v sviazi s zadachami ekonomicheskoi geografii)," *Izvestiia AN SSSR, seriia geograficheskaia,* 1959, no. 4, 106–116.

Davidovich, V. G. and Lappo, G. M. "Voprosy razvitiia gorodskikh aglomeratsii v SSSR," in *Sovremennye problemy geografii; nauchnye soobshcheniia sovetskikh geografov po programme XX Mezhdunarodnogo geograficheskogo kongressa (London, 1964.)* M. "Nauka," 1964,

43–49. English abstract: "Problems of the development of urban agglomeration in the USSR," 49.

D'iakonov, Fëdor Vasil'evich. "Nauchnoe soveshchanie po voprosam formirovaniia naseleniia i ispol'zovaniia trudovykh resursov v raionakh Severa SSSR," *Izvestiia AN SSSR, seriia geograficheskaia*, 1966, no. 2, 145–148.

Dubrovin, Pëtr Iosifovich. "Aglomeratsii gorodov (genezis, ekonomika, morfologiia)," *Voprosy geografii*, sbornik 45, M. Geografgiz, 1959, 23–36.

Dzenis, Zigrid Iakubovich. "K voprosu o metodike ekonomgeograficheskogo analiza predposylok razvitiia promyshlennosti v malykh i srednikh gorodakh," *Trudy konferentsii po voprosam razmeshcheniia promyshlennosti i razvitiia gorodov.* Vil'nius: AN Litovskoi SSR, 1963, 151–156.

Dzenis, Z. E., Kolotievskii, A. M., Volrats, U. Ia., Kholtsmanis, A. V., and Barashkov, D. A. "Pasport naselennogo punkta gorodskogo tipa," *Materialy I Mezhduvedomstvennogo soveshchaniia po geografii naseleniia (ianvar'-fevral' 1962 g.)*, vypusk 3, Sektsiia geografii gorodov. Doklady i reziume dokladov. M-L. Geograficheskoe obshchestvo Soiuza SSR, 1961, 115–135. Rotaprint.

Geograficheskoe obshchestvo SSSR. Moskovskii filial. Materialy. *Geografiia naseleniia*, vypusk 1 1967, 45 p., vypusk 2, 1968, 19 p. vypusk 3 (1969), 39 p. (Abstracts of papers).
stracts of papers).

Gokhberg, M. Ia. "Velichina gorodskikh poselenii v neftedobyvaiushchikh raionakh," *Izvestiia VGO*, 1967, no. 6, 483–491.

Gokhman, Veniamin Maksovich, and Lipets, Iulii Grigor'evich. "Some trends in Soviet regional studies," *Regional science association, papers*, vol. 18 (1967), 223–229.

"Gorod," *Bol'shaia sovetskaia entsiklopediia.* M. 1st ed., vol. 18, 1930, 17–159.

"Gorod," *Bol'shaia sovetskaia entsiklopediia.* M. 2nd ed., vol. 12, 1952, 172–209.

Gorod i raion kak ob"ekty geograficheskogo izucheniia; sbornik statei. R. M. Kabo, ed. *Uchenye zapiski Moskovskogo gosudarstvennogo pedagogicheskogo instituta imeni V. I. Lenina*, tom 54, 1949, 188 p.

Goroda feodal'noi Rossii. M. AN SSSR, Institut istorii, 1966. 563 p. (Reviewed by Samuel H. Baron, "The town in 'feudal' Russia," *Slavic review*, vol. 28, no. 1 March, 1969, pp. 116-122.)

Goroda kotorykh ne bylo na karte. (Sbornik.) Georgii Aleksandrovich Mariagin, ed. M. "Sovetskaia Rossiia," 1960, 372 p. (discussion of 13 new cities.)

Gozulov, Avdei Il'ich. "Osnoynye izmeneniia v chislennosti, razmeshchenii, i sostave naseleniia SSSR," *Materialy I Mezhduvedomstven-*

nogo soveshchaniia po geografii naseleniia, vypusk 7. L. Geograficheskoe obshchestvo SSSR, 1965, 12–25. Rotaprint.

Gurevich, Boris Lazarevich. "Plotnost' naseleniia goroda i plotnost' veroiatnosti sluchainoi velichiny," *Vestnik Moskovskogo universiteta, seriia 5, geografiia,* 1967, no. 1, 15–21.

Ianitskii, Nikolai Fedorovich. "Territorial'noe razdelenie truda," chapter 2 in *Metodologicheskie voprosy ekonomicheskoi geografii,* P.M. Alampiev and Ia. G. Feigin, eds. M. Ekonomizdat, 1962, 58–87. Segments in English "The territorial division of labor," *Soviet geography: review & translation,* vol. 4, no. 10. (December 1963), 54–55.

Ivanter, Anna Abramovna. "Opyt izucheniia gorodov na polevoi praktike studentov III kursa," *Uchenye zapiski Moskovskogo gorodskogo pedagogicheskogo instituta imeni Potemkina,* tom 101, Geografiia, vypusk 6, 1959, 207–229.

Kabo, Rafail Mikhailovich. "Naselenie SSSR," chapter 2 in *Geografiia SSSR; posobie dlia uchitelei* N. I. Lialikov, and others, eds. M. Uchpedgiz, 1955, 79–91.

Kargalova, S. F. "Prakticheskie raboty pri izuchenii gorodov SSSR," in *Prakticheskie raboty na urokakh ekonomicheskoi geografii SSSR.* M. Uchpedgiz, 1962, 102–110.

Khauke, Mikhail Ottovich. "Ogranichenie rosta krupnykh gorodov," in *Planirovka i zastroika bol'shikh gorodov.* M. Gostroiizdat, 1961, 5–27.

Khodzhaev, D. G. "Planirovanie razmeshcheniia proizvodstva v naselennykh punktakh i nekotorye problemy geografii naseleniia," in *Nauchnye problemy geografii naseleniia.* M. Izd. Moskovskogo universiteta, 1967, 7–19. In English: "The planning of the distribution of production in population centers and some problems in population geography," *Soviet geography: review and translation,* vol. 8, no. 8 (October, 1967), 619–629.

———. "Problemy razvitiia gorodov i nauka o narodonaselenii," in *Narodonaselenie i ekonomika,* D. I. Valentei, and others, eds. M. Izd. "Ekonomika," 1967, 37–50.

Khorev, Boris Sergeevich. "Obzor raboty Komissii geografii naseleniia i gorodov Moskovskogo filiala Geograficheskogo obshchestva Soiuza SSR (1945–1957 gg.)," *Voprosy geografii,* sbornik 45. M. Geografgiz, 1959, 227–245.

———. "Itogi diskussi, posviashchennoi gorodam-sputnikam," in *Goroda-sputniki; sbornik statei.* M. Geografgiz, 1961, 173–178.

———. "K voprosu o meste geografii naseleniia i naselennykh punktov v sisteme geograficheskikh nauk (v poriadke obsuzhdeniia)," *Voprosy geografii,* sbornik 56. M. Geografgiz, 1962, 178–181.

———. "Novye goroda Sovetskogo Soiuza," *Geografiia v shkole,* 1963, no. 6. 5-10.

———. "Issledovanie funktsional'noi struktury gorodskikh poselenii SSSR (v sviazi s zadachami ikh ekonomiko- geograficheskoi tipologii," *Voprosy geografii,* sbornik 66, M. "Mysl," 1965. 34–58. In English: "A study of the functional structure of urban places of the USSR (in connection with the tasks of an economic-geographic typology)," *Soviet geography: review and translation,* vol, 7, no. 1 (January, 1966), 31–51.

———. "Opyt kolichestvennoi otsenki uslovii zhizni naseleniia nebol'-shkikh gorodov," *Vestnik Moskovskogo universiteta, seriia 5, geografiia,* 1966, no. 6, 52–55.

———. "Narodokhoziaistvennaia struktura gorodov kak osnovnoi element ihk tipologii," in *Problemy rasseleniia.* Kiev: "Budivel'nik," 1966, 12–19.

———. "Poselki gorodskogo tipa i prochie naselennye punkty kak rezerv popolneniia seti gorodov," *Izvestiia VGO,* 1966, no. 6, 494–499.

———. "Goroda rozhdennye oktiabrem (ob izmeneniiakh v seti gorodov SSSR za 50 let)," *Geografiia v shkole,* 1967, no. 4, 9–18.

———. "Funktsional'naia tipologiia malykh i srednikh gorodov i puti razvitiia gorodov razlichnogo tipa," in *Puti razvitiia malykh i srednikh gorodov tsentral'nikh ekonomicheskikh raionov,* M. "Nauka," 1967, 20–48.

———. "Problemy razvitiia gorodov i ispol'zovaniia trudovykh resursov: soveshchanie v Vil'niuse," *Izvestiia AN, seriia geograficheskaia,* 1968, no. 4, 148–150.

———. *Gorodskie poseleniia SSSR (problemy rosta i ikh izuchenie); ocherki geografii rasseleniia.* M. Izd. "Mysl'," 1968. 254 p.

Kibal'chich, Oleg Alekseevich. "Nekotorye osobennosti passazhirskikh sviazei krupnykh gorodov SSSR," *Voprosy geografii,* sbornik 66. M. Izd. "Mysl'," 1965, 141–152.

———. "Voprosy geografii naseleniia i perspektivnoe planirovanie passazhirskikh perevozok," *Materialy I Mezhduvedomstvennogo soveshchaniia po geografii naseleniia,* vypusk 7. L. Geograficheskoe obshchestvo SSSR, 1965, 26–33. Rotaprint.

Knobel'sdorf, Eduard Vil'gel'movich. "Tipologiia sovetskikh gorodov i zadachi ikh ekonomiko-geograficheskogo izucheniia," *Materialy gertsenoviskikh chtenii 1955 g. Uchenye zapiski Leningradskogo gosudarstvennogo pedagogicheskogo instituta imeni A. I. Gertsena,* tom 111, 1955, 194–199.

———. "Sovremennye problemy geografii sovetskikh gorodov," *Voprosy geografii gorodov Pribaltiki.* Publikatsii Estonskogo geograficheskogo obshchestva, 5. Tallin: Izd. AN Estonskoi SSR, 1962, 5–25. English summary: "The problem of Soviet urban geography at its present stage of development," 24–25.

———. "O sinteticheskoi tipologii sovetskikh gorodov," *Izvestiia VGO,* 1965, no. 2, 119–127.

———. "Raionoobrazuiushchaia rol' gorodov i krupnykh sel'skikh pose-lenii," in *Geografiia naseleniia i naselennykh punktov SSSR*, L. "Na-uka," 1967, 69–89. English abstract: "Region-forming role of towns and large rural settlements," 88–89.

Kolotijevski, A. (Kolotievskii, Anton Mikhailovich). "O sisteme raionno-gorodskikh vzaimosviazei i ikh arealakh," *Voprosy geografii gorodov Pribaltiki*. Publikatsii Estonskogo geograficheskogo obshchestva, 5, 1962, 34–54. English summary: "On the system of district-and-town interrelations and their areas," 51–54.

———. "K voprosu o roli prirodnykh uslovii i resursov v formirovanii i razvitii gorodskikh poselenii," *Zinatn. raksti. Latv. Univ.* (Uchenye zapiskogo Latviiskogo universiteta), vol. 75 1966, 174–179.

Komar, Igor' Valer'ianovich, Pomus, M. I., and Riazantsev, S. N. "O vnutrioblastnom raionirovanii," *Materialy k III s"ezdu geografiche-skogo obshchestva soiuza SSR*. L. Geograficheskoe obshchestvo SSSR, 1959. Especially pp. 7–9. Rotaprint. In English "Intra-oblast regionali-zation," in *Soviet geography: review translation*, vol. 1, no. 8. (Oc-tober 1960), 16–22.

Konstantinov, Oleg Arkad'evich. "K voprosu ob ekonomiko-geogra-ficheskom izuchenii gorodov SSSR," *Trudy geografo-ekonomicheskogo nauchno-issledovatel'skogo instituta pri LGU*, vypusk 2, L., 1934, 8–33.

———. "Osnovnye problemy ekonomiko-geograficheskogo izucheniia gorodov SSSR," *Trudy pervogo Vsesoiuznogo geograficheskogo s"ezda*, vypusk 4, L. 1934, 67–95.

———. "Opyt izucheniia vliianiia osobennostei raiona na kharakter gorodskikh poselenii," *Trudy Leningradskogo instituta inzhenerno-kommunal'nogo stroitel'stva*, vypusk 3. L. 1936.

———. "Geograficheskie sdvigi v razmeshchenii bol'shikh gorodov SSSR," *Izvestiia VGO*, 1941, no. 1, 23–30.

———. "Ob ekonomiko-geograficheskom polozhenii gorodov," *Geografiia v shkole*, 1941, no. 3, 56–61.

———. "Geograficheskie razlichiia v dinamike gorodskogo naseleniia SSSR," *Izvestiia VGO*, 1943, no. 6, 11–25.

———. "Ekonomiko-geograficheskoe polozhenie bol'shikh gorodov SSSR," *Izvestiia VGO*, 1946, no. 2, 171–182.

———. "Izmeneniia v geografii gorodov SSSR za sovetskii period," *Vo-prosy geografii*, sbornik 6, M. Geografgiz, 1947, 11–46.

———. "Amerikanskaia klassifikatsiia sovetskikh gorodov," *Izvestiia VGO*, 1947, no. 2, 218–223.

———. "Problema ekonomiko-geograficheskoi klassifikatsii gorodov," *Vtoroi Vsesoiuznyi geograficheskii s"ezd. Tezisy dokladov po sektsii ekonomischeskoi geografii*. M-L. Izd. AN SSSR, 1947.

———. "O tak nazyvaemom 'zakone pervenstvuiushchego gorod' (giper-trofiia glavnykh gorodov)," *Izvestiia VGO*, 1949, no. 2, 198–212.

———. "Tempy rosta gorodov SSSR i kapitalisticheskikh stran," *Izvestiia VGO,* 1949, no. 6, 577–583.

———. "Novye gorodskie poseleniia pervoi poslevoennoi piatiletki i ikh geograficheskoe razmeshchenie," *Izvestiia VGO,* 1952, no. 2.

———. "Goroda i gorodskoe naselenie SSSR k nachalu shestoi piatiletki," *Geografiia v shkole,* 1956, no. 5, 5–13.

———. "Ogranichenie rosta gorodov kak faktor pravil'nogo razmeshcheniia promyshlennosti," in *Voprosy geografii; sbornik statei dlia XVIII Mezhdunarodnogo geograficheskogo kongressa.* M-L. AN SSSR, 1956, 319–326. In French: "Limitation de l'accroisement des villes comme facteur de la répartition rationnelle de l'industrie," in *Essais de géographie; recueil des articles pour le XVIIIe congrès international géographique.* M-L.: Éditions de l'Académie des Sciences de l'URSS, 1956, 332–340.

———. "Novye gorodskie poseleniia SSSR perioda Velikoi Otechestvennoi voiny," *Nauchnye zapiski Leningradskogo finansovo-ekonomicheskogo instituta,* Kafedra ekonomicheskoi geografii, vypusk 12, 1956, 67-137. (Bibliography, pp. 133–137, 112 entries).

———. "O klassifikatsii gorodov v ekonomicheskoi geografii," *Voprosy geografii,* sbornik 41, M. Geografgiz, 1957, 65–92.

———. "Sovremennoe sostoianie deleniia naselennykh punktov SSSR na gorodskie i sel'skie," *Izvestiia AN SSSR, seriia geograficheskaia,* 1958, no. 6, 69–78.

———. "Nekotorye vyvody o geografii gorodov i gorodskogo naseleniia SSSR iz itogov perepisi 1959 goda," *Izvestiia AN SSSR, seriia geograficheskaia,* 1959, no. 6, 44–56. In English: "Some conclusions about the geography of cities and the urban population of the USSR based on the results of the 1959 census," *Soviet geography: review and translation,* vol. 1, no. 7 (September, 1960), 59–75.

———. "Istoriia formirovaniia v SSSR geografii gorodov kak osoboi otrasli geograficheskikh znanii (Materialy k dokladu Geograficheskoe izuchenie gorodskikh poselenii v SSSR)," in *Materialy po geografii naseleniia,* vypusk 1. L. Geograficheskoe obshchestvo Soiuza SSR. Otdelenie ekonomicheskoi geografii, 1962, 109–151. Rotaprint.

———. "Tipologiia i klassifikatsiia gorodskikh poselenii v sovetskoi ekonomiko-geograficheskoi nauke," in *Materialy po geografii naseleniia,* vypusk 2, L. Geografisheskoe obshchestvo SSSR, Komissiia geografii naseleniia i gorodov, 1963, 5–53. Rotaprint. (Bibliography of 93 items).

———. "Nekotorye itogi Pervogo Mezhduvedomstvennogo soveshchaniia po geografii naseleniia (Moskva, 30 ianvaria-3 fevralia, 1962 g.)", *Izvestiia VGO,* 1963, no. 1, 32–40.

———. "O seti gorodov na territoriiakh, voshedshikh v sostav SSSR s 1939 g.", *Izvestiia AN SSSR, seriia geografisheskaia,* 1963, no. 4, 23–34. In English: "The network of cities in areas annexed by the USSR since 1939," *Soviet geography; review and translation,* vol. 5, no. 1 (January, 1964), 26–39.

———. "Geograficheskoe izuchenie gorodskikh poselenii v SSSR," in *Geografiia naseleniia v SSSR; osnovnye problemy.* M-L. Izd. "Nauka," 1964, 32–68.

———. "Sravnitel'naia kharakteristika tipov poselenii SSSR," in *Sovremennye problemy geografii; nauchnye soobshcheniia sovetskikh geografov po programme XX Mezhdunarodnogo geograficheskogo kongressa (London, 1964).* M. Izd. "Nauka," 1964, 38–43. English abstract: "Comparative characteristics of settlement types in the USSR," 43.

———. "Izuchenie seti gorodskikh poselenii SSSR v sovetskoi ekonomiko-geograficheskoi nauke," in *Materialy I Mezhduvedomstvennogo soveshchaniia po geografii naseleniia,* vypusk 7. L. Geograficheskoe obshchestvo SSSR, 1965, 69–96. Rotaprint.

———. "Wissenschaftliche Grundprobleme der sowjetischen Stadtgeographie," *Geographische Berichte,* vol. 10, no. 36 (1965, no. 3), 202–211.

———. "Dinamika i razmeshchenie malykh gorodov SSSR," *Voprosy geografii naseleniia* Uchenye zapiski Leningradskogo gos. pedagogicheskogo instituta im. A. I. Gertsena, tom 279. L. 1966, 4–24.

———. "Migratsiia naseleniia iz sel'skikh mestnostei v goroda, kak faktor ekonomicheskogo razvitiia i privedeniia proportsii mezhdu gorodskim i sel'skim naseleniem v sootvetstvie s obshchim urovnem proizvoditel'nykh sil," in *Voprosy narodonaseleniia i demograficheskoi statistiki; doklady sovetskikh uchenykh i spetsialistov na Vsemirnoi konferentsii OON po Voprosam narodonaseleniia 1965 goda.* P. G. Pod"iachikh and others, eds. M. "Statistika," 1966, 96–106. In English: "Rural-urban migration as a factor of economic development and adjustment of the ratio of urban-rural population to the general level of productive forces," *Proceedings of the World population conference Belgrade, 30 August–10 September 1965.* vol. 4, *Selected papers and summaries: migration, urbanization, economic development* (United Nations, Department of economic and social affairs). New York: United Nations (66.XIII.8), 1967, 499–504.

———. "Nekotorye itogi II Vsesoiuznogo mezhduvedomstvennogo soveshchaniia po geografii naseleniia," *Izvestiia VGO,* 1967, no. 3, 223–229. In English: "Some results of the second national interagency conference on population geography," *Soviet geography: review and translation,* vol. 8, no. 8 (October, 1967), 652–660.

———. "Opyt vyiavleniia raionov rasseleniia SSSR," in *Geografiia naseleniia i naselennykh punktov SSSR.* L. Izd. "Nauka," 1967, 5–68. English abstract: "An experiment in definition of settlement regions in the USSR," 67–68.

———. "Raionirovanie rasseleniia SSSR," in *Nauchnye problemy geografii naseleniia.* M. Izd. Moskovskogo universiteta, 1967, 48–70.

Korovitsyn, Vasilii Petrovich. "Karta razvitiia seti gorodskikh poselenii SSSR (za 1926–1959 gg.)", *Vestnik Moskovskogo universiteta, seriia 5, geografiia,* 1961, no. 6, 18–24.

———. "Sdvigi v geografii gorodskikh poselenii SSSR (1926–1959 gg.)", *Izvestiia AN SSSR, seriia geograficheskaia,* 1961, no. 6, 47–68.

———. "Voprosy kartografirovaniia naseleniia," in *Geografiia naseleniia v SSSR; osnovnye problemy.* M-L. Izd. "Nauka," 1964, 94–105.

Kosheleva, E. S. "Izuchenie gorodov v kurse geografii dorevoliutsionnoi shkoly," *Uchenye zapiski Leningradskogo gosudarstvennogo pedagogicheskogo instituta imeni A. I. Gertsena,* tom 206, 1962, 297–308.

Kovalëv, Sergei Aleksandrovich. "Razvitie seti gorodskikh poselenii v sovetskom soiuze za pervye tri goda piatoi piatiletki, *Geografiia v shkole,* 1954, no. 6, 1–8. In German: "Die Entwicklung des Netzes der städtischen Siedlungen in der Sowjetunion in den ersten drei Jahren des fünften Fünfjahrplans," *Petermanns geographische Mitteilungen,* vol. 99, no. 2 1955, 159–163.

———. "Sdvigi v geografii naseleniia SSSR za 40 let," *Geografiia v shkole,* 1957, no. 5, 11–22.

———. *Geograficheskoe izuchenie sel'skogo rasselennia (zadachi, metodika, materialy, spets. karty rasseleniia).* M. Moskovskii universitet. Geograficheskii fakul'tet Kafedra ekonomicheskoi geografii SSSR, 1960. 340 p.

———. "Izmeneniia v geografii sel'skikh raionnykh tsentrov SSSR (1954–1960 gg.)", *Geografiia i khoziaistvo,* sbornik 10, 1961, 24–28.

———. "Geografiia naseleniia v Moskovskom universitete," *Vestnik Moskovskogo universiteta, seriia 5, geografiia,* 1961, no. 6, 9–17.

———. "Tipy poselenii – raionnykh tsentrov SSSR," *Voprosy geografii,* sbornik 56. M. Geografgiz, 1962, 54–72.

———. "O rabote pervogo Mezhduvedomstvennogo nauchnogo soveshchaniia po geografii naseleniia (30 ianvaria-3 fevralia 1962 g.)," *Vestnik Moskovskogo universiteta, seriia 5, geografiia,* 1962, no. 3, 67–69.

———. *Sel'skoe rasselenie (geograficheskoe issledovanie).* M. Izd. Moskovskogo universiteta, 1963. 370 p.

———. "Geografiia potrebleniia i geografiia obsluzhivaniia naseleniia," *Vestnik Moskovskogo universiteta, seriia 5, geografiia,* 1966, no. 2, 3–10. In English: "A geography of consumption and a geography of services," *Soviet geography: review and translation,* vol. 7, no. 7 (September, 1966), 65–73.

———. "Voprosy geografii obsluzhivaniia naseleniia," in *Geografiia naseleniia,* vypusk 1. M. Geograficheskoe obshchestvo, Moskovskii filial, 1967, 33–37.

———. "Mezhvuzovskoe soveshchanie po problemam migratsii naseleniia, Rostov 18–20 maia 1967 g.," *Vestnik Moskovskogo universiteta, seriia 5, geografiia,* 1967, no. 6, 115–116.

———. "Izmeneniia v razmeshchenii naseleniia SSSR za gody sotsialisticheskogo stroitel'stva," *Vestnik Moskovskogo universiteta, seriia 5, geografiia*, 1968, no. 3, 3–13. English abstract: "Changes in population distribution in the U.S.S.R. during the years of socialist construction," 13.

Kovalëv, S. A., Liamin, E. A., and Pekel', Anna I. "Ob izuchenii migratsionnykh sviazei gorodov SSSR," *Voprosy geografii*, sbornik 38. M. Geografgiz, 1956, 196–210.

Kovalëv, S. A. and Pokshishevskii, V. V. "Geografiia naseleniia i geografiia obsluzhivaniia," in *Nauchnye problemy geografii naseleniia.* M. Izd. Moskovskogo universiteta, 1967, 34–47. In English: "The geography of population and the geography of services," *Soviet geography: review & translation*, vol. 8, no. 8 (October, 1967), 641–652.

Koval'skaia, Natalia Iakovlevna. "Ekonomiko-geograficheskoe izuchenie goroda," chapter 3 in her *Metodika ekonomiko-geograficheskikh issledovanii (uchebnoe posobie dlia geograficheskikh fakul'tetov universitetov).* M. Izd. MGU, 1963, 131–167.

———. "Krupnomasshtabnoe izuchenie gorodov," in *Sovremennaia geografiia v period stroitel'stva kommunizma.* M. Geografgiz, 1963, 203–212.

"Kratkaia promyshlennaia kharakteristika gorodov i poselenii gorodskogo tipy," *Trudy tsentral'nogo statisticheskogo upravleniia*, tom 22, vypusk 2. M. 1926.

Kudriavstev, Orest Konstantinovich. "Passazhirskie sviazi gorodov-sputnikov," in *Goroda-sputniki; sbornik statei.* M. Geografgiz, 1961, 150–165.

———. "Izuchenie plotnosti naseleniia v gorodakh i prigorodakh," *Voprosy geografii*, sbornik 56. M. Geografgiz, 1962, 173–177.

Lappo, Georgii Mikhailovich. "Izuchenie gorodskikh aglomeratsii," in *Sovremennaia geografiia v period stroitel'stva kommunizma,* M. Geografgiz, 1963, 213–224.

———. "Problemy malykh gorodov," in *Narodonaselenie i ekonomika,* M. Izd. "Ekonomika," 1967, 170–186.

———. "Formirovanie seti gorodskikh poselenii SSSR i sdvigi v razmeshchenii naseleniia strany," *Voprosy geografii*, sbornik 75, M. "Mysl'," 1968. 107–128. English summary.

Lappo, G. M., and Listengurt, F. M. "O putiakh razvitiia v SSSR gorodov raznykh tipov," in *Nauchnye problemy geografii naseleniia,* M. Izd. Moskovskogo universiteta, 1967, 113–124.

Lappo, G. M. and Troitskaia, E. Kh. "Puti razvitiia krupnykh gorodov v SSSR," in *Nauchny problemy geografii naseleniia.* M. Izd. Moskovskogo universiteta, 1967, 125–137.

Lialikov, Nikolai Ivanovich. *Geografiia naseleniia SSSR.* M. Tip. Gosfinizdata, 1946, 24 p.

———. "Ocherki po geografii naseleniia SSSR," *Geografiia v shkole*, 1948, no. 2, 15–23; no. 3, 4–14; 1948, no. 5, 1–14; 1949, no. 2, 3–13; and 1949, no. 3, 19–32.

——. "O geograficheskom izuchenii goroda," *Moskovskii gosudarstvennyi pedagogicheskii institut imeni Lenina. Uchenye Zapiski,* tom 54; geograficheskii fakul'tet, vypusk 1, Gorod i raion kak ob"ekty geograficheskogo izucheniia. R. M. Kabo, ed. M. 1949, 135–152.

——. "Geografiia naseleniia SSSR," in *Ekonomicheskaia geografiia SSSR: obshchaia kharakteristika i geografiia otraslei narodnogo khoziaistva SSSR,* G. N. Cherdantsev, and others, eds. M. Uchpedgiz, 1958, 68–91.

Liashchenko, Petr Ivanovich. *Istoriia narodnogo khoziaistva SSSR.* M. 1939; 2nd ed. M. Gospolitizdat, 1947–1948, 2 vols.; 3rd ed., 1952; 4th ed., 1956. First edition in English as Peter I. Lyashchenko, *History of the national economy of Russia to the 1917 revolution.* New York: Macmillan, 1949. 880 p.

Listengurt, Feliks Mikhailovich. "Nekotorye izmeneniia v geografii naseleniia SSSR s 1939 po 1956 g. (opyt ischisleniia sdvigov)," *Moskovskii gosudarstvennyi pedagogicheskii institut imeni Lenina. Uchenye zapiski,* tom 117, Ekonomicheskaia geografiia SSSR, vypusk 5, 1960.

——. "Perspektivnye izmeneniia gorodskogo naseleniia v SSSR," *Izvestiia AN SSSR, seriia geograficheskaia,* 1969, no. 1, 59–68.

Lizogub, Vladimir Kipriianovich. "Sud'ba byvshikh 'fabrichnykh sel' v sovetskii period," *Doklady po geografii naseleniia* (Geograficheskoe obshchestvo SSSR, Komissiia geografii naseleniia i gorodov), vypusk 2 (4). L. Geograficheskoe obshchestvo SSSR, 1964, 2–14.

——. "Gradoobrazovanie, kategorii gorodov i drugikh gorodskikh poselenii," *Geografiia v shkole,* 1966, no. 2, 74–76.

Lopatina, Elena Brunovna, Tikhonov, A. V., and Shatsilo, E. S. "Vsesoiuznoe soveshchanie po geografii naseleniia," *Izvestiia AN SSSR, seriia geograficheskaia,* 1962, no. 3, 144–148.

Lukhmanov, D. N. "Stepen' reguliarnosti seti obsluzhivaniia," *Voprosy geografii,* sbornik 77. M. Izd. "Mysl'," 1968, 136–147. English abstract, "The extent of regularity in networks of different service establishments," 204.

Maergoiz, Isaak Moiseevich. "K ekonomiko-geograficheskomu izucheniiu gorodov," *Voprosy geografii,* sbornik 38. M. Geografgiz, 1956, 5–26.

——. "Nekotorye voprosy izucheniia ekonomiko-geograficheskogo polozheniia gorodov SSSR," *Materialy vtorogo mezhduvedomstvennogo soveshchaniia po geografii naseleniia,* vypusk 1. M. Geograficheskoe obshchestvo Soiuza SSR, Moskovskii filial, 1968, 92–96.

Makhrachev, A. Ia. *Osnovnye printsipy sotsialisticheskogo rasseleniia i rost gorodskikh poselenii v SSSR i USSR.* Kiev: AN USSR, 1964. 41 p.

Markus, B. L. "Naselenie SSSR i ego razmeshchenie," chapter 4 in *Ekonomicheskaia geografiia SSSR,* S. S. Bal'zak, V. F. Vasiutin, and Ia. G. Feigin, eds. M. Gossotsekizd., Chast' I, 1940, 129–154. In English: "The population of the USSR and its distribution," chapter 4 in *Economic geography of the USSR.* New York: Macmillan, 1949, 167–200.

Matematika v ekonomicheskoi geografii. Voprosy geografii, sbornik 77. Iu. V. Medvedkov and Iu. G. Saushkin, eds. M. "Mysl'," 1968. 208 p. Supplementary English title, table of contents and abstracts: Mathematics in economic geography, *Problems in geography,* volume 77.

Materialy I mezhduvedomstvennogo soveshchaniia po geografii naseleniia, vypusk 7. L. Geograficheskoe obshchestvo SSSR, 1965. 190 p. Rotaprint. (Contains reports of discussions and a checklist of places of publication of papers presented at First Inter-agency conference on geography of population, Moscow, 1962.)

Materialy vtorogo mezhduvedomstvennogo soveshchaniia po geografii naseleniia (Moskva, 30-ianv.-4 fevr. 1967g.), vypusk 1. Plenarnye zasedaniia; simposiumy: pervyi, vtoroi i tretii. M. Geograficheskoe obshchestvo Soiuza SSR, Moskovskii filial, 1968. 277 p. "Vtoroi simpozium: Puti razvitiia gorodov raznykh tipov," 90–183 (abstracts of 44 papers in urban geography presented at the Second Inter-agency conference on the geography of population, Moscow, 1967).

Matlin, I. S. "Modeli optimal'noi organizatsii seti obsluzhivaniia v raione," *Voprosy geografii,* sbornik 77. M. Izd. "Mysl'," 1968, 123–135. In English: "Models of an optimally organized network of service establishments in a region," *Soviet geography: review and translation,* vol. 10, no. 9 (November, 1969), 537–548.

Matveev, Gennadii Petrovich. "O dissertatsiiakh, posviashchennykh gorodam," *Voprosy geografii,* sbornik 38. M. Geografgiz, 1956, 246–247.

———. "Dissertatsii po geografii naseleniia i gorodam," *Voprosy geografii,* sbornik 45. M. Geografgiz, 1959, 267–269.

Medvedkov, Iurii Vladimirovich. "O razmerakh gorodov, ob"edinennykh v sistemu" in *Kolichestvennye metody issledovaniia v ekonomicheskoi geografii* (sbornik dokladov na seminare), I. M. Maergoiz, ed. M. VINITI, 1964, 90–121. Rotaprint.

———. "Matematika v mikrogeografii gorodov (odna iz glav spetsial'noi teorii kul'turnogo landshafta)", in AN SSSR, Institut nauchnoi informatsii. *Geograficheskii sbornik,* 2 (Metody geograficheskogo izucheniia. Ispol'zovanie prirodnykh resursov). M. VINITI, 1966, 27–56.

———. "Reguliarnaia komponenta v setiakh rasseleniia izobrazhennykh na karte," *Izvestiia AN SSSR, seriia geograficheskaia,* 1966, no. 4, 110–122. In English: "The regular component in settlement patterns as shown on a map," *Soviet geography: review & translation,* vol. 8, no. 3 (March 1967), 150–168.

———. "Prilozheniia matematiki v geografii naseleniia," in *Nauchnye problemy geografii naseleniia.* M. Izd. Moskovskogo universiteta, 1967, 225–237. In English: "Applications of mathematics to population geography," *Soviet geography: review and translation,* vol. 8, no. 9 (November, 1967), 709–722.

———. "The concept of entropy in settlement pattern analysis," *Regional science association, papers,* vol. 18 (1967), 165–168.

————. "Topologicheskii analiz setei naselennykh mest," *Voprosy geografii*, sbornik 77. M. Izd. "Mysl'," 1968, 159–167. In English: "An application of topology in central place analysis," *Regional science association, papers*, vol. 20. 1968, 77–84.

Mikhailov, Nikolai Nikolaevich, "The new distribution of the population," in his *Soviet geography: the new industrial and economic distributions of the U.S.S.R.* London: Methuen, 1935, 199–220.

————. "New towns," in his *Glimpses of the U.S.S.R.: its economy and geography*. M. Foreign languages publishing house, 1960, 112–115.

Mikhailov, N. N. with the collaboration of V. V. Pokshishevskii. *Soviet Russia: the land and its people*. New York: Sheridan house, 1948 (descriptions of many cities).

Mints, Aleksei Aleksandrovich. "Osnovnye izmeneniia v geografii naseleniia SSSR za poslednie desiatiletiia (po itogam Vsesoiuznoi perepisi naseleniia 1959 g.), *Voprosy geografii*, sbornik 71. M. "Mysl'," 1966, 4–19.

Mints, A. A., and Khorev, B. S. "Nekotorye voprosy ekonomiko-geograficheskoi tipologii gorodov," in *Voprosy geografii naseleniia SSSR; Sbornik statei k I mezhduvedomstvennomu soveshchaniiu po geografii naseleniia*. M. Institut geografii AN SSSR, Otdel geografii SSSR, 1961, 44–70. Rotaprint.

Mongait, Aleksandr L'vovich. *Arkheologia v SSSR*. M. Izd. AN SSSR, 1955. 433 p. In English: *Archeology in the U.S.S.R.* Translated by David Skvirsky. M. Foreign languages publishing house, 1959. 427 p., or *Archeology in the U.S.S.R.* Translated and adapted by M. W. Thompson. Harmondsworth, England, or Baltimore, Maryland: Penguin books, 1961. 313 p.

Moskvin, D. D. "Problema gorodov," chapter 8 in *Metodologicheskie voprosy ekonomicheskoi geografii*. P. M. Alampiev and Ia. G. Feigin, eds. M. Ekonomizdat, 1962, 222–239. Segments translated as: "VIII. The problem of cities," in *Soviet geography: review and translation*, vol. 4, no. 10 (December, 1963), 69–70.

Nikitin, Nikolai Pavlovich, Prozorov, E. D., and Tutykhin, B. A., eds. *Ekonomicheskaia geografia SSSR*. M. Izd. "Prosveshchenie," 1966. Heading: "Naselenie" in each republic or region; index for individual cities.

Nikol'skii, Igor' Vladimirovich. *Geografiia transporta SSSR*. M. Geografgiz, 1960. 406 p. Extensive excerpts published in English as: "Railroad freight traffic of the USSR," *Soviet geography: review and translation*, vol. 2, no. 6 (June, 1961), 39–92.

————. "Geografiia transporta Kazakhstana," *Geografiia i khoziaistvo*, sbornik 3–4, 1958, 47–54. In English as "The geography of transportation of Kazakhstan," *Soviet geography: review and translation*, vol. 2, no. 3 (March, 1961), 44–54.

Nõmmik, S. (Nymmik, Sal'ma Ianovna). "K voprosu izucheniia khinterlanda goroda," *Voprosy geografii gorodov pribaltiki*. Publikatsii

Estonskogo geograficheskogo obshchestva, 5, 1962, 55–72. English summary: "On the study of the hinterland of towns," 69–72.

——. "Regional'nye sistemy poselenii kak karkas raionoobrazovaniia," *Vestnik Moskovskogo universiteta, seriia 5, geografiia,* 1969, no. 3, 33–45. English abstract: "Regional systems of settlement as a framework of regionalization," 45.

Orekhov, Vladimir Mikhailovich. "Osnovnye zadachi razvitiia gorodov na sovremennom etape," *Gradostroitel'stvo. Planirovka i zastroika gorodov,* Kiev: "Budivel'nik," 1966, 5–14.

Osnovy sovetskogo gradostroitel'stva. tom 1. *Rasselenie i regulirovanie rosta gorodov; planirovka novykh gorodov; rekonstruktsiia gorodov; gorodskoe dvizhenie i transport.* M. Stroiizdat, 1966. 415 p.

Osnovy sovetskogo gradostroitel'stva. tom 2. *Planirovka i zastroika promyshlennykh raionov; planirovka i zastroika zhilykh raionov, kul'turno-bytovoe obsluzhivanie naseleniia; ozelenie gorodov.* M. Stroiizdat, 1967. 343 p.

Pavchinskii, Boris Rostislavovich. "Problemy razvitiia malykh gorodov (v poriadke obsuzhdeniia)," *Doklady po geografii naseleniia* (Geograficheskoe obshchestvo SSSR. Komissiia geografii naseleniia i gorodov), vypusk 2 (4). L. Geograficheskoe obshchestvo SSSR, 1965, 15–33.

Perevedentsev, Viktor Ivanovich. "Voprosy metodiki izucheniia sovremennoi migratsii naseleniia v SSSR," in *Voprosy trudovykh resursov v raionakh Sibiri.* Novosibirsk: Sibirskoe otdelenie AN SSSR, 1961, 128–145.

——. "Nekotorye voprosy metodiki izucheniia migratsii naseleniia," *Voprosy geografii naseleniia SSSR; Sbornik statei k I Mezhduvedomstvennomu soveshchaniiu po geografii naseleniia.* M. Institut geografii AN SSSR. Otdel geografii SSSR, 1961, 72–92. Rotaprint.

——. "O vliianii etnicheskikh faktorov na territorial'noe pereraspredelenie naseleniia," *Izvestiia AN SSSR, seriia geograficheskaia,* 1965, no. 4, 31–39. In English: "The influence of ethnic factors on the territorial redistribution of population," *Soviet geography: review and translation,* vol. 6, no. 8 (October, 1965), 40–50.

Perevendentsev, V. I., and Zaionchkovskaia, Z. A. *Sovremennaia migratsiia naseleniia Krasnoiarskogo kraia.* Novosibirsk, 1964. 104 p.

Pod"iachikh, Petr Gavrilovich. "Pokazateli territorial'nykh itogov Vsesoiuznoi perepisi naseleniia 1959 g.," *Materialy I Mezhduvedomstvennogo soveshchaniia po geografii naseleniia,* vypusk 7, L. Geograficheskoe obshchestvo SSSR, 1965, 5–11. Rotaprint.

Pokshishevskii, Vadim Viacheslavovich. "O probleme vnutrigorodskoi khoziaistvennoi geografii," *Kommunal'noe delo,* 1929, no. 7.

——. "O kraevednoi rabote po kompleksnomu izucheniiu gorodov," *Sovetskoe kraevedenie,* 1931, no. 2.

——. "Grafo-analiticheskie metody v izuchenii gorodov i ikh planirovke," *Planirovka i stroitel'stvo gorodov,* 1935, no. 2.

——. "O nektotorykh zadachakh kompleksnykh fiziko-geograficheskikh issledovanii gorodov," *Voprosy geografii*, sbornik 28. M. Geografgiz, 1952, 177–191.

———. "Opyt postanovki kursa geografii gorodov na geograficheskom fakul'tete MGU," *Voprosy geografii*, sbornik 38. M. Geografgiz, 1956, 223–231.

———. "Vnutrennie migratsii naseleniia, kak ob"ekt geograficheskogo izucheniia," *Voprosy geografii. Sbornik statei dlia XVIII Mezhdunarodnogo geograficheskogo kongressa.* M-L. AN SSSR, 1956, 249–260. In French: "Les migrations intérieures en tant qu'objet d'étude géographique," in *Essais de géographie; recueil des articles pour le XVIIIe congrès international géographique.* M–L. Éditions de l'académie des sciences de l'URSS, 1956, 260–271.

———. "Nekotorye voprosy mikro-geograficheskogo izucheniia gorodov SSSR," *Geograficheskii sbornik,* sbornik 11. Ekonomicheskaia geografiia (Geograficheskoe obshchestvo Soiuza SSR). M–L. Izd. AN SSSR, 1957, 90–109.

———. *Zaselenie Sibiri; istoriko-geograficheskii ocherk.* Irkutsk: Irkutskoe oblastnoe gosudarstvennoe izd., 1959. 208 p.

———. "V poiskakh 'ierarkhii' gorodov," *Voprosy Geografii,* sbornik 45. M. Geografgiz, 1959, 259–263.

———. "Geografiia naseleniia i naselennykh punktov," in *Sovetskaia geografiia: itogi i zadachi.* M. Geografgiz, 1960, 232–244. In English: "Geography of population and populated points," in *Soviet geography: accomplishments and tasks.* N. Y.: American Geographical Society, 1962, 141–150.

———. "Geografiia naseleniia," *Kratkaia geograficheskaia entsiklopediia,* tom 1. M. 1960, 428–429.

———. "Rizhskoe soveshchanie po geografii naseleniia. (22–27 avg. 1961 g.)," *Izvestiia AN SSSR, seriia geograficheskaia,* 1961, no. 6, 154–157.

———. "Predmet, sostoianie i zadachi geografii naseleniia," *Materialy I Mezhduvedomstvennogo soveshchaniia po geografii naseleniia (ianvar'-fevral' 1962 g.). Vypusk 1. Doklady i reziume dokladov na plenume.* M-L. Geograficheskoe obshchestvo Soiuza SSR, 1961, 1–25.

———. "Tipy gorodskikh i sel'skikh poselenii SSSR i teorii 'gorodov-tsentral'nykh mest'," *XIX Mezhdunarodnyii geograficheskii kongress v Stokgol'me.* (AN SSSR. Natsional'nyi komitet sovetskikh geografov). M. Izd. AN SSSR, 1961, 240–244.

———. "Naselennye punkty — mestnye tsentry i problemy ikh sopodchineniia," *Voprosy geografii,* sbornik 56. M. Geografgiz, 1962, 30–53.

———. "Perspektivy migratsii naseleniia v SSSR (voprosy metodiki postroeniia rabochei gipotezy)," in *Geografiia naseleniia Vostochnoi Sibiri.* M. Izd. AN SSSR, 1962, 63–81.

———. "Geografiia naseleniia i ee zadachi," *Izvestiia AN SSSR, seriia geograficheskaia,* 1962, no. 4, 3–11. In English: "Geography of population and its tasks," *Soviet geography: review & translation,* vol. 3, no. 9 (November, 1962), 3–13.

———. "Printsipy metodiki otsenki uslovii obitaniia naseleniia v raznoi geograficheskoi obstanovke," *Izvestiia AN SSSR, seriia geograficheskaia,* 1964, no. 3, 89–101.

———. "Soderzhanie i osnovnye zadachi geografii naseleniia," in *Geografiia naseleniia v SSSR; osnovnye problemy* (Geograficheskoe obshchestvo Soiuza SSR). M-L. Izd. "Nauka," 1964, 3–31.

———. "Razvitie v SSSR geografii naseleniia (obzor rabot 1961–1965 gg.)," *Itogi Nauki: seriia geografiia, geografiia SSSR,* vypusk 3. M. VINITI, 1966, 7–33. English summary: Trends of population geography in the USSR (a review of studies reported 1961–1965), 31–33.

———. "O geografii naseleniia, zaniatogo v SSSR v sfere nonmaterial'nogo proizvodstva i obsluzhivaniia," in *Geografiia naseleniia i naselennykh punktov SSSR.* L. "Nauka," 1967, 103–128. English abstract, "On the geography of population employed in the USSR in the sphere of services and non-material production," 127–128.

Pokshishevskii, V. V. and Vorob'ev, V. V. *Geografiia naseleniia Vostochnoi Sibiri* (AN SSSR, Sibirskoe otdelenie, Institut geografii Sibiri i Dal'nego Vostoka). M. Izd. AN SSSR, 1962. 163 p.

Pomus, Moisei Isaakovich. "Osveshchenie voprosov geografii naseleniia na stranitsakh ekonomiko-geograficheskoi pechati," *Izvestiia AN SSSR, seriia geograficheskaia,* 1951, no. 4, 57–67.

———. "Opyt ekonomiko-geograficheskogo izucheniia gorodov SSSR," *Izvestiia AN SSSR, seriia geograficheskaia,* 1958, no. 1, 129–133. In English: "An experiment in the economic-geographic study of the cities of the USSR", *Soviet geography: review and translation,* vol. 1, no. 1–2 (January-February, 1960), 43–47.

Puti razvitiia malykh i srednikh gorodov tsentral'nykh ekonomicheskikh rainov SSSR. D. G. Khodzhaev, ed. (Gosplan SSSR. Sovet po izucheniiu proizvoditel'nykh sil). M. Izd. "Nauka," 1967. 206 p.

Raionnaia planirovka. Gorodskie agglomeratsii (Mezhvedomstvennyi respublikanskii nauchno-tekhnicheskii sbornik). Kiev: "Budivel'nik," 1968. 132 p.

Rashin, Adol'f Grigor'evich. "Sdvigi v territorial'nom razmeshchenii naseleniia Rossii v XIX i v nachale XX v.," *Voprosy geografii,* sbornik 20. M. Geografgiz, 1950, 99–121.

Rudnitskii, Andrei Markovich, Serediuk, I. I., and Serediuk, S. P. "Sovremennoe gradostroitel'stvo i geografiia," *Vestnik Moskovskogo universiteta, seriia 5, geografiia,* 1965, no. 5, 41–46.

Saushkin, Iulian Glebovich. "Programma geograficheskogo izucheniia sovetskogo goroda," *Spravochnik puteshestvennika i kraeveda,* tom II. M. Geografgiz, 1950.

———. "Geography of urban and rural population in the USSR," in his *Economic geography of the Soviet Union* (8 lectures March-April 1956 at the Department of Geography, University of Oslo). Oslo: Oslo University Press, 1956, 28–43. Mimeographed.

———. "Ob izuchenii sistemy gorodov Sovetskogo Soiuza," *Vestnik*

Moskovskogo universiteta, seriia 5, geografiia, 1960, no. 1, 23–30. In English: "The study of a system of cities of the Soviet Union", *Soviet geography: review and translation,* vol. 1, no. 9 (November, 1960), 43–51.

———. "Geografiia naseleniia i smezhnye nauki," *Materialy I Mezhduvedomstvennogo soveshchaniia po geografii naseleniia (ianvar'-fevral' 1962 g),* vypusk 1. Doklady i reziume dokladov na plenume. M.-L. Geograficheskoe obshchestvo Soiuza SSR, 1961, 82–90. Rotaprint.

———. "Large areal complexes of productive forces in the Soviet Union," *Regional science association, papers,* vol. 8 (1962), 93–104.

Saushkin, Iu. G., Nikol'skii, I. V., and Korovitsyn, V. P., eds. *Ekonomicheskaia geografiia Sovetskogo Soiuza.* M. Izd. Moskovskogo universiteta, 1967. Especially "Geografiia gorodskikh poselenii," 79–97.

Semenov-Tian-Shanskii, Veniamin Petrovich. "Gorod i derevnia v Evropeiskoi Rossii: ocherk po ekonomicheskoi geografii," *Zapiski Russkogo geograficheskogo obshchestva po otdeleniiu statistiki,* tom 10, vypusk 2, SPb., 1910, 212 p.

———. "Russia: territory and population, a perspective on the 1926 census," *Geographical review,* vol. 18, no. 4 (October, 1928), 616–640, especially 632–637.

Smeile, Iu. V. "Novye goroda SSSR i faktory ikh obrazovaniia," in *Materialy I Mezhduvedomstvennogo soveshchaniia po geografii naseleniia (ianvar'-fevral' 1962 g),* vypusk 3, Sektsiia geografii gorodov. Doklady 1 reziume dokladov. M.-L. Geograficheskoe obshchestvo Soiuza SSR, 1962, 49–51. Rotaprint.

———. "O statistiko-ekonomicheskoi funksional'noi klassifikatsii gorodov," *Uchenye zapiski Rostovskogo finansovo-ekonomicheskogo instituta,* vypusk 2, Rostov-na-Donu, 1964, 85–95.

———. "Ekonomicheskaia struktura i funktsional'no-geneticheskaia tipologiia gorodov Sovetskogo Soiuza," *Uchenye zapiski Rostovskogo instituta Narodnogo khoziaistva,* Rostov-na-Donu, vypusk 3, 1967, 61–72.

SSSR. Narodnyi komissariat vnutrennikh del. Statisticheskii otdel. *Goroda Soiuza SSR.* M. Izd. Narodnogo komissariata vnutrennikh del., 1927. 160 p.

Stepanov, Mikhail Nikolaevich, and Vorob'ev, Vladimir Vasilevich. "O mestnykh izdanniakh, posviashchennykh otdel'nym gorodam," *Voprosy geografii,* sbornik 38. M. Geografgiz, 1956, 266–270.

Tikhomirov, Mihail Nikolaevich. *Drevnerusskie goroda.* M. Gospolitizdat, 2nd ed., 1956. 477 p. (1st ed. 1946) In English: *The towns of ancient Rus.* M. Foreign language publishing house, 1959. 502 p.

Trube, Lev Liudvigovich. "Ob ekonomiko-geograficheskom izuchenii poselkov gorodskogo tipa" in *Geografiia naseleniia v SSSR; osnovnye problemy* (Geograficheskoe obshchestvo Soiuza SSR). M.-L. Izd. "Nauka," 1964, 113–121.

———. "Izuchenie gorodov v sisteme raionnykh tsentrov dlia tselei raionnoi planirovki," *Teoriia i praktika ekonomicheskogo mikroraionirovaniia,* A. M. Kolotievskii, ed. Riga: Izd. "Zinatne," 1969, 93–100.

Tverskoi, Lev Mikhailovich. "Puti preobrazovaniia sushchestvuiushchikh bol'shikh gorodov," in *Geograficheskoe obshchestvo SSSR. Komissiia geografii naseleniia i gorodov, doklady,* vypusk 1 (3). L. Geograficheskoe obshchestvo SSSR, 1965, 92–123.

Valentei, Dmitrii Ignat'evich, and Khorev, Boris Sergeevich. "Problemy gorodov," *Ekonomicheskaia Gazeta,* July 1967, no. 29, 18–19. In English: "The problems of the cities," *Current digest of the Soviet press,* vol. 19, no. 38 (October 11, 1967), 3–5.

Varlamov, Viktor Sergeevich. "Geografiia naseleniia v novykh monografiiakh po ekonomicheskim raionam i soiuznym respublikam." *Voprosy geografii,* sbornik 45. M. Geografgiz, 1959, 253–258.

———. "O kolichestvennoi otsenke ekonomiko-geograficheskogo polozheniia gorodov," *Voprosy geografii,* sbornik 66. M. "Mysl'," 1965, 130–140. In English: "On a quantitative assessment of the economic-geographic situation of cities," *Soviet geography: review and translation,* vol. 7, no. 1 (January, 1966), 52–59.

Vladimirov, Viktor Vladimirovich. "Rasselenie v lesopromyshlennykh raionakh SSSR," *Izvestiia AN SSSR, seriia geograficheskaia,* 1966, no. 4, 64–76. In English: "Settlement in lumber-industry regions of the USSR," *Soviet geography: review and translation,* vol. 9, no. 8 (October, 1968), 710–725.

Vol'f, Mark Borisovich. "O geografichnosti sovetskikh statisticheskikh sbornikov," *Geografiia i khoziaistvo,* sbornik 10, 1961, 90–93.

Vorob'ëv, Vladimir Vasilevich, and Khorev, Boris Sergeevich. Issledovaniia po geografii naseleniia v vuzakh i nauchnykh uchrezhdeniiakh SSSR," *Materialy I Mezhduvedomstvennogo soveshchaniia po geografii naseleniia (ianvar'-fevral' 1961 g.),* vypusk 6. Obzor issledovanii po geografii naseleniia v SSSR. M-L. Geograficheskoe obshchestvo Soiuza SSR, 1962, 3–28.

Vorob'ëv, V. V., Gladysheva, E. N., Perevedentsev, V. I., and Pokshishevskii, V. V. "Ob osnovnykh zakonomernostiakh migratsii," *Materialy k IV s"ezdu geograficheskogo obshchestva SSSR. Simpozium B, osnovnye voprosy ekonomicheskoi geografii SSSR. Doklady.* Chast' 2. L. Geograficheskoe obshchestvo SSSR, 1964, 32–51. Rotaprint. In English "On basic migration patterns," *Soviet geography: review and translation,* vol. 5, no. 10 (December, 1964), 3–18.

Voronin, N. N. *Drevnerusskie goroda.* M-L. AN SSSR, 1945. 109 p.

Voskoboinikova, Sara Mironovna. "O vzaimosviaziakh mezhdu ekonomiko-geograficheskim polozheniem gorodov, ikh proizvodstvennymi funktsiiami i planirovkoi gorodskoi territorii, *Ocherki po istorii geologo-geograficheskikh znanii,* Yaroslavl', 1968, 235-241.

"Vtoroe vsesoiuznoe soveshchanie po geografii nasaleniia," *Izvestiia AN*

SSR, seriia geograficheskaia, 1967, no. 3, 134–136. In English: "The second interagency conference on population geography," *Soviet geography: review and translation,* vol. 8, no. 8 (October, 1967), 613–618.

Zolotnitskaia, R. L. "Otchet o deiatel'nosti Komissii geografii naseleniia i gorodov (1947–1964)," *Geograficheskoe obshchestvo SSSR, komissiia geografii naseleniia i gorodov. Doklady,* vypusk 1 (3). L. Geograficheskoe obshchestvo SSSR, 1965, 124–139.

III: REGIONAL STUDIES OF CITIES
1. The Northwest

Afonskaia, Margarita Osval'dovna. "Goroda Komi ASSR i puti ikh razvitiia," *Voprosy geografii naseleniia,* Uchenye zapiski Leningradskogo Gos. Pedagogicheskogo instituta im. A. I. Gertsena, tom 279. L. 1966, 114–127.

Bubes, E. Ia., and Kantor, E. L. Formirovanie sistemy gorodskikh poselenii Leningradskoi oblasti," *Doklady po geografii naseleniia* (Geograficheskoe obshchestvo SSSR. Komissiia geografii naseleniia i gorodov), vypusk 2 (4). L. Geograficheskoe obshchestvo SSSR, 1965, 34–55.

Chertov, Leonid Georgievich. "Lesopromyshlennye poselki Severo-zapada RSFSR," in *Geografiia naseleniia v SSSR; osnovnye problemy.* (Geograficheskoe obshchestvo Soiuza SSR.) M-L. Izd. "Nauka", 1964, 257–267.

Ginzburg, Natal'ia Solomonovna. "Trudovye resursy malykh gorodov Karel'skoi ASSR i puti ikh ispol'zovaniia," *Voprosy geografii naseleniia,* Uchenye zapiski Leningradskogo Gos. pedagogicheskogo instituta im A. I. Gertsena, tom 279, L. 1966, 99–113.

Knobel'sdorf, Eduard Vil'gel'movich. "Goroda Severo-Zapada RSFSR (formirovanie seti gorodov)," in *Voprosy ekonomiko-geograficheskogo izucheniia raionov i gorodov SSSR,* Leningradskii gosudarstvennyi pedagogicheskii institut imeni A. I. Gertsena. Uchenye zapiski, tom 206, L., 1962, 11–44.

———. "Raionoobrazuiushchaia rol' sovetskikh gorodov (na primere nekotorykh gorodov Leningradskogo ekonomicheskogo administrativnogo raiona)," in *Materialy po geografii naseleniia,* vypusk 1. L. Geograficheskoe obshchestvo Soiuza SSR, Otdelenie ekonomicheskoi geografii, 1962, 18–60. Rotaprint.

———. "Tipy gorodov Severo-zapada RSFSR," *Eesti geograafiia seltsi aastaraamat* (Ezhegodnik Estonskogo geograficheskogo obshchestva), 1960/61. Tallinn, 1962, 261–284. English summary.

———. "Zona khoziaistvennogo tiagoteniia Velikikh Luk," *Doklady po geografii naseleniia* (Geograficheskoe obshchestvo SSSR. Komissiia geografii naseleniia i gorodov). L. Geograficheskoe Obshchestvo SSSR. 1965, 56–82.

———. "Goroda Pskovskoi oblasti i puti ikh razvitiia (v sviazi s ispol'zovaniem trudovykh resursov)," *Voprosy geografii naseleniia,* Uchenye zapiski Leningradskogo gos. pedagogicheskogo instituta im. A. I. Gertsena, tom 279. L. 1966, 47–66.

———. "Sistema khoziaistvennykh tsentrov Leningradskoi zony," *Teoriia i praktika ekonomicheskogo mikroraionirovaniia,* A. M. Kolotievskii, ed. Riga: Izd. "Zinatne," 1969, 57–75.

Krasnova, K. A. "Formirovanie seti naselennykh punktov iugo-vostochnoi chasti Leningradskoi oblasti," *Voprosy geografii naseleniia* Uchenye zapiski Leningradskogo Gos. pedagogicheskogo instituta im A. I. Gertsena, tom 279. L. 1966, 251–263.

———. "Mestnye khoziaistvennye tsentry iugo-vostochnoi chasti Leningradskoi oblasti," *Voprosy geografii naseleniia* Uchenye zapiski Leningradskogo Gos. pedagogicheskogo instituta im A. I. Gertsena, tom 279. L. 1966, 264–280.

Lopatina, Elena Brunovna. *Leningrad. Ekonomiko-geograficheshkii ocherk.* M. Geografgiz, 1959, 216 p.

———. "Formirovanie poselenii-sputnikov Leningrada," in *Gorodasputniki; sbornik statei.* M. Geografgiz, 1961, 50–59. In English: "The formation of Leningrad's satellite places," *Soviet geography: review and translation,* vol. 3, no. 3 (March, 1962), 43–50.

Nevel'shtein, Grigorii Solomonovich. "Naselenie," in *Severo-zapad RSFSR: ekonomiko-geograficheskaia kharakteristika* (AN SSSR. Institut geografii *and* Leningradskii gosudarstvennyi universitet, Geograficheskii nauchnoissledovatel'skii institut). M. Izd. "Mysl'," 1964, 135–155, especially pp. 138–145.

———. "K voprosu o razvitii malykh i srednikh gorodov Severo-zapada RSFSR," *Voprosy geografii naseleniia,* Uchenye zapiski Leningradskogo Gos. pedagogicheskogo instituta im A. I. Gertsena, tom 279. L. 1966, 25–46.

Pokshishevskii, Vadim Viacheslavovich. "Leningrad (opyt vnutrigorodskoi kraevednoi kharakteristiki," *Sovetskoe kraevedenie,* 1931, no. 6.

———. "Territorial'noe formirovanie promyshlennogo kompleksa Peterburga v XVIII-XIX vekakh (opyt istoricheskoi mikrogeografii promyshlennosti krupnogo goroda)", *Voprosy geografii,* sbornik 20. M. Geografgiz, 1950, 122–162.

———. "Nekotorye voprosy ekonomiko-geograficheskogo polozheniia Leningrada," *Voprosy geografii,* sbornik 38. M. Geografgiz, 1956, 104–130.

Veselovskaia, Valentina Ivanovna. "Goroda Vologodskoi oblasti," *Vologodskii Krai,* vypusk 1, Vologda, 1959, 74–93.

———. "Nekotorye voprosy geografii gorodov Evropeiskogo Severa,"

Uchenye zapiski Vologodskogo gos. pedagogicheskogo instituta, 24 (1959), 145–158.

———. "Novye gorodskie poseleniia Vologodskoi oblasti," in *Vologodskii Krai*, vypusk 3, Vologda, 1962, 60–80.

———. "Puti razvitiia malykh i srednikh gorodskikh poselenii Vologodskoi oblasti," *Voprosy geografii naseleniia*, Uchenye zapiski Leningradskogo Gos. pedagogicheskogo instituta im. A. I. Gertsena, tom 279. L. 1966, 85–98.

2. The Center

Bukhgol'ts, Ol'ga Eduardovna, and Storozhenko, V. P. "Opyt obsledovaniia nekotorykh podmoskovnykh gorodov i problema sputnikov Moskvy," *Geografiia i khoziaistvo*, sbornik 2, 1958, 8–16.

Knobel'sdorf, Eduard Vil'gel'movich. "K voprosu o tipakh sovetskikh gorodov," *Geograficheskii sbornik*, tom 11, ekonomicheskaia geografiia (Geograficheskoe obshchestvo Soiuza SSR). M-L. Izd. AN SSSR, 1957, 75–89.

Lappo, Georgii Mikhailovich. "Geograficheskaia literatura o gorodakh Promyshlennogo Tsentra," *Voprosy geografii*, sbornik 38. M. Geografgiz, 1956, 261–265.

———. "Puti razvitiia starykh promyshlennykh tsentrov Podmoskov'ia," *Voprosy geografii*, sbornik 41. M. Geografgiz, 1957, 224–236.

———. "Set' gorodov Podmoskov'ia (eë formirovanie i opyt tipologii gorodov)," in *Sbornik statei aspirantov*. M. Geograficheskii Fakul'tet Moskovskogo gos. universiteta, 1958, 161–184. Rotaprint.

———. "Sovremennoe rasselenie i puti razvitiia gorodov v Moskovskom prigorodnom raione," in *Planirovka i zastroika bol'shikh gorodov*. M. Gosstroiizdat, 1961, 89–104.

———. "Nekotorye cherty istoricheskoi geografii gorodov Moskovskoi oblasti," *Voprosy geografii*, sbornik 51. M. Geografgiz, 1961, 27–51.

———. "Geograficheskoe izuchenie naselennykh punktov, zanimaiushchikh promezhutochnoe polozhenie mezhdu gorodskimi i sel'skimi poseleniiami (na primere Moskovskoi oblasti)," in *Geografiia naseleniia v SSSR: osnovnye problemy* (Geograficheskoe obshchestvo SSSR). M.-L. Izd. "Nauka," 1964, 245–256.

Listengurt, Feliks Mikhailovich. "Razvitie gorodov Iaroslavlia, Kalinina i Rybinska v sviazi s nekotorymi osobennostiami ikh ekonomikogeograficheskogo polozheniia" Moskovskii gosudarstvennyi pedagogicheskii institut imeni V. I. Lenina. Geografo-biologicheskii fakul'tet, *Ekonomicheskaia geografiia SSSR*, vypusk 5, M. 1960, 124–134.

———. "Rol' ekonomiko-geograficheskogo polozheniia razvitii gorodov Iaroslavlia, Tveri i Rybinska v epokhy feodalizma," in *Ekonomicheskaia geografiia, toponomika; sbornik statei*. M. Moskovskii gosudarstvennyi pedagogicheskii institut imeni V. I. Lenina, 1960, 88–131.

———. "Perspektivy ekonomicheskogo i territorial'nogo rosta malykh i srednikh gorodov Tsentral'nogo ekonomicheskogo raiona," *Izvestiia AN SSSR, seriia geograficheskaia,* 1965, no. 4, 61–69. In English: "Prospects of economic and territorial growth of small and medium cities of the Central economic region," *Soviet geography: review & translation,* vol. 6, no. 8 (October, 1965), 51–59.

Listengurt, F. M., and Smoliar, I. M. "Izuchenie nekotorykh predposylok promyshlennogo razvitiia malykh i srednikh gorodov Tsentral'nogo ekonomicheskogo raiona," *Izvestiia AN SSSR, seriia geograficheskaia,* 1964, no. 4, 79–90.

———. "O razgranichenii poniatii 'malye' i 'srednie' goroda (po materialam izucheniia gorodov Tsentral'nogo ekonomicheskogo raiona)," *Vestnik Moskovskogo universiteta, seriia 5, geografiia,* 1965, no. 5, 74–77.

Liubovnyi, Vladimir Iakovlevich. "O nekotorykh voprosakh formirovaniia gorodskogo naseleniia," *Geografiia i khoziaistvo,* vypusk 9, 1961, 60–64. In English: "Some questions relating to the formation of urban population," *Soviet geography: review & translation,* vol. 2, no. 10 (December, 1961), 51–57.

———. "Opyt izucheniia formirovaniia gorodskogo naseleniia (na primere nekotorykh gorodskikh poselenii iugovostochnoi chasti Moskovskoi oblasti)," *Voprosy geografii naseleniia SSSR; Sbornik statei k I Mezhduvedomstvennomu soveshchaniiu po geografii naseleniia.* M. Institut geografii AN SSSR, Otdel geografii SSSR, 1962, 93–110.

Makukha, Aleksei Ivanovich. "O nekotorykh osobennostiakh gorodov raionnogo podchineniia Iaroslavskoi oblasti," *Uchenye Zapiski Iaroslavskogo gosudarstvennogo pedagogicheskogo instituta,* vypusk 24 (34), Estestvoznanie, geografiia (chast' 1), 1958, 259–284.

———. "O nekotorykh osobennosti ekonomicheskykh sviazei promyshlennosti gorodov Iaroslavskoi oblasti," *Uchenye zapiski.* Smolenskii pedagogicheskii institut imeni K. Marksa, vypusk 12, 1963, 276–302.

Mints, Aleksei Aleksandrovich. "Voprosy ekonomiko-geograficheskoi tipologii sotsialisticheskikh gorodov (po materialam Tsentral'no-promyshlennogo raiona)," *Tezisy dokladov IV konferentsii molodykh uchenykh instituta geografii AN SSSR.* M. 1957, 26–28.

———. *Podmoskov'e; ekonomiko-geograficheskaia kharakteristika.* M. Geografgiz, 1961. 303 p. "Naselenie," 67–83.

———. "Naselenie," in *Tsentral'nyi raion; ekonomiko-geograficheskaia kharakteristika* (Institut geografii AN SSSR). M. Geografgiz, 1962, 114–151.

Mints, A. A., and Khorev, B. S. "Opyt ekonomiko-geograficheskoi tipologii sovetskikh gorodov (po materialam Tsentral'no-promyshlennogo raiona)," *Voprosy geografii,* sbornik 45. M. Geografgiz, 1959, 72–88.

Mishchenko, Grigorii E. "Goroda i poselki-sputniki Moskvy," in *Goroda-sputniki; sbornik statei.* M. Geografgiz. 1961, 40–49. In English: "Satellite cities and towns of Moscow," *Soviet geography: review & translation,* vol. 3, no. 3 (March, 1962), 35–43.

Monakhov, V. "Raspredelenie i rost gorodov Tsentral'noi promyshlennoi oblasti," *Zemlevedenie,* tom 27, vypusk 3/4, 1927, 43–60.

Rodoman, Boris Borisovich. "Stroitel'stvo novykh gorodov-sputnikov vokrug Moskvy i okhrana prirody," in *Goroda-sputniki; sbornik statei.* M. Geografgiz, 1961, 169–172.

Saushkin, Iulian Glebovich. *Moskva.* M. Geografgiz, 1950. 87 p. 2nd ed. 1953.

———. *Moskva: geograficheskaia kharakteristika.* M. Geografgiz. 3rd ed. 1955. 192 p.

———. *Moskva: geograficheskaia kharakteristika.* M. Izd. "Mysl'," 4th ed. 1964. 238 p. In English: *Moscow.* M. Progress publishers, 1966. 186 p.

———. "Opyt geograficheskogo analiza materialov o planirovke i zastroike Moskvy v poslevoennye gody (1945–1957)." *Voprosy geografii,* sbornik 51. M. Geografgiz, 1961, 176–182.

Semenov-Tian-Shanskii, Veniamin Petrovich. *Antropogeografiia Tsentral'noi promyshlennoi oblasti (raspredelenie naseleniia TsPO v sviazi s estesvennymi usloviiami.* Petrograd, 1924.

Serdobova, M. and Khorev, B. S. "Soveshchanie po izucheniiu malykh i srednikh gorodov Tsentral'nogo ekonomicheskogo raiona," *Izvestiia AN SSSR, seriia geograficheskaia,* 1964, no. 4, 165–166.

Skobeev, Dmitrii Aleksandrovich. "Promyshlennost' Moskvy," *Voprosy geografii,* sbornik 51. M. Geografgiz, 1961, 58–75.

Trube, Lev Liudvigovich. "Tipy gorodov Tsentral'no-promyshlennogo raiona," *Geografiia v shkole,* 1955, no. 5, 10–14.

Veselovskaia, Valentina Ivanovna. "Nekotorye osobennosti razmeshcheniia gorodov Tsentral'no-promyshlennogo raiona," *Uchenye zapiski Vologodskogo gosudarstvennogo pedagogicheskogo instituta imeni Molotova,* tom 8, 1951, 33–50.

———. "Formirovanie seti gorodov Tsentral'no-promyshlennogo raiona," *Uchenye zapiski Vologodskogo gosudarstvennogo instituta imeni Molotova,* tom 15, 1954, 443–455.

Vilenberg, B., and Loginov, S. "Kriukovo—pervyi 'gorod-sputnik' Moskvy," *Voprosy geografii,* sbornik 51. M. Geografgiz, 1961, 52–57.

Voskoboinikova, Sara Mironovna. "K voprosu o probleme malykh i srednikh gorodov (na primere gorodov Iaroslavskoi oblasti)," *Trudy konferentsii po voprosam razmeshcheniia promyshlennosti i razvitiia gorodov* (Vil'nius, 20–23 avgusta 1962 g). Vil'nius: AN Litovskoi SSR, 1963, 73–79.

———. "K voprosu o razvitii srednikh i malykh gorodov Iaroslavskoi oblasti," *Doklady na nauchnykh konferentsiiakh. Iaroslavskii gos. pedagogicheskii institut,* 1964, 2, no. 4, 117–122.

3. The Volga-Vyatka Region

Khorev, Boris Sergeevich. "Gor'kovskii proizvodstvenno-territorial'nyi kompleks i ego razvitie v semiletke," *Izvestiia AN SSSR, seriia geograf-cheskaia,* 1960, no. 6, 46–54.

———. "Geograficheskie osobennosti 'Selk'skogo nesel'skokhoziaistven-nogo' naseleniia (na materiale Volgo-Viatskogo raiona," in *Voprosy geografii naseleniia SSSR. Sbornik statei k I Mezhduvedomstvennomu soveshchaniiu po geografii naseleniia.* M. AN SSSR Institut geografii, Otdel geografii SSSR, 1961, 111–146.

———. "Goroda i poselki-sputniki Gor'kogo," in *Goroda-sputniki; sbornik statei.* M. Geografgiz, 1961, 60–77. In English: "Satellite cities and towns of Gor'kiy," *Soviet geography: review and translation,* vol. 3, no. 3 (March, 1962), 51–64.

———. "Gorodskie poseleniia," in *Volgo-Viatskii raion, ekonomiko-geograficheskaia kharakteristika* (AN SSSR, Institut geografii). M. Geografgiz, 1961, 63–70.

———. "Ocherk geografii naseleniia i naselennykh punktov Gor'kovskoi oblasti," *Voprosy geografii,* sbornik 56. M. Geografgiz, 1962, 110–140.

———. "Puti razvitiia promyshlennogo kompleksa Volgo-Viatskogo krup-nogo ekonomicheskogo raiona," *Izvestiia AN SSSR, seriia geografi-cheskaia,* 1962, no. 4, 52–61.

———. "Gorodskie poseleniia," in his *Gor'kovskaia oblast'; ekonomiko-geograficheskie ocherki; priroda, naselenie, khoziaistvo.* Gor'kiy: Volgo-Viatskoe knizhnoe izd., 1967, 81–100.

Khorev, B. S., and Rogov, N. A. "O putiakh razvitiia byvshikh 'kustar-nykh' promyslov (na primere Gor'kovskoi oblasti)," *Izvestiia VGO,* 1962, no. 5, 414–424. In English: "On ways of developing former handicraft industries (as illustrated by Gork'iy Oblast)," *Soviet geography: review & translation,* vol. 4, no. 4 (April, 1963), 31–46.

Matveev, Gennadii Petrovich. *Ekonomiko-geograficheskii ocherk Chu-vashii.* Cheboksary: Chuvashskoe gosud. izd., 1959.

Trube, Lev Liudvigovich. *Nashi goroda, ekonomiko-geograficheskie ocherki o gorodakh Gor'kovskoi i Arzamasskoi oblasti.* Gorkiy: Knizh-noe izd., 1954. 244 p.

———. "Poselki Gor'kovskoi oblasti (obshchaia kharakteristika)," *Uchenye zapiski Gor'kovskogo gosudarstvennogo pedagogicheskogo instituta,* vypusk 20 1958, 15–33.

———. "Izmeneniia v sostave raionnykh tsentrov Gor'kovskoi oblasti (v sviazi s izmeneniiami v administrativnom delenii)," *Uchenye zapiski Gor'kovskogo gos. pedagogicheskogo instituta,* vypusk 46 1964, 12–21.

———. "Tipy poselkov Volgo-Viatskogo raiona," *Uchenye zapiski Gor'kov-skogo gos. pedagogicheskogo instituta,* vypusk 51 1964, 35–43.

——. "Izmeneniia v sostave gorodov Volgo-Viatskogo raiona v sovetskoe vremia i problemy ikh razvitiia," *Izvestiia VGO*, 1966, no. 3, 225–229.

——. "Malye goroda i bol'shie poselki i problemy ikh razvitiia (na primere Volgo-Viatskogo raiona)," in *Geografiia naseleniia i naselennykh punktov SSSR*. L. "Nauka," 1967, 144–156. English abstract: "Development problems of small towns and large settlements (as illustrated by the Volga-Vyatka region)," 156.

4. The Black-Earth Center

Grishin, Grigorii Terent'evich. "Ekonomicheskie raiony i goroda Voronezhskoi gubernii nakanune 1917 goda," *Trudy Voronezhskogo universiteta*, tom 53 (1957), 27–45.

Kapitonov, Evgenii Ivanovich. "O nekotorykh sdvigakh v gorodskom naselenii Kurskoi oblasti po dannym perepisei 1939 i 1959 godov," *Uchenye zapiski Kurskogo gos. pedagogicheskogo instituta*, vypusk 19 (1963), 181–189.

Korzhov, Nikolai Ivanovich. "O raionoobrazuiushchei roli gorodov Voronezhskoi oblasti," *Izvestiia Voronezhskogo otdela Geograficheskogo obshchestva SSSR*, vypusk 3 (1961), 45–52.

Rybin, Iu. V. "Sakharnaia promyshlennost' Voronezhskoi oblasti i ee vliianie na formirovanie gorodskikh poselenii," *Voprosy geografii naseleniia*, Uchenye zapiski Leningradskog gos. pedagogicheskogo instituta A. I. Gertsena, tom 279. L. 1966, 218–235.

Snytko, Mikhail Kirillovich. "Goroda Tambovskogo kraia (istoriko-geograficheskii ocherk)," *Nash Krai*, vypusk 1. Voronezh-Tambov: Tsentral'no-Chernozemnoe knizhnoe izd. 1964, 109–134.

——. "Nekotorye voprosy formirovaniia seti gorodov Tsentral'no-chernozemnogo raiona," *Nash Krai*, vypusk 1. Voronezh-Tambov: Tsentral'no-chernozemnoe knizhnoe izd. 1964, 142–157.

Zinenko, Petr Fedorovich, and Gurevich, Mark Iakovlevich. *Goroda Tambovskoi oblasti (ekonomiko-geograficheskii ocherk)*. Tambov: "Tambovskaia pravda." 1956. 111 p. (Tambovskii otdel Geograficheskogo obshchestva).

5. The Volga

Aleksandrova, Tat'iana Aleksandrovna. "Goroda i rabochie poselki Kuibyshevskoi oblasti," *Uchenye zapiski Kuibshevskogo plan. instituta*, vypusk 5 (1958), 3–44.

Dolgopolov, Konstantin Vasil'evich, and Fedorova, Evgeniia Fedorovna. "Naselenie," in their *Povolzh'e: ekonomiko-geograficheskii ocherk*. M. Izd. "Prosveshchenie," 1967, 41–47.

Kavunov, Petr Aleksandrovich. *Goroda Saratovskoi oblasti; ekonomiko-geograficheskii ocherk*. Saratov: Saratovskoe knizhnoe izd. 1958. 175 p. 2nd ed., 1963, 212 p.

Maergoiz, Isaak Moiseevich. "Geograficheskoe polozhenie goroda Stalingrada," *Voprosy geografii*, sbornik 2. M. Geografgiz, 1946, 63–110.

Saushkin, Iulian Glebovich, and Shaposhnikov, Anatolii Sergeevich. "Promyshlennye uzly Srednego Povolzh'ia," *Vestnik Moskovskogo universiteta, seriia 5, geografiia*, 1965, no. 3, 31–40.

Skliar, Mikhail Ivanovich. "Gorodskie poseleniia Tatarii (osobennosti razvitiia i tipologiia)," *Uchenye zapiski Kazanskogo finansovo-ekonomicheskogo instituta*, vypusk 14 1960, 205–237.

Trube, Lev Liudvigovich. "Volzhskie goroda," *Voprosy geografii*, sbornik 45. M. Geografgiz, 1959, 89–98.

Vladimirov, Viktor Vladimirovich, Listengurt, F. M., and Naimark, N. I. "Nekotorye osobennosti formirovaniia sistem gorodskogo rasseleniia (na primere Tatarskoi ASSR, Bashkirskoi ASSR i Kuibyshevskoi oblasti)," *Izvestiia AN SSSR, seriia geograficheskaia*, 1966, no. 5, 57–67. In English: "Some aspects of the formation of urban settlement patterns (illustrated by the Tatar ASSR, Bashkir ASSR and Kuybyshev Oblast)," *Soviet geography: review & translation*, vol. 8, no. 2 (February, 1967), 58–70.

6. The North Caucasus

Fedorova, Aleksandra Georgievna. "Tipy gorodskikh poselenii Dagestanskoi ASSR," in *Materialy po geografii naseleniia*, vypusk 1. L. Geograficheskoe obshchestvo Soiuza SSR, Otdelenie ekonomicheskoi geografii, 1962, 73–81.

Kapitonov, Evgenii Ivanovich. "O nekotorykh izmeneniiakh v gorodskom naselenii i poseleniiakh gorodskogo tipa Krasnodarskogo kraia v sovetskoe vremia," *Uchenye zapiski Krasnodarskogo gosudarstvennogo pedagogicheskogo instituta*, vypusk 19, 1957, 75–86.

Perfil'ev, Andrei Il'ich. "K voprosu obrazovaniia i razvitiia tipov poselenii na Kubani i Chernomorskom poberezh'e Severo-Zapadnogo Kavkaza," *Uchenye zapiski Krasnodarskogo gosudarstvennogo pedagogicheskogo instituta*, vypusk 19 1957, 61–73.

Shevtsov, Boris Mikhailovich. "Formirovanie Sadono-Mizuro-Alagirskogo gornopromyshlennogo uzla i ego gorodskie poseleniia," *Voprosy geografii naseleniia*, Uchenye zapiski Leningradskogo Gos. pedagogicheskogo instituta im A. I. Gertsena, tom 279. L. 1966, 199–217.

7. The Urals

Animitsa, E. G. "Voprosy formirovaniia seti gorodov Sverdlovskoi oblasti," in *Voprosy ekonomicheskoi istorii i ekonomicheskoi geografii*, Sverdlovsk, 1964, 136–151.

Chepkasov, P. N. "Velichina gorodskikh poselenii Permskoi oblasti," in *Ekonomicheskaia geografiia Zapadnogo Urala*, vypusk 1, *Uchenye zapiski Permskogo universiteta*, tom 101 1963, 20–56.

Eropkina, N. D., and Khorev, B. S. "Nauchnaia sessiia po problemam razvitiia gorodov Urala," *Izvestiia AN SSSR, seriia geograficheskaia,* 1966, no. 4, 155–157.

Iofa, Leonid Evgen'evich. *Goroda Urala,* Chast' I: Feodal'nyi period. M. Geografgiz. 1951. 424 p.

Komar, Igor' Valer'ianovich. *Ural: ekonomiko-geograficheskaia kharakteristika.* M. Izd. AN SSSR, 1959. 367 p., especially 157–179.

Konstantinov, Oleg Arkad'evich. "Gorodskie poseleniia Urala," *Voprosy geografii,* sbornik 38. M. Geografgiz, 1956, 78–103.

Stepanov, Mikhail Nikolaevich. "Razvitie poselenii-sputnikov Permi," in *Goroda-sputniki; sbornik statei.* M. Geografgiz, 1961, 78–82. In English: "Development of the satellite places of Perm'," *Soviet geography: review and translation,* vol. 3, no. 3 (March, 1962), 65–68.

———. "Funktsional'no-geneticheskie tipy gorodskikh poselenii Permskoi oblasti," *Uchenye zapiski Permskogo universiteta,* tom 21, vypusk 3 1962, 25–32.

Trube, Lev Liudvigovich. "Nauchnaia sessiia po problemam razvitiia gorodskikh poselenii Urala," *Izvestiia VGO,* 1966, no. 5, 467.

Ural'skaia, E. M. "Osnovnye cherty seti gorodskikh poselenii i tipy otraslevykh tsentrov Sverdlovskoi oblasti," *Vestnik Leningradskogo universiteta, seriia geologii i geografii.* 1966, no. 1, 101–111. English summary, 110.

Varlamov, Viktor Sergeevich. "Ob ekonomicheskikh sviaziakh promyshlennosti Orenburga," *Geografiia i khoziaistvo,* sbornik 3–4 1958, 64–70. In English: "On the economic links of the industry of Orenburg," *Soviet geography: review and translation,* vol. 2, no. 3 (March, 1961), 54–60.

———. "Ob ekonomiko-geograficheskom polozhenii Orenburga," *Vestnik Moskovskogo universiteta, seriia 5, geografiia,* 1960, no. 6, 55–60. In English: "The economic-geographic situation of Orenberg," *Soviet geography: review and translation,* vol. 2, no. 6 (June, 1961), 14–21.

———. "Zadachi kompleksnogo razvitiia promyshlennykh tsentrov (na primere izucheniia ekonomicheskikh sviazei Orenburga)," *Voprosy geografii,* sbornik 61. M. Geografgiz, 1963, 74–86.

8. Siberia and the Far East

Baturina, Eva Anatol'evna. "Izmenenie geografii gorodov Zapadnoi Sibiri," *Uchenye zapiski Novosibirskogo pedagogicheskogo instituta,* vypusk 12 1957, 57–75.

———. "Nekotorye voprosy geografii gorodov Novosibirskoi oblasti," in *Materialy I Mezhduvedomstvennogo soveshchaniia po geografii naseleniia (ianvar'-fevral' 1962 g.),* vypusk 3. Sektsiia geografii gorodov. Doklady i reziume dokladov, M.-L. Geograficheskoe obshchestvo Soiuza SSR, 1961, 73–74.

———. "Osobennosti razvitiia i razmeshcheniia gorodov Novosibirskoi oblasti," in *Trudy 2-i nauchnoi konferentsii prepodavatelei kafedr geografii pedagogicheskikh institutov Sibiri,* Novokuznetsk, 1963, 82–92.

Buiantuev, Bal'zhan Rinchinovich, and Vorob'ev, Vladimir Vasil'evich. "Gorodskie poseleniia Buriatii (opyt istoriko-geograficheskogo analiza etapov formirovaniia gorodskoi seti)," *Kraevedcheskii sbornik (Buriatskogo filiala Geograficheskogo obshchestva SSSR),* vypusk 4 1959, 42–71.

Burmantov, G. G. "Formirovanie funktsional'nykh tipov poselenii v raionakh iuzhnoi taigi (na primere Krasnoiarskogo Priangar'ia)," *Doklady Instituta Geografii Sibiri i Dal'nego Vostoka,* vypusk 13 (1966), 56–62. In English: "The formation of functional types of settlements in the southern tayga (with particular reference to the Angara River district of Krasnoyarsk Kray)," *Soviet geography: review and translation,* vol. 9, no. 2 (February, 1968), 112–119.

Gorban', N. V. "Iz istorii stroitel'stva krepostei na iuge Zapadnoi Sibiri; Novo-Ishimskaia liniia krepostei," *Voprosy geografii,* sbornik 31. M. Geografgiz, 1953, 206–227.

Iurasova, Mariia Kliment'evna. *Goroda Omskoi oblasti.* Omsk: Knigoizdat, 1959. 172 p.

Kabo, Rafail Mikhailovich. *Goroda Zapadnoi Sibiri: ocherki istoriko-ekonomicheskoi geografii (XVII-pervaia polovina XIX vv.).* M. Geografgiz, 1949. 220 p.

Khrushchev, Anatolii Timofeevich. "Osobennosti promyshlennykh uzlov Irkutsko-Cheremkhovskogo raiona," in *Voprosy geografii Vostochnoi Sibiri, Trudy Seminara,* tom 1. M. Geograficheskii fakul'tet MGU, 1957, 11–56.

Kolesnikov, A. D. "Osnovanie Omskoi kreposti i ee rol' v zaselenii Priirtysh'ia," *Izvestiia Omskogo otdela Geograficheskogo obshchestva SSSR,* vypusk 7 1965, 133–160.

Kosmachev, Kirill Petrovich, and Nedeshev, Aleksei Aleksandrovich. "O nekotorykh osobennostiakh formirovaniia seti gornopromyshlennykh poselenii (na primere Iakutii i Chitinskoi oblasti)," in *Geografiia naseleniia Vostochnoi Sibiri.* M. Izd. AN SSSR, 1962, 118–125.

Kurakin, Anatolii Fedorovich. "Formirovanie gorodskikh poselenii Altaiskogo kraia," in *Materialy I Mezhduvedomstvennogo soveshchaniia po geografii naseleniia (ianvar'-fevral' 1962 g.),* vypusk 3, sektsiia geografii gorodov, doklady i reziume dokladov. M-L. Geograficheskoe obshchestvo Soiuza SSR, 1961, 81–86.

———. "Razvitie seti gorodskikh poselenii na territorii Altaiskogo kraia," *Uchenye zapiski Permskogo universiteta,* tom 23, no. 4 1963, 63–71.

Losiakova, K. M. "O razmeshchenii gorodskogo naseleniia na territorii Iakutskoi ASSR," in *Voprosy geografii Iakutii,* vypusk 2 1962, Yakutsk, 128–133.

Margolin, Adol'f Borisovich. "Goroda zapoliar'ia," *Sovetskaia Arktika,* 1937, no. 7, 82–96.

Meerson, E. G. "Naselenie" in *Dal'nii Vostok: ekonomiko-geograficheskaia kharakteristika* (Akademiia Nauk SSSR, Institut geografii). M. Izd. "Mysl'," 1966, 91–111.

Mytarev, Aleksandr Alekseevich. *Iuzhnyi Kuzbass (ekonomiko-geograficheskii ocherk).* Kemerovo: Knizhnoe izd., 1957, 123 p.

———. "Istoriia zaseleniia i obrazovaniia gorodskikh poselenii na territorii Kemerovskoi oblasti," in *Materialy I Mezhduvedomstvennogo soveshchaniia po geografii naseleniia (ianvar'-fevral' 1962 g.),* vypusk 3, sektsiia geografii gorodov, doklady i reziume dokladov. M.-L. Geograficheskoe obshchestvo Soiuza SSR, 1961, 75–77.

———. "Iz istorii zaseleniia i formirovaniia naselennykh punktov Kuzbassa," in *Doklady VI nauchnoi konferentsii (aprel'-mai 1963 g.).* Sektsiia geografii i kraevedeniia. (Novokuznetskii pedagogicheskii institut.) Novokuznetsk, 1963, 3–13.

———. "Nekotorye osobennosti razvitiia i razmeshcheniia poselkov gorodskogo tipa Kuzbassa," in *Ocherki naseleniia i khoziaistva Zapadnoi Sibiri; sbornik statei.* Novosibirsk, 1965, 3–21.

Penzin, Il'ia Dmitrievich. "Gorodskie poseleniia Priamur'ia," in *Voprosy geografii Dal'nego Vostoka,* sbornik 6, Khabarovsk 1963, 55–71.

———. "Istoriko-geograficheskie usloviia formirovaniia gorodskikh poselenii iuzhnoi chasti Dal'nego Vostoka," in *Voprosy geografii Priamur'ia,* Khaborovsk, 1965, 76–109.

Pertsik, Evgenii Naumovich. "Razvitie promyshlennykh uzlov i gorodov Tsentral'noi Sibiri v perspektive," *Voprosy geografii,* sbornik 57. M. Geografgiz, 1962, 250–274.

———. "Formirovanie sistemy gorodov Kuzbassa," in *Geografiia naseleniia v SSSR; osnovnye problemy.* M.-L. Izd., "Nauka," 1964, 183–190.

Pokshishevskii, Vadim Viacheslavovich. *Zaselenie Sibiri: istoriko-geograficheskii ocherk.* Irkutsk: Irkutskoe oblastnoe gosudarstvennoe izd., 1951, 208 p.

———. "K geografii dooktiabr'skikh kolonizatsionno-migratsionnykh protsessov v iuzhnoi chasti Dal'nego Vostok," *Sibirskii geograficheskii sbronik,* no. 1, 1962, 85–95. In English: "On the geography of prerevolutionary colonization and migration processes in the southern part of the Soviet Far East," *Soviet geography: review and translation,* vol. 4, no. 4 (April, 1963), 17–31.

Pomus, Moisei Isaakovich. *Zapadnaia Sibir' (ekonomiko-geograficheskaia kharakteristika).* M. Geografgiz, 1956, 643 p., especially pp. 143–151.

———. "Gorodskoe naselenie i tipy gorodskikh poselenii," in *Vostochnaia Sibir'; ekonomiko-geograficheskaia kharakteristika.* (AN SSSR, Institut geografii *and* Institut geografii Sibiri i Dal'nego Vostoka). M. Geografgiz, 1963, 177–194.

Potanin, Grigorii Nikolaevich. "Goroda Sibiri," in *Sibir', ee sovremennoe sostoianie i ee nuzhdy.* St. Peterburg, 1908, 234–259.

Sergeev, V. I. "Pervye sibirskie goroda, ikh voennoe, ekonomicheskoe i kul'turnoe znachenie," *Vestnik istorii mirovoi kultury*, 1960, kniga 3, 113–124.

Spidchenko, Konstantin Ivanovich. *Goroda Kuzbassa; (ekonomiko-geograficheskii ocherk)*. M. Geografgiz, 1947, 148 p. (Bibliography, 138–145, 217 entries.)

Tiunov, V. F. ed. *Zapadno-sibirskii krai; goroda i raiony; osnovnye pokazateli*. Novosibirsk: Zapsibkraiizdat, 1936, 373 p.

Turchainov, N. V. "Goroda Aziatskoi Rossii," in *Aziatskaia Rossiia*, tom 1. St. Peterburg, 1914, 285–360.

Vorob'ev, Vladimir Vasil'evich. *Izmeneniia v geografii gorodov iuga Vostochnoi Sibiri za 40 let Sovetskoi vlasti*. V. P. Shotskii, ed. Irkutsk. Geograficheskoe obshchestvo SSSR, Vostochno-Sibirskii otdel, 1957, 32 p.

———. *Formirovanie gorodskoi seti iuga Vostochnoi Sibiri*. V. P. Shotskii, ed. Irkutsk. Geograficheskoe obshchestvo SSSR, Vostochno-Sibirskii otdel, 1958. 26 p.

———. "Osnovnye izmeneniia v geografii gorodskikh poselenii iuga Vostochnoi Sibiri za 40 let (1917–1957 gg.)," *Nauchnye doklady vysshei shkoly; geologo-geograficheskie nauki*, 1958, no. 2, 230–234.

———. *Goroda iuzhnoi chasti Vostochnoi Sibiri; istoriko-geograficheskie ocherki*. Trudy Vostochno-Sibirskogo filiala Sibirskogo otdeleniia Akademii nauk SSSR, vypusk 28, seriia ekonomiko-geograficheskaia. Irkutskoe knizhnoe izd. 1959, 147 p. (Bibliography, 136–146, 394 entries.)

———. "Tipy gorodskikh poselenii iuga Vostochnoi Sibiri," *Voprosy geografii*, sbornik 45. M. Geografgiz, 1959, 99–112.

———. "Novye gorodskie poseleniia Vostochnoi Sibiri, voznikshie v poslevoennyi period," in *Materialy pervogo soveshchaniia geografov Sibiri i Dal'nego Vostoka, 1, Tezisy dokladov*. Irkutsk, 1959, 92–96.

———. "Nekotorye voprosy ekonomiko-geograficheskogo polozheniia goroda Irkutska," *Trudy Vostochno-Sibirskogo filiala Sibirskogo otdeleniia AN SSSR*, vypusk 32, seriia ekonomicheskaia geografiia 1960, 61–79.

———. "Sotsialisticheskie goroda-novostroiki Sibiri i Dal'nego Vostoka, vyrosshie za gody Sovetskoi vlasti," in *Tret'ia nauchnaia konferentsiia po istorii, arkheologii i etnografii Dal'nego Vostoka*, vypusk 1, *Doklady i soobshcheniia po istorii Sovetskogo Dal'nego Vostoka, epokhi sotsializma i kommunizma* (1917–1962). Vladivostok, 1962, 107–110.

———. "The principal changes in the geography of urban population and urban settlements of the Soviet Far East," *Eleventh Pacific Science Congress, Tokyo, 1966. Proceedings*, vol. 10, Abstracts of papers related with geography and scientific information-museum. Tokyo: Science Council of Japan. "Urbanization and industrialization," p. 26.

Vorob'ev, Vladimir Vasil'evich, and Kozhukhovskaia, N. F. "Geograficheskie razlichiia v kharaktere dinamiki gorodskogo i sel'skogo naseleniia (na primere Iuzhnoi chasti Vostochnoi Sibiri)," in *Geografiia naseleniia i naselennykh punktov SSSR*. L. Izd. "Nauka," 1967, 90–102. English abstract: "Geographic differences in urban and rural population changes (as illustrated by the southern part of Eastern Siberia), 102.

Zaionchkovskaia, Zhanna Antonovna. "Nekotorye voprosy prizhivaemosti pereselentsev v gorodakh Vostochnoi Sibiri (na primere trëkh gorodov Krasnoiarskogo kraia)," *Materialy I Mezhduvedomstvennogo soveshchaniia po geografii naseleniia (ianvar'-fevral' 1962 g.)*. vypusk 2. M-L. Geograficheskoe obshchestvo SSR, 1961, 45–47. Rotaprint.

Zykov, Sergei Sergeevich. "Voprosy razvitiia gorodov Sibiri (nekotorye ekonomicheskie faktory razvitiia gorodov)," *Izvestiia Sibirskogo otdeleniia AN SSSR*, 1964, no. 1, seriia obshchestvennykh nauk, vypusk 1, 1964, 63–69.

9. The Ukraine

Blazhko, Nina Ivanovna. "O metodakh izucheniia mesta goroda v sisteme gorodov Sovetskogo Soiuza (na primere Odessy)," *Vestnik Moskovskogo universiteta, seriia 5, geografiia*, 1961, no. 6, 25–29. In English: "On methods of studying the place of a city in the system of cities of the USSR (as illustrated by Odessa)," *Soviet geography: review and translation*, vol. 3, no. 3 (March, 1963), 69–74.

———. "Odessa, Nikolaev, Kherson — sravnitel'naia kharakteristika," *Voprosy geografii*, sbornik 56. M. Geografgiz, 1962, 95–109.

———. "Donetskaia gorodskaia aglomeratsiia Ukrainskoi SSR," *Materialy po geografii naseleniia*, vypusk 2. L. Geograficheskoe obshchestvo SSSR, 1963, 54–79. Rotaprint.

———. "Sistema gorodskikh poselenii Donetskogo proizvodstvenno-territorial'nogo kompleksa," *Vestnik Moskovskogo universiteta, seriia 5, geografiia*, 1963, no. 6, 24–32. In English: "The system of urban places of the Donets territorial-production complex," *Soviet geography: review & translation*, vol. 5, no. 2 (February, 1964), 11–16.

———. "O sisteme gorodov Prikarpat'ia," in *Geografiia naseleniia v SSSR. Osnovnye problemy* (Geograficheskoe obshchestvo Soiuza SSR). M.-L. Izd. "Nauka," 1964, 191–200.

Bogorad, Daniil Il'ich. "Tipy i razmeshchenie gorodskikh poselenii Ukrainskoi SSR," in *Voprosy gorodskogo raseleniia*. Kiev: Izd. "Budivel'nik," 1964, 26–34.

———. "Osnovnye problemy rasseleniia v Donetsko-pridneprovskom ekonomicheskom raione," *Gradostroitel'stvo: voprosy rasseleniia* (Mezhvedomstvennyi respublikanskii nauchno-technicheskii sbornik). Kiev: Izd. "Budivel'nik," 1966, 3–19.

———. *Gorodskie aglomeratsii Ukrainskoi SSR (osnovnye polozheniia i vyvody)*. Kiev: Izd. AN USSR, 1966.

Bogunenko, Dmitrii Il'ich. "Tipologiia gorodov i sel'skikh raionnykh tsentrov Odesskoi oblasti," *Nauchnye doklady vysshei shkoly, geologo-geograficheskie nauki,* 1958, no. 2, 223–229.

———. "Znachenie gorodov v khoziaistvennom komplekse Odesskoi oblasti," *Nauchnyi ezhegodnik Odesskogo gosudarstvennogo universiteta: geograficheskii fakul'tet,* vypusk 2, 1960, 139–142.

———. "Goroda Odesskoi oblasti," *Trudy Odesskogo universiteta, seriia geologicheskikh i geograficheskikh nauk,* tom 152, no. 10 1962, 187–195.

Bondarenko, Iaroslav Ivanovich, and Vitebskii, R. Ia. "O tipologii gorodov Zakarpatskoi oblasti," *Tezisy dokladov XXI nauchnoi sessii. Sektsiia geograficheskikh nauk (mai-iiun'),* Chernovitskii gos. universitet. Chernovtsy, 1965, 67–71.

Dagaeva, Tat'iana Konstantinovna, and Ignatenko, Nikolai Grigor'evich. "Malye i srednie goroda Podol'ia i Severnoi Bukoviny (Klassifikatsiia i puti razvitiia)," in *Geografiia naseleniia i naselennykh punktov.* L. "Nauka," 1967, 157–174. English abstract: "Small and medium towns of Podolye and Northern Bukovina (classification and ways of development), 173–174.

Denisiuk, L. M. "Osobennosti razmeshcheniia i struktura gorodskogo naseleniia v Iugo-Zapadnom ekonomicheskom raione," *Iugo-Zapadnyi ekonomicheskii raion: ekonomicheskaia geografiia.* Resp. mezhved. nauchnyi sbornik, 1964, vypusk 2, 23–28.

Konstantinov, Oleg Arkad'evich. "Goroda Ukrainskoi SSR," *Izvestiia VGO,* 1954, no. 3, 215–228.

Maergoiz, Isaak Moiseevich (under the name of I. M. Marchenko). *Kiev: stolitsa Ukrainskoi SSR.* M. Geografgiz, 1959, 72 p.

Makarenko, Gurii Karpovich. "Goroda Cherkasskoi oblasti," *Voprosy ekonomiko-geograficheskogo izucheniia rainov i gorodov SSSR.* Uchenye zapiski Leningradskogo gosudarstvennogo pedagogicheskogo instituta imeni A. I. Gertsena, tom 206, 1962, 205–236.

Materialy Mezhvedomstvennoi Nauchnoi Konferentsii po problemam razvitiia gorodov i sel'skikh poselenii Zapadnykh oblastei USSR, L'vov, Sentiabr' 1966 g. (L'vovskii gosudarstvennyi universitet im Iv. Franko, L'vovskii otdel Geograficheskogo obshchestva USSR, *and* L'vovskoe otdelenie Soiuza Arkhitektorov USSR). L'vov: Izd. L'vovskogo universiteta, 1966.

Pitiurenko, Iukhim (Efim) Ivanovich. "Zmini v geografii mist Stalinskoi oblasti za roki radianskoi vladi," *Geografichnyi zbirnik* (Geografichne tovarystvo U.R.S.S.), vypusk 3 (1960), 191–197. Russian summary: "Izmeneniia v geografii gorodov Stalinskoi oblasti za gody Sovetskoi vlasti," *Geograficheskii sbornik* (Ukrainskoe geograficheskoe obshchestvo).

———. "Rost gorodov i gorodskogo naseleniia Stalinskoi oblasti," *Vestnik Kievskogo universiteta,* no. 3, seriia geologii i geografii, vypusk 2. Izd. Kievskogo un-ta. 1961, 102–110.

————. "Tipy gorodskikh poselenii Donetskoi oblasti i perspektivy ikh razvitiia" in *Geografiia naseleniia v SSSR: osnovnye problemy*. M-L. Izd. "Nauka," 1964, 168–182.

Vologodtsev, Ippolit Konstantinovich. "Osobennosti razvitiia gorodov Ukrainy," *Trudy komissii po izucheniiu perspektiv razvitiia gorodov*, vypusk 2, Khar'kov: Izd. Gosplana USSR, 1930, 91–205.

Zhembrovskii, Mikhail Aleksandrovich. "Poseleniia-sputniki Kieva i Khar'kova," in *Goroda-sputniki; sbornik statei*. M. Geografgiz, 1961, 83–93.

10. The Baltic

Blazhis, R. "Litovskaia SSR: naselenie, trudovye resursy i rasselenie," *Sovetskaia Pribaltika: problemy ekonomicheskoi geografii* (AN SSSR, Institut geografii). M. "Nauka," 1966, 243–247.

Dzenis, Zigrid Iakubovich. "Par dažiem Latvijas PSR pilsētu geografijas lautājumiem," *Latvijas universitate, Zinātniskie raksti* (Uchenye zapiski Latviiskogo universiteta), tom 27 (1959), 25–54. Russian summary: "O nekotorykh voprosakh geografii gorodov Latviiskoi SSR."

————. "Latviiskaia SSR: naselenie trudovye resursy i rasselenie," *Sovetskaia Pribaltika: problemy ekonomicheskoi geografii* (AN SSSR. Institut geografii). M. "Nauka," 1966, 202–205.

Januskevičius, V., and Skupeika, A. "Razmeshchenie promyshlennosti i razvitie gorodov v Litovskoi SSR," *Trudy konferentsii po voprosam razmeshcheniia promyshlennosti i razvitiia gorodov*. Vil'nius: AN Litovskoi SSR, 1963, 47–56.

Kaufman, V. "O razvitii poselkov i melkikh gorodov v Estonskoi SSR," *Trudy konferentsii po voprosam razmeshcheniia promyshlennosti i razvitiia gorodov*. Vil'nius: AN Litovskoi SSR, 1963, 137–150.

Khalifman, Lev Iakovlevich. "Ekonomicheskie sviazi goroda Daugav-pilsa," in *Materialy po geografii naseleniia*, vypusk 1. L. Geografi-cheskoe obshchestvo Soiuza SSR, otdelenie ekonomicheskoi geografii, 1962, 61–72. Rotaprint.

————. "O raionoobrazuiushchei roli srednikh gorodov Vostochnoi Latvii," *Trudy konferentsii po voprosam razmeshcheniia promyshlen-nosti i razvitiia gorodov*. Vil'nius: AN Litovskoi SSR, 1963, 181–197.

————. "Nekotorye metodicheskie priemy opredeleniia zon transportnogo tiagoteniia gorodov Latviiskoi SSR (po passazhirskim avtopere-vozkam)," *Teoriia i praktika ekonomicheskogo mikroraionirovaniia*, A. M. Kolotievskii, ed. Riga: Izd. "Zinatne," 1969, 113–119.

————. "K voprosu o razvitii srednikh i malykh gorodov Latviiskoi SSR," *Izvestiia VGO*, 1969, no. 4, 337–342.

Knobel'sdorf, Eduard Vil'gel'movich. "Rizhskoe soveshchanie po ge-ografii naseleniia (22–24 avgusta 1961)" *Izvestiia VGO*, 1961, no. 6, 549–551.

Kolotievskii (Kolotijevski), Anton Mikhailovich. "Rol' prirodnykh uslovii i resursov v formirovanii i razvitii gorodskikh poselenii zapadnogo
raiona SSSR," *Soveshchanie ekonomiko-geografov pribaltiiskikh
soiuznykh respublik po voprosam razmeshchaniia promyshlennosti i
razvitiia gorodov* (20–25 avgusta 1962). Tezisy dokladov. Vil'nius: AN
Litovskoi SSR, Institut geologi i geografii, 1962, 22–24. Rotaprint.

Mints, Aleksei Aleksandrovich, and Nazarevskii, Oleg Rostislavovich.
"Regional'noe soveshchanie ekonomiko-geografov pribaltiiskikh
respublik," *Izvestiia AN SSSR, seriia geograficheskaia,* 1967, no. 1,
166–168.

Nõmmik, S. (Nymmyk, Sal'ma Ianovna). "K voprosu vnutrirespubli-
kanskogo ekonomicheskogo raionirovaniia (na primere Estonskoi
SSR)," *Teoriia i praktika ekonomicheskogo mikroraionirovaniia,* A. M.
Kolotievskii, ed. Riga: Izd. "Zinatne," 1969, 39–55.

Pokshishevskii, Vadim Viacheslavovich. "Rizhskoe soveshchanie po
voprosam geografii naseleniia," *Izvestiia AN SSSR, seriia geograficheskaia,* 1961, no. 6, 154–157.

Pragi, U. "Parametry formuly Zipfa dlia sistemy gorodskikh poselenii
Estonskoi SSR za 1922–1965 gg," *Voprosy geografii,* sbornik 77. M.
"Mysl'," 1968, 175–178. English abstract: "Zipf's formula applied to
the cities of Estonian SSR in 1922–1965," 206.

Rea, Taimo Borisovich. "Linnade rahvaarvu muutumisest kodanlikus
Eestis," *Eesti geograafia seltsi aastaraamat (Ezhegodnik Estonskogo
geograficheskogo obshchestva), 1958.* Tallin, 1959, 230–237. Russian
summary: "O roste naseleniia gorodov Estonii v period burzhuazno-
natsionalisticheskoi diktatury."

———. "Eestii NSV linnaliste asulate geneetilisest klassifikatsioonist
(sotsialismieelsel periodil)," *Tartu riikliku ülikooli toimetised, vihik
88, geograafia-alaseid töid.* Tartu, 1960, 18–44. Russian summary: "O
geneticheskoi klassifikatsii gorodskikh poselenii Estonskoi SSSR
(Dosovetskii period)," *Uchenye zapiski Tartuskogo universiteta,*
vypusk 88, *Trudy po geografii.*

———. "Eesti ala linnade funktsionaalsed tüübid XX saj. alguses,"
Tartu riikliku ülikooli toimetised, vihik 88, *geograafia-alaseid töid,*
Tartu, 1960, 45–61. Russian summary: "Funktsional'nye tipy gorodov
Estonskogo kraia v nachale XX veka," *Uchenye zapiski Tartuskogo
universiteta,* vypusk 88, *Trudy po geografii.*

———. "Ekonomicheskaia geografiia: Izuchenie gorodov," in *O razvitii
geografii v Estonskoi SSR 1940–1960.* Tallin: AN Estonskoi SSR, 1960,
80–82.

———. "O poniatii geneticheskoi klassifikatsii gorodov," *Voprosy geografii
gorodov Pribaltiki.* Publikatsii Estonskogo Geograficheskogo obshchestva, 5, 1962, 26–33. English summary: "On the conception of
the genetic classification of towns," 33.

———. "On the ways of development and genetic classification of Estonian urban settlements," *Tartu riikliku ülikooli toimetised: Geograafia-alaseid töid* (Uchenye zapiski Tartuskogo gos. universiteta. Trudy po geografii), no. 156 (1964), 87–105. Russian summary: "O putiakh razvitiia i geneticheskoi klassifikatsii gorodskikh poselenii Estonii." (On the occassion of the XXth International Geographical Congress)

Rostovtsev, Mikhail Ivanovich. "Geografiia naseleniia," *Sovetskaia Pribaltika; problemy ekonomicheskoi geografii.* M. Izd. "Nauka," 1966, 51–76. (AN SSSR, Institut geografii)

Saunoris, V. "Sostav osnovnykh grupp gorodskogo naseleniia v raionnykh tsentrakh Litovskoi SSR," *Trudy konferentsii po voprosam razmeshcheniia promyshlennosti i razvitiia gorodov.* Vil'nius: AN Litovskoi SSR, 1963, 125–129.

Šešelgis (Sheshel'gis), Kazis Kazisovich. "Voprosy issledovaniia seti naselennykh mest pri sostavlenii skhem raionnoi planirovki (na primere Litovskoi SSR)," *Trudy konferentsii po voprosam razmeshcheniia promyshlennosti i razvitiia gorodov.* Vil'nius: AN Litovskoi SSR, 1963, 81–99.

Šešelgis, K. and Miliukštis, V. "Lietuvos TSR miestų, tinklo desningas vystymas," *Lietuvos TSR architektūros klausimai,* tom 1. Kaunas: Statybos ir architekturos instituto, 1960, 245–261. Russian summary: "Razvitie seti gorodov v Litovskoi SSR," 337.

Skupeika, Alfonsas Kostovich. "Opyt issledovaniia promyshlennykh tsentrov Litovskoi SSR," *Voprosy geografii gorodov Pribaltiki.* Publikatsii Estonskogo Geograficheskogo Obshchestva, 5, 1962, 101–117. English summary: "A study of the industrial centers of the Lithuanian SSR," 114–117.

———. "Promyshlennye goroda Litovskoi SSR i razmeshchenie promyshlennosti," *Soveshchanie ekonomiko-geografov pribaltiiskikh soiuznykh respublik po voprosam razmeshcheniia promyshlennosti i razvitiia gorodov (Vil'nius 20–25 avgusta 1962). Tezisy dokladov.* Vil'nius: AN Litovskoi SSR. Institut geologii i geografii *and* Institut ekonomiki, 1962, 52–55. Rotaprint.

Stulginskis, Stepanas. "Perspektivnoe rasselenie Litovskoi SSR v raionnoi planirovke respubliki," *Trudy konferentsii po voprosam razmeshcheniia promyshlennosti i razvitiia gorodov.* Vil'nius: AN Litovskoi SSR, 1963, 111–123.

Soveshchanie ekonomiko-geografov pribaltiiskikh soiuznykh respublik po voprosam geografii gorodov. Tartu, 24–28 sent. 1960. Tezisy dokladov. Tartu: Estonskoe geograficheskoe obshchestvo, 1960, 26 p.

Tarmisto, Vello Iuliusovich. "O zaniatosti v promyshlennosti naseleniia gorodov i poselkov Estonskoi SSR," *Tezisy dokladov soveshchaniia po geografii naseleniia Pribaltiiskikh Soiuznykh Respublik i Belorussi.* Riga: Izd. Latviiskogo gosudarstvennogo universiteta, 1961, 28–30.

———. "O nekotorom opyte ekonomiko-geograficheskogo issledovaniia promyshlennykh tsentrov (na osnove materialov g. Tallina)," *Voprosy geografii gorodov Pribaltiki*. Publikatsii Estonskogo geograficheskogo obshchestva, 5, 1962, 73–87. English summary: "On some experiences of an economic-geographic study of industrial centres (on the materials of Tallinn)," 85–87.

———. "O prichinakh rosta gorodov Estonskoi SSR v poslevoennyi period," in *Geografiia naseleniia v SSSR; osnovnye problemy* (Geograficheskoe obshchestvo Soiuza SSR). M-L. Izd. "Nauka," 1964, 239–244.

———. "Estonskaia SSR: naselenie, trudovye resursy i rasselenie," in *Sovetskaia Pribaltika; problemy ekonomicheskoi geografii* M. "Nauka," 1966, 162–164. (AN SSSR, Institut Geografii).

Tarvydas, Stasys. "A short review of Lithuanian urban geography," *Collected papers for the XIX International Geographical Congress.* Vil'nius, 1960, 431–436. Russian summary: "Kratkii ocherk gorodov Litovskoi SSR," 434–436.

Tarvydas, S., and Gudonyte, M. "Šiaurines vidurio Lietuvos dalies miestai," *Geografinis metraštis* (Lietuvos geogr. dragija), 3 1960, 137–147. Russian summary: "Goroda severa Srednei Litvy," *Geograficheskii ezhegodnik Geograficheskogo obshchestva Litovskoi SSR.*

———. "Goroda severa Srednei Litvy," *Voprosy geografii gorodov Pribaltiki,* Publikatsii Estonskogo Geograficheskogo Obshchestva, 5, 1962, 88–100. English summary: "The towns of the northern part of Central Lithuania," 98–100.

Teoriia i praktika ekonomicheskogo mikroraionirovaniia (v sviazi s raionnoi planirovkoi) (Latviiskii gosudarstvennyi universitet im. P. Stuchki and Geograficheskoe obshchestvo Latviiskoi SSR). A. M. Kolotievskii, ed. Riga: Izd. "Zinatne," 1969, 211 p. (papers given at the 6th regional conference of Baltic geographers in 1967 in Riga).

Tezisy dokladov soveshchaniia po geografii naseleniia Pribaltiiskikh soiuznykh respublik i Belorussii. Riga, 22–24 avgusta 1961. Riga: Izd. Latviiskogo gosudarstvennogo universiteta, 1961, 67 p.

Trudy konferentsii po voprosam razmeshcheniia promyshlennosti i razvitiia gorodov (Vil'nius, 20–23 avg. 1962 g.). Vil'nius: AN Litovskoi SSR, Institut geologii i geografii and Institut ekonomiki, 1963. 200 p.

Voprosy geografii gorodov pribaltiki, Publikatsii Estonskogo geograficheskogo obshchestva, 5. Tallin: AN Estonskoi SSR, 1962. 123 p. (in Russian with summaries of articles in Estonian and English).

Zagorskis, I. I. "Kaunas kak raionoformiruiushchii gorod," *Liet. TSR Mokslu Akad. darbai* (Trudy AN Litovskoi SSR), 1965, A, no. 1 (18), 3–13.

———. "Ekonomiko-geograficheskoe izuchenie krupnykh i bol'shikh gorodov kak glavnykh raionoformiruiushchikh tsentrov Litovskoi SSR," *Teoriia i praktika ekonomicheskogo mikroraionirovaniia.* A. M. Kolotievskii, ed. Riga: Izd. "Zinatne," 1969, 85–92.

11. Belorussia

Belogortsev, Igor' Dmitrievich. "Gorodskie poseleniia-sputniki v Belorussii," *Goroda-sputniki; sbornik statei.* M. Geografgiz, 1961, 94–100.

——. "Razvitie seti gorodov Belorussii," *Materialy I Mezhduvedomstvennogo soveshchaniia po geografii naseleniia,* vypusk 7. L. Geograficheskoe obshchestvo SSSR, 1965, 56–68. Rotaprint.

Bogdanovich, Antolii Vladimirovich, and Sidorov, Petr Aleksandrovich. "Problemy razvitiia nebol'shikh gorodov Belorussii," *Vestnik Moskovskogo universiteta, seriia 5, geografiia,* 1966, no. 3, 83–85.

——. *Goroda Belorussii: Kratkii ekonomicheskii ocherk.* Minsk: Nauka i Tekhnika, 1967. 183 p.

Nemtsova, L. E. "Formirovanie seti gorodskikh poselenii na territorii Brestskoi oblasti," *Voprosy geografii naseleniia* Uchenye zapiski Leningradskogo gos. pedagogicheskogo instituta im. A. I. Gertsena, tom 279, L. 1966, 178–198.

Zhuchkevich, Vadim Andreevich, Malyshev, A. Ia., and Rogozin, N. E. *Goroda i sela Belorusskoi SSR; istoriko-geograficheskie ocherki.* Minsk: Uchpedgiz BSSR, 1959. 279 p.

12. The Caucasus

Dzhaoshvili, Vakhtam Shalvovich. "K klassifikatsii gorodov Gruzii," *Soobshcheniia Akademii nauk Gruzinskoi SSR,* tom 19, no. 5 (1957), 563–570.

——. "K sravnitel'noi kharakteristike gorodskikh poselenii Gruzinskoi SSR," in *Materialy I Mezhduvedomstvennogo soveshchaniia po geografii naseleniia (ianvar'-fevral' 1962 g.),* vypusk 3, Sektsiia geografii gorodov, doklady i resiume dokladov. M-L. Geograficheskoe obshchestvo Soiuza SSR, 1961, 99–106. Rotaprint.

——. "K probleme razvitiia malykh gorodskikh poselenii i ogranicheniia rosta krupnykh gorodov (iz praktiki gradostroitel'stva v Gruzii)," *Izvestiia AN SSSR, seriia geograficheskaia,* 1964, no. 2, 60–68.

——. "K sravnitel'noi kharakteristike gorodskikh poselenii Gruzinskoi SSR" in *Geografiia naseleniia v SSSR; osnovy problemy.* M-L. Izd. "Nauka," 1964, 214–229.

——. "Gruzinskaia SSR: geografiia naseleniia," in *Geografiia khoziaistva respublik Zakavkaz'ia,* M. Izd. "Nauka," 1966, 72–80.

——. *Naselenie Gruzii: ekonomiko-geograficheskoe issledovanie.* Tbilisi: Izd. "Metsniereba," 1968. 398 p. English subtitle: Population of Georgia: economic-geographical study. English table of contents, 396–398.

Gadzhi-Zade, Abduragim Mamediiaevich. "Sovremennaia vzaimossviaz' sotsialisticheskoi stolitsy Azerbaidzhana Baku s raionami respubliki," *Uchenye zapiski Azerbaidzhanskogo universiteta,* 1958, no. 6, 81–89.

——. "Azerbaidzhanskaia SSR: geografiia naseleniia," in *Geografiia khoziaistva respublik Zakavkaz'ia.* M. Izd. "Nauka," 1966, 139–143.

Grgearian, Akop Kazarosovich. "Armianskaia SSR: geografiia naseleniia," in *Geografiia khoziaistva respublik Zakavkaz'ia.* M. Izd. "Nauka," 1966, 216–221.

Mikhel's, B. N. "Dinamika sostova gorodov i chislennosti gorodskogo naseleniia Azerbaidzhanskoi SSR," *Uchenye zapiski Azerbaidzhanskogo universiteta, seriia geologo-geograficheskikh nauk,* 1965, no. 5, 93–101.

Mints, Aleksei Aleksandrovich. "Geografiia naseleniia" in *Geografiia khoziaistva respublik Zakavkaz'ia.* M. Izd. "Nauka," 1966, 29–35.

Nadirov, Asaf Abbas-Kuli ogly. *Voprosy ekonomicheskogo razvitiia gorodov Azerbaidzhana* (AN Azerbaidzhanskoi SSR, Institut Geografii). Baku: Izd. AN Azerbaidzhanskoi SSR, 1966.

13. Middle Asia and Kazakhstan

Akhmedov, Erkin Agzamovich. "Tashkentskaia oblast' i ee novye goroda," *Nauchnye raboty i soobshcheniia otdela obshchestvennykh nauk Uzbekskoi SSSR,* kniga 1. Tashkent, 1960, 205–215.

———. "Nekotorye voprosy razvitiia novykh gorodov Tashkent-Chirchik-Angrenskogo promyshlennogo raiona," *Obshchestvennye nauki v Uzbekistane,* 1962, no. 3, 12–18.

Akhmedov, E. A., Zakirov, Sh. N., and Kravets, F. F. "Nekotorye problemy razvitiia gorodov Uzbekistana," in *Problemy razvitiia ekonomiki Uzbekistana.* Tashkent: Izd. AN Uzbekskoi SSR, 1963, 88–99.

Akramov, Ziiavitdin Mukhitdinovich, and Raimov, Tursun. "Ob ekonomiko-geograficheskom izuchenii gorodov Uzbekistana," *Nauchnye Trudy Tashkentskogo Gos. universiteta,* vypusk 248, 1964, 3–32.

Andreeva, V. M., Kniazhinskaia, L. A., Nazarevskii, O. R., and Freikin, Z. L. "Voprosy geografii naseleniia na nauchnoi konferentsii po narodonaseleniiu Srednei Azii," *Izvestiia AN SSSR, seriia geograficheskaia,* 1966, no. 1, 145–148.

Chavchanidze, Irina Ivanovna. "Ekonomiko-geograficheskoe issledovanie trudovykh resursov na primere Vostochno-Kazakhstanskoi oblasti," in *Geografiia naseleniia v SSSR; osnovnye problemy.* M-L. Izd. "Nauka," 1964, 160–167.

Faiziev, N. "Nekotorye voprosy formirovaniia novykh gorodov Uzbekistana," *Nauchnye trudy Tashkentskogo gos. universiteta,* vypusk 251 1964, 18–23.

———. "K voprosu o tipologii novykh gorodov Uzbekskoi SSR," in *Materialy mezhvuzovskoi nauchnoi konferentsii po problemam narodonaseleniia Srednei Azii.* Tashkent: Tashkentskii gosudarstvennyi universitet, 1965, 106–107.

Fesenko, T. M. "Formirovanie gorodskikh poselenii Zapadnogo Pridzhungar'ia," *Voprosy geografii Kazakhstana,* vypusk 10. Alma-Ata: AN Kazakhskoi SSR, 1963, 163–179.

Ginzburg, Natal'ia Solomonovna. "Novye goroda Uzbekskoi SSR," *Izvestiia VGO,* 1957, no. 5, 445–456.

460
Cities of the Soviet Union

——. "Molodye goroda Uzbekistana segodnia i zavtra," *Narodnoe Khoziaistvo Uzbekistana,* 1961, no. 12, 71–75.

——. "Perspektivy razvitiia novykh gorodov Uzbekskoi SSR," in *Materialy po geografii naselenii,* vypusk 1. L. Geograficheskoe obshchestvo SSSR, 1962, 82–108.

Gladysheva, Ekaterina Nikolaevna. "Ekonomicheskaia struktura gorodov Tselinnogo kraia i vliianie ee na zaniatost' naseleniia," in *Problemy sovremennoi ekonomiki Kazakhstana,* vypusk 1. Alma-Ata: Institut ekonomiki AN Kazakhskoi SSR, 1965, 216–248.

Gladysheva, Ekaterina Nikolaevna, and Nazarevskii, Oleg Rostislavovich. "Gorodskie poseleniia Kazakhstana-novostroiki stalinskikh piatiletok," *Voprosy geografii,* sbornik 19. M. Geografgiz, 1950, 6–19.

Goroda Uzbekistana: Ukazatel' literatury. Gosudarstvennaia respublikanskaia biblioteka UzSSR im A. Navoi. Tashkent: Gosudarstvennoe izd. Uzbekskoi SSR, 1964, 95 p.

Inamov, I. I. "Opyt kharakteristiki promyshlennosti gorodov nizov'ev Amu-Dar'i v predelakh Uzbekistana," *Nauchnye zapiski Tashkentskogo finansovo-ekonomicheskogo instituta,* vypusk 15, 1961, 139–151.

——. "Nekotorye voprosy tipologii gorodskikh poselenii nizov'ev Amu-Dar'i," *Nauchnye zapiski Tashkentskogo instituta narodnogo khoziaistva,* vypusk 20, 1963, 177–188.

——. "O vliianii prirodnykh uslovii i resursov na razvitie gorodov nizov'ev Amu-Dar'i," *Nauchnye zapiski Tashkentskogo instituta narodnogo khoziaistva,* vypusk 26, 1964, 197–220.

Karakhanov, Murtoza K. "K izucheniiu naseleniia i naselennykh punktov gornykh raionov Uzbekstana," *Izvestiia Uzbekistanskogo geograficheskogo obshchestva,* tom 8, 1964, 47–51.

——. "Naselenie i naselennye punkty raionov predgornoi i gornoi zony Tashkentskoi oblasti," *Nauchnye trudy Tashkentskogo Gos. universiteta im. V. I. Lenina,* vypusk 248, 1964, 33–57.

——. "O chislennosti naseleniia Uzbekskoi SSR po dannym perepisi 1897 g.", *Nauchnye trudy Tashkentskogo universiteta im. V. I. Lenina,* vypusk 266, geografiia, 1965, 56–68.

Konobritskaia, Evgeniia Mitrofanovna. *Novye goroda tsentral'nogo Kazakhstana.* Alma-Ata: AN Kazakhskoi SSR, 1950. 38 p.

Konstantinov, Oleg Arkad'evich. "Osobennosti rasseleniia sovetskoi Srednei Azii," *Voprosy geografii naseleniia,* Uchenye zapiski Leningradskogo Gos. pedagogicheskogo instituta im A. I. Gertsena, tom 279. L. 1966, 128–152.

Kravets, Fania Fatelevna. "O perspektivakh razvitiia malykh gorodov Iugo-zapadnogo Uzbekistana," in *Obshchestvennye nauki v Uzbekistane,* kniga 1. Tashkent: Izd. AN Uzbekskoi SSR, 1963, 20–26.

Kurambaev, Makham. "Naselenie i tipy gorodskikh poselenii Zapadnogo Turkmenistana," *Uchenye zapiski Turkmenskogo gos. pedago-*

gicheskogo instituta im V. I. Lenina (seriia biologicheskikh i geograficheskikh nauk), vypusk 2, Chardzhou, 1965, 35–46.

Leizerovich, E. E. "Funktsional'nye tipy gorodskikh poselenii Kirgizii i ikh razvitie v perspektive," *Vestnik Moskovskogo universiteta, seriia 5, geografiia,* 1964, no. 6, 45–54.

Materialy Mezhvuzovskoi nauchnoi konferentsii po problemam narodonaseleniia Srednei Azii. M. K. Karakhanov, ed. Tashkent: Tashkentskii gosudarstvennyi universitet, 1965. "Problemy gorodskogo rasseleniia," 79–121. Short papers by O. A. Konstantinov, N. V. Smirnov, B. S. Khorev, A. N. Zotov, T. Raimov, S. A. Pol'skii, O. Ata-Mirzaev, V. Zh. Grundmanis, E. A. Akhmedov, N. Faiziev, M. K. Karakhanov, I. Inamov, and others.

Nazarevskii, Oleg Rostislavovich. "Gorodskoe naselenie i tipy gorodov," in *Kazakhskaia SSR; ekonomiko-geograficheskaia kharakteristika* (AN SSSR, Institut geografii, *and* AN Kazakhskoi SSR, sektor geografii). M. Geografgiz, 1957, 134–145.

———. "Formirovanie poselenii-sputnikov v Kazakhstane i sredneaziatskikh respublikakh SSSR" in *Goroda-sputniki; sbornik statei.* M. Geografgiz, 1961, 101–114.

———. "Tipologiia i osobennosti formirovaniia novykh poselenii Kazakhstana i sredneaziatskikh respublik," *Voprosy geografii,* sbornik 56. M. Geografgiz, 1962, 73–94.

Raimov, Tursun. "Gorod Tashkent (formirovanie millionnogo stolichnogo goroda, osobennosti ego funktsional'noi struktury i perspektivy razvitiia)," *Nauchnye trudy Tashkentskogo gos. universiteta im V. I. Lenina,* vypusk 248, 1964, 58–79.

———. "Formirovanie Bol'shogo goroda — stolitsa Sovetskoi sotsialisticheskoi respubliki," in *Sovremennye problemy geografii: nauchnye soobshcheniia sovetskikh geografov po programme XX Mezhdunarodnogo geograficheskogo kongressa (London, 1964).* M. Izd. "Nauka," 1964, 60–65. English abstract: "Formation of a big city—a capital of Soviet Socialist Republic (on the example of Tashkent)," 65.

———. "K ekonomiko-geograficheskomu issledovaniiu naseleniia stolichnykh gorodov," *Nauchnye trudy Tashkentskogo universiteta,* vypusk 310, 1967, 133–148.

Smirnov, Nikolai Vasil'evich. "Goroda Ferganskoi doliny (ekonomiko-geograficheskii ocherk)," *Trudy Sredneaziatskogo gosudarstvennogo universiteta,* novaia seriia, vypusk 95. Geograficheskie nauki, kniga 9, 1957. 152 p.

———. "Dinamicheskaia klassifikatsiia gorodskikh poseleniia Uzbekistana," *Vestnik Moskovskogo universiteta, seriia 5, geografiia,* 1966, no. 6, 47–51.

Zotov, A. N., Iakubov, B., Smirnov, N. V., and Chabrov, G. *Goroda Ferganskoi doliny; kratkii spravochnik.* Tashkent: Gosizdat Uzbekskoi SSR, 2nd ed., 1963. 158 p.

462

Cities of the Soviet Union

Zotov, A. N., Raimov, T., Smirnov, N. V., and Iakubov, B. *Goroda Uzbekistana.* Tashkent: Izd. "Uzbekistan," 1965. 286 p.

IV. FOREIGN WORKS ON SOVIET CITIES

Armstrong, Terence. *Russian settlement in the north.* "Scott polar research institute, special publication no. 3." Cambridge: University press, 1965. 223 p.

Barr, Brenton M., "The Krasnoyarsk region — an emerging industrial center," *Occasional papers, British Columbia division, Canadian association of geographers,* no. 4 (June, 1963, reprinted 1965), 26–38.

Beaujeu-Garnier, Jacqueline. "Les villes de l'U.R.S.S." in Jacqueline Beaujeu-Garnier and Georges Chabot, *Traité de géographie urbaine.* Paris: Armand Colin, 1963, 63–70. In English: "The world's towns: the USSR," in their *Urban geography.* London: Longmans, and New York: Wiley, 1967, 61–68.

Borchert, John R. "The Soviet city," chapter 2 in *Soviet Union, paradox and change,* ed. by Robert T. Holt and John E. Turner. New York: Holt, Rinehart and Winston, 1962, 35–61.

Cole, John P. "Urban population," in his *A geography of the U.S.S.R.* Harmondsworth, England, or Baltimore, Maryland: Penguin Books, 1967, 70–75.

———. "Urban population changes in the U.S.S.R. 1939–1956," *Tijdschrift voor economische en sociale geografie,* vol. 48. no. 3 (March, 1957), 80–83.

Dewdney, John C. "Urbanization," in his *A geography of the Soviet Union.* Oxford: Pergamon Press, 1965, 137–140.

Dienes, Leslie. *Locational factors and locational developments in the Soviet chemical industry.* Chicago: University of Chicago, Department of Geography, Research paper no. 119, 1969. 262 p. (Chemical centers).

Field, Neil C. "Land hunger and the rural depopulation problem in the U.S.S.R.," *Annals of the Association of American geographers,* vol. 53, no. 4 (December, 1963), 465–478.

———. "Administrative and constitutional changes in Arctic territories: the USSR," in *The Arctic frontier,* R. St. J. MacDonald, ed. Toronto: University of Toronto press, 1966, 160–193.

Fischer, Dora. "Siedlungsgeographie in der Sowjetunion," *Erdkunde; archiv für wissenschaftliche Geographie,* Band 20, Heft 3 (September, 1966), 211–227.

French, R. A. "Recent population trends in the USSR," *St Antony's papers,* no. 19, Soviet affairs, no. 4 (1966), 68–95.

Frolic, B. Michael. "The Soviet city," *Town planning review,* vol. 34, no. 4 (January, 1964), 285–306.

Fuchs, Roland J. "Soviet urban geography: an appraisal of postwar research," *Annals of the Association of American Geographers,* vol. 54, no. 2 (June, 1964), 276–289.

Gellert, Johannes F., and Engelmann, Gerhard. "Entwicklung und Struktur einiger sowjetischer Grossstädte in Mittelasien," *Geographische Berichte*, vol. 12, no. 44 (1967, no. 3), 175–203. English and Russian summaries, 202.

George, Pierre. "La place de la ville dans l'économie et la société soviétique," in his *L'U.R.S.S.* Paris: Presses universitaires de France, 2nd ed., 1962, 408–438. (1st ed., 1947, pp. 359–381.)

———. "Population urbaine et population rurale en U.R.S.S.," *Annales de géographie*, vol. 70, no. 378 (March-April 1961), 206–210.

———. "Les formes de developpement urbain en U.R.S.S.," *Bulletin de l'Association de géographes français*, no. 322–323 (March-April, 1964), 36–42.

Gley, Werner. "Bevölkerungs- und Siedlungsfragen: die Verstädterung in Russland," *Zeitschrift für Erdkunde*, vol. 8, no. 17/18 (September, 1940), 439–444.

———. "Lage und Verteilung der Städte im alten Russland: ein Beitrag zum Problem der zentralen Orte," *Die Erde*, 3 (1951), 319–338.

Gregory, James S. *Russian land, Soviet people; a geographical approach to the U.S.S.R.* London: George G. Harrap, 1968. 947 p. (See index for individual cities).

Hall, Peter. "Moscow," chapter 6 in his *The world cities*. World university library. London: Weidenfeld and Nicholson, and New York: McGraw-Hill, 1966, 158–181.

Harris, Chauncy D. "The cities of the Soviet Union," *Geographical review*, vol. 35, no. 1 (January, 1945), 107–121.

———. "Ethnic groups in cities of the Soviet Union," *Geographical review*, vol. 35, no. 3 (July, 1945), 466–473.

———. "City and region in the Soviet Union," chapter XI in *Urbanization and its problems: essays in honour of E. W. Gilbert*, Robert P. Beckinsale and James M. Houston, eds., Oxford: Basil Blackwell, 1968, 277–296.

———. Population of cities of the Soviet Union, 1897, 1926, 1939, 1959, and 1967: tables, maps, and gazetteer, "Soviet geography: review and translation," Vol. 11, no. 5 (May, 1970), 1–138.

Hettner, Alfred. "Städte," in his *Russland: eine geographische Betrachtung von Volk, Staat und Kultur*. Leipzig: B. G. Teubner, 3rd ed., 1916, 135–142.

Hooson, David, J. M. *A new Soviet heartland?* Princeton, N. J.: Van Nostrand, 1964. 132 p.

———. "The growth of cities," in his *The Soviet Union: people and regions*. Belmont, California: Wadsworth, 1966, 112–116.

———. "The growth of cities in pre-Soviet Russia," chapter X in *Urbanization and its problems: essays in honour of E. W. Gilbert*, Robert P. Beckinsale and James M. Houston, eds., Oxford: Basil Blackwell, 1968, 254–276.

Houston, Cecil. "Market potential and potential transportation costs: an evaluation of the concepts and their surface patterns in the U.S.S.R.," *The Canadian Geographer,* vol. 13, no. 3 (fall, 1969), 216–236.

Howe, G. Melvyn. "Urban development," in his *The Soviet Union.* London: MacDonald and Evan, 1968, 119–121.

Hruska, E. "Sozialistischer Städtebau mit besonderer Berücksichtigung der UdSSR," *Tidjschrift voor economische en sociale geografie,* vol. 56, no. 6 (1965), 209–220.

Jensen, Robert G., and Karaska, Gerald J. "The mathematical thrust in Soviet economic geography: its nature and significance," *Journal of regional science,* vol. 9, no. 1 (April, 1969), 141–152.

———. "Application of mathematical methods in Soviet economic geography," *Soviet geography: review and translation,* vol. 10, no. 9 (November, 1969), 501–506.

Karger, Adolf, "Ausgewählte industrielle Ballungsräume," and "Bratsk als Beispiel für die industrielle Erschliessung Sibiriens," in his *Die Sowjetunion als Wirtschaftsmacht.* Frankfurt am Main: Verlag Moritz Diesterweg, 1967, 69–87 and 90–95.

Knübel, Hans. "Verstädterung und Grossstadtentwicklung in der Sowjetunion," *Geographische Rundschau,* vol. 16, no. 6 (1964), 244–246.

Langbein, Otto. "Die Grosstädte der Sowjetunion," *Mitteilungen der geographischen Gesellschaft Wien,* vol. 80 (1937), 265–269.

———. "Städtische Bevölkerung und Grossstädte der UdSSR," *Mitteilungen der Geographischen Gesellschaft Wien,* vol. 98, no. 3 (1956), 250–256.

———. "Les grandes villes de l'U.R.S.S." *Annales de géographie,* vol. 67, no. 361 (1958), 282–288.

Leasure, J. William and Lewis, Robert A. "Internal migration in the USSR: 1897–1926," *Demography,* vol. 4 no. 2 (1967), 479–496.

Leimbach, Werner. "Städtische Siedlungen," in his *Die Sowjetunion: Natur, Volk und Wirtschaft.* Stuttgart: Franckh'sche Verlagshandlung, 1950, 218–231.

Lewis, Robert A. "The postwar study of internal migration in the USSR," *Soviet geography: review and translation,* vol. 10, no. 4 (April, 1969), 157–166.

Lewis, Robert A. and Leasure, J. William. "Regional population changes in Russia and the USSR since 1851," *Slavic review; American quarterly of Soviet and East European studies,* vol. 25, no. 4 (December, 1966), 663–668.

Lewis, Robert A., and Rowland, Richard H. "Urbanization in Russia and the USSR: 1897–1966," *Annals of the Association of American geographers,* vol. 59, no. 4 (December, 1969), 776–796.

Lonsdale, Richard E., and Thompson, John H. "A map of the USSR's manufacturing," *Economic geography,* vol. 36, no. 1 (January, 1960), 35–52.

Lydolph, Paul E. "Urbanization," in his *Geography of the U.S.S.R.* New York: John Wiley, 1964, 275–277.

——. "The population of the U.S.S.R.," chapter 6 in *Geography of population: a teacher's guide.* The 1970 yearbook of the National council for geographic education. Paul F. Griffin, ed. Palo Alto, California: Fearon, 1969, 85–116.

Lydolph, Paul E., and Shabad, Theodore. "The oil and gas industries in the U.S.S.R.," *Annals of the Association of American geographers,* vol. 50, no. 4 (December, 1960), 461–486.

Mathieson, Raymond S. "The Soviet contributions to regional science: a review article," *Journal of regional science,* vol. 9, no. 1 (April, 1969), 125–140. (100 references).

Meckelein, Wolfgang. "Gruppengrosstadt und Grosstadtballung in der Sowjetunion," *Deutscher Geographentag, Berlin, 20. bis 25. Mai. 1959. Tagunsbericht und wissenschaftliche Abhandlungen,* vol. 32. Wiesbaden: F. Steiner Verlag, 1960, 168–185.

——. "Jüngere siedlungsgeographische Wandlungen in der Sowjetunion," *Geographische Zeitschrift,* vol. 52, no. 3 (August 1964), 242–270, especially 257–269. English summary: "Recent changes of the geographic patterns of settlement within the Soviet Union," 269–270.

Meijide Pardo, Antonio. "El nuevo dinamismo urbano y la geografía de la ciudad," and "Las ciudades-hongo," in his *La U.R.S.S.: geografía, economia, industria.* Madrid: Instituto Juan Sebastian Elcano, Consejo Superior de Investigaciones Científicas, 1952, 33–42.

Melezin, Abraham. "Trends and issues in the Soviet geography of population," *Annals of the Association of American geographers,* vol. 53, no. 2 (June, 1963), 144–160.

Mellor, Roy E. H. "The Soviet town," *Town and country planning,* February, 1963.

——. "Town. . . in the Soviet Union," in his *Geography of the U.S.S.R.* London: Methuen, 1965, 145–163.

Mieczkowski, Zbigniew. "The major economic regions of the USSR in the Khrushchev era," *Canadian geographer,* vol. 9, no. 1 (1965), 19–30.

——. "The 1962–63 reforms in Soviet economic regionalization," *Slavic review,* vol. 24, no. 3 (September, 1965), 479–496.

——. "The economic regionalization of the Soviet Union in the Lenin and Stalin periods," *Canadian slavonic papers,* vol. 8 (1966), 89–124.

——. "The economic administrative regions in the U.S.S.R.," *Tijdschrift voor economische en sociale geografie,* vol. 58, no. 4 (July-August, 1967), 209–219.

——. "The Soviet post-Stalin approach to the unity of economic and administrative divisions," *Études slaves et est européennes,* vol. 12 (été-automne, 1967), 84–98.

Olbricht, Konrad. "Neue Städte in der Sowjetunion," *Geographische Wochenschrift,* vol. 1, no. 6 (February 20, 1933), 142–148.

Osborn, Robert J., and Reiner, Thomas A. "Soviet city planning: current issues and future perspectives," *Journal of the American institute of planners,* 1962, no. 4, 239–250.

Parker, William Henry. *An historical geography of Russia.* London: University of London Press Ltd., 1968, 62–64, 74–76, 91–92, 95–97, 129–136, 198–208, 261–265, 314–318, and 343–345.

Parkins, Maurice F. *City planning in Soviet Russia, with an interpretative bibliography.* Chicago: University of Chicago press, 1953. 257 p. (Extensive bibliography.)

Pullè, Giorgio. "La città della Russia," *Bollettino della R. Società geografica italiana,* serie VII, vol. 1, no. 8–9 1936, 523–540.

———. "Origini e trasformazioni della cittè russe," *Le vie del mondo,* vol. 10, no. 10 1942, 689–700.

Rogers, Allan. "Changing locational patterns in the Soviet pulp and paper industry," *Annals of the Association of American geographers,* vol. 45, no. 1 (March, 1955), 85–104.

———. "Coking coal supply: its role in the expansion of the Soviet steel industry," *Economic geography* vol. 40, no. 2 (April, 1964), 113–150.

Roof, Michael K., and Leedy, Frederick A. "Population redistribution in the Soviet Union, 1939–1956," *Geographical review,* vol. 49, no. 2 (April, 1959), 208–221.

Schultz, Arved. "Russische Stadtlandschaften," in Siegfried Passarge, *Stadtlandschaften der Erde.* Hamburg, 1930, 41–70.

Shabad, Theodore. *Geography of the USSR: a regional survey.* New York: Columbia University press, 1951. (Comments on a large number of individual cities).

———. *Basic industrial resources of the U.S.S.R.* New York: Columbia University press, 1969. 393 p. (See index for names of cities covered).

Shimkin, Demitri B. "Demographic changes and socio-ecnomic forces within the Soviet Union, 1939–1959," in *Population trends in eastern Europe, the USSR, and mainland China.* New York: The Milbank memorial fund, 1960, 224–262.

Shkvarikov, V. and others. "The building of new towns in the USSR," *Ekistics* (Athens) vol. 18 1964, 108: 307–319.

Täubert, Heinrich. "Typengliederung der sowjetischen Städte," *Petermanns geographische Mitteilungen,* vol. 102, no. 3 (1958), 234–239.

"Turkmenistan: urban development," *Central Asian Review,* vol. 2, no. 1 1954, 76–84.

Verlet, Bruno. "Villes d'aujourd'hui en U.R.S.S." *Revue de géographie de Lyon,* vol. 40, no. 2, 1965, 159–173.

Zile, Zigurds. "Programs and problems of city planning in the Soviet Union (part of symposium: land use planning)," *Washington University Law Quarterly,* February, 1963, 19–59.

V. GENERAL WORKS ON CITIES

Beckmann, Martin J. "City hierarchies and the distribution of city size," *Economic development and cultural change,* vol. 6 1958, 243–248.

Berry, Brian J. L. "Cities as systems within systems of cities," in *Regional development and planning: a reader,* John Friedmann and William Alonso, eds., Cambridge, Mass.: M.I.T. Press, 1964, 116–137.

———. "City size distribution and economic development," *Economic development and cultural change,* vol. 9, no. 4, part 1 (July, 1961), 573–588.

Berry, Brian J. L. and Garrison, William L. "Alternate explanations of urban rank-size relationships," *Annals of the Association of American geographers,* vol. 48, no. 1 (March, 1958), 83–91.

Berry, Brian J. L. and Harris, Chauncy D. "Central place," *International encyclopedia of the social sciences,* New York: Macmillan and the Free Press, 1968, vol. 2, 365–370.

Berry, Brian J. L. and Pred, Allan R. *Central place studies: a bibliography of theory and applications.* Philadelphia: Regional Science research institute, 1961. "Bibliography series no. 1." 153 p.

———. ———. *Supplement through 1964,* by H. Gardiner Barnum, Roger Kasperson, and Shinzo Kiuchi. 1965. 50 p.

Christaller, Walter. *Die zentralen Orte in Süddeutschland: eine ökonomisch-geographische Untersuchung über die Gesetzmässigkeit der Verbreitung und Entwicklung der Siedlungen mit städtischen Funktionen.* Jena, Fischer, 1933. 331 p.

Davis, Kingsley. "The urbanization of the human population," *Scientific American,* vol. 213, no. 3 (September, 1965), 41–53.

Haggett, Peter. *Locational analysis in human geography.* London: Edward Arnold, 1965. 339 p. In Russian: *Prostranstvennyi analiz v ekonomicheskoi geografii.* Foreword by V. M. Gokhman and Iu. V. Medvedkov. M. Izd. "Progress," 1968.

Harris, Chauncy D. "A functional classification of cities in the United States," *Geographical review,* vol. 33, no. 1 (January, 1943), 86–99.

———. "Suburbs," *American journal of sociology,* vol. 49, no. 1 (July, 1943), 1–13.

———. "The market as a factor in the localization of industry in the United States," *Annals of the Association of American geographers,* vol. 44, no. 4 (December, 1954), 315–348.

———. "Methods of research in economic regionalization," *Geographia Polonica,* no. 4 (1964), 59–86. Shorter version in Russian: "Metody issledovanii v oblasti ekonomicheskogo raionirovaniia," *Izvestiia AN SSSR, seriia geograficheskaia,* 1963, no. 4, 128–136.

Harris, Chauncy D., and Ullman, Edward L. "The nature of cities,"

Annals of the American academy of political and social science, vol. 242 (November, 1945), 7–17.

Hassert, Kurt, *Die Städte geographisch betrachtet*. Leipzig, 1907. 137 p. In Russian: *Goroda, geograficheskii etiud*, v perevode i peredelke s nemetskogo dobavleniiamii L. D. Sinitskogo. M. 1912.

Hauser, Philip M., and Schnore, Leo F., eds. *The study of urbanization*. New York: John Wiley, 1965. 554 p.

Hoover, Edgar M. "The concept of a system of cities," *Economic development and cultural change*, vol. 3 (1955), 196–198.

Isard, Walter, and others. *Methods of regional analysis: an introduction to regional science*. Cambridge, Mass.: Technology press of the Massachusetts institute of technology, and New York: John Wiley, 1960. 784 p. In Russian: *Metody regional'nogo analiza: vvedenie v nauku o regionakh*. Foreword by A. E. Probst. M. Izd. "Progress," 1966. 659 p.

Jefferson, Mark. "How American cities grow," *Bulletin of the American geographical society*, vol. 47, no. 1 1915, 19–37.

———. "The law of the primate city," *Geographical review*, vol. 29, no. 2 (April, 1939), 226–232.

Mayer, Harold M., and Kohn, Clyde F., eds. *Readings in urban geography*. Chicago: University of Chicago press, 1959. 625 p. In Russian: *Geografiia gorodov*. Abridged translation by V. M. Gokhman. Introduction and editing by V. V. Pokshishevskii. M. Izd. "Progress," 1965. 440 p.

Olsson, Gunnar. *Distance and human interaction: a review and a bibliography*. Philadelphia: Regional science research institute, 1965. "Bibliography series no. 2." 112 p.

———. "Central place systems, spatial interaction, and stochastic processes," *Regional science association, papers*, vol. 18 1967, 13–45. (Extensive bibliography).

Ray, D. Michael. *Market potential and economic shadow: a quantitative analysis of industrial location in Southern Ontario*. Chicago: University of Chicago, Department of geography, Research paper no. 101, 1965. 164 p.

Weber, Adna Ferrin. *The growth of cities in the nineteenth century: a study in statistics*. "Columbia University studies in history, economics and public law, vol. 11," New York: Macmillan, 1899. 495 p. Reprinted: Ithaca, N.Y.: Cornell University press, 1963. 495 p. In Russian as: *Rost gorodov v deviatnadtsom stoletii*. St. Petersburg: Izd. E. D. Kuskovoi, 1903.

Zelinsky, Wilbur. *A Bibliographic guide to population geography*. Chicago: University of Chicago, Department of geography, Research paper no. 80, 1962. 257 p.

Zipf, G. K. *National unity and disunity: the nation as a bio-social organism*. Bloomington, Indiana: The Principia Press, 1941. 408 p.

Index

469

470

478

484

PRINTED IN U.S.A.